VECTORS, MATRICES AND ALGEBRAIC STRUCTURES

H. A. Elliott

Associate Director

Service for Admission to College and University

Ottawa, Ontario

K. D. Fryer

Associate Dean, Faculty of Mathematics

University of Waterloo

Waterloo, Ontario

J. C. Gardner

Superintendent of Schools

The Carleton Board of Education

Ottawa, Ontario

Norman J. Hill

Head of Mathematics Department

St. Mary's Collegiate and Vocational Institute

St. Mary's, Ontario

VECTORS, MATRICES AND ALGEBRAIC STRUCTURES

ELLIOTT
FRYER
GARDNER
HILL

Holt, Rinehart and Winston of Canada, Limited
Toronto

CONTENTS

VECTORS

1.1. Lines and Planes in Space

In most of our geometrical work in previous years, we studied lines and other figures in a plane. However, geometrical figures do exist in 3-dimensional space and not just in the 2-dimensional space that we studied previously. It is, of course, a little more difficult to represent 3-dimensional figures on the 2-dimensional surface of a sheet of paper. Certain conventions have been established to enable us to make this representation without ambiguity.

A region of a plane is represented by a parallelogram. Lines and line segments are represented by line segments.

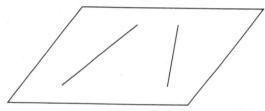 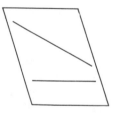

A line can intersect a plane. We show this situation in the diagram below. The plane I is cut by the line l at a point P. The dotted segment of the line indicates where the line is behind the plane from our point of view.

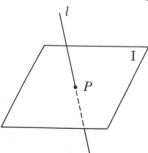

In 3-dimensional geometry, we require certain axioms and definitions in addition to those that we have already used in 2-dimensional geometry.

Axiom 1.   If two points A and B lie in a plane I, then the line AB determined by these points lies entirely in the plane I; that is, all points on the line are coplanar in I.

Axiom 2.   If two distinct planes I and II intersect, they intersect in a line m.

Axiom 3.   Through any three distinct noncollinear points, there is one and only one plane.

We note, as a consequence of Axiom 1, that a plane I and a line l not lying entirely in the plane can intersect in at most one point.   If the line does not intersect the plane, then it is parallel to the plane.

The diagram shows two planes I and II intersecting in a line.

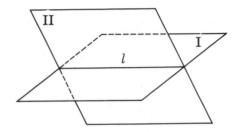

DEFINITION.   Skew lines are lines in space which do not intersect and are not parallel.

In the diagram below, the lines l and m are coplanar in I and do not intersect. They are, therefore, parallel lines by definition.   The lines l and n are not coplanar but do intersect at A.   (An enlarged dot is, by convention, used to indicate the point of intersection.) l and n are, therefore, not skew lines.

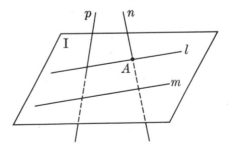

Line p is not coplanar with l and m, nor does it intersect either l or m. By definition, p and l are skew lines as are p and m.

DEFINITION.   A line l is perpendicular to a plane I at a point N if it is perpendicular to every line in the plane passing through N.

In the diagram, the line l is perpendicular to both m and n which are coplanar in I . l is perpendicular to both m and n and this is indicated by the usual marking for indicating right angles. It can be proved that a line is perpendicular to any line in a plane if it is perpendicular to any two distinct lines in the plane. l is, therefore, perpendicular to I . Similarly, p is perpendicular to I .

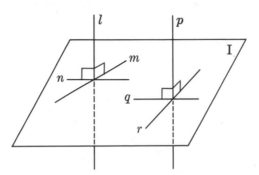

In plane geometry we have proved that if two lines are both perpendicular to the same line, then they are parallel to each other. In the same way, it may be proved that if two lines are both perpendicular to the same plane, then they are parallel to each other. In the diagram, $l \parallel p$.

When two planes intersect, they form an angle between the two planes called the *dihedral angle*. How do we measure such an angle?

In the diagram below, N is any point on the line l of intersection of the two planes. ON is perpendicular to l in plane I and PN is perpendicular to l in plane II . $\angle ONP$ can be measured in the usual way and the measure of $\angle ONP$ is defined to be the measure of the dihedral angle.

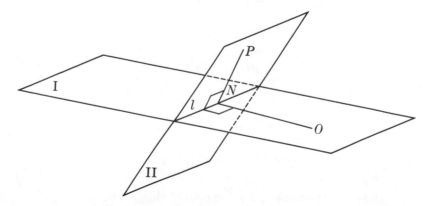

DEFINITION.   The measure of a dihedral angle is the measure of the plane angle formed by the perpendiculars to the line of intersection of the planes at any point on the line of intersection.

Example 1.   In the diagram, the figure represents a rectangular prism.   If $CD = 8$ in., $DE = 5$ in., and $BC = 6$ in., calculate the length of the diagonal GH and the measure of $\angle GHD$.

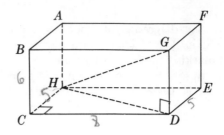

Solution: In $\triangle HCD$,
$$\angle HCD = 90°.$$

Therefore,
$$HD^2 = HC^2 + CD^2$$
$$= 25 + 64.$$
$$HD = \sqrt{89} \text{ in.}$$

In $\triangle GHD$,
$$\angle GDH = 90°.$$

Therefore,
$$GH^2 = GD^2 + HD^2$$
$$= 36 + 89$$
$$= 125.$$
$$GH = 5\sqrt{5} \text{ in.}$$
$$\sin \angle GHD = \frac{GD}{GH}$$
$$= \frac{6}{5\sqrt{5}}$$
$$= \frac{6\sqrt{5}}{25}$$
$$\simeq .5366.$$

Hence,
$$\angle GHD \simeq 32°.$$

EXERCISE 1.1

1. Sketch
    (a) two intersecting planes,
    (b) two skew lines,
    (c) two skew lines and a third line intersecting them,
    (d) a line and a plane intersecting,
    (e) three planes intersecting in a point,
    (f) three planes intersecting in a line.

2. How many planes can be passed through (a) a line? (b) two intersecting lines? (c) two skew lines?

3. How many planes can be passed through (a) a point? (b) two points? (c) three points? State any special cases.

4. What is the measure of the dihedral angle between a wall and the floor of your classroom?

5. Calculate the length of the diagonal of a rectangular prism if the lengths of the sides are 12 in., 9 in., and 8 in.

6. In the diagram, which represents a rectangular prism, $CG = 12$ in., $GH = 5$ in., $BC = 6$ in. Calculate the length of the diagonal DF and the measures of $\angle CDG$ and $\angle EDG$.

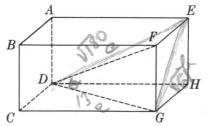

1.2. Vectors

The mass of an object in some particular unit can be expressed by a single real number; the length of a line segment in some particular unit can be expressed by a single real number. Such quantities are known as *scalar* quantities. A scalar quantity has only magnitude and is specified completely in size by a number. In this text all scalars will be real numbers.

However, many physical quantities cannot be completely specified by magnitude alone. A force acting on a body is not completely specified by stating only its magnitude. We must also know the direction in which that force is acting. Such quantities are known as vector quantities and must be specified by a real number called the magnitude, and by a direction in space.

While it is not possible to adequately define a vector, it is possible to understand intuitively the basic idea. Vectors were originally devised for the purpose of dealing with physical quantities such as force and velocity involving both magnitude and direction. However, vectors are now fundamental to many branches of mathematics and, while the application of vectors to physical problems is still of great importance, the application to other subject areas is now of even greater value.

We may describe a nonzero vector as having two fundamental properties: a positive real number called its magnitude or length, and a direction in space. A vector may then be represented by a directed line segment drawn to a suitable scale. Such vectors are usually known as geometric vectors.

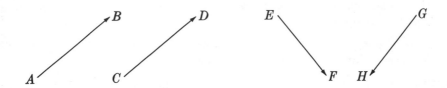

In the diagram, AB, CD, EF, and GH represent vectors with A, C, E, and G, the initial points of the line segments. If drawn to the same scale, vectors AB, CD, and GH are all equal in magnitude. AB and CD are also equal in direction (they are parallel) but GH is opposite in direction to AB and CD. The vectors AB and CD are defined to be equal.

DEFINITION.   Two geometric vectors are equal if and only if they have the same magnitude and the same direction.

Various symbols are used to name vectors. The vectors in the diagram may be named $\overrightarrow{AB}$, $\overrightarrow{CD}$, $\overrightarrow{EF}$, $\overrightarrow{GH}$, the arrow indicating that the direction of $\overrightarrow{AB}$ is from A to B. The vector $\overrightarrow{BA}$ is not equal to $\overrightarrow{AB}$ since, although they have the same magnitude, they are opposite in direction. In the diagram,

$$\overrightarrow{AB} = \overrightarrow{CD}, \qquad \overrightarrow{AB} \neq \overrightarrow{GH}.$$

Another way of naming vectors in print is by bold-face single letters, **u**, **v**, **w**, etc. This is not too useful in written work but, if the single letter representation is desirable, it may be written as $\vec{u}$, $\vec{v}$, $\vec{w}$, etc., to indicate that we are discussing a vector and not a scalar.

Frequently we are interested in the magnitude of a vector. The magnitude of vector $\overrightarrow{AB}$ or of vector **v** is indicated by

$$|\overrightarrow{AB}| \qquad \text{or} \qquad |\mathbf{v}|.$$

Note, that in the diagram above, although

$$\overrightarrow{AB} \neq \overrightarrow{GH},$$

it is true that

$$|\overrightarrow{AB}| = |\overrightarrow{GH}|.$$

When we state that $\overrightarrow{AB} = \overrightarrow{CD} = \overrightarrow{EF} = \overrightarrow{GH}$, we understand from the definition that these vectors have the same magnitude and the same direction. Such vectors belong to an equivalence class of vectors. By this we understand that in any discussion involving vectors any one of these vectors may be used as a representative of that class.

In previous work we have used any member of the equivalence class of fractions $\frac{1}{2}, \frac{2}{4}, \frac{3}{6}, \cdots$ as a representative of that class. In any discussion involving fractions, we may substitute any one of $\frac{1}{2}, \frac{2}{4}, \frac{3}{6}, \cdots$ for any other member of the class; they are equivalent fractions. In the same way, we may substitute any one of $\overrightarrow{AB}, \overrightarrow{CD}, \overrightarrow{EF}, \overrightarrow{GH}, \cdots$ for any other member of the class of equivalent vectors.

1.3. Addition of Vectors

When the symbols $+, -, \times, \div$ are associated with numbers, we have already assigned a meaning to them. However, when we talk about addition of vectors, the symbols $\overrightarrow{PQ} + \overrightarrow{QR}$, $\mathbf{v} + \mathbf{u}$, $\mathbf{u} - \mathbf{v}$, have, as yet, no meaning, Consequently, we are free to define them as we please but, unless the meaning we assign is of some value, it is unlikely that it will prove acceptable. The actual definition used has arisen because of its application in physics.

DEFINITION. If $\mathbf{u}$ and $\mathbf{v}$ are two vectors represented by $\overrightarrow{PQ}$ and $\overrightarrow{QR}$, respectively, so that the endpoint of the line segment PQ is the initial point of the line segment QR, then the sum of $\mathbf{u}$ and $\mathbf{v}$ is represented by $\overrightarrow{PR}$.

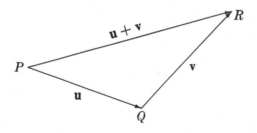

We note that two vectors $\mathbf{u}$ and $\mathbf{v}$ may be represented by any two line segments $\overrightarrow{PQ}$ and $\overrightarrow{QR}$, provided that $\overrightarrow{PQ}$ and $\mathbf{u}$ are equal in magnitude and direction and also that $\overrightarrow{QR}$ and $\mathbf{v}$ are equal in magnitude and direction.

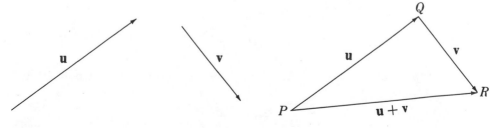

Some special cases are worth noting.

(a) If **u** and **v** have the same direction, then Q lies between P and R and we see an immediate analogy to addition on the real number line.

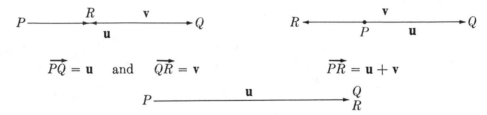

$$\vec{PR} = \mathbf{u} + \mathbf{v}$$

(b) If **u** and **v** are opposite in direction, then R lies between P and Q or P lies between R and Q and we see the analogy to subtraction on the real number line.

$$\vec{PQ} = \mathbf{u} \quad \text{and} \quad \vec{QR} = \mathbf{v} \qquad\qquad \vec{PR} = \mathbf{u} + \mathbf{v}$$

(ċ) If Q and R coincide so that $\mathbf{v} = \vec{QR} = \vec{QQ}$, then

$$\mathbf{u} + \mathbf{v} = \vec{PQ} + \vec{QQ} = \vec{PQ}.$$

Vector **v** or $\vec{QQ}$ is, in this case, defined to be the zero vector, denoted by **0**, and we can write

$$\mathbf{u} + \mathbf{0} = \mathbf{u}.$$

The analogy with the algebra of real numbers is immediately apparent. Although the zero vector has no direction, it is convenient to regard it as parallel to every vector. The zero vector has magnitude zero.

(d) If $\vec{PQ}$ and $\vec{QR}$ are equal in magnitude but opposite in direction, P and R will coincide.

Therefore, $\vec{PQ} + \vec{QR} = \vec{PR} = \mathbf{0}$ or

$$\vec{PQ} + \vec{QP} = \mathbf{0}.$$

Since $\vec{PQ}$ has been denoted by **u**, it would seem appropriate to denote $\vec{QP}$ by $-\mathbf{u}$ and we can write that

$$\mathbf{u} + (-\mathbf{u}) = \mathbf{0}.$$

This equation suggests that we define the negative of a vector as follows.

DEFINITION: The negative of a vector **u** is a vector equal in magnitude to **u** but opposite in direction, and is denoted by −**u**.

We note that

$$-(-\mathbf{u}) = \mathbf{u}.$$

This result enables us to define subtraction of vectors in the same way as we define subtraction of real numbers.

$$\mathbf{u} - \mathbf{v} = \mathbf{u} + (-\mathbf{v})$$

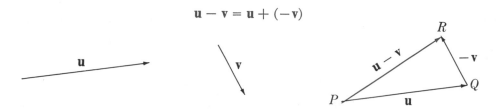

If $\overrightarrow{PQ} = \mathbf{u}$ and $\overrightarrow{RQ} = \mathbf{v}$, then $\overrightarrow{QR} = -\mathbf{v}$ and $\overrightarrow{PR} = \mathbf{u} - \mathbf{v}$. Let us consider the parallelogram $PQRS$.

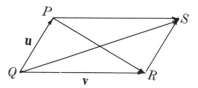

If $\overrightarrow{QP} = \mathbf{u}$ and $\overrightarrow{QR} = \mathbf{v}$, then $\overrightarrow{PS} = \mathbf{v}$ and $\overrightarrow{RS} = \mathbf{u}$. Thus,

$$\begin{aligned}
\mathbf{u} + \mathbf{v} &= \overrightarrow{QP} + \overrightarrow{QR} \\
&= \overrightarrow{QP} + \overrightarrow{PS} \\
&= \overrightarrow{QS}.
\end{aligned}$$

That is, the sum of the vectors can either be obtained from the sides of $\triangle QPS$ or as the diagonal QS of parallelogram $PQRS$. If, instead of drawing the two given vectors so that the endpoint of one is the initial point of the second, as in the triangle method, we prefer to draw both vectors with a common initial point, then we obtain the sum as the diagonal of the parallelogram in which the two given vectors are adjacent sides. The diagonal required will have the same common initial point.

The diagonal PR also represents a vector.

$$\begin{aligned}
\overrightarrow{PR} &= \overrightarrow{PS} + \overrightarrow{SR} \\
&= \mathbf{v} - \mathbf{u}. \\
\overrightarrow{RP} &= \overrightarrow{RS} + \overrightarrow{SP} \\
&= \mathbf{u} - \mathbf{v}.
\end{aligned}$$

Example 1.   Two vectors **u** and **v** have a common initial point and form an angle of 60°.   If $|\mathbf{u}| = 6$ and $|\mathbf{v}| = 8$, find $|\mathbf{u} + \mathbf{v}|$ and the angle between $\mathbf{u} + \mathbf{v}$ and **v**.

Solution: In $\triangle QRS$,

$$QR = 8, \quad RS = 6, \quad \angle QRS = 120°.$$
$$QS^2 = RQ^2 + RS^2 - 2RQ \cdot RS \cos \angle QRS$$
$$= 64 + 36 + 2\,(8)\,(6) \cos 60°$$
$$= 148.$$
$$QS = 2\sqrt{37}$$
$$\simeq 12.2.$$

Hence, $|\mathbf{u} + \mathbf{v}| \simeq 12.2.$

$$\frac{\sin \angle SQR}{RS} = \frac{\sin \angle QRS}{QS}.$$

$$\frac{\sin \angle SQR}{6} = \frac{\sin 120°}{12.2}.$$

$$\sin \angle SQR = \frac{6 \sin 60°}{12.2}$$

$$\simeq \frac{6\sqrt{3}}{12.2 \times 2}$$

$$\simeq .426.$$

Therefore,

$$\angle SQR \simeq 25°.$$

The angle between $\mathbf{u} + \mathbf{v}$ and **v** is 25°.

When three or more vectors are involved in a problem they are, in general, not in the same plane. Any two vectors, however, are coplanar, and in certain circumstances, three or more vectors may be coplanar.

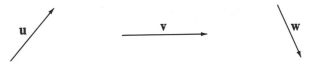

If **u**, **v**, and **w** are three coplanar vectors, as in the diagram, they may be represented by the equivalent parallel vectors $\overrightarrow{PQ}$, $\overrightarrow{QR}$, and $\overrightarrow{RS}$. Then

$$\overrightarrow{PR} = \overrightarrow{PQ} + \overrightarrow{QR}$$

and

$$\overrightarrow{PS} = \overrightarrow{PR} + \overrightarrow{RS}$$
$$= (\overrightarrow{PQ} + \overrightarrow{QR}) + \overrightarrow{RS}$$
$$= (\mathbf{u} + \mathbf{v}) + \mathbf{w}.$$

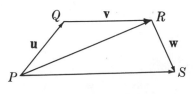

In the same way, if **u**, **v**, and **w** are not coplanar, as in the diagram, then

$$\overrightarrow{PV} = (\mathbf{u} + \mathbf{v}) + \mathbf{w}.$$

$\overrightarrow{PQ}$ and $\overrightarrow{PR}$ are coplanar in the plane $PQSR$ and

$$\overrightarrow{PS} = \overrightarrow{PQ} + \overrightarrow{PR}.$$

$\overrightarrow{PS}$ and $\overrightarrow{PT}$ are coplanar in the plane $PSVT$ and

$$\overrightarrow{PV} = \overrightarrow{PS} + \overrightarrow{PT}.$$

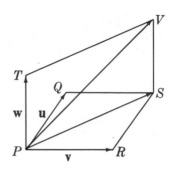

Therefore,

$$\begin{aligned}\overrightarrow{PV} &= \overrightarrow{PS} + \overrightarrow{PT} \\ &= (\overrightarrow{PQ} + \overrightarrow{PR}) + \overrightarrow{PT} \\ &= (\mathbf{u} + \mathbf{v}) + \mathbf{w}.\end{aligned}$$

Example 2. Two vectors **u** and **v** have a common initial point and form an angle of 75°. A third vector **w** has the same initial point and is perpendicular to the plane containing **u** and **v**. If $|\mathbf{u}| = 4$, $|\mathbf{v}| = 7$, and $|\mathbf{w}| = 6$, calculate $|(\mathbf{u} + \mathbf{v}) + \mathbf{w}|$.

Solution:

$$\begin{aligned}(\mathbf{u} + \mathbf{v}) + \mathbf{w} &= (\overrightarrow{QT} + \overrightarrow{QR}) + \overrightarrow{QP} \\ &= \overrightarrow{QS} + \overrightarrow{QP} \\ &= \overrightarrow{QW}.\end{aligned}$$

In $\triangle SQR$,

$$\begin{aligned}SQ^2 &= RQ^2 + RS^2 - 2RQ \cdot RS \cos \angle QRS \\ &= 49 + 16 + 2\,(7)\,(4) \cos 75° \\ &\simeq 65 + 56\,(.2588) \\ &\simeq 79.45.\end{aligned}$$

In $\triangle WQS$,

$$\begin{aligned}QW^2 &= QS^2 + SW^2 \\ &\simeq 79.45 + 36 \\ &= 115.45 \\ &\simeq 2\sqrt{29} \\ &\simeq 10.7.\end{aligned}$$

Therefore,

$$|(\mathbf{u} + \mathbf{v}) + \mathbf{w}| \simeq 11.$$

EXERCISE 1.3

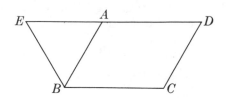

1. $ABCD$ is a parallelogram and $EB = AB$. State which vectors (if any) are equal to $\overrightarrow{AB}$, $\overrightarrow{DA}$, $\overrightarrow{EB}$, $\overrightarrow{BC}$, $\overrightarrow{ED}$.

2. $PQRS$ is a parallelogram. $\overrightarrow{QP} = \mathbf{u}$ and $\overrightarrow{PS} = \mathbf{v}$. State which vectors are equal to $\mathbf{u} + \mathbf{v}$, $\mathbf{v} + \mathbf{u}$, $\mathbf{u} - \mathbf{v}$, $\mathbf{v} - \mathbf{u}$.

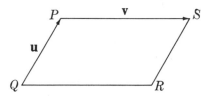

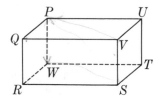

3. The diagram on the right represents a rectangular prism. State a single vector equal to each of the following.
   (a) $\overrightarrow{RQ} + \overrightarrow{RS}$
   (b) $\overrightarrow{RQ} + \overrightarrow{QV}$
   (c) $\overrightarrow{RW} + \overrightarrow{RS}$
   (d) $\overrightarrow{RQ} + \overrightarrow{RT}$
   (e) $\overrightarrow{PW} + \overrightarrow{WS}$
   (f) $(\overrightarrow{RQ} + \overrightarrow{RS}) + \overrightarrow{VU}$
   (g) $\overrightarrow{RQ} + (\overrightarrow{RS} + \overrightarrow{VU})$
   (h) $\overrightarrow{PW} - \overrightarrow{VP}$

4. Three vectors $\mathbf{f}$, $\mathbf{g}$, and $\mathbf{h}$ form a triangle ABC with $\overrightarrow{AB} = \mathbf{f}$, $\overrightarrow{BC} = \mathbf{g}$, $\overrightarrow{CA} = \mathbf{h}$. State a single vector equal to each of $(\mathbf{f} + \mathbf{g}) + \mathbf{h}$ and $\mathbf{f} + (\mathbf{g} + \mathbf{h})$.

5. If two vectors $\mathbf{u}$ and $\mathbf{v}$ are perpendicular, show that
$$|\mathbf{u} + \mathbf{v}| = |\mathbf{u} - \mathbf{v}|.$$

6. Show that for any two vectors $\mathbf{u}$ and $\mathbf{v}$,
$$\mathbf{u} + \mathbf{v} = \mathbf{v} + \mathbf{u}.$$

7. If $\mathbf{u} = \overrightarrow{AB}$, $\mathbf{v} = \overrightarrow{BC}$, $\mathbf{w} = \overrightarrow{CD}$, show that
$$(\mathbf{u} + \mathbf{v}) + \mathbf{w} = \mathbf{u} + (\mathbf{v} + \mathbf{w}).$$

8. The diagram shows a square-based right pyramid. State any vectors equal to each of the following.
   (a) $\overrightarrow{CB}$
   (b) $\overrightarrow{AB}$
   (c) $\overrightarrow{BE}$
   (d) $\overrightarrow{AB} + \overrightarrow{BC}$
   (e) $\overrightarrow{AB} - \overrightarrow{AE}$
   (f) $\overrightarrow{DE} - \overrightarrow{DA}$
   (g) $(\overrightarrow{AE} + \overrightarrow{ED}) + \overrightarrow{DC}$
   (h) $\overrightarrow{AE} + (\overrightarrow{ED} + \overrightarrow{DC})$

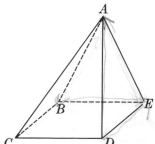

9. Vectors $\overrightarrow{PQ}$ and $\overrightarrow{PR}$ are inclined at an angle of 45° and $|\overrightarrow{PQ}| = 6$, $|\overrightarrow{PR}| = 10$. Calculate, to the nearest integer, the value of $|\overrightarrow{PQ} + \overrightarrow{PR}|$ and, to the nearest degree, the angle between $\overrightarrow{PQ} + \overrightarrow{PR}$ and $\overrightarrow{PR}$.

10. Two vectors **u** and **v** have a common initial point and form an angle of 120°. Calculate, to the nearest integer, the value of $|\mathbf{u} + \mathbf{v}|$ and, to the nearest degree, the angle between $\mathbf{u} + \mathbf{v}$ and **v**, given that $|\mathbf{u}| = 10$ and $|\mathbf{v}| = 12$.

11. The diagram below shows a rectangular prism. If $|\overrightarrow{UQ}| = 3$, $|\overrightarrow{UT}| = 4$, and $|\overrightarrow{UV}| = 12$, calculate

$$|(\overrightarrow{UQ} + \overrightarrow{UT}) + \overrightarrow{UV}|$$

and $\angle SUW$, to the nearest degree.

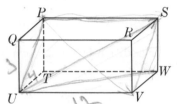

12. Two vectors **u** and **v** have a common initial point and form an angle of 60°. A third vector **w** has the same initial point and is perpendicular to the plane containing **u** and **v**. If $|\mathbf{u}| = 5$, $|\mathbf{v}| = 6$, and $|\mathbf{w}| = 3$, calculate the value of $|(\mathbf{u} + \mathbf{v}) + \mathbf{w}|$, to the nearest integer.

1.4. Algebraic Properties of Vector Addition

Algebraic addition of real numbers has certain properties with which we are familiar.   If a, b, and c are real numbers, then

$$a + b = b + a \qquad \text{Commutative property,}$$
$$(a + b) + c = a + (b + c) \qquad \text{Associative property,}$$
$$a + 0 = 0 + a = a \qquad \text{Identity property,}$$
$$a + (-a) = (-a) + a = 0 \qquad \text{Inverse property.}$$

From the work of the previous sections it would appear that vectors also have this set of properties.

1. *Commutative Property*   If **u** and **v** are vectors, then

$$\mathbf{u} + \mathbf{v} = \mathbf{v} + \mathbf{u}.$$

As with the commutative property of addition of numbers, this is really an axiom of vector addition.   However, its plausibility can be illustrated intuitively by letting $\mathbf{u} = \overrightarrow{PQ}$ and $\mathbf{v} = \overrightarrow{QR}$ and using our definition of vector addition.

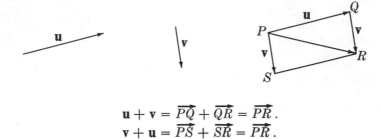

$$\mathbf{u} + \mathbf{v} = \overrightarrow{PQ} + \overrightarrow{QR} = \overrightarrow{PR}.$$
$$\mathbf{v} + \mathbf{u} = \overrightarrow{PS} + \overrightarrow{SR} = \overrightarrow{PR}.$$

Therefore,

$$\mathbf{u} + \mathbf{v} = \mathbf{v} + \mathbf{u}.$$

2. *Associative Property*

$$(\mathbf{u} + \mathbf{v}) + \mathbf{w} = \mathbf{u} + (\mathbf{v} + \mathbf{w}).$$

Again this is an axiom for vector addition but it may be illustrated by the addition of geometrical vectors in a diagram.

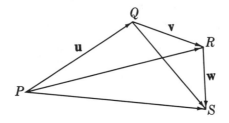

$$\begin{aligned}
(\mathbf{u} + \mathbf{v}) + \mathbf{w} &= (\overrightarrow{PQ} + \overrightarrow{QR}) + \overrightarrow{RS} \\
&= \overrightarrow{PR} + \overrightarrow{RS} \\
&= \overrightarrow{PS}. \\
\mathbf{u} + (\mathbf{v} + \mathbf{w}) &= \overrightarrow{PQ} + (\overrightarrow{QR} + \overrightarrow{RS}) \\
&= \overrightarrow{PQ} + \overrightarrow{QS} \\
&= \overrightarrow{PS}.
\end{aligned}$$

Therefore,

$$(\mathbf{u} + \mathbf{v}) + \mathbf{w} = \mathbf{u} + (\mathbf{v} + \mathbf{w}).$$

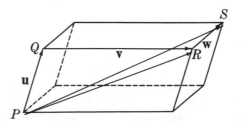

Note that this last equation applies whether the vectors are coplanar or not. Both diagrams indicate the same result.   Remember that, while any two vectors are coplanar, three vectors, in general, are not coplanar.

These two properties indicate that vector addition may be performed in any order.   The brackets in $(\mathbf{u} + \mathbf{v}) + \mathbf{w}$ are no longer necessary and may now be omitted.

It should also be noted that this may be extended to include any number of vectors in any number of planes.

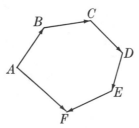

In the diagram,

$$\vec{AB} + \vec{BC} + \vec{CD} + \vec{DE} + \vec{EF} = \vec{AF}.$$

Remember again that although the diagram is drawn on a sheet of paper, the vectors need not be coplanar.   It is useful to make a three dimensional "diagram" or model of wire, or drinking straws, or pipe cleaners.

3. *Identity Property*   In Section 1.3, we have defined the zero vector $\mathbf{0}$ and, by our definition, this is the identity element for vector addition.

$$\mathbf{v} + \mathbf{0} = \mathbf{0} + \mathbf{v} = \mathbf{v}.$$

4. *Inverse Property*   Again in Section 1.3, we have defined the negative of a vector.   If $\mathbf{u} = \vec{PQ}$, then $-\mathbf{u} = \vec{QP}$, and

$$\mathbf{u} + (-\mathbf{u}) = (-\mathbf{u}) + \mathbf{u} = \mathbf{0}.$$

Example 1.   Prove that

$$(\mathbf{u} + \mathbf{v}) + (\mathbf{w} + (-\mathbf{u})) = \mathbf{v} + \mathbf{w}.$$

Solution:

$$
\begin{aligned}
(\mathbf{u} + \mathbf{v}) + (\mathbf{w} + (-\mathbf{u})) &= (\mathbf{v} + \mathbf{u}) + (-\mathbf{u} + \mathbf{w}) & (1)\\
&= [(\mathbf{v} + \mathbf{u}) + (-\mathbf{u})] + \mathbf{w} & (2)\\
&= [\mathbf{v} + (\mathbf{u} + (-\mathbf{u}))] + \mathbf{w} & (3)\\
&= [\mathbf{v} + \mathbf{0}] + \mathbf{w} & (4)\\
&= \mathbf{v} + \mathbf{w}. & (5)
\end{aligned}
$$

In step (1) we used the commutative property twice, in steps (2) and (3) we made use of the associative property, in step (4) we used the inverse property, and in step (5), the identity property.

It should be mentioned that, while we proved this identity in detail using only the four properties, it would be more usual to eliminate most of the steps as we do in proving algebraic identities.

The result may be indicated diagrammatically.

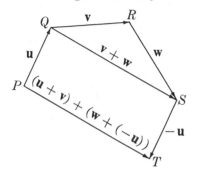

$$\vec{QS} = \mathbf{v} + \mathbf{w}.$$
$$\vec{PT} = (\mathbf{u} + \mathbf{v}) + (\mathbf{w} + (-\mathbf{u})).$$

$PQST$ is a parallelogram; therefore

$$\vec{QS} = \vec{PT}.$$

EXERCISE 1.4

1. Using the diagram, show that
$$\vec{PQ} + \vec{QR} + \vec{RS} + \vec{ST} + \vec{TU} = \vec{PU}.$$

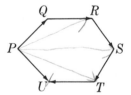

2. Using the diagram of question (1), show that
$$\vec{PQ} + \vec{QR} + \vec{RS} + \vec{ST} + \vec{TU} + \vec{UP} = \mathbf{0}.$$

3. Prove that
$$(\mathbf{u} + \mathbf{v}) + (-\mathbf{u}) = \mathbf{v}.$$

4. Prove that for given vectors $\mathbf{u}$ and $\mathbf{v}$, there is always a vector $\mathbf{w}$ such that
$$\mathbf{u} + \mathbf{w} = \mathbf{v}.$$

5. Prove that
$$\mathbf{u} + \mathbf{v} + (-\mathbf{u}) + \mathbf{w} + (-\mathbf{v}) = \mathbf{w}.$$

6. From the diagram, state a single vector equal to each of the following.
   (a) $\vec{RQ} + \vec{QV} + \vec{VS} + \vec{ST}$
   (b) $\vec{RS} + \vec{RQ} + \vec{VP} + \vec{PW}$

   (Note that all opposite planes are parallel.)

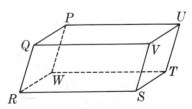

7. From the diagram, state a single vector equal to each of the following.

(a) $\vec{PQ} + \vec{QR} + \vec{RS}$

(b) $\vec{PS} + \vec{ST} + \vec{TQ} + \vec{QR} + \vec{RP}$

(c) $\vec{PR} - \vec{PQ}$

(d) $\vec{PQ} - \vec{PR}$

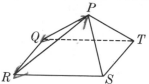

1.5. Force and Velocity

The mathematics of vectors was first developed to simplify working with such physical quantities as force and velocity where both magnitude and direction are of importance. We will now look at some examples of this application.

To represent a physical vector, we draw an arrow whose length and direction indicate the magnitude and direction of the vector.

A force of 50 pounds acting on a body at an angle of 40° to the horizontal would be represented by a vector drawn at an angle of 40° to the horizontal. If we decide that a suitable scale is 1 inch to represent 10 pounds, then the length of the vector would be 5 inches. A velocity of 30 m.p.h. at a bearing of 240° would be represented by a vector of magnitude 30 on some suitable scale. The 240° angle is, by convention, measured in a clockwise direction from north. This latter vector may also be given as a velocity of 30 m.p.h. at an angle of S 60° W indicating that the velocity is in a direction of 60° to the west of south.

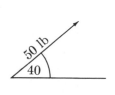

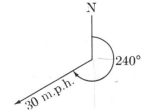

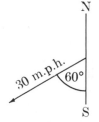

When two or more forces act on a body, the resultant effect depends on the magnitude and direction of the given forces.

The diagram indicates three forces acting at a point on a body: a force of 60 pounds acting in a horizontal direction, a force of 40 pounds acting at an angle of 45° to the horizontal, and a force of 30 pounds acting at an angle of −60° to the horizontal.

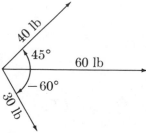

The resultant of two or more forces acting at a point on a body may be defined in terms of the forces or in terms of the associated vectors.

DEFINITION.   The resultant of two or more forces acting at a point on a body is that single force which would have the same effect as the given forces.   The resultant of two or more physical vectors representing forces with a common initial point is the sum of the given vectors.

DEFINITION.   The equilibrant of two or more forces acting at a point on a body is that single force which, when applied to the body, maintains it in a state of equilibrium.

In the diagram, $\mathbf{F}_1$ and $\mathbf{F}_2$ are two forces represented by $\overrightarrow{AB}$ and $\overrightarrow{AD}$, acting on a body at A.

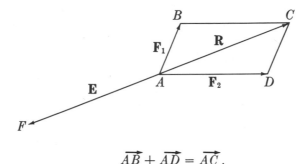

$$\overrightarrow{AB} + \overrightarrow{AD} = \overrightarrow{AC}.$$

Hence vector $\overrightarrow{AC}$ represents in magnitude and direction the resultant $\mathbf{R}$ of $\mathbf{F}_1$ and $\mathbf{F}_2$.   The body would tend to move in the direction represented by $\overrightarrow{AC}$. If a force equal in magnitude to $\mathbf{R}$ were applied at A, but in the opposite direction, it would counteract the resultant $\mathbf{R}$ and the body would be maintained in a state of equilibrium.   Such a force is the equilibrant $\mathbf{E}$ and is represented by $\overrightarrow{AF}$ where $\overrightarrow{AF} = -\overrightarrow{AC}$.

The equilibrant of two or more forces acting at a point is equal in magnitude but opposite in direction to the resultant.

In the diagram, three forces $\mathbf{F}_1$, $\mathbf{F}_2$, and $\mathbf{F}_3$ act on a body at O.   These forces are represented by $\overrightarrow{AB}$, $\overrightarrow{BC}$, and $\overrightarrow{CD}$.   By definition, the resultant $\mathbf{R}$ is represented by $\overrightarrow{AD}$ and the equilibrant by $\overrightarrow{DA}$ or $-\overrightarrow{AD}$.

If an aircraft is flying on a bearing of 80° at 300 m.p.h., and a wind is blowing from 120° at 20 m.p.h., as shown in the diagram, the resultant **R** of the two velocities will give the actual ground speed and direction of the aircraft.

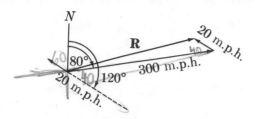

Example 1.   Two forces of 20 pounds and 30 pounds act on a body at an angle of 50° to each other.   Find the magnitude and direction of the resultant, to the nearest pound and the nearest degree.

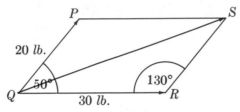

Solution: In △PQR,

$$QS^2 = RQ^2 + RS^2 - 2RQ \cdot RS \cos \angle QRS$$
$$= 900 + 400 - 2(30)(20) \cos 130°$$
$$= 1300 + 1200 \cos 50°$$
$$\simeq 1300 + 1200(.6428)$$
$$= 2071.36 .$$

Therefore,

$$QS \simeq 46 .$$

$$\frac{\sin \angle SQR}{RS} = \frac{\sin \angle SRQ}{QS} .$$

$$\sin \angle SQR \simeq \frac{20 \sin 50°}{46}$$

$$\simeq \frac{20 (.7660)}{46}$$

$$\simeq .333 .$$

Thus,

$$\angle SQR \simeq 19° .$$

Therefore, the resultant force has a magnitude of 46 pounds and acts at an angle of 19° to the 30-pound force.

Example 2. Three forces of 30 pounds, 45 pounds, and 50 pounds act on a body. The first two act at an angle of 120° to each other and the third is perpendicular to the plane of the first two. Find, to the nearest pound, the magnitude of the resultant and the angle which the resultant makes with the plane containing the first two forces.

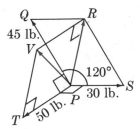

Solution: In $\triangle PRS$,

$$PR^2 = SP^2 + SR^2 - 2SP \cdot SR \cos \angle RSP$$
$$= 900 + 2025 - 2\,(30)\,(45) \cos 60°$$
$$= 2925 - 1350$$
$$= 1575 .$$

In $\triangle PTV$, $\angle PTV = 90°$.

$$PV^2 = PT^2 + TV^2$$
$$= PT^2 + PR^2$$
$$= 2500 + 1575$$
$$= 4075 .$$

Therefore,

$$PV \simeq 64 .$$

$$\sin \angle VPR = \frac{VR}{PV}$$
$$= \frac{50}{64}$$
$$\simeq .781 .$$

Therefore,

$$\angle VPR \simeq 51° .$$

Therefore, the resultant is a force of 64 pounds acting at an angle of 51° to the plane containing the first two forces.

Example 3. An aircraft is flying at 300 m.p.h. on a bearing of 80°. A wind is blowing at 50 m.p.h. from a bearing of 120°. Determine the actual ground speed and direction of the aircraft.

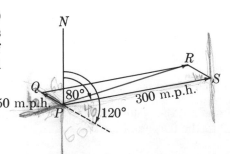

Solution: In $\triangle PRS$, $\angle RSP = 40°$.

$$PR^2 = SP^2 + SR^2 - 2SP \cdot SR \cos \angle RSP$$
$$= 90000 + 2500 - 2(300)(50) \cos 40°$$
$$= 92500 - 30000(.7660)$$
$$= 92500 - 22,980$$
$$= 69,520 .$$

Therefore,

$$PR \simeq 264 .$$

$$\frac{\sin \angle RPS}{RS} = \frac{\sin \angle RSP}{PR} .$$

$$\sin \angle RPS = \frac{50 \sin 40°}{264}$$

$$\simeq \frac{50 (.6428)}{264}$$

$$\simeq .1217 .$$

Thus,

$$\angle RPS \simeq 7° .$$

Therefore, the ground speed is 264 m.p.h. on a bearing of 73°.

EXERCISE 1.5

1. Calculate the magnitude of the resultant force of each of the following pairs of forces.   All forces should be given to the nearest pound and all angles to the nearest degree.

    (a) 30 pounds and 40 pounds at an angle of 90° to each other

    (b) 40 pounds and 40 pounds at an angle of 60° to each other

    (c) 50 pounds and 80 pounds at an angle of 120° to each other

    (d) 10 pounds and 12 pounds at an angle of 30° to each other

    (e) 20 pounds and 15 pounds at an angle of 180° to each other

    (f) 120 pounds and 100 pounds at an angle of 100° to each other

2. Two forces act on a body: a force of 50 pounds at an angle of 30° to the horizontal, and a force of 20 pounds at an angle of −90° to the horizontal. Calculate the magnitude of the resultant force and the angle which it makes with the horizontal.

3. Two forces act on a body: a force of 12 pounds at an angle of 60° to the horizontal, and a force of 20 pounds at an angle of 120° to the horizontal. Calculate the magnitude and direction of the equilibrant for e.

4. Two equal forces acting at an angle of 90° to each other have a resultant force of 40 pounds.   Calculate the magnitude of the two forces.

5. Two equal forces acting at an angle of 150° to each other have a resultant force of 50 pounds.   Calculate the magnitude of the two forces.

6. Three coplanar forces act on a body: a force of 30 pounds at an angle of 30° to the horizontal, a force of 40 pounds at an angle of 120° to the horizontal, and a force of 20 pounds at an angle of −90° to the horizontal.   Calculate the magnitude of the resultant force and the angle which it makes with the horizontal.

7. Three coplanar forces of x pounds, 10 pounds, and 20 pounds act on a body and maintain it in a state of equilibrium.   If the x-pound force acts along the horizontal and the 10-pound force at an angle of 90°, find the value of x and the direction of the 20-pound force.

8. Three coplanar forces of x pounds, 10 pounds, and 20 pounds act on a body and maintain it in a state of equilibrium.   If the x-pound force acts along the horizontal and the 10-pound force at an angle of 60°, find the value of x and the direction of the 20-pound force.

9. An aircraft is flying at 500 m.p.h. on a bearing of 60°.   A 60 m.p.h. wind is blowing from a bearing of 90°.   Calculate the ground speed and direction of the aircraft.

10. An aircraft is flying at 600 m.p.h. on a bearing of 60°.   An 80 m.p.h. wind is blowing from a bearing of 270°.   Calculate the ground speed and direction of the aircraft.

11. A ship is sailing on a compass bearing of 320° at a speed of 20 knots.   A current of 6 knots is travelling from a compass bearing of 230°.   Calculate the actual direction of travel and the actual speed of the ship.

12. A fisherman wishes to cross a river from A to B as shown in the diagram. $\angle BAC = 50°$ and his outboard motor produces a speed of 10 m.p.h.   If there is a current of 4 m.p.h. downstream as shown, in what direction should he travel and what will be his actual speed?

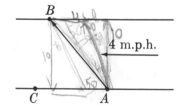

13. An aircraft pilot wishes to fly from A to B.   The distance is 400 miles on a bearing of 160° and the cruising speed of the aircraft is 350 m.p.h.   If there is a wind of 50 m.p.h. blowing from a bearing of 280°, what heading should the pilot take in order to reach his destination and how long will the flight take, to nearest minute?

14. Three forces act on a body: a force of 10 pounds and a force of 20 pounds at an angle of 60° to each other, and a force of 30 pounds perpendicular to the plane containing the first two forces.   Calculate the magnitude of the resultant force and the angle which it makes with the plane containing the first two forces.

15. Three forces act on a body: a force of 20 pounds and a force of 30 pounds at an angle of 120° to each other, and a force of 30 pounds perpendicular to the plane of the first two forces.   Calculate the magnitude of the resultant force and the angle which it makes with the plane of the first two forces.

1.6. Resolution of Forces

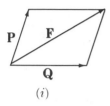

(i)

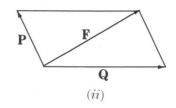

(ii)

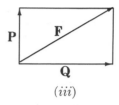

(iii)

In the diagram, two forces **P** and **Q** have a force **F** as their resultant.   All three resultants are equal in magnitude and direction.   Two given forces have only one resultant but one given force may be the resultant of any number of different pairs of given forces.   **F** is the resultant of **P** and **Q**; **P** and **Q** are the components of **F**.   A given force has an unlimited number of possible components in a given plane.   In Figure (iii), the components are perpendicular to each other.   Such components are called rectangular components.   Again it is possible to have an unlimited number of pairs of rectangular components of a given force.   However, if the angle between the given force and one of its rectangular components is given, then only one pair of rectangular components is possible.

In studying forces it is very often of value to find two rectangular components of the given force. The force is then said to have been resolved into rectangular components.   While it is possible to resolve a force into nonrectangular components, this is rarely required and, unless stated otherwise, we shall assume that when we state that a force has been resolved into components, we mean rectangular components.   As well it should be noted that it is also possible to resolve a force into more than two components not necessarily in the same plane.

In the diagram below, a force **F** has been resolved into rectangular components **P** and **Q** so that the angle between **F** and **Q** is θ.

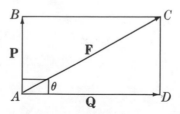

Thus,

$$\frac{AD}{AC} = \cos \theta .$$

$$AD = AC \cos \theta .$$

Hence,

$$|\mathbf{Q}| = |\mathbf{F}| \cos \theta .$$
$$\frac{AB}{AC} = \cos (90° - \theta) .$$
$$AB = AC \sin \theta .$$

Therefore,

$$|\mathbf{P}| = |\mathbf{F}| \sin \theta .$$

We see that the component of a force $\mathbf{F}$, resolved at an angle of θ to the force, has magnitude $|\mathbf{F}| \cos \theta$, and that the magnitude of the associated rectangular component is $|\mathbf{F}| \sin \theta$.

Example 1. A body weighing 60 pounds rests on a smooth ramp which is inclined at an angle of 50° to the horizontal.   What force must be applied in the direction of the ramp in order to maintain the body at rest?

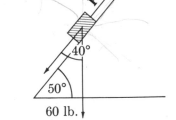

Solution: Let the required force be $\mathbf{P}$ pounds. To maintain equilibrium,

$$|\mathbf{P}| = 60 \cos 40°$$
$$\simeq 60 (.7660)$$
$$= 45.96 .$$

Therefore, the required force is 46 pounds in the direction of the ramp.

Example 2. Two boys are pulling a sled along smooth level ice.   Each boy is exerting a pull of 30 pounds at an angle of 30° to the horizontal and at an angle of 30° on either side of the direction of travel.   Find the force that draws the sled forward and the force tending to lift the sled.

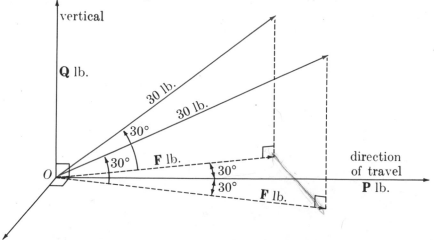

Solution: Let the force drawing the sled forward be **P** pounds. Let the force tending to lift the sled be **Q** pounds. Let the horizontal component of each applied force be **F** pounds.

$$|\mathbf{F}| = 30 \cos 30° .$$
$$|\mathbf{P}| = |\mathbf{F}| \cos 30° + |\mathbf{F}| \cos 30°$$
$$= 2\,|\mathbf{F}| \cos 30°$$
$$= 2(30 \cos 30°)\,(\cos 30°)$$
$$= 60 \cos^2 30°$$
$$= \frac{60 \times 3}{4}$$
$$= 45 .$$
$$|\mathbf{Q}| = 30 \sin 30° + 30 \sin 30°$$
$$= 15 + 15$$
$$= 30 .$$

Therefore, the force drawing the sled forward is 45 pounds and the force tending to lift the sled is 30 pounds.

EXERCISE 1.6

Give all solutions correct to the nearest unit.

1. In the diagram, **P** and **Q** are rectangular components of the force **F**. Find **P** and **Q** for each of the following values for **F** and θ.

    (a) $|\mathbf{F}| = 40$ pounds, $\theta = 30°$
    (b) $|\mathbf{F}| = 60$ pounds, $\theta = 45°$
    (c) $|\mathbf{F}| = 200$ pounds, $\theta = 60°$
    (d) $|\mathbf{F}| = 20$ pounds, $\theta = 35°$
    (e) $|\mathbf{F}| = 72$ pounds, $\theta = 54°$
    (f) $|\mathbf{F}| = 45$ pounds, $\theta = 20°$

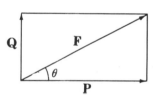

2. Resolve a 35-pound force into two rectangular components so that the magnitudes of the components are in the ratio 3 : 4. Calculate the angle between the 35-pound force and the larger component.

3. A boy pulls a sled along smooth level ice exerting a force of 20 pounds at an angle of 45° to the horizontal. What is the magnitude of the force which moves the sled forward and what is the magnitude of the force tending to lift the sled?

4. A telephone pole is anchored by means of a guy wire as shown in the sketch. What is the magnitude of the force **P**, perpendicular to the pole, if the tension in the guy wire is 300 pounds and the wire makes an angle of 55° with the ground?

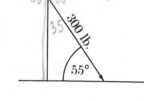

5. A 100-pound trunk rests on a smooth ramp inclined at an angle of 25° to the horizontal.   Find the force which must be applied parallel to the ramp to keep the trunk stationary on the ramp.

6. Two horses are hauling a load of logs along a smooth level road.   If each horse is exerting a pull of 500 pounds at an angle of 25° to the horizontal and at an angle of 30° on each side of the direction of travel, find the force moving the load along the road.

7. A force of 12 pounds is resolved into two components of 8 pounds and 7 pounds (not necessarily rectangular).   Find the angle which each component makes with the 12-pound force.

8. Resolve a force of 50 pounds into two equal rectangular components.

9. A smooth road is inclined at an angle of 20° to the horizontal.   What force must be applied at an angle of 20° to the road, to maintain a sled weighing 50 pounds in equilibrium on the road?

10. An aircraft is climbing at an angle of 15° to the horizontal and at a speed of 400 m.p.h.   What is its rate of climb in feet per minute and its horizontal ground speed in miles per hour?

11. A rocket is moving at an angle of 60° to the horizontal and at a speed of 10,000 m.p.h.   What is its rate of climb in feet per minute and its horizontal ground speed in miles per hour?

12. An aircraft headed due north is climbing at an angle of 20° and at an air speed of 400 m.p.h.   It is affected by a horizontal easterly wind of 60 m.p.h.   What is the rate of climb in feet per minute and the horizontal ground speed in miles per hour?

1.7. Multiplication by a Scalar

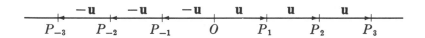

Let us consider the vector $\mathbf{u} = \overrightarrow{OP_1}$ in the diagram.

$$\overrightarrow{OP_2} = \mathbf{u} + \mathbf{u},$$
$$\overrightarrow{OP_3} = \mathbf{u} + \mathbf{u} + \mathbf{u},$$

and it would seem appropriate to represent $\overrightarrow{OP_3}$ by $3\mathbf{u}$ as in the algebra of real numbers. Similarly, it would seem natural to represent $\overrightarrow{OP_{-3}}$ by $(-3)\mathbf{u}$. In general,

$$\overrightarrow{OP}_n = \mathbf{u} + \mathbf{u} + \mathbf{u} + \cdots + \mathbf{u} \qquad\qquad (n \text{ terms})$$
$$= n\mathbf{u}.$$

If n is a positive scalar, then $n\mathbf{u}$ is a vector in the same direction as $\mathbf{u}$ but with magnitude n times as great. If n is a negative scalar, then $n\mathbf{u}$ is a vector in the opposite direction to that of $\mathbf{u}$ and with magnitude $|n|$ times the magnitude of $\mathbf{u}$.

This suggests the following definition of the multiplication of a vector by a scalar.

DEFINITION.   If $\mathbf{u}$ is a *nonzero* vector and k, a *nonzero* real number, the vector $k\mathbf{u}$ is defined by the following rules.

(1) $|k\mathbf{u}| = |k| \, |\mathbf{u}|$.

(2) The directions of $k\mathbf{u}$ and $\mathbf{u}$ are the same if $k > 0$ and opposite if $k < 0$.

This definition may be extended to include the zero vector or the scalar zero.

DEFINITION. $k\mathbf{0} = \mathbf{0}$ and $0\mathbf{u} = \mathbf{0}$.

That is, the product of any real number and the zero vector is the zero vector, and the product of the number zero and any vector is the zero vector.

Properties of Multiplication by a Scalar

For the following properties, $\mathbf{u}$ and $\mathbf{v}$ are vectors and k and l are real numbers.

(1) $k\mathbf{u}$ is a vector.

(2) $k\mathbf{u} = \mathbf{u}k$.

(3) If $k = l$ and $\mathbf{u} = \mathbf{v}$, then $k\mathbf{u} = l\mathbf{v}$.

(4) $(kl)\mathbf{u} = k(l\mathbf{u})$.

(5) $1\mathbf{u} = \mathbf{u}$.

(6) $(-1)\mathbf{u} = -\mathbf{u}$.

(7) $k(\mathbf{u} + \mathbf{v}) = k\mathbf{u} + k\mathbf{v}$.

(8) $(k + l)\mathbf{u} = k\mathbf{u} + l\mathbf{u}$.

(9) $|k\mathbf{u}| = |k| \, |\mathbf{u}|$. *length of vector*

We note that there are two distributive properties. Property (7) states that multiplication by a scalar is distributive over vector addition; property (8) states that multiplication by a given vector is distributive over scalar addition. The validity of these properties may be demonstrated by using geometric vectors. We shall demonstrate some of them and leave the others as exercises.

Property (7) $k(\mathbf{u} + \mathbf{v}) = k\mathbf{u} + k\mathbf{v}$.

  Case 1. $k > 0$.

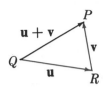

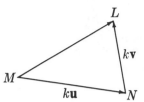

Let $\overrightarrow{QR} = \mathbf{u}$ and $\overrightarrow{RP} = \mathbf{v}$; then $\overrightarrow{QP} = \mathbf{u} + \mathbf{v}$.

Construct $\triangle LMN$ with $MN \parallel QR$, $NL \parallel RP$, $ML \parallel QP$, and $\overrightarrow{MN} = k\mathbf{u}$.   Then

$$\triangle LMN \parallel\!\parallel\!\parallel \triangle PQR.$$

Therefore,

$$\overrightarrow{NL} = k\,\overrightarrow{RP} = k\mathbf{v}$$

and

$$\overrightarrow{ML} = k\,\overrightarrow{QP} = k(\mathbf{u} + \mathbf{v}).$$

But

$$\overrightarrow{ML} = \overrightarrow{MN} + \overrightarrow{NL}$$

$$= k\mathbf{u} + k\mathbf{v}.$$

Therefore,

$$k(\mathbf{u} + \mathbf{v}) = k\mathbf{u} + k\mathbf{v}.$$

The following cases are also possible and demonstrations of these are asked for in Exercise 1.7.

  Case 2. $k < 0$.

  Case 3. $k = 0$.

  Case 4. $\mathbf{u}$ and $\mathbf{v}$ are collinear.

Property (8) $(k + l)\mathbf{u} = k\mathbf{u} + l\mathbf{u}$.

  Case 1. $k > 0$, $l > 0$, $\mathbf{u} \neq \mathbf{0}$.

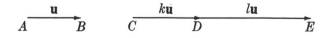

Since $k > 0, l > 0$, vectors $k\mathbf{u}$ and $l\mathbf{u}$ have the same direction as $\mathbf{u}$.   Also,

$$|k\mathbf{u}| + |l\mathbf{u}| = |k||\mathbf{u}| + |l||\mathbf{u}|$$
$$= |k + l||\mathbf{u}|. \qquad\qquad (|k|, |l|, |\mathbf{u}| \text{ are scalars}$$
$$\text{and } k > 0, l > 0)$$

Therefore, $k\mathbf{u} + l\mathbf{u}$ and $(k + l)\mathbf{u}$ are vectors equal in magnitude and direction. Thus

$$(k + l)\mathbf{u} = k\mathbf{u} + l\mathbf{u}.$$

Case 2. $\qquad\qquad k > 0, \quad l < 0, \quad |k| > |l|.$

Let $r = k + l$ and $s = -l$.

$$r > 0 \text{ and } s > 0.$$
$$(r + s)\mathbf{u} = r\mathbf{u} + s\mathbf{u}. \qquad\qquad \text{(Case 1)}$$
$$(k + l - l)\mathbf{u} = (k + l)\mathbf{u} - l\mathbf{u}.$$
$$k\mathbf{u} = (k + l)\mathbf{u} - l\mathbf{u}.$$

Therefore,

$$k\mathbf{u} + l\mathbf{u} = (k + l)\mathbf{u}.$$

Case 3. $\qquad\quad k > 0, \quad l < 0, \quad |k| < |l|.$

Case 4. $\qquad\quad k < 0, \quad l > 0, \quad |k| > |l|.$

Case 5. $\qquad\quad k < 0, \quad l > 0, \quad |k| < |l|.$

Case 6. $\qquad\qquad\quad k < 0, \quad l < 0.$

Case 7. $\qquad\qquad\quad k = 0 \quad \text{or} \quad l = 0.$

Case 8. $\qquad\qquad\qquad k + l = 0.$

Case 9. $\qquad\qquad\qquad\qquad \mathbf{u} = \mathbf{0}.$

Demonstration of these cases is asked for in Exercise 1.7.

Example 1. $ABCD$ is a quadrilateral with $\overrightarrow{AD} = \mathbf{u}, \overrightarrow{AB} = \mathbf{v}, \overrightarrow{AC} = \mathbf{u} + 2\mathbf{v}.$
Express $\overrightarrow{BC}$ and $\overrightarrow{DC}$ in terms of $\mathbf{u}$ and $\mathbf{v}$.

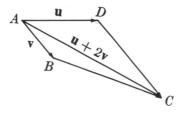

Solution:

$$\overrightarrow{BC} = \overrightarrow{AC} - \overrightarrow{AB}$$
$$= \mathbf{u} + 2\mathbf{v} - \mathbf{v}$$
$$= \mathbf{u} + \mathbf{v}.$$
$$\overrightarrow{DC} = \overrightarrow{AC} - \overrightarrow{AD}$$
$$= \mathbf{u} + 2\mathbf{v} - \mathbf{u}$$
$$= 2\mathbf{v}.$$

Example 2. $\overrightarrow{OP}, \overrightarrow{OQ}, \overrightarrow{OR}$ are three vectors which are mutually perpendicular.   If $\overrightarrow{OP} = 2\mathbf{u}$, $\overrightarrow{OQ} = 3\mathbf{v}$, and $\overrightarrow{OR} = 4\mathbf{w}$, express $\overrightarrow{OP} + \overrightarrow{OQ} + \overrightarrow{OR}$ in terms of $\mathbf{u}$, $\mathbf{v}$, and $\mathbf{w}$.   If $|\mathbf{u}| = 2$, $|\mathbf{v}| = 1$, and $|\mathbf{w}| = 3$, calculate $|\overrightarrow{OP} + \overrightarrow{OQ} + \overrightarrow{OR}|$.

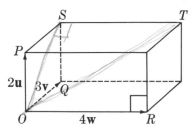

Solution:

$$\overrightarrow{OP} + \overrightarrow{OQ} + \overrightarrow{OR} = 2\mathbf{u} + 3\mathbf{v} + 4\mathbf{w}.$$

$$\begin{aligned}
|\overrightarrow{OP} + \overrightarrow{OQ} + \overrightarrow{OR}| &= |\overrightarrow{OS} + \overrightarrow{OR}| \\
&= |\overrightarrow{OT}| \\
&= \sqrt{|\overrightarrow{OS}|^2 + |\overrightarrow{OR}|^2} \\
&= \sqrt{|\overrightarrow{OP}|^2 + |\overrightarrow{OQ}|^2 + |\overrightarrow{OR}|^2} \\
&= \sqrt{|2\mathbf{u}|^2 + |3\mathbf{v}|^2 + |4\mathbf{w}|^2} \\
&= \sqrt{16 + 9 + 144} \\
&= 13.
\end{aligned}$$

EXERCISE 1.7

1. Demonstrate that
$$k(\mathbf{u} + \mathbf{v}) = k\mathbf{u} + k\mathbf{v}$$
    when
    (a) $k < 0$,   (b) $k = 0$,   (c) $\mathbf{u}$ and $\mathbf{v}$ are collinear.

2. Use geometric vectors to demonstrate that
$$(-1)\mathbf{u} = -\mathbf{u}.$$

3. Show that
$$(k + l)\mathbf{u} = k\mathbf{u} + l\mathbf{u}$$
    when
    (a) $k > 0, l < 0, |k| < |l|$,   (b) $k < 0, l > 0, |k| > |l|$,
    (c) $k < 0, l < 0$,   (d) $k = 0$ or $l = 0$,
    (e) $k + l = 0$,   (f) $\mathbf{u} = \mathbf{0}$.

4. $PQRS$ is a quadrilateral with $\overrightarrow{PQ} = 2\mathbf{u}$, $\overrightarrow{QR} = 3\mathbf{v}$, $\overrightarrow{QS} = 3\mathbf{v} - 3\mathbf{u}$.   Express $\overrightarrow{PS}$ and $\overrightarrow{RS}$ in terms of $\mathbf{u}$ and $\mathbf{v}$.

5. $ABCD$ is a quadrilateral and $\overrightarrow{AB} = \mathbf{u}$, $\overrightarrow{CD} = 2\mathbf{v}$, $\overrightarrow{AC} = 3\mathbf{u} - \mathbf{v}$.   Express $\overrightarrow{BD}$ and $\overrightarrow{BC}$ in terms of $\mathbf{u}$ and $\mathbf{v}$.

6. If $\mathbf{u} = k\mathbf{v}$, $k \neq 0$, prove that

$$v = \frac{1}{k}\mathbf{u}.$$

7. If A, B, and C are three collinear points with B the midpoint of AC and O is any point not on the line AC, prove that

$$\overrightarrow{OA} + \overrightarrow{OC} = 2\,\overrightarrow{OB}.$$

(*Note*: $\overrightarrow{AB} = \overrightarrow{BC}$.)

8. If A, B, and C are three collinear points with B between A and C such that

$$AB : BC = 2 : 1,$$

prove that

$$\overrightarrow{OB} = \frac{2\,\overrightarrow{OC} + \overrightarrow{OA}}{3},$$

where O is any point not on the line AC.

9. $\overrightarrow{PQ}$, $\overrightarrow{PR}$, and $\overrightarrow{PS}$ are three mutually perpendicular vectors. $\overrightarrow{PQ} = 2\mathbf{u}$, $\overrightarrow{PR} = \mathbf{v}$, $\overrightarrow{PS} = 5\mathbf{w}$, $|\mathbf{u}| = 2$, $|\mathbf{v}| = 5$, and $|\mathbf{w}| = 4$. Express $\overrightarrow{PQ} + \overrightarrow{PR} + \overrightarrow{PS}$ in terms of $\mathbf{u}$, $\mathbf{v}$, and $\mathbf{w}$, and calculate $|\overrightarrow{PQ} + \overrightarrow{PR}|$, $|\overrightarrow{PR} + \overrightarrow{PS}|$, and $|\overrightarrow{PQ} + \overrightarrow{PR} + \overrightarrow{PS}|$.

10. A, B, C are three collinear points with B between A and C so that

$$AB : BC = r : s.$$

If O is any point not on the line AC, prove that

$$\overrightarrow{OB} = \frac{s\,\overrightarrow{OA} + r\,\overrightarrow{OC}}{s + r}.$$

1.8. Linear Combination of Vectors

If we consider two nonzero parallel vectors $\mathbf{u}$ and $\mathbf{v}$, it is possible to cut off on $\mathbf{v}$ a vector $\mathbf{w}$ equal to $\mathbf{u}$. $\mathbf{u}$ and $\mathbf{w}$ are equal vectors since they are equal in magnitude and direction. Also, for some scalar k, $\mathbf{v} = k\mathbf{w} = k\mathbf{u}$. $\mathbf{v}$ is a scalar multiple of $\mathbf{w}$ and $\mathbf{u} = \frac{1}{k}\mathbf{v}$ is a scalar multiple of $\mathbf{v}$.

If the two vectors **u** and **v** are not parallel, it is impossible to express one as a scalar multiple of the other. By the definition of multiplication by a scalar, the directions of $k\mathbf{u}$ and **u** are the same if $k > 0$ and opposite if $k < 0$. Hence, $\mathbf{v} \neq k\mathbf{u}$ for any scalar k, since the direction of **v** cannot be the same as the direction of $k\mathbf{u}$, although it is possible to find a vector $k\mathbf{u}$ such that

$$|\mathbf{v}| = |k\mathbf{u}|.$$

In the first diagram, **u** and **w** are equal vectors. In any discussion it is possible to replace one with the other. They are members of an equivalence class of vectors all equal in magnitude and direction. In practice we are always using one member of this class of vectors and we may call any such representative vector **u**. Note that any two vectors in the equivalence class are either parallel to, or collinear with, **u**. It follows that any vector $\mathbf{v} = k\mathbf{u}$ must also be parallel to or collinear with **u**.

To simplify the situation we say that if $\mathbf{v} = k\mathbf{u}$, then **u** and **v** are collinear realizing that this means only that we can find a representative vector **v** which is collinear with **u**.

DEFINITION.   Two coplanar vectors are said to be collinear if and only if one is a scalar multiple of the other.

For example, if $\mathbf{v} = k\mathbf{u}$, then **v** and **u** are collinear.

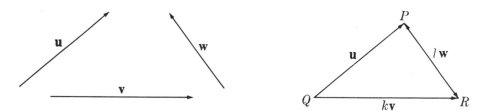

If we consider three coplanar, noncollinear vectors **u**, **v**, and **w** as shown, it is possible to construct $\triangle PQR$ in which $\overrightarrow{QP} = \mathbf{u}$, $\overrightarrow{QR} = k\mathbf{v}$, and $\overrightarrow{RP} = l\mathbf{w}$; that is, $\overrightarrow{QR}$ is parallel to **v** and $\overrightarrow{RP}$ is parallel to **w**.

$$\overrightarrow{QP} = \overrightarrow{QR} + \overrightarrow{RP}.$$

Therefore,

$$\mathbf{u} = k\mathbf{v} + l\mathbf{w}.$$

This construction is possible for any three coplanar, noncollinear vectors, and we say that **u** is a linear combination of **v** and **w**. Also in this case, since $k \neq 0$, $l \neq 0$,

$$\mathbf{v} = \frac{1}{k}\mathbf{u} - \frac{l}{k}\mathbf{w}, \text{ and } \mathbf{v} \text{ is a linear combination of } \mathbf{u} \text{ and } \mathbf{w},$$

$$\mathbf{w} = \frac{1}{l}\mathbf{u} - \frac{k}{l}\mathbf{v}, \text{ and } \mathbf{w} \text{ is a linear combination of } \mathbf{u} \text{ and } \mathbf{v}.$$

If **u** and **v** are collinear (or parallel) vectors, and **w** is not parallel to **u** and **v**, then **w** is not a linear combination of **u** and **v**, but **u** is a linear combination of **v** and **w**, and **v** is a linear combination of **u** and **w**.

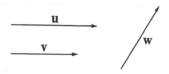

Since **u** and **v** are collinear, then for some scalar k, $\mathbf{u} = k\mathbf{v}$, and

$$\mathbf{u} = k\mathbf{v} + \mathbf{0}$$
$$= k\mathbf{v} + 0\mathbf{w}.$$

Therefore,

$$\mathbf{v} = \frac{1}{k}\mathbf{u} + 0\mathbf{w}.$$

u is a linear combination of **v** and **w**, **v** is a linear combination of **u** and **w**, but **w** is not a linear combination of **u** and **v**.

DEFINITION.   Three vectors are coplanar if and only if at least one is a linear combination of the other two.

The word "coplanar" can include parallel planes in the same way as the word collinear included parallel lines when discussing vectors.

In the diagram, I and II are parallel planes with **u** a vector in I, and **v** a vector in II.   A plane III intersects plane I in the line through **u** and plane III is perpendicular to I.   Plane III is also perpendicular to II and intersects II in a line parallel to its line of intersection with I. Hence a vector equal to **u** in magnitude and direction can be drawn in plane II. Thus **u** and **v** are coplanar.   It should again be emphasized that, in this way, any two vectors are coplanar, although two line segments are not necessarily coplanar.

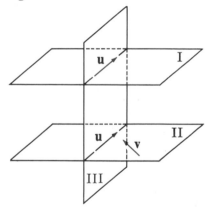

If **u** and **v** are vectors in two non-parallel planes I and II, representative vectors **u** and **v** can be drawn with initial points on the line of intersection of the planes.   In this case, however, the plane in which both **u** and **v** lie is a plane different from I and II.   The initial point common to both **u** and **v** is the point of intersection of the three planes.   We suggest that these cases be examined by using sheets of paper to represent the planes.

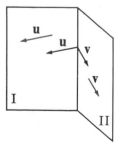

In the diagram P, Q, and R are collinear and are the endpoints of $\overrightarrow{OP} =$ **u**, $\overrightarrow{OQ} = \mathbf{w}$, $\overrightarrow{OR} = \mathbf{v}$. The vectors have a common initial point O. These vectors are known as the position vectors of P, Q, and R relative to the reference point O. Since a line and a point not on the line determine a plane, the vectors are all coplanar, and any one of **u**, **v**, and **w** is a linear combination of the other two.

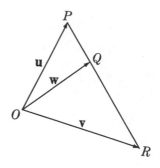

Theorem. If $\mathbf{u} = \overrightarrow{OP}$, $\mathbf{w} = \overrightarrow{OQ}$, and $\mathbf{v} = \overrightarrow{OR}$ are three vectors with P, Q, and R collinear, and $\overrightarrow{PQ} = k\overrightarrow{QR}$, then

$$\mathbf{w} = \frac{k\mathbf{v} + \mathbf{u}}{k + 1}.$$

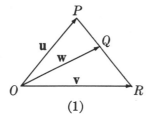
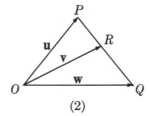
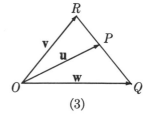

(1)   (2)   (3)

In case (1), $k > 0$ and Q is between P and R.

In case (2), $|k| > 1$, since $|\overrightarrow{PQ}| > |\overrightarrow{QR}|$, and k is negative because $\overrightarrow{PQ}$ and $\overrightarrow{QR}$ are opposite in direction; thus $k < -1$.

In case (3), $|k| < 1$, since $|\overrightarrow{PQ}| < |\overrightarrow{QR}|$, and k is negative because $\overrightarrow{PQ}$ and $\overrightarrow{QR}$ are opposite in direction; thus $-1 < k < 0$.

Note that $\overrightarrow{PQ} = k\overrightarrow{QR}$ may be written in the form $PQ : QR = k : 1$, which shows that Q divides the line segment PR in the ratio $k : 1$.

Proof:

$$P, Q, R \text{ are collinear}$$

and

$$\overrightarrow{PQ} = k\,\overrightarrow{QR}.$$

Therefore,

$$\overrightarrow{PO} + \overrightarrow{OQ} = k\,(\overrightarrow{QO} + \overrightarrow{OR}).$$

Hence,

$$-\mathbf{u} + \mathbf{w} = k(-\mathbf{w} + \mathbf{v}).$$
$$\mathbf{w} + k\mathbf{w} = k\mathbf{v} + \mathbf{u}.$$

Therefore,

$$\mathbf{w} = \frac{k\mathbf{v} + \mathbf{u}}{k + 1}.$$

Note that if Q is the midpoint of PR so that $k = 1$, then

$$\mathbf{w} = \frac{\mathbf{v} + \mathbf{u}}{2} = \tfrac{1}{2}\mathbf{v} + \tfrac{1}{2}\mathbf{u}.$$

Since all the steps in the solution are reversible, the converse theorem may be proved by simply reversing the steps in the solution.

Converse Theorem.   If $\mathbf{u} = \overrightarrow{OP}$, $\mathbf{w} = \overrightarrow{OQ}$, and $\mathbf{v} = \overrightarrow{OR}$ are such that

$$\mathbf{w} = \frac{k\mathbf{v} + \mathbf{u}}{k + 1},$$

then P, Q, and R are collinear, and Q divides the line segment PR in the ratio $k : 1$.

The proof is required in the exercises.

The definitions of parallel or collinear vectors and coplanar vectors together with the theorem just proved enable us to prove many theorems of deductive geometry by vector methods.   We should note that if

$$\overrightarrow{AB} = k\overrightarrow{CD},$$

then the lines containing $\overrightarrow{AB}$ and $\overrightarrow{CD}$ are either collinear or parallel.   If these lines have no point in common, then

$$AB \parallel CD.$$

If they have one point in common, then AB and CD are collinear.

Example 1.   Three coplanar vectors $\mathbf{u}$, $\mathbf{v}$, and $\mathbf{w}$ make angles of 40°, 130°, and 250°, respectively, with the horizontal.   If $|\mathbf{u}| = 4$, $|\mathbf{v}| = 6$, and $|\mathbf{w}| = 12$, express $\mathbf{w}$ as a linear combination of $\mathbf{u}$ and $\mathbf{v}$.

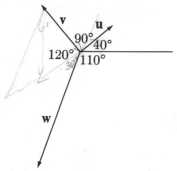
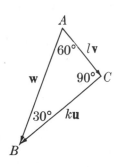

Solution: Let

$$\mathbf{w} = l\mathbf{v} + k\mathbf{u}.$$

In $\triangle ABC$, $AB = 12$, $AC = 6|l|$, $BC = 4|k|$, $\angle ABC = 30°$, $\angle ACB = 90°$, $\angle BAC = 60°$.

$$AC = AB \sin 30°.$$

Thus,

$$6|l| = 12 \times \tfrac{1}{2}.$$
$$|l| = 1.$$
$$BC = AB \cos 30°.$$
$$4|k| = \tfrac{12\sqrt{3}}{2}.$$

Therefore,

$$|k| = \tfrac{3\sqrt{3}}{2}.$$

From the diagram, $k < 0$, $l < 0$; therefore $l = -1$, $k = -\tfrac{3\sqrt{3}}{2}$, and

$$\mathbf{w} = -\mathbf{v} - \tfrac{3\sqrt{3}}{2}\mathbf{u}.$$

Note also that

$$\tfrac{3\sqrt{3}}{2}\mathbf{u} = -\mathbf{v} - \mathbf{w}.$$

Therefore,

$$\mathbf{u} = -\tfrac{2}{3\sqrt{3}}\mathbf{v} - \tfrac{2}{3\sqrt{3}}\mathbf{w}$$
$$= -\tfrac{2\sqrt{3}}{9}(\mathbf{v} + \mathbf{w}).$$

Example 2.   Prove that the line segment joining the midpoints of two sides of a triangle is parallel to the third side and equal in length to one half of it.

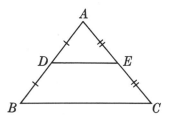

Given: $\triangle ABC$ with D the midpoint of AB and E the midpoint of AC.

Required: To prove $DE \parallel BC$ and

$$DE = \tfrac{1}{2}BC.$$

Proof:

$$\overrightarrow{DE} = \overrightarrow{DA} + \overrightarrow{AE}$$
$$= \tfrac{1}{2}\overrightarrow{BA} + \tfrac{1}{2}\overrightarrow{AC}$$
$$= \tfrac{1}{2}(\overrightarrow{BA} + \overrightarrow{AC})$$
$$= \tfrac{1}{2}\overrightarrow{BC}.$$

Therefore, $DE \parallel BC$ and $DE = \tfrac{1}{2}BC$.

Example 3. Prove that the medians of a triangle intersect at a point two thirds of the distance from each vertex to the midpoint of the opposite side.

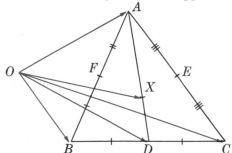

Given: $\triangle ABC$.

Required: To prove that the medians of $\triangle ABC$ intersect at a point two thirds of the distance from each vertex to the midpoint of the opposite side.

Proof: Let D, E, F be midpoints of BC, AC, and AB, respectively. Let X be the point on AD such that

$$AX : XD = 2 : 1.$$

Let O be any point not necessarily in the plane of ABC. Therefore,

$$\overrightarrow{OX} = \frac{2\overrightarrow{OD} + \overrightarrow{OA}}{2 + 1}$$
$$= \tfrac{2}{3}\overrightarrow{OD} + \tfrac{1}{3}\overrightarrow{OA},$$

but

$$\overrightarrow{OD} = \tfrac{1}{2}\overrightarrow{OB} + \tfrac{1}{2}\overrightarrow{OC}.$$

Therefore,

$$\overrightarrow{OX} = \tfrac{2}{3}(\tfrac{1}{2}\overrightarrow{OB} + \tfrac{1}{2}\overrightarrow{OC}) + \tfrac{1}{3}\overrightarrow{OA}$$
$$= \tfrac{1}{3}(\overrightarrow{OA} + \overrightarrow{OB} + \overrightarrow{OC}).$$

Similarly, if Y is the point on BE such that

$$BY : YE = 2 : 1,$$

then

$$\overrightarrow{OY} = \tfrac{1}{3}(\overrightarrow{OB} + \overrightarrow{OC} + \overrightarrow{OA}),$$

and if Z is the point on CF such that

$$CZ : ZE = 2 : 1,$$

then

$$\overrightarrow{OZ} = \tfrac{1}{3}(\overrightarrow{OC} + \overrightarrow{OA} + \overrightarrow{OB}).$$

Therefore,

$$\overrightarrow{OX} = \overrightarrow{OY} = \overrightarrow{OZ},$$

and X, Y, Z are the same point. Therefore, the medians intersect at a point two thirds of the distance from each vertex to the midpoint of the opposite side.

The final part may be shortened by noting that the result

$$\overrightarrow{OX} = \tfrac{1}{3}(\overrightarrow{OA} + \overrightarrow{OB} + \overrightarrow{OC})$$

is completely symmetrical in A, B, and C and is independent of the median used. Therefore, X is on all three medians.

Example 4. If $\overrightarrow{OA}$, $\overrightarrow{OB}$, $\overrightarrow{OC}$ are such that A, B, and C are collinear and $AB:BC = -5:3$, express $\overrightarrow{OB}$ as a linear combination of $\overrightarrow{OA}$ and $\overrightarrow{OC}$.

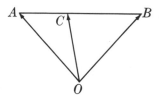

Solution:

$$AB:BC = -\tfrac{5}{3}:1.$$
$$\overrightarrow{OB} = \frac{-\tfrac{5}{3}\overrightarrow{OC} + \overrightarrow{OA}}{-\tfrac{5}{3} + 1}.$$
$$= \frac{-5\,\overrightarrow{OC} + 3\,\overrightarrow{OA}}{-5 + 3}$$
$$= \tfrac{5}{2}\,\overrightarrow{OC} - \tfrac{3}{2}\,\overrightarrow{OA}.$$

Example 5. If $\overrightarrow{OP} = 3\,\overrightarrow{OQ} - 2\,\overrightarrow{OR}$, prove that P, Q, and R are collinear, and find the value of the ratio $PQ:QR$.

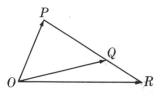

Solution:

$$\overrightarrow{PQ} = \overrightarrow{PO} + \overrightarrow{OQ}$$
$$= \overrightarrow{OQ} - \overrightarrow{OP}$$
$$= \overrightarrow{OQ} - 3\,\overrightarrow{OQ} + 2\,\overrightarrow{OR}$$
$$= 2\,(\overrightarrow{OR} - \overrightarrow{OQ}).$$
$$\overrightarrow{QR} = \overrightarrow{QO} + \overrightarrow{OR}$$
$$= \overrightarrow{OR} - \overrightarrow{OQ}.$$

Thus,

$$\overrightarrow{PQ} = 2\,\overrightarrow{QR}.$$

Therefore, P, Q and R are collinear and $PQ:QR = 2:1$.

EXERCISE 1.8

1. In the diagram, **u**, **v**, **w** represent three coplanar vectors. If $|\mathbf{u}| = 10$, $|\mathbf{v}| = 12$, and $|\mathbf{w}| = 12$, express **w** as a linear combination of **u** and **v**. Also express **v** as a linear combination of **u** and **w**.

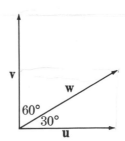

2. In the diagram, $\overrightarrow{RP} = \mathbf{w}$, $\overrightarrow{RQ} = k\mathbf{u}$, $\overrightarrow{QP} = l\mathbf{v}$ with $k > 0$, $l > 0$. If $|\mathbf{u}| = 4$, $|\mathbf{v}| = 5$, and $|\mathbf{w}| = 16$, find the values of k and l correct to 2 decimal places.

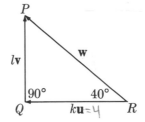

3. In the diagram, $\overrightarrow{QP} = \mathbf{w}$, $\overrightarrow{QR} = k\mathbf{u}$, $\overrightarrow{RP} = l\mathbf{v}$ with $k > 0$, $l > 0$. If $|\mathbf{u}| = 2$, $|\mathbf{v}| = 4$, and $|\mathbf{w}| = 10$, express **w** as a linear combination of **u** and **v**.

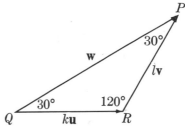

4. $\overrightarrow{OA}$, $\overrightarrow{OB}$, and $\overrightarrow{OC}$ are such that A, B, and C are collinear with
$$AB : BC = 3 : 2 .$$
Express $\overrightarrow{OB}$ as a linear combination of $\overrightarrow{OA}$ and $\overrightarrow{OC}$.

5. If $\overrightarrow{OP} = \mathbf{u}$, $\overrightarrow{OQ} = \mathbf{v}$, $\overrightarrow{OR} = \mathbf{w}$ and P, Q, and R are collinear with
$$PQ : QR = -1 : 4,$$
express **v** as a linear combination of **u** and **w**.

6. If $\overrightarrow{OQ} = \frac{2}{5}\overrightarrow{OP} + \frac{3}{5}\overrightarrow{OR}$, prove that P, Q, and R are collinear and that $PQ : QR = 3 : 2$.

7. If $\mathbf{u} = \overrightarrow{OP}$, $\mathbf{w} = \overrightarrow{OQ}$, and $\mathbf{v} = \overrightarrow{OR}$ are such that
$$\mathbf{w} = \frac{k\mathbf{v} + \mathbf{u}}{k + 1},$$
prove that P, Q, and R are collinear and that $PQ : QR = k : 1$.

Use vector methods to prove each of the following.

8. Prove that if one pair of opposite sides of a quadrilateral are equal and parallel, then the other pair of opposite sides are also equal and parallel.

9. Prove that the diagonals of parallelogram $ABCD$ bisect each other. (Hint: Let E be the midpoint of AC and F the midpoint of BD. Prove $\overrightarrow{AE} = \overrightarrow{AF}$.)

10. In $\triangle ABC$, D and E are points on AB and AC, respectively, such that $AD:DB = AE:EC$. Prove that $DE \parallel BC$ and that $DE:BC = AD:AB$.

11. AC and BD are two line segments which bisect each other at E. Prove $ABCD$ is a parallelogram.

12. $ABCD$ is a parallelogram with E the midpoint of AD. Prove that AC and BE trisect each other (see hint to question (9)).

13. In $\triangle ABC$, D is the midpoint of AB and $DE \parallel BC$ meets AC at E. Prove that E is the midpoint of AC.

14. $ABCD$ is a parallelogram with E the midpoint of AD and F the midpoint of BC. Prove that BE and DF trisect AC.

15. P, Q, R, and S are the centroids of triangles ABC, ABD, DEF, and CEF, respectively. Prove that $PQRS$ is a parallelogram. (Let O be any point and note that $\overrightarrow{OP} = \frac{1}{3}(\overrightarrow{OA} + \overrightarrow{OB} + \overrightarrow{OC})$.)

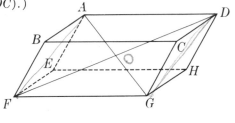

16. The diagram shows a parallelopiped (opposite faces are parallel and congruent parallelograms). Prove that the diagonals AG and DF bisect each other.

17. Prove that the three line segments joining the midpoints of pairs of opposite edges of a tetrahedron bisect each other. A tetrahedron is a pyramid with a triangular base as shown in the diagram. AB and CD are opposite edges, as are AD and BC, and AC and BD.

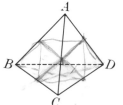

Chapter Summary

Definitions

Skew lines are lines in space which do not intersect and are not parallel.

A line l is perpendicular to a plane I at a point N if it is perpendicular to every line in the plane passing through N.

The measure of a dihedral angle is the measure of the plane angle formed by the perpendiculars in each plane at a point on the line of intersection of the planes.

Two vectors are equal if and only if they have the same magnitude and the same direction.

If $\mathbf{u}$ and $\mathbf{v}$ are two vectors represented by $\overrightarrow{PQ}$ and $\overrightarrow{QR}$, respectively, so that the endpoint of the line segment PQ is the initial point of the line segment QR, then the sum of $\mathbf{u}$ and $\mathbf{v}$ is represented by $\overrightarrow{PR}$.

The negative of a vector $\mathbf{u}$ is a vector equal in magnitude to $\mathbf{u}$ but opposite in direction, and is denoted by $-\mathbf{u}$.

The resultant force of two or more forces is that single force that would have the same effect as the given forces.

The equilibrant force of two or more forces acting on a body is that single force which, when applied to the body, maintains it in a state of equilibrium.

If $\mathbf{u}$ is a nonzero vector and k a nonzero real number (scalar), the vector $k\mathbf{u}$ is defined by the following rules.

(1) $|k\mathbf{u}| = |k||\mathbf{u}|$.

(2) The directions of $k\mathbf{u}$ and $\mathbf{u}$ are the same if $k > 0$ and opposite if $k < 0$. Also

$$k\mathbf{0} = \mathbf{0} \quad \text{and} \quad 0\mathbf{u} = \mathbf{0}.$$

Two coplanar vectors are collinear if one is a scalar multiple of the other.

Three vectors are coplanar if at least one is a linear combination of the other two.

Algebraic Properties of Vectors

For the following properties, $\mathbf{u}$, $\mathbf{v}$, $\mathbf{w}$ are vectors.

(1) $\mathbf{u} + \mathbf{v}$ is a vector.   Closure property

(2) $\mathbf{u} + \mathbf{v} = \mathbf{v} + \mathbf{u}$.   Commutative property

(3) $(\mathbf{u} + \mathbf{v}) + \mathbf{w} = \mathbf{u} + (\mathbf{v} + \mathbf{w})$.   Associative property

(4) $\mathbf{u} + \mathbf{0} = \mathbf{0} + \mathbf{u} = \mathbf{u}$.   Identity property (zero vector)

(5) $\mathbf{u} + (-\mathbf{u}) = -\mathbf{u} + \mathbf{u} = \mathbf{0}$.   Inverse property

Properties of Multiplication by a Scalar

For the following properties, $\mathbf{u}$ and $\mathbf{v}$ are vectors and k and l are real numbers.

(1) $k\mathbf{u}$ is a vector.

(2) $k\mathbf{u} = \mathbf{u}k$.

(3) If $k = l$ and $\mathbf{u} = \mathbf{v}$, then $k\mathbf{u} = l\mathbf{v}$.

(4) $(kl)\mathbf{u} = k(l\mathbf{u})$.

(5) $1\mathbf{u} = \mathbf{u}$.

(6) $(-1)\mathbf{u} = -\mathbf{u}$.

(7) $k(\mathbf{u} + \mathbf{v}) = k\mathbf{u} + k\mathbf{v}$.

(8) $(k + l)\mathbf{u} = k\mathbf{u} + l\mathbf{u}$.

(9) $|k\mathbf{u}| = |k||\mathbf{u}|$.

Theorem.

If $\mathbf{u} = \overrightarrow{OP}$, $\mathbf{w} = \overrightarrow{OQ}$, and $\mathbf{v} = \overrightarrow{OR}$ are three vectors with P, Q, and R collinear and $\overrightarrow{PQ} = k\overrightarrow{QR}$, then

$$\mathbf{w} = \frac{k\mathbf{v} + \mathbf{u}}{k + 1}.$$

REVIEW EXERCISE 1

1. $PQRST$ is a pentagon.   State a single vector equal to each of the following.
   (a) $\overrightarrow{PQ} + \overrightarrow{QR}$
   (b) $\overrightarrow{PQ} + \overrightarrow{QR} + \overrightarrow{RT}$
   (c) $\overrightarrow{QR} + \overrightarrow{RT}$
   (d) $\overrightarrow{ST} - \overrightarrow{PT}$
   (e) $\overrightarrow{PQ} + \overrightarrow{QR} - \overrightarrow{TR}$
   (f) $\overrightarrow{PR} - (\overrightarrow{PT} - \overrightarrow{ST})$

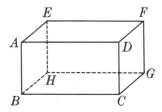

2. The diagram above represents a rectangular prism.   State a single vector equal to each of the following.
   (a) $\overrightarrow{AB} + \overrightarrow{BG}$
   (b) $\overrightarrow{EH} + \overrightarrow{HG}$
   (c) $\overrightarrow{AB} + \overrightarrow{HG}$
   (d) $\overrightarrow{BC} + \overrightarrow{DF} + \overrightarrow{GH}$
   (e) $\overrightarrow{FG} - \overrightarrow{BH}$
   (f) $\overrightarrow{CG} - \overrightarrow{EH}$
   (g) $\overrightarrow{AD} - \overrightarrow{HC} - \overrightarrow{GH}$
   (h) $\overrightarrow{DF} + \overrightarrow{GC}$

3. Two vectors $\mathbf{u}$ and $\mathbf{v}$ have a common initial point and form an angle of 140°. If $|\mathbf{u}| = 4$ and $|\mathbf{v}| = 8$, calculate, to the nearest integer, the value of $|\mathbf{u} + \mathbf{v}|$ and, to the nearest degree, the size of the angle between $\mathbf{u} + \mathbf{v}$ and $\mathbf{v}$.

4. Simplify $3\mathbf{u} + 2\mathbf{v} - 2(\mathbf{v} - \mathbf{u}) + (-3\mathbf{u})$.

5. Two forces of 40 pounds and 60 pounds act on a body at an angle of 60° to each other.   Find the magnitude and direction of the resultant force, to the nearest pound and the nearest degree.

6. Two forces of 50 grams and 80 grams act on a body at an angle of 130° to each other.   Find the magnitude and direction of the equilibrant, to the nearest gram and nearest degree.

7. Two equal forces acting at an angle of 80° to each other have a resultant of 60 pounds.   Calculate the magnitude of the two forces, to the nearest pound.

8. A light aircraft is flying at a speed of 160 m.p.h. on a bearing of 140°.   A 30 m.p.h. wind is blowing from a bearing of 290°.   Calculate the ground speed and direction of flight of the aircraft, to the nearest m.p.h. and the nearest degree.

9. A ship's navigator wishes to set a course for a port which is 300 nautical miles distant from his present position on a bearing of 220°. The ship's speed is 18 knots and a current of 6 knots is travelling from a bearing of 100°. What course should he set and what will be the actual speed of the ship, to the nearest degree and nearest knot?

10. A force of 40 pounds acts at an angle of 50° to the horizontal. Calculate the horizontal and vertical components of the force, to the nearest pound.

11. Resolve a force of 65 pounds into two rectangular components so that the magnitude of the components are in the ratio $5:12$. Calculate the angle between the 65-pound force and the larger component. Give the results to the nearest unit.

12. An aircraft is climbing at an angle of 20° to the horizontal and at a speed of 120 m.p.h. What is its rate of climb in feet per minute and its horizontal ground speed in miles per hour, each to nearest unit.

13. Three coplanar vectors **u**, **v**, and **w** make angles of 30°, 60°, and 120°, respectively, with the horizontal. If $|\mathbf{u}| = 5, |\mathbf{v}| = 6, |\mathbf{w}| = 8$, express **v** as a linear combination of **u** and **w**.

14. Three coplanar vectors **u, v,** and **w** make angles of 60°, 180°, and −30° with the horizontal. If $|\mathbf{u}| = 3, |\mathbf{v}| = 2, |\mathbf{w}| = 5$, express **u** as a linear combination of **v** and **w**.

15. In $\triangle ABC$, E is the midpoint of AC and BE is produced to D so that $ED = BE$. Using vector methods, prove $AB \parallel CD$ and $AB = CD$.

16. In $\triangle PQR$, S is a point on QR such that
$$QS : SR = 3 : 2,$$
and T is a point on PS such that
$$PT : TS = -5 : 2.$$
Using vector methods, prove $PQ \parallel RT$.

17. $ABCD$ is a quadrilateral with P, Q, R, and S the midpoints of AB, BC, CD, and DA, respectively. Using vector methods, prove that $PQRS$ is a parallelogram.

18. $\overrightarrow{OA} = \mathbf{u}$, $\overrightarrow{OB} = \mathbf{v}$, $\overrightarrow{OC} = \mathbf{w}$, and A, B, C are collinear with $AB : BC = 2 : 1$. Express **v** as a linear combination of **u** and **w**.

19. $\overrightarrow{OP}$, $\overrightarrow{OQ}$, and $\overrightarrow{OR}$ are such that P, Q, R are collinear with $PQ : QR = -2 : 5$. Express $\overrightarrow{OQ}$ as a linear combination of $\overrightarrow{OP}$ and $\overrightarrow{OR}$.

20. If $\overrightarrow{OQ} = \frac{3}{7}\overrightarrow{OP} + \frac{4}{7}\overrightarrow{OR}$, prove that P, Q, R are collinear and that
$$PQ : QR = 4 : 3.$$

21. If $\overrightarrow{OQ} = \dfrac{s}{r}\overrightarrow{OP} + \dfrac{r-s}{r}\overrightarrow{OR}$, prove that P, Q, R are collinear and that $PQ:QR = (r-s):s$.

22. In a tetrahedron $ABCD$, P, Q, R, and S are the centroids of faces ABC, BCD, CDA, and ABD, respectively. Prove that DP, AQ, BR, and CS intersect at X so that
$$DX:XP = AX:XQ = BX:XR = CX:XS = 3:1.$$
(Hint: take as the origin of the position vectors any point not on the faces of the tetrahedron.)

23. Show that the point X found in question (22) is also the point of intersection of the line segments joining the midpoints of the opposite edges of the tetrahedron (see question (17), Exercise 1.8).

24. Prove that the diagonals of a cube intersect in a point and show that the line segments joining the midpoints of the opposite edges intersect in this point.

25. State and prove results for a rectangular prism similar to those in question (24) for the cube. Do similar results hold for the general parallelopiped?

Chapter **2**

ALGEBRAIC VECTORS

2.1. Graphical Representation of Triplets of Real Numbers

A pair (x, y) of real numbers may be represented geometrically by a point in a plane using a Cartesian co-ordinate system with a frame of reference consisting of two lines (the x- and y-axes) intersecting at right angles in a point (the origin). The real numbers, x and y, are the co-ordinates of the particular point.

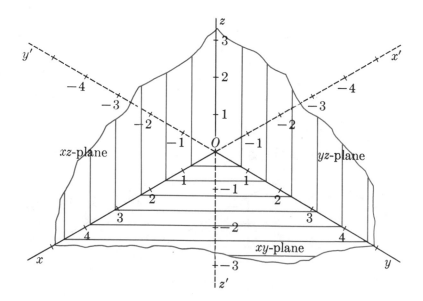

Figure 2.1

The points of a particular plane may all be represented by pairs of real numbers. Therefore, the consideration of triplets of real numbers would suggest going *outside* a particular plane. Indeed, triplets (x, y, z) of real numbers are represented by points in space. In this case, our frame of reference consists of three mutually perpendicular number lines (the x-, y-, and z-co-ordinate axes) intersecting in a point O (the origin). Such a frame of reference is shown in Figure 2.1. The three axes are at right angles to each other but, of course, cannot be drawn as such in the plane of the page; they are drawn at an angle of 120° to each other and the student must visualize the x- and y-axes as coming out of the page.

The x-, y-, and z-axes are three number lines and, by convention, the solid rays represent the positive directions of these number lines.

Note that the co-ordinate axes, taken in pairs, form three mutually perpendicular planes called the co-ordinate planes, namely, the xy-plane, the yz-plane, and the xz-plane.

To determine the point represented by the triplet (x, y, z) of real numbers, we start at the origin O, move x units along the x-axis, then y units in the xy-plane parallel to the y-axis, and finally z units from that point parallel to the z-axis. Distances are measured to the same scale along all three axes. Figure 2.2 shows the representation of some typical points.

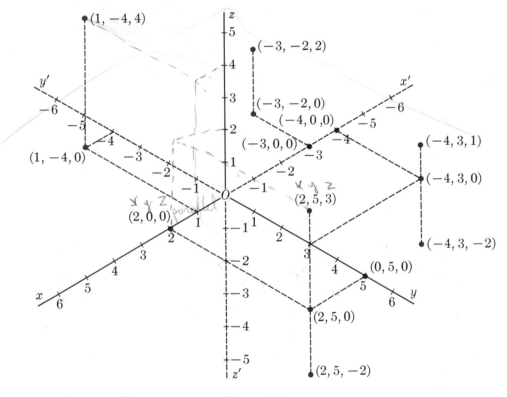

Figure 2.2

Conversely, a point in space determines a triplet of real numbers with respect to such a co-ordinate system, namely, real numbers x (perpendicular distance of the point from the yz-plane), y (distance of the point from the xz-plane), and z

(distance of the point from the xy-plane). Then there is a one-to-one correspondence between the set of points in space and the set of ordered triplets (x, y, z) of real numbers, just as there is a one-to-one correspondence between the set of points in a plane and the set of ordered pairs (x, y) of real numbers.

EXERCISE 2.1

1. Plot the following triplets of real numbers on a suitably drawn co-ordinate system.

$(1, 1, 1)$	$(1, 3, -4)$	$(0, -5, 2)$	$(1, -3, -6)$
$(-4, 3, 5)$	$(-3, 6, -2)$	$(-3, -2, 0)$	$(3, -4, -4)$
$(-2, -3, -4)$	$(-5, 1, 6)$	$(4, -3, 0)$	$(-1, 0, -6)$
$(-5, 0, 0)$	$(3, 0, 0)$	$(0, -4, 0)$	$(0, 0, 7)$.

2. The three co-ordinate axes in space divide space into eight regions called octants. The region bounded by the boldfaced rays is called the first octant (the others are not numbered). What characterizes points in the first octant? How would you refer to any particular octant (without attempting to number the octants)?

3. What characterizes points on the yz-plane? on the xz-plane? on the xy-plane? What, then, are the equations of these planes?

4. What characterizes points on the x-axis? on the y-axis? on the z-axis?

5. A line in space does not have a single equation as does a line in a plane, but rather a pair of equations. What are the pairs of equations for the x-axis? the y-axis? the z-axis?

2.2. Two- and Three-Dimensional Vectors

In the preceding section, ordered pairs and triplets of real numbers were given geometric interpretations as points in a plane and in space, respectively. In the present section, we define a (real) two-dimensional vector to be an ordered pair of real numbers and a (real) three-dimensional vector to be an ordered triplet of real numbers, and we shall consider some algebraic properties of these mathematical objects.

Example 1. $(0, 0)$, $(3, 6)$, $(-\frac{1}{2}, 5)$, $(\pi, -\pi)$ are two dimensional vectors; $(0, 0, 0)$, $(-1, 3, 6)$, $(-\frac{1}{2}, 5, 0)$, $(\pi, 3.14, \frac{22}{7})$ are three-dimensional vectors.

The real numbers involved in the symbols in the example above are called the components of the vector. We normally use a bold-faced letter (in print) to refer to a vector: thus $\mathbf{u} = (1, 2)$, $\mathbf{v} = (3, 2, 5)$, etc. In writing, we may use either $\underline{u} = (1, 2)$ or $\vec{u} = (1, 2)$.

Let us now consider the set V_2 of all ordered pairs, and the set V_3 of all ordered triplets of real numbers. When we consider sets of mathematical objects, it is important that we know when two of the elements are equal. We have the following definitions in V_2 and V_3.

DEFINITION. $(a, b) = (c, d)$ if and only if $a = c$ and $b = d$.

$(a, b, c) = (d, e, f)$ if and only if $a = d$, $b = e$, and $c = f$.

Two vectors are equal if and only if they have the same dimension and corresponding components are equal.

Example 2. $(2, -1) \neq (3, 2, -1)$.   (Why?)
$(2, 3, 1) \neq (2, 3, -1)$.   (Why?)
$(a, 3) = (-2, b)$ if and only if $a = -2$ and $b = 3$.
$(3, -1, 2) \neq (-3, a, b)$ for any values of a and b.

Vectors may be added according to the following definition.

DEFINITION. $(a, b) + (c, d) = (a + c, b + d)$.

$(a, b, c) + (d, e, f) = (a + d, b + e, c + f)$.

Notice that addition is defined only for equidimensional vectors and that equidimensional vectors are added by the addition of corresponding components. Obviously both V_2 and V_3 are closed under this operation of addition.

Example 3. $(-1, 5) + (3, 4) = (2, 9)$.
$(6, -4, 2) + (-1, 0, 5) = (5, -4, 7)$.
$(2, 3) + (2, 3, 0)$ is not defined.

A vector may be multiplied by a real number according to the following definition.

DEFINITION. $t(a, b) = (ta, tb)$.

$t(a, b, c) = (ta, tb, tc)$.

According to this definition, a vector is multiplied by a real number by the multiplication of each component by that real number. The product of a two- (three-) dimensional vector and a real number is a two- (three-) dimensional vector; V_2 and V_3 are closed under multiplication by real numbers.

Example 4. $3(5, -1) = (15, -3)$.
$-2(6, -1, 4) = (-12, 2, -8)$.

It is easy to verify that $(0, 0)$ and $(0, 0, 0)$ are identities under addition in V_2 and V_3, respectively; we call them zero vectors and often refer to them simply as **0**.

Note that
$$(a, b) + (-a, -b) = (0, 0),$$
and
$$(a, b, c) + (-a, -b, -c) = (0, 0, 0).$$

We call $(-a, -b)$ the additive inverse or negative of (a, b), and $(-a, -b, -c)$ the additive inverse or negative of (a, b, c). Then, as usual, the subtraction of one vector from a second is defined as the addition of the negative of that vector to the second.

DEFINITION. $(a, b) - (c, d) = (a, b) + (-c, -d)$
$$= (a - c, b - d).$$

$$(a, b, c) - (d, e, f) = (a, b, c) + (-d, -e, -f)$$
$$= (a - d, b - e, c - f).$$

Example 5. The negative of $(3, -7, 5)$ is $(-3, 7, -5)$.

Check: $(3, -7, 5) + (-3, 7, -5) = (0, 0, 0).$

Example 6. $(4, -7, 3) - (3, 2, -4) = (4, -7, 3) + (-3, -2, 4)$
$$= (1, -9, 7).$$

As usual, the second step in the subtraction operation is normally omitted and we simply subtract corresponding components of the vectors.

Note that
$$(-1)(a, b, c) = (-a, -b, -c),$$
so that
$$(-1)(a, b, c)$$
is the negative of (a, b, c).

EXERCISE 2.2

1. Express the following as single vectors.
   (a) $(2, 3) + (4, 6)$
   (b) $(3, 2) + (-5, 1)$
   (c) $(4, 7) + (0, 0)$
   (d) $(3, -1, 4) + (2, 0, 1)$
   (e) $(3, 0, -5) + (-3, -2, 1)$
   (f) $(0, 0, -5) + (4, 0, 0)$
   (g) $5(2, 8)$
   (h) $-3(4, 7)$
   (i) $0(0, 0)$
   (j) $3(-2, -1, 4)$
   (k) $-2(-4, -1, 3)$
   (l) $\frac{1}{2}(4, 2, -6)$
   (m) $(4, 7) - (4, 7)$
   (n) $(4, 7) - (3, 2)$
   (o) $(-4, 7) - (-5, -3)$
   (p) $(3, 2, 1) - (1, 2, 3)$
   (q) $(-4, 1, 2) - (3, -1, -2)$
   (r) $(-2, -1, 6) - (3, -1, 0)$

2. Show that

   (a) $(-1, 3) + (4, 5) = (4, 5) + (-1, 3)$,

   (b) $(2, 1, 6) + (-3, 2, 5) = (-3, 2, 5) + (2, 1, 6)$.

3. Use the vectors

   (a) $(3, 1)$, $(2, -4)$, $(5, -3)$,

   (b) $(4, 2, 1)$, $(3, -2, 0)$, $(5, -2, -1)$,

   to demonstrate that addition of vectors is associative.

4. Evaluate $3[(2, 1, 5) + (-2, 4, 6)]$ in two ways to illustrate that multiplication by a real number is distributive over the addition of vectors.

5. Find a and b if
   $$3(a, 1) - 2(2, b) = (2, 1).$$

6. Find a, b, and c if
   $$2(a, -1, 4) - 3(-4, b, 6) - \tfrac{1}{2}(4, -2, c) = (0, 0, 0).$$

7. Find x, y, and z if
   $$3[(x, 1, -1) + (3, -2, z)] - (4, 3, -1) = 6(-3, -y, 5).$$

8. Find p, q, and r if
   $$(p, -6, 4) - 2(q, p, 3) + (5, q, r) = (0, 0, 0).$$

9. Prove that addition of two- and three-dimensional vectors is commutative.

10. Prove that addition of two- and three-dimensional vectors is associative.

11. Prove that multiplication by a real number is distributive over addition of two- and three-dimensional vectors.

2.3. Identification of Algebraic and Geometric Vectors

In Chapter 1, we discussed physical vectors represented geometrically by directed line segments in a plane (2-space) or in a space of three dimensions (3-space). It was pointed out that the characteristics of such representations, called geometric vectors, were length and direction. Two geometric vectors are equal if they are line segments having the same length and the same direction, and equal geometric vectors are normally interchangeable in a geometric discussion.

Consider the ordered pair $(2, 3)$ of real numbers, that is, the algebraic vector $(2, 3)$ in V_2. Moving $+2$ units in the x direction from the origin O of a plane Cartesian co-ordinate system, and then $+3$ units in the y direction brings us to a point P in the plane whose co-ordinates are $(2, 3)$; O and P are the initial and terminal points, respectively, of a directed line segment or vector $\overrightarrow{OP}$ (Figure 2.3). Indeed, associated with every nonzero algebraic vector (a, b) in V_2 there is a geometric vector with initial point O and terminal point P with co-ordinates (a, b).

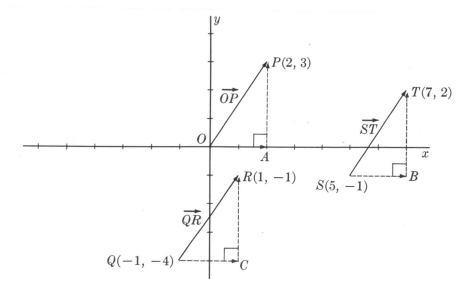

Figure 2.3

Now choose an arbitrary point, say $Q(-1, -4)$, and move $+2$ units in the x direction and $+3$ units in the y direction; this procedure determines the point $R(1, -1)$ and a vector $\overrightarrow{QR}$. Similarly, starting at $S(5, -1)$ determines the point $T(7, 2)$ and the vector $\overrightarrow{ST}$ (Figure 2.3). Obviously, $\overrightarrow{OP} = \overrightarrow{QR} = \overrightarrow{ST}$, since $\overrightarrow{OP}$, $\overrightarrow{QR}$, and $\overrightarrow{ST}$ are line segments with the same length and the same direction (OAP, QCR, and SBT are congruent right-angled triangles). We may also say that $\overrightarrow{OP}$, $\overrightarrow{QR}$, $\overrightarrow{ST}$ are vectors of the same equivalence class.

Thus, each nonzero algebraic vector in V_2 has an infinite number of equivalent geometric representatives in the plane. In particular, there is a one-to-one correspondence between the nonzero vectors of V_2 and the geometric vectors *with initial point at the origin* in a fixed plane.

Note the double interpretation that we now have for an ordered pair (a, b) of real numbers

(i)   as an algebraic vector of V_2,

(ii) as the co-ordinates of a point P in the plane that is the terminal point of a geometric vector with initial point at the origin.

The geometric vector $\overrightarrow{OP}$ from the origin O to the point P with co-ordinates (a, b) can thus be identified with the algebraic vector (a, b).

In the same way, an ordered triplet (a, b, c) of real numbers can be considered as an algebraic vector of V_3, or as the co-ordinates of a point P in space that determines, with the origin O, the geometric vector $\overrightarrow{OP}$. For example, $(3, -2, 2)$ is an algebraic vector in V_3; also, the point P with co-ordinates $(3, -2, 2)$ determines the geometric vector $\overrightarrow{OP}$ (Figure 2.4). Again, starting at any point Q in space and moving $+3$ units in the x direction, -2 units in the y direction, and $+2$ units in the z direction determines a point R and a vector $\overrightarrow{QR}$ such that $\overrightarrow{QR} = \overrightarrow{OP}$ $(OAB$ and QCD are congruent right triangles, as are OBP and QDR).

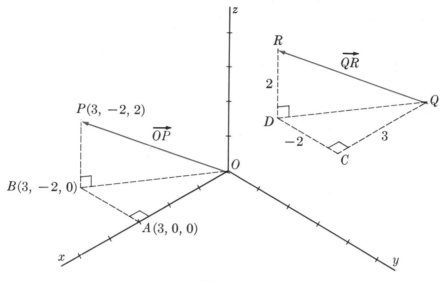

Figure 2.4

Thus, there is a one-to-one correspondence between nonzero algebraic vectors of V_3 and geometric vectors in 3-space *with initial point at the origin*, but each nonzero algebraic vector in V_3 has an infinite number of equivalent geometric representatives in 3-space.

EXERCISE 2.3

1. Draw representatives in 2-space with initial point at
    (i) the origin,   (ii) $(3, 4)$,   (iii) $(-1, 5)$,   (iv) $(-3, -5)$,   (v) $(4, -3)$,
    for the following vectors in V_2.
    (a) $(1, 1)$ (b) $(2, 3)$ (c) $(-3, 4)$ (d) $(-4, 3)$
    (e) $(3, 5)$ (f) $(2, 0)$ (g) $(-1, -2)$ (h) $(0, -3)$

2. Draw representatives in 3-space with initial point at
    (i) the origin, (ii) $(3, 3, 4)$, (iii) $(-2, 1, 5)$, (iv) $(3, -2, 4)$, (v) $(-2, -2, -2)$,
    for the following vectors in V_3.
    (a) $(1, 1, 1)$ (b) $(2, 3, 1)$
    (c) $(-3, 4, 2)$ (d) $(2, 2, 2)$
    (e) $(-4, 3, 0)$ (f) $(2, 0, 0)$
    (g) $(-1, -2, -2)$ (h) $(0, 0, -3)$

3. What algebraic vectors in V_2 correspond to geometric vectors $\overrightarrow{PQ}$ if P and Q are the following points?

(a) $P(0, 0), Q(2, 5)$ (b) $P(0, 0), Q(-3, 1)$

(c) $P(0, 0), Q(-5, -2)$ (d) $P(2, 5), Q(0, 0)$

(e) $P(-3, 1), Q(0, 0)$ (f) $P(-5, -2), Q(0, 0)$

(g) $P(3, 4), Q(5, 7)$ (h) $P(3, -4), Q(-2, 5)$

(i) $P(-3, -1), Q(-5, -5)$ (j) $P(-4, 2), Q(-7, -3)$

4. What point P in the plane is the terminal point of a geometric vector $\overrightarrow{OP}$ that is equivalent to $\overrightarrow{RS}$ for the following points R and S?

(a) $R(4, 3), S(2, 1)$ (b) $R(6, 3), S(-5, 3)$

(c) $R(-3, 2), S(5, 7)$ (d) $R(-1, -3), S(-7, -2)$

5. What algebraic vectors in V_3 correspond to geometric vectors $\overrightarrow{PQ}$ if P and Q are the following points?

(a) $P(0, 0, 0), Q(3, -1, 4)$ (b) $P(3, 2, 4), Q(0, 0, 0)$

(c) $P(-2, -1, -1), Q(0, 0, 0)$ (d) $P(3, 3, 1), Q(7, 2, 1)$

(e) $P(-2, 5, 1), Q(7, 3, 2)$ (f) $P(-1, 3, -4), Q(-1, -5, -4)$

6. What point P in 3-space is the terminal point of a geometric vector $\overrightarrow{OP}$ that is equivalent to $\overrightarrow{RS}$ for the following points R and S?

(a) $R(2, -3, 1), S(-4, -2, 1)$ (b) $R(3, -1, -2), S(5, 4, 3)$

(c) $R(-1, -2, -5), S(-3, -4, -1)$ (d) $R(-1, 2, 1), S(6, 0, -2)$

7. What is the connection between the algebraic vectors corresponding to $\overrightarrow{PQ}$ and $\overrightarrow{QP}$?

8. Compare geometric vectors representing (a, b, c) and $(-a, -b, -c)$.

9. Is there a geometric vector representing the algebraic vector $(0, 0, 0)$?

10. When the geometric vector has the indicated property, what can be said about the corresponding algebraic vector (a, b, c) in each of the following cases?

(a) parallel to the x-axis   (b) parallel to the y-axis

(c) parallel to the z-axis   (d) perpendicular to the x-axis

(e) perpendicular to the y-axis   (f) perpendicular to the z-axis

2.4. Geometric Interpretation of $u + v$ and $t u$

The parallelogram law for the addition of geometric vectors in two and three dimensions was established in Chapter 1. In this section, we shall show that this addition of geometric vectors corresponds to the addition of algebraic vectors as defined in Section 2.2.

Example 1. Draw geometric vectors $\overrightarrow{OP}$ and $\overrightarrow{OQ}$ corresponding to the algebraic vectors (5, 2) and (2, 4). Find the sum $\overrightarrow{OR}$ of these vectors by using the parallelogram law, and show that this vector represents the algebraic sum of (5, 2) and (2, 4).

Solution: Figure 2.5 shows vectors $\overrightarrow{OP}$ and $\overrightarrow{OQ}$ corresponding to algebraic vectors (5, 2) and (2, 4). If R is such that $OPRQ$ is a parallelogram, then $\overrightarrow{OR} = \overrightarrow{OP} + \overrightarrow{OQ}$ by the parallelogram law.

Draw $QA \perp x$-axis, $RB \perp x$-axis, and $PB \perp RB$. Then triangles OAQ and PBR are congruent (why?) so that PB and BR have lengths 2 and 4 units, respectively, and R has co-ordinates $(7, 6)$.

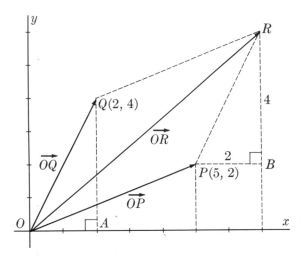

Figure 2.5

But, by the definition of algebraic vectors,

$$(2, 4) + (5, 2) = (7, 6)$$

and so $\overrightarrow{OR}$ is the geometric vector corresponding to the algebraic vector $(7, 6)$.

Example 2. Draw vectors $\overrightarrow{OP}$, $\overrightarrow{OQ}$, and $\overrightarrow{OR}$ corresponding to the algebraic vectors (4, 1), (−3, 4), and (4, 1) + (−3, 4). Show that $OPRQ$ is a parallelogram.

Solution: Figure 2.6 shows vectors $\overrightarrow{OP}$, $\overrightarrow{OQ}$, and $\overrightarrow{OR}$; R has co-ordinates $(1, 5)$.

$$OP \text{ has slope } \tfrac{1}{4}.$$
$$QR \text{ has slope } \frac{5 - 4}{1 - (-3)} = \frac{1}{4}.$$

Therefore,
$$OP \parallel QR.$$

$$OQ \text{ has slope } \frac{4}{-3}.$$

$$PR \text{ has slope } \frac{5-1}{1-4} = \frac{4}{-3}.$$

Therefore,

$$OQ \parallel PR.$$

Therefore, $OPRQ$ is a parallelogram and, by the parallelogram law, $\overrightarrow{OR} = \overrightarrow{OP} + \overrightarrow{OQ}$.

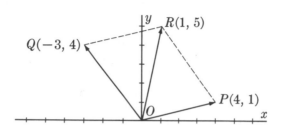

Figure 2.6

In Chapter 1, it was pointed out that the geometric vectors **u** and k**u** were collinear or parallel. The next example verifies that the vectors (a, b) and $k(a, b)$ are represented by parallel geometric vectors.

Example 3. Draw vectors $\overrightarrow{OP}$ and $\overrightarrow{OQ}$ corresponding to the algebraic vectors $(2, 1)$ and $(6, 3)$; show that O, P, and Q are collinear.

Solution: Figure 2.7 shows the required vectors $\overrightarrow{OP}$ and $\overrightarrow{OQ}$; P has co-ordinates $(2, 1)$ and Q has co-ordinates $(6, 3)$.

$$OP \text{ has slope } \tfrac{1}{2}.$$
$$OQ \text{ has slope } \tfrac{3}{6} = \tfrac{1}{2}.$$

Therefore,

$$OP \parallel OQ,$$

and so O, P, and Q are collinear.

We may conclude from this result that *any* geometric representative of **u** = $(2, 1)$ is parallel to *any* geometric representative of 3**u** = $3(2, 1)$.

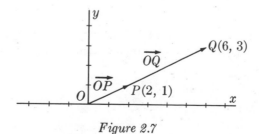

Figure 2.7

The examples of this section have illustrated in the two-dimensional case

(i) that addition of algebraic vectors corresponds to the addition of geometric vectors using the parallelogram law,

(ii) that multiplication of an algebraic vector by a real number produces a vector whose geometric representatives are parallel to the representatives of the original vector; in other words, (a, b) and $k(a, b)$ are represented by parallel vectors.

These two facts are also true in the three-dimensional case. Their verification will be easier when we have further information about lines in space at our disposal. (See question (10), Exercise 4.6.)

Of course, the vectors $\mathbf{v} = (a_1, b_1, c_1)$ and $\mathbf{w} = (a_2, b_2, c_2)$ are represented by the line segments OP and OQ joining the origin to the points $P(a_1, b_1, c_1)$ and $Q(a_2, b_2, c_2)$. These three points O, P, and Q determine a plane and the result above on addition of vectors then applies in this plane.

EXERCISE 2.4

1. Draw geometric vectors $\overrightarrow{OP}$ and $\overrightarrow{OQ}$ corresponding to the following pairs of algebraic vectors. Find the sum $\overrightarrow{OR} = \overrightarrow{OP} + \overrightarrow{OQ}$ using the parallelogram law and show that $\overrightarrow{OR}$ represents the sum of the given pair of vectors.
   (a) $(3, 2), (6, 1)$ (b) $(-4, 3), (2, 3)$
   (c) $(2, -3), (-3, 1)$ (d) $(4, -3), (-2, -3)$
   (e) $(-2, -3), (5, 3)$ (f) $(-3, -1), (-4, 3)$

2. Draw vectors $\overrightarrow{OP}$, $\overrightarrow{OQ}$, and $\overrightarrow{OR}$ corresponding to the following pairs of algebraic vectors and their sums, respectively, and show in each case that $OPRQ$ is a parallelogram.
   (a) $(1, 4)$ and $(3, 5)$ (b) $(-2, 6)$ and $(4, -2)$
   (c) $(5, 2)$ and $(-3, -2)$ (d) $(-3, -6)$ and $(-1, 4)$

3. Find geometrically the sum of the following vectors; check your results algebraically.
   (a) $(1, 1), (3, -2), (2, 1)$ (b) $(-3, 1), (2, -4), (-3, -4)$

4. Draw three representatives of the vector $(-1, 3)$ and of the vector $(-2, 6)$, and show that the first set is parallel to the second.

5. Show that the geometric vectors representing $(-1, 4)$ and $2(-1, 4)$ are parallel.

6. Show that the geometric vector representing $(1, 3)$ with initial point at $(2, 0)$ is parallel to the geometric vector representing $-2(1, 3)$ with initial point at $(0, 3)$.

7. Find geometrically the following vectors.
   (a) $2(3, 1) + 3(1, 1)$ (b) $2(-1, 2) + 3(2, -1)$
   (c) $-1(2, -3) + 3(-1, 2)$ (d) $-2(1, 3) - 3(2, -1) + \frac{1}{4}(4, -6)$

8. Prove that geometric vectors representing (a, b) and $k(a, b)$ are parallel.

9. Prove that if $\overrightarrow{OP}$, $\overrightarrow{OQ}$, and $\overrightarrow{OR}$ represent (a, b), (c, d), and $(a + c, b + d)$, respectively, then $OPRQ$ is a parallelogram.

10. Show algebraically and geometrically that if $\mathbf{u} = (2, 1)$ and $\mathbf{v} = (-1, 3)$, then $2(\mathbf{u} + \mathbf{v}) = 2\mathbf{u} + 2\mathbf{v}$.

11. Show algebraically and geometrically that $-3(\mathbf{u} + \mathbf{v}) = -3\mathbf{u} - 3\mathbf{v}$ if $\mathbf{u} = (3, -2)$ and $\mathbf{v} = (-1, 4)$.

12. Show algebraically and geometrically that if $\mathbf{u} = (2, -1)$ and $\mathbf{v} = (-1, 3)$, $2(\mathbf{u} - \mathbf{v}) = 2\mathbf{u} - 2\mathbf{v}$.

2.5. Lines Through the Origin • Collinear Vectors

We have already seen that the geometric vectors corresponding to the algebraic vectors $\mathbf{u}$ and $k\mathbf{u}$, where k is a real number, are parallel line segments. If we restrict our geometric vectors to those with initial point at the origin, then $\mathbf{u}$ and $k\mathbf{u}$ lie along the same line through the origin, and hence are collinear.

Thus, for a given nonzero vector $\mathbf{u}$, the set

$$\{k\mathbf{u} \mid k \in Re\}$$

is represented by the set of all line segments OP joining the origin to the points P of a certain line; that is, there is a one-to-one correspondence between the set

$$\{k\mathbf{u} \mid k \in Re\}$$

and the set of points on a particular line through the origin (either in 2- or 3-space). In this sense, we say that the set of all scalar multiples of a fixed nonzero vector *determines* or *is* a line through the origin.

Example 1. $\{k(1, 2) \mid k \in Re\}$ determines the line in 2-space through the origin and the point with co-ordinates $(1, 2)$.

Example 2. $\{k(-1, 3, 2) \mid k \in Re\}$ determines the line in 3-space through the origin and the point with co-ordinates $(-1, 3, 2)$.

Two nonzero vectors are said to be collinear if their geometric representatives with initial point at the origin lie along the same line. Therefore, the condition that two nonzero vectors be collinear is that each vector be a scalar multiple of the other.

$\mathbf{u}$ and $\mathbf{v}$ are collinear if and only if $\mathbf{u} = k\mathbf{v}$.

Obviously, $\mathbf{0} = 0\mathbf{u}$ and $\mathbf{0}$ is considered to be collinear with every vector.

Example 3.   Are the vectors

(a) $(1, 3, -2)$ and $(4, 12, -8)$,   (b) $(2, 3)$ and $(-4, -7)$ collinear?

Solution:

(a) $(4, 12, -8) = 4(1, 3, -2)$,   and $(1, 3, -2) = \frac{1}{4}(4, 12, -8)$. These two vectors are collinear.

(b) There is no real number k such that $(-4, -7) = k(2, 3)$.   For there to be agreement in the first components, k would have to have the value -2, but $(-2)(3) \neq -7$.   The two vectors are not collinear.

EXERCISE 2.5

1. State the sets of vectors determining lines parallel to the following vectors.
    (a) $(1, 3)$
    (b) $(-3, 4)$
    (c) $(3, 5, -2)$
    (d) $(-6, -1, 5)$
    (e) $(1, -2, 0)$
    (f) $(-2, 4, 6)$

2. State the sets of vectors determining lines parallel to $\overrightarrow{PQ}$ if P and Q are the following points.
    (a) $P(2, 3), Q(5, 7)$
    (b) $P(-3, 1), Q(5, -2)$
    (c) $P(4, -4), Q(-3, -2)$
    (d) $P(-1, -5), Q(-6, -3)$
    (e) $P(2, 3, 1), Q(-3, 1, 5)$
    (f) $P(-1, 3, -4), Q(3, 0, -2)$

3. Are the following pairs of vectors collinear?
    (a) $(4, -2), (-2, 1)$
    (b) $(-4, 2), (-2, -1)$
    (c) $(1, 3, -2), (\frac{1}{2}, \frac{3}{2}, -1)$
    (d) $(3, -6, 5), (\frac{3}{2}, 3, \frac{5}{2})$
    (e) $(1, -2, 2), (-4, 8, -8)$
    (f) $(3, -1, -5), (6, -3, -10)$

4. Find values of the variable involved (if possible) so that the following pairs of vectors are collinear.
    (a) $(3, -2), (6, k)$
    (b) $(-3, 1), (-6, -k)$
    (c) $(1, 5, -3), (-2, k, 6)$
    (d) $(4, -1, 1), (\frac{1}{2}, k, l)$
    (e) $(3, -1, 4), (k, -3, l)$
    (f) $(0, 2, -4), (k, 4, l)$

5. The following vectors determine lines through the origin.   Give the co-ordinates of two points on each line.
    (a) $k(2, 3)$
    (b) $(3k, -k)$
    (c) $(2k, 0, -k)$
    (d) $(k, 2k, -3k)$
    (e) $(a, -a, \sqrt{2}a)$
    (f) $(\pi p, -2\pi p, 0)$

2.6. Planes Through the Origin · Coplanar Vectors

Suppose that **u** and **v** are two noncollinear vectors. Their geometric representatives with initial point at the origin determine two distinct lines, which intersect in the origin. But two intersecting lines determine a plane and so two noncollinear vectors determine a plane passing through the origin.

The sum **u** + **v** of the noncollinear vectors **u** and **v** is represented geometrically by the diagonal of the parallelogram determined by **u** and **v**. This diagonal is a geometric vector in the plane determined by **u** and **v**. It follows that, for any real numbers k and l, the vector $k\mathbf{u} + l\mathbf{v}$ has a geometric representative having its initial point at the origin and lying in the plane determined by **u** and **v**. Indeed, it is obvious from the geometry (Figure 2.8) that, for given noncollinear vectors **u** and **v**, $k\mathbf{u} + l\mathbf{v}$ determines a point P in the plane determined by **u** and **v** (the point P such that $\overrightarrow{OP} = k\mathbf{u} + l\mathbf{v}$), and conversely, corresponding to every point P in the plane determined by **u** and **v**, there are two real numbers k and l such that $\overrightarrow{OP} = k\mathbf{u} + l\mathbf{v}$. (Note that we have not specified whether **u** and **v** are both two- or three-dimensional vectors; they can be either, provided they both have the same dimensions.)

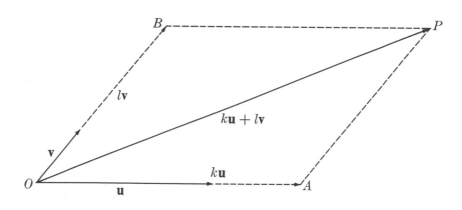

Figure 2.8

In the converse, given the point P in the plane determined by **u** and **v**, we need draw lines only through P parallel to **v** intersecting the line of **u** at A and through P parallel to **u** intersecting the line of **v** at B. Then $\overrightarrow{OA} = k\mathbf{u}$ for some k, and $\overrightarrow{OB} = l\mathbf{v}$ for some l.

Thus, for noncollinear vectors **u** and **v**, there is a one-to-one correspondence between the set

$$\{k\mathbf{u} + l\mathbf{v} \mid k, l \in Re\}$$

and the set of points in the plane through the origin determined by **u** and **v**. We call $k\mathbf{u} + l\mathbf{v}$ a linear combination of the vectors **u** and **v**.

Example 1. Sketch the plane through the origin determined by the vectors $\mathbf{u} = (2, 5, 4)$ and $\mathbf{v} = (-3, 1, 2)$. State the set of vectors determined by this plane.

Solution: The required plane is represented by the triangle OPQ in which $\overrightarrow{OP} = \mathbf{u}$ and $\overrightarrow{OQ} = \mathbf{v}$ (Figure 2.9). The set determined by this plane is

$$\{k(2, 5, 4) + l(-3, 1, 2) \mid k, l \in Re\}.$$

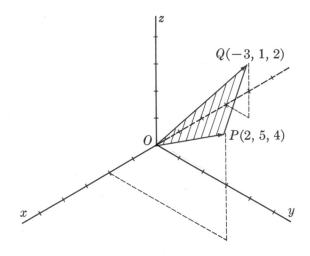

Figure 2.9

Three nonzero vectors are said to be coplanar if their geometric representatives with initial point at the origin lie in the same plane. The condition for three vectors to be coplanar is that at least one of the vectors be a linear combination of the other two.

Example 2. Show that the vector $(9, -10, -3)$ is a linear combination of the vectors $(-1, 2, 1)$ and $(3, -2, 0)$.

Solution: We must show that real numbers k and l exist such that

$$\begin{aligned}
(9, -10, -3) &= k(-1, 2, 1) + l(3, -2, 0) \\
&= (-k, 2k, k) + (3l, -2l, 0) \\
&= (-k + 3l, 2k - 2l, k).
\end{aligned}$$

Thus we must find k and l such that

$$\begin{aligned}
-k + 3l &= 9, \\
2k - 2l &= -10, \\
k &= -3.
\end{aligned}$$

We find that $k = -3$ and $l = 2$, so that

$$(9, -10, -3) = -3(-1, 2, 1) + 2(3, -2, 0).$$

The vectors $(9, -10, -3)$, $(-1, 2, 1)$, and $(3, -2, 0)$ are coplanar.

Example 3. Show that the vectors $(1, 0, 6)$, $(1, 2, -1)$, and $(3, 0, 4)$ are not coplanar; that is, none of the vectors is a linear combination of the others.

Solution: We can see at once that none of these vectors is a scalar multiple of either of the others. Thus any pair of the vectors, for example, the second and third, will determine a plane. Then, to show that $(1, 0, 6)$ is not in the plane they determine, we must show that $(1, 0, 6)$ is not a linear combination of $(1, 2, -1)$ and $(3, 0, 4)$; that is, we must show that it is impossible to find real numbers k and l such that

$$\begin{aligned}
(1, 0, 6) &= k(1, 2, -1) + l(3, 0, 4) \\
&= (k, 2k, -k) + (3l, 0, 4l) \\
&= (k + 3l, 2k, -k + 4l).
\end{aligned}$$

Suppose it were possible; then the system

$$\begin{aligned}
k + 3l &= 1, \\
2k &= 0, \\
-k + 4l &= 6,
\end{aligned}$$

would have a solution. From the second equation, $k = 0$ and so from the first, $l = \frac{1}{3}$. But this pair of values does not satisfy the third equation.

$$-0 + 4(\tfrac{1}{3}) = \tfrac{4}{3} \neq 6.$$

The system of equations is inconsistent and has no solution; that is, k and l do not exist such that

$$(1, 0, 6) = k(1, 2, -1) + l(3, 0, 4),$$

and so $(1, 0, 6)$ is not coplanar with $(1, 2, -1)$ and $(3, 0, 4)$. Thus, $(1, 0, 6)$, $(1, 2, -1)$, and $(3, 0, 4)$ are noncoplanar.

EXERCISE 2.6

1. Sketch the planes through the origin determined by the following pairs of vectors and state the set of vectors determined by each plane.
   (a) $(1, 0, 0)$, $(0, 2, 0)$
   (b) $(1, 2, 0)$, $(2, 0, -1)$
   (c) $(3, 2, 2)$, $(-2, 5, -3)$
   (d) $(-3, 2, 4)$, $(1, 0, 3)$
   (e) $(-2, -2, 5)$, $(0, -3, 4)$
   (f) $(-4, 0, 0)$, $(3, -1, 5)$

2. Find k, if possible, so that
   (a) $2(-1, 3) - (k, 3) = (-7, 3)$,
   (b) $3(1, 1, -3) + 2(-3, k, 4) = (-3, 3, -1)$,
   (c) $3(-1, 1, 2) - 2(4, 1, k) = (-11, 0, 4)$.
   (d) $2(1, 2, -k) + (4, -1, 5) = 3(2, 1, k)$.

3. Establish whether the first vector in each of the following is coplanar with, that is, a linear combination of, the other two vectors.
   (a) $(-3, 1), (1, 0), (0, 1)$ (b) $(2, 3), (0, -1), (1, 0)$
   (c) $(3, 5), (0, 1), (-1, 0)$ (d) $(-3, 4), (0, 5), (2, 0)$
   (e) $(2, 3), (1, -1), (1, 0)$ (f) $(-2, -2), (1, 2), (2, 1)$
   (g) $(2, 3, -5), (1, 0, 0), (0, 1, 0)$ (h) $(2, 2, -5), (1, 1, 0), (0, 0, 1)$
   (i) $(3, 1, 1), (0, 1, 1), (1, 1, 0)$ (j) $(3, 1, 1), (0, 1, 1), (1, 0, 0)$
   (k) $(3, 3, -1), (1, 1, 1), (1, 1, -1)$ (l) $(10, -3, 1), (1, 3, -2), (4, 1, -1)$
   (m) $(10, -3, 0), (1, 3, -2), (4, 1, -1)$
   (n) $(-3, 11, -16), (1, 3, -4), (2, 1, -1)$

4. Are the following sets of vectors coplanar?
   (a) $(0, 0, 0), (3, -1, 2), (1, 1, 4)$ (b) $(1, 1, -3), (4, -1, 2), (2, 2, -6)$
   (c) $(1, 0, 0), (0, 1, 0), (2, 3, 4)$ (d) $(0, 1, -1), (5, 5, -5), (0, 5, -5)$

5. If three 3-dimensional vectors are coplanar, must each be a linear combination of the other two?   (Refer to the results in question (4).)

6. Are the following sets of vectors coplanar?
   (a) $(3, -1, 1), (2, -1, 0), (3, 1, 4)$ (b) $(-1, 0, 3), (5, 2, 1), (-1, 1, 2)$
   (c) $(0, -1, 3), (3, -1, 0), (3, 0, -1)$ (d) $(1, 1, 1), (1, -1, 1), (3, 0, 4)$

2.7. Bases for V_2

In any set consisting of two vectors $\mathbf{u}$ and $\mathbf{v}$ in V_2, there are two possibilities: *either* $\mathbf{u}$ and $\mathbf{v}$ are scalar multiples of each other; that is, $\mathbf{u}$ and $\mathbf{v}$ are collinear, *or* $\mathbf{u}$ and $\mathbf{v}$ are not scalar multiples of each other; that is, they are not collinear.

In the latter case, we have seen in Section 2.6 that the set of vectors

$$\{k\mathbf{u} + l\mathbf{v} \mid k, l \in Re\}$$

corresponds to the entire set of points in the plane determined by $\mathbf{u}$ and $\mathbf{v}$, that is, in this case, to the entire 2-space.   This fact implies that any other vector in V_2 is a linear combination of $\mathbf{u}$ and $\mathbf{v}$.   It is this idea that we shall investigate in this section.

Example 1.   Given the vectors $\mathbf{u} = (1, 2)$, $\mathbf{v} = (3, 5)$, and $\mathbf{w} = (2, 4)$, show that at least one of the vectors is a linear combination of the other two.

Solution: In this case, $\mathbf{u}$ and $\mathbf{w}$ are scalar multiples of each other and so it is obvious that $\mathbf{w} = 2\mathbf{u} + 0\mathbf{v}$.

Example 2.   Given $\mathbf{u} = (1, 2)$, $\mathbf{v} = (3, 5)$, and $\mathbf{w} = (2, 6)$, show that at least one of the vectors is a linear combination of the others.

Solution: In this case, no two of the vectors are scalar multiples of each other. We must find k and l such that

$$\mathbf{u} = k\mathbf{v} + l\mathbf{w},$$

that is,

$$(1, 2) = k(3, 5) + l(2, 6)$$
$$= (3k, 5k) + (2l, 6l)$$
$$= (3k + 2l, 5k + 6l).$$

$$3k + 2l = 1.$$
$$5k + 6l = 2.$$

The solution of this system of equations is $k = \frac{1}{4}$, $l = \frac{1}{8}$.   Therefore,

$$(1, 2) = \tfrac{1}{4}(3, 5) + \tfrac{1}{8}(2, 6);$$

that is,

$$\mathbf{u} = \tfrac{1}{4}\mathbf{v} + \tfrac{1}{8}\mathbf{w}.$$

Example 3.   Show that, in Example 1, $\mathbf{v}$ is not a linear combination of $\mathbf{u}$ and $\mathbf{w}$.

Solution: Geometrically, $\mathbf{u}$ and $\mathbf{w}$ are collinear vectors and any linear combination of $\mathbf{u}$ and $\mathbf{w}$ will be a vector collinear with $\mathbf{u}$ and $\mathbf{w}$.   Since $\mathbf{v}$ is not collinear with $\mathbf{u}$ or $\mathbf{w}$, it follows that $\mathbf{v}$ cannot be a linear combination of $\mathbf{u}$ and $\mathbf{w}$. Algebraically, this means that it should be impossible to find k and l such that

$$(3, 5) = k(1, 2) + l(2, 4)$$
$$= (k, 2k) + (2l, 4l)$$
$$= (k + 2l, 2k + 4l),$$

that is, such that

$$k + 2l = 3,$$

$$2k + 4l = 5.$$

It should be immediately obvious that this system of equations is inconsistent and does not have a solution.

Example 4. In Example 2, it was shown that $\mathbf{u} = \frac{1}{4}\mathbf{v} + \frac{1}{8}\mathbf{w}$. Show that this expression for $\mathbf{u}$ is unique; that is, that $\mathbf{u}$ is no other linear combination of $\mathbf{v}$ and $\mathbf{w}$.

Solution: It has already been pointed out that no two of the vectors are scalar multiples of each other. Now suppose that

$$\mathbf{u} = \tfrac{1}{4}\mathbf{v} + \tfrac{1}{8}\mathbf{w} \quad \text{and} \quad \mathbf{u} = a\mathbf{v} + b\mathbf{w},$$

where

$$(a, b) \neq (\tfrac{1}{4}, \tfrac{1}{8}).$$

[handwritten: for ordered pairs to be equal, both terms must be equal.]

Then

$$\tfrac{1}{4}\mathbf{v} + \tfrac{1}{8}\mathbf{w} = a\mathbf{v} + b\mathbf{w}$$

and

$$(\tfrac{1}{4} - a)\mathbf{v} = (b - \tfrac{1}{8})\mathbf{w}.$$

By assumption, either $a \neq \frac{1}{4}$ or $b \neq \frac{1}{8}$. Suppose $b \neq \frac{1}{8}$; then

$$\mathbf{w} = \frac{\tfrac{1}{4} - a}{b - \tfrac{1}{8}}\mathbf{v}.$$

[handwritten: expressing w as scalar multiple of v]

This result violates the known fact that no two of the vectors are scalar multiples of each other. We conclude that no such real number pair (a, b) exists, and that

$$\mathbf{u} = \tfrac{1}{4}\mathbf{v} + \tfrac{1}{8}\mathbf{w}$$

is the only linear combination of $\mathbf{v}$ and $\mathbf{w}$ possible for $\mathbf{u}$.

Theorem. If $\mathbf{u}$ and $\mathbf{v}$ are noncollinear vectors of V_2, then any vector $\mathbf{w}$ in V_2 is a linear combination of $\mathbf{u}$ and $\mathbf{v}$.

[handwritten: since zero vectors are collinear with all vectors, but they're not collinear]

Proof: Obviously, $\mathbf{u}$ and $\mathbf{v}$ are both nonzero vectors. We must show that, if $\mathbf{u} = (a, b)$ and $\mathbf{v} = (c, d)$ are not scalar multiples of each other, and if $\mathbf{w} = (e, f)$ is any vector in V_2, then

$$\mathbf{w} = k\mathbf{u} + l\mathbf{v}$$

for some real numbers k and l. But

$$
\begin{aligned}
(e, f) &= k(a, b) + l(c, d) \\
&= (ka, kb) + (lc, ld) \\
&= (ka + lc, kb + ld)
\end{aligned}
$$

if and only if

$$
\begin{aligned}
ka + lc &= e, \\
kb + ld &= f.
\end{aligned}
$$

This system of equations will have a unique solution

$$k = \frac{cf - de}{bc - ad}, \quad l = \frac{be - af}{bc - ad}$$

provided $bc - ad \neq 0$. But $bc - ad = 0$ if and only if $\mathbf{u}$ and $\mathbf{v}$ are collinear (see question (5), Exercise 2.7). Hence, k and l exist such that

$$\mathbf{w} = k\mathbf{u} + l\mathbf{v}.$$

Corollary. The expression for $\mathbf{w}$ as a linear combination of $\mathbf{u}$ and $\mathbf{v}$ is unique.

A set of vectors such as those described in the above theorem is called a basis for V_2. Thus a basis for V_2 is any pair of noncollinear vectors of V_2; any vector of V_2 is a linear combination of the vectors of a basis.

The natural basis for V_2 is the pair of noncollinear vectors

$$\mathbf{e}_1 = (1, 0), \quad \mathbf{e}_2 = (0, 1).$$

It is immediately obvious that

$$(a, b) = a(1, 0) + b(0, 1)$$
$$= a\mathbf{e}_1 + b\mathbf{e}_2.$$

EXERCISE 2.7

1. In the following sets, show that at least one vector is a linear combination of the other two.
   (a) $(0, 0), (3, 5), (2, -3)$
   (b) $(0, 1), (1, 0), (3, -4)$
   (c) $(1, -1), (4, 7), (-3, 3)$
   (d) $(4, 4), (-1, -1), (-3, -3)$
   (e) $(3, 7), (0, 0), (2, 9)$
   (f) $(4, 2), (5, 9), (2, 1)$
   (g) $(1, 1), (3, 2), (1, 0)$
   (h) $(3, -2), (0, 1), (5, 2)$
   (i) $(3, 2), (-1, 1), (5, 7)$
   (j) $(-2, -1), (3, 1), (2, -5)$

2. Which of the following sets of vectors are bases for V_2? In the case of a basis, express $(5, -2)$ as a linear combination of the basis vectors.
   (a) $(0, 0), (3, 5)$
   (b) $(1, 0), (0, 3)$
   (c) $(-1, 5), (2, -10)$
   (d) $(-2, 0), (0, -3)$
   (e) $(1, 3), (2, -6)$
   (f) $(2, -4), (-1, 3)$
   (g) $(3, -1), (5, -2)$
   (h) $(2, 0), (4, 2)$
   (i) $(1, -1), (-1, 1)$

3. Express the following vectors as ordered pairs of real numbers.
   (a) $3\mathbf{e}_1 + 2\mathbf{e}_2$
   (b) $-\mathbf{e}_1 + 4\mathbf{e}_2$
   (c) $6\mathbf{e}_1$
   (d) $-\mathbf{e}_1 - 2\mathbf{e}_2$

4. Show that a basis for V_2 cannot contain the zero vector.

5. Show that (a, b) and (c, d) are collinear if and only if $ad - bc = 0$. *Hint:* consider the following cases.
   (i) $a = b = c = d = 0$
   (ii) $a = b = 0$
   (iii) $c = d = 0$
   (iv) $a = c = 0$, b, d nonzero
   (v) $b = d = 0$, a, c nonzero
   (vi) a, b, c, d nonzero.

6. Prove the corollary to the theorem of this section as in Example 4.

2.8. Sets of Vectors in V_3

Let $\mathbf{u}$ and $\mathbf{v}$ be distinct nonzero vectors in V_3. There are two possibilities:

(i) $\mathbf{u}$ and $\mathbf{v}$ are collinear; then each vector is a scalar multiple of the other;

(ii) $\mathbf{u}$ and $\mathbf{v}$ are not collinear; they are not scalar multiples of each other.

In the latter case, $\mathbf{u}$ and $\mathbf{v}$ determine a plane through the origin in 3-space.

Example 1. $\mathbf{u} = (-1, 3, 2)$ and $\mathbf{v} = (2, -6, -4)$ are collinear vectors;

$$\mathbf{u} = -\tfrac{1}{2}\mathbf{v} \quad \text{and} \quad \mathbf{v} = -2\mathbf{u}.$$

Example 2. $\mathbf{u} = (-1, 3, 2)$ and $\mathbf{v} = (2, 0, -1)$ are not collinear; they determine a plane through the origin consisting of the vectors

$$\{a\mathbf{u} + b\mathbf{v} \mid a, b \in Re\}.$$

If $\mathbf{u}$, $\mathbf{v}$, and $\mathbf{w}$ are distinct nonzero vectors of V_3, there are three possibilities:

(i) $\mathbf{u}$, $\mathbf{v}$, and $\mathbf{w}$ are collinear; then the vectors are scalar multiples of each other;

(ii) two of the vectors, say $\mathbf{u}$ and $\mathbf{v}$, determine a plane through the origin and the third is a vector in that plane; that is, $\mathbf{w}$ is a linear combination of $\mathbf{u}$ and $\mathbf{v}$;

(iii) no one of the vectors is in the plane determined by the other two; that is, none of the vectors is a linear combination of the other two.

Example 3. $\mathbf{u} = (-1, 3, 2)$, $\mathbf{v} = (2, -6, -4)$, and $\mathbf{w} = (-5, 15, 10)$ are collinear vectors;

$$\mathbf{v} = -2\mathbf{u} \quad \text{and} \quad \mathbf{w} = 5\mathbf{u}.$$

Example 4. $\mathbf{u} = (-1, 3, 2)$ and $\mathbf{v} = (2, 0, -1)$ determine a plane through the origin and

$$\begin{aligned}
\mathbf{w} &= (-8, 6, 7) \\
&= 2(-1, 3, 2) + (-3)(2, 0, -1)
\end{aligned}$$

is in this plane.

Example 5. $\mathbf{u} = (1, 0, 0)$, $\mathbf{v} = (0, 2, 0)$, and $\mathbf{w} = (0, 0, 3)$ are such that none of the vectors is in the plane determined by the other two; that is, none of the vectors is a linear combination of the other two, since a nonzero component cannot be a linear combination of two zero components.

Now consider a set of four distinct vectors of V_3. The possibilities are the following:

(i) all four vectors are collinear; that is, each vector is a scalar multiple of each of the others;

(ii) all four vectors are coplanar; that is, two of the vectors determine a plane and the other two are both in this plane;

(iii) three of the vectors are coplanar but the fourth does not lie in their plane;

(iv) no three of the vectors are coplanar.

The fourth possibility will be considered in the next section.

Example 6.   The vectors **u, v, w,** as given in Example 3, and $x = (-3, 9, 6)$ are four nonzero collinear vectors in V_3.

Example 7.   The vectors **u, v, w,** given in Example 4, and

$$x = (5, -9, -7)$$
$$= -3(-1, 3, 2) + (2, 0, -1)$$
$$= -3u + v$$

are such that **w** and **x** both lie in the plane determined by **u** and **v.**

Example 8.   The vectors **u** and **v,** as given in Example 5, determine a plane and

$$x = (3, 4, 0)$$
$$= 3u + 2v$$

lies in this plane, but **w** does not; that is, we have three vectors that are coplanar and a fourth that does not lie in their plane.

EXERCISE 2.8

1. Determine whether the following vectors are collinear.
    (a) $(3, 1, 1)$, $(-6, 2, 0)$ (b) $(4, -1, 3)$, $(2, -\frac{1}{2}, -\frac{3}{2})$
    (c) $(4, -4, 2)$, $(-2, 2, 1)$ (d) $(3, -1, 0)$, $(-6, 2, 2)$

2. State whether the following vectors are collinear. If they are not, select two vectors which determine a plane. Then determine whether the third vector lies in that plane (if so, express the third vector as a linear combination of the other two).
    (a) $(1, -1, 0)$, $(-2, 2, 0)$, $(\frac{1}{2}, -\frac{1}{2}, 0)$ (b) $(1, -1, 0)$, $(-3, 3, 0)$, $(-1, 1, 1)$
    (c) $(1, 0, 0)$, $(0, 1, 0)$, $(1, 1, 0)$ (d) $(1, 0, 0)$, $(0, 1, 0)$, $(0, 1, 1)$
    (e) $(1, 0, 0)$, $(0, 1, 0)$, $(1, 0, 1)$ (f) $(0, 2, \frac{1}{2})$, $(0, 4, 1)$, $(0, -16, -8)$
    (g) $(-3, 1, 2)$, $(1, 1, 4)$, $(-2, 1, 0)$ (h) $(1, -1, 4)$, $(3, -1, 1)$, $(1, -2, -1)$

3. State whether the following vectors are collinear, coplanar, or noncoplanar. If they are coplanar, express two of the vectors as linear combinations of the other two.
   (a) $(1, -1, 0)$, $(-3, 3, 0)$, $(4, -4, 0)$, $(\frac{1}{2}, -\frac{1}{2}, 0)$
   (b) $(-3, 1, 0)$, $(2, 1, 4)$, $(6, -2, 0)$, $(-12, 4, 0)$
   (c) $(2, 3, -1)$, $(5, 1, 2)$, $(-4, -6, 2)$, $(-10, -2, -4)$
   (d) $(1, 0, 3)$, $(0, 2, 0)$, $(-2, 0, -6)$, $(1, 2, 3)$
   (e) $(0, 0, -2)$, $(-3, 1, 0)$, $(0, 4, 0)$, $(1, 1, 1)$
   (f) $(-1, 2, 0)$, $(0, 3, -1)$, $(2, 0, -1)$, $(1, 2, 1)$
   (g) $(3, 1, 1)$, $(1, -1, 2)$, $(4, 0, 3)$, $(2, 2, -1)$

2.9. Bases for V_3

In Section 2.7, we showed that, in a set of three vectors of V_2, at least one of the vectors is a linear combination of the other two. Further, we showed that, if **u** and **v** are noncollinear vectors in V_2, then any vector **w** in V_2 is a *unique* linear combination of **u** and **v**.

In this section, we shall illustrate the following theorem (the proof in general follows the method of the example).

Theorem. If **u, v,** and **w** are three noncoplanar vectors of V_3, then any vector of V_3 is a linear combination of **u, v,** and **w.**

Corollary 1. In any set of four vectors of V_3, at least one of the vectors is a linear combination of the other three (see question (5), Exercise 2.9).

Example. Show that no three of the vectors

$$\mathbf{u} = (-1, 0, 3), \quad \mathbf{v} = (1, -1, 4), \quad \mathbf{w} = (3, -2, 1), \quad \mathbf{x} = (1, 1, -2)$$

are coplanar and that **x** is a linear combination of **u, v,** and **w.**

Solution: It can be seen immediately that none of the vectors is a scalar multiple of one of the others. Then **u** and **v** determine a plane, and we shall show that **w** does not lie in this plane. Assume that it does; that is, assume that real numbers k and l exist such that

$$\begin{aligned}(3, -2, 1) &= k(-1, 0, 3) + l(1, -1, 4) \\ &= (-k, 0, 3k) + (l, -l, 4l) \\ &= (-k + l, -l, 3k + 4l),\end{aligned}$$

and hence

$$\begin{aligned}-k + l &= 3, \\ -l &= -2, \\ 3k + 4l &= 1.\end{aligned}$$

The first two of these equations have the solution $k = -1, l = 2$, and substitution of these values in the third equation shows that this system of three equations in k and l is inconsistent and does not have a solution. Thus, **w** does not lie in the plane determined by **u** and **v**.

We must now show that **x** is not coplanar with any pair of the vectors **u**, **v**, and **w**. This involves showing, possibly as above, that $\{$**u, v, x**$\}$, $\{$**u, w, x**$\}$, and $\{$**v, w, x**$\}$ are not sets of coplanar vectors.

However, rather than carry out the above analysis three times, we proceed as follows. We express **x** as a linear combination, a**u** $+ b$**v** $+ c$**w**, of **u**, **v**, and **w**.

Suppose that one of a, b, or c is zero. Then we may write **x** as a linear combination of two of the vectors. Therefore, **x** is coplanar with these vectors.

Suppose that none of a, b, and c is zero. We shall argue that **x** cannot be coplanar with any pair of the vectors **u**, **v**, and **w**.

We wish to find real numbers a, b, and c such that

$$(1, 1, -2) = a(-1, 0, 3) + b(1, -1, 4) + c(3, -2, 1)$$
$$= (-a, 0, 3a) + (b, -b, 4b) + (3c, -2c, c)$$
$$= (-a + b + 3c, -b - 2c, 3a + 4b + c),$$

that is, such that

$$-a + b + 3c = 1,$$
$$-b - 2c = 1,$$
$$3a + 4b + c = -2.$$

We now have the problem of finding the solution of a system of three equations in the variables a, b, and c. By the method of elimination or any suitable method, the solution is found to be $a = -4$, $b = 3$, $c = -2$, so that

$$(1, 1, -2) = -4(-1, 0, 3) + 3(1, -1, 4) - 2(3, -2, 1).$$

We have now expressed **x** as a linear combination of **u**, **v**, and **w**, and we shall now show that this expression is unique. Assume that it is not; that is, assume that

$$-4(-1, 0, 3) + 3(1, -1, 4) - 2(3, -2, 1) = d(-1, 0, 3) + e(1, -1, 4) + f(3, -2, 1),$$

where $(-4, 3, -2) \neq (d, e, f)$. Then

$$[d + 4](-1, 0, 3) + [e - 3](1, -1, 4) + [f + 2](3, -2, 1) = (0, 0, 0).$$

Now either $d \neq -4$ or $e \neq 3$ or $f \neq -2$. If $d \neq -4$, we have

$$(-1, 0, 3) = -\frac{e - 3}{d + 4}(1, -1, 4) - \frac{f + 2}{d + 4}(3, -2, 1)$$
$$= -\frac{e - 3}{d + 4}\mathbf{v} - \frac{f + 2}{d + 4}\mathbf{w}.$$

This result gives us a contradiction since it has been shown that $\mathbf{u}$ is not a linear combination of $\mathbf{v}$ and $\mathbf{w}$. (Similar contradictions exist if $e \neq 3$ or $f \neq -2$.) This contradiction means that it is impossible to have

$$\mathbf{x} = d\mathbf{u} + e\mathbf{v} + f\mathbf{z}$$

in which one of d, e, and f is 0 and so $\mathbf{x}$ is not coplanar with any pair of vectors of the set $\{\mathbf{u}, \mathbf{v}, \mathbf{w}\}$.

In the study of this example, we have seen verified the following corollary to the theorem of this section.

Corollary 2.   The expression of any vector in V_3 as a linear combination of three noncoplanar vectors of V_3 is unique.

A set of three noncoplanar vectors of V_3 is called a basis for V_3; any vector in V_3 can be expressed uniquely as a linear combination of a set of basis vectors.

The natural basis for V_3 is the set $\{\mathbf{e}_1, \mathbf{e}_2, \mathbf{e}_3\}$ where

$$\mathbf{e}_1 = (1, 0, 0), \quad \mathbf{e}_2 = (0, 1, 0), \quad \mathbf{e}_3 = (0, 0, 1) .$$

It is immediately seen that these vectors are noncoplanar and that any vector $\mathbf{u} = (a, b, c)$ of V_3 can be expressed as

$$(a, b, c) = a(1, 0, 0) + b(0, 1, 0) + c(0, 0, 1) ;$$

that is,

$$\mathbf{u} = a\mathbf{e}_1 + b\mathbf{e}_2 + c\mathbf{e}_3 .$$

There should be no confusion in our using $\mathbf{e}_1$, $\mathbf{e}_2$ as the symbols for the natural basis for V_2 and $\mathbf{e}_1$, $\mathbf{e}_2$, $\mathbf{e}_3$ as symbols for the natural basis for V_3. In each case it should be known whether we are discussing two- or three-dimensional vectors.

EXERCISE 2.9

1. Do the following sets of vectors form bases for V_3; that is, are they noncoplanar?
   (a) $(0, 1, 0)$, $(1, 0, 0)$, $(0, 0, 2)$ (b) $(-1, 0, 0)$, $(0, 3, 0)$, $(0, 0, -2)$
   (c) $(-1, 0, 1)$, $(0, 1, 0)$, $(0, 0, 1)$ (d) $(-1, 0, 1)$, $(0, 0, 1)$, $(1, 0, 0)$
   (e) $(1, -1, 2)$, $(3, -1, 5)$, $(-2, 2, -4)$
   (f) $(3, -1, 1)$, $(2, -1, 1)$, $(1, 1, 2)$

2. Express the vector $(1, 1, 1)$ as a linear combination of the basis vectors in question (1).

3. Express the following vectors as triples of real numbers.
   (a) $3\mathbf{e}_1 - 2\mathbf{e}_2 + \mathbf{e}_3$ (b) $-4\mathbf{e}_1 + 2\mathbf{e}_3$ (c) $5\mathbf{e}_1 - 3\mathbf{e}_2 - \mathbf{e}_3$

4. Express the fourth vector in each of the following sets as a linear combination of the first three if possible.
   (a) $(1, 0, 0)$, $(0, 2, 0)$, $(0, 0, 3)$, $(-1, 2, 1)$
   (b) $(3, 1, 0)$, $(0, 3, 1)$, $(1, 0, 3)$, $(2, 2, 1)$
   (c) $(-3, 2, 1)$, $(-3, 0, 0)$, $(0, 2, 1)$, $(1, 1, -2)$
   (d) $(4, -1, 1)$, $(3, 0, -1)$, $(0, 1, -1)$, $(1, 1, 4)$
   (e) $(3, -3, 1)$, $(2, 0, 0)$, $(1, 3, 0)$, $(5, 2, 1)$

5. Prove Corollary 1 of the theorem in this section.

6. Prove Corollary 2 of the theorem.

Chapter Summary

Cartesian co-ordinate system in three dimensions · Two- and three-dimensional algebraic vectors: V_2 and V_3 · Equality of vectors · Addition of vectors; multiplication of a vector by a scalar; geometric interpretation · Identification of algebraic and geometric vectors · Lines through the origin; collinear vectors · Planes through the origin; coplanar vectors · Bases for V_2 and V_3

REVIEW EXERCISE 2

1. Express the following as single vectors.
   (a) $4(3, -1) + 3(-5, 2)$
   (b) $3(1, 0, -5) + 2(6, -3, -3)$
   (c) $5(2, 2) - 4(3, -1) + \frac{1}{2}(4, 8)$
   (d) $-2(1, 1, 5) - 3(2, -1, 4) + 2(0, 3, 5)$
   (e) $3e_1 - 5e_2 + 6e_3$
   (f) $6e_1 - 4e_2 - 5e_3$

2. What algebraic vectors correspond to geometric vectors $\overrightarrow{PQ}$ if P and Q are the following points?
   (a) $P(6, -1)$, $Q(-1, 6)$ (b) $P(-2, -4)$, $Q(3, -6)$
   (c) $P(-3, 1, -3)$, $Q(4, -1, 4)$ (d) $P(-1, -1, -5)$, $Q(3, -2, 6)$

3. Find the following vectors geometrically.
   (a) $3(1, 1) + 2(-1, 3)$ (b) $-2(3, 1) + 4(2, 2)$

4. Find the values of the variable involved (if possible) so that the following pairs of vectors are collinear.
   (a) $(6, -3)$, $(4, k)$ (b) $(3, -2, -4)$, $(\frac{1}{2}, k, l)$

5. Establish whether the first vector in each of the following is a linear combination of the other two vectors.

(a) $(3, 5)$, $(-2, 4)$, $(1, 1)$ (b) $(4, 1)$, $(3, -1)$, $(-6, 2)$

(c) $(1, 3, -3)$, $(4, 2, 1)$, $(1, 0, 1)$ (d) $(2, 3, -4)$, $(6, -1, 3)$, $(-4, 1, 1)$

6. Are the following sets of vectors coplanar?

(a) $(3, 2, -1)$, $(-6, -4, 2)$, $(1, 1, 1)$ (b) $(1, 0, 0)$, $(0, 5, 0)$, $(1, 1, 5)$

(c) $(3, -1, 0)$, $(1, 0, 1)$, $(0, -1, 3)$ (d) $(1, 1, 2)$, $(3, -1, 1)$, $(4, 2, 2)$

7. Which of the following sets of vectors are bases for V_2? In the case of a basis, express $(4, -3)$ as a linear combination of the basis vectors.

(a) $(0, 0)$, $(2, 1)$ (b) $(-1, 3)$, $(2, 1)$

(c) $(-4, 2)$, $(2, -1)$ (d) $(3, -1)$, $(3, -2)$

(e) $(2, 0)$, $(0, 5)$ (f) $(1, 1)$, $(2, 3)$

8. State whether the following vectors are collinear. If they are not, select two vectors which determine a plane. Then determine whether or not the third vector lies in that plane.

(a) $(1, 1, -2)$, $(2, 2, -4)$, $(3, 3, 6)$ (b) $(1, 3, 1)$, $(-2, -6, -2)$, $(3, 9, 3)$

(c) $(1, 1, 0)$, $(0, 1, 1)$, $(1, 0, 1)$ (d) $(4, 1, 1)$, $(3, -1, 1)$, $(2, -1, 1)$

9. State whether the following vectors are collinear, coplanar, or noncoplanar.

(a) $(1, 0, 0)$, $(3, 0, 0)$, $(0, 2, 0)$, $(0, 4, 0)$

(b) $(1, 0, 0)$, $(-3, 0, 0)$, $(0, 2, 0)$, $(0, 0, 4)$

(c) $(2, -1, 1)$, $(4, -2, 2)$, $(1, 1, 0)$, $(2, 1, 3)$

10. Do the first three vectors of each of the following sets form a basis for V_3? If so, express the fourth vector in each set as a linear combination of the first three.

(a) $(0, 2, 0)$, $(3, 0, 0)$, $(0, 0, -2)$, $(5, 1, -2)$

(b) $(3, -1, 0)$, $(-1, 0, 3)$, $(0, -1, 3)$, $(2, 2, -5)$

(c) $(4, -1, 2)$, $(1, 0, 3)$, $(2, -1, 0)$, $(3, 2, 3)$

Chapter 3

LENGTH AND INNER PRODUCT

3.1. Length of Line Segments in One and Two Dimensions

In this chapter, we shall assume that a fixed unit of measurement has been established. We can then set up a frame of reference to provide co-ordinates for points in one-, two-, and three-dimensional space. In one-dimensional space, that is, along a line, this unit of measurement allows us to assign the integer 1 to a certain point of the line after an origin for measurement has been established on the line, and hence to set up the real number line. With this fixed unit of measurement, we then make the following definition.

DEFINITION. The distance $d(P, Q)$ between the two points P and Q on the number line representing the real numbers x_1 and x_2, is defined to be

$$d(P, Q) = |x_2 - x_1|.$$

This definition assigns to each pair of points on the number line a unique nonnegative real number called the distance between the two points. This real number is positive if and only if the two points are distinct.

Example 1.

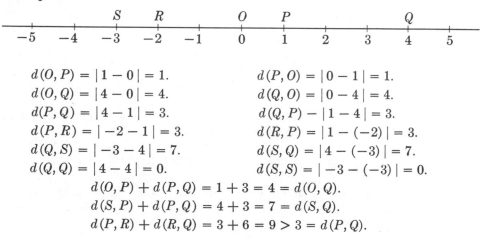

$$d(O, P) = |1 - 0| = 1. \qquad d(P, O) = |0 - 1| = 1.$$
$$d(O, Q) = |4 - 0| = 4. \qquad d(Q, O) = |0 - 4| = 4.$$
$$d(P, Q) = |4 - 1| = 3. \qquad d(Q, P) = |1 - 4| = 3.$$
$$d(P, R) = |-2 - 1| = 3. \qquad d(R, P) = |1 - (-2)| = 3.$$
$$d(Q, S) = |-3 - 4| = 7. \qquad d(S, Q) = |4 - (-3)| = 7.$$
$$d(Q, Q) = |4 - 4| = 0. \qquad d(S, S) = |-3 - (-3)| = 0.$$
$$d(O, P) + d(P, Q) = 1 + 3 = 4 = d(O, Q).$$
$$d(S, P) + d(P, Q) = 4 + 3 = 7 = d(S, Q).$$
$$d(P, R) + d(R, Q) = 3 + 6 = 9 > 3 = d(P, Q).$$

An examination of the results of Example 1 verifies that the distance $d(P, Q)$ we have defined for ordered pairs of points (P, Q) satisfies the following properties.

(i) $d(P, Q) > 0$ if $P \neq Q$.

(ii) $d(P, Q) = 0$ if $P = Q$.

(iii) $d(P, Q) = d(Q, P)$.

(iv) $d(P, Q) + d(Q, R) \geq d(P, R)$.

DEFINITION.   The length PQ of a line segment with endpoints P and Q is defined to be the distance between the endpoints.

$$PQ = d(P, Q) .$$

Example 2.   Using the points O, P, Q, R, S of Example 1,

$OP = PO = 1,$	$OQ = QO = 4,$
$PQ = QP = 3,$	$PR = RP = 3,$
$QS = SQ = 7,$	$QQ = SS = 0,$
$OP + PQ = OQ,$	$SP + PQ = SQ,$
$PR + RQ > PQ.$	

Note that these results for length agree with those we have used for many years based on a less formal definition of distance.

It follows immediately, from the properties of the distance $d(P, Q)$, that

(i) $PQ > 0$ if $P \neq Q$,

(ii) $PQ = 0$ if $P = Q$,

(iii) $PQ = QP$,

(iv) $PQ + QR \geq PR$.

We now use the definition of the length of a line segment in one dimension and the theorem of Pythagoras, to determine the length of a line segment, and hence the distance between two points, in two dimensions, that is, in the plane.

Theorem.   The distance $d(P, Q)$ between two points $P(x_1, y_1)$ and $Q(x_2, y_2)$ in the plane and the length of the line segment PQ is

$$d(P, Q) = PQ = \sqrt{(x_2 - x_1)^2 + (y_2 - y_1)^2} .$$

Proof: Let $P(x_1, y_1)$ and $Q(x_2, y_2)$ be two arbitrary points in the plane (Figure 3.1).   The relative positions of the particular points shown in the diagram are not important; the points may be in any position.

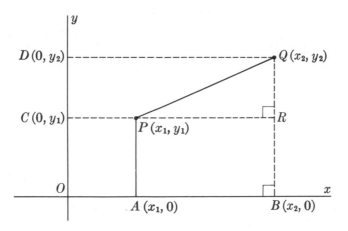

Figure 3.1

Construction: Draw PA and $QB \perp x$-axis, and PC and $QD \perp y$-axis; extend CP and QB to intersect in R.   Then

$$PR = AB = |x_2 - x_1|$$

and

$$RQ = CD = |y_2 - y_1|.$$

Proof: By the theorem of Pythagoras,

$$PQ = \sqrt{PR^2 + RQ^2} = \sqrt{|x_2 - x_1|^2 + |y_2 - y_1|^2},$$

or simply

$$PQ = \sqrt{(x_2 - x_1)^2 + (y_2 - y_1)^2}.$$

It follows by our definition that $d(P, Q)$ has this same value.

Example 3.   Let $P(2, 3)$, $Q(-1, 4)$, and $R(-3, -5)$ be three points in the plane.

(a) Find PQ, QR, and PR.
(b) Check that $PQ + QR \geq PR$.

Solution:

(a) $PQ = \sqrt{(-1 - 2)^2 + (4 - 3)^2} = \sqrt{10}.$

(b) $QR = \sqrt{(-3 + 1)^2 + (-5 - 4)^2} = \sqrt{85}.$

            $PR = \sqrt{(-3 - 2)^2 + (-5 - 3)^2} = \sqrt{89}.$

            $PQ \simeq 3.162, \quad QR \simeq 9.220, \quad PR \simeq 9.434.$

Therefore,

$$PQ + QR > PR.$$

EXERCISE 3.1

1. Find
$$d(A, B), \quad OC, \quad d(D, C), \quad AD, \quad d(B, B), \quad AC, \quad d(E, D), \quad d(C, D), \quad DA, \quad CB$$
   for the points and line segments of the following diagram.

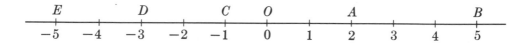

2. Verify that
   (a) $ED + DA \geq EA$ (b) $d(O, C) + d(C, B) \geq d(O, B)$
   (c) $AD + DB \geq AB$ (d) $d(C, D) + d(D, A) \geq d(C, A)$
   (e) $CE + ED \geq CD$ (f) $d(E, D) + d(C, D) \geq d(E, C)$
   (g) $DC + CA \geq DA$ (h) $d(A, E) + d(E, D) \geq d(A, D)$
   for the points and line segments in the above diagram.

3. Find
$$d(A, C), \quad AB, \quad d(D, E), \quad BC, \quad d(E, A), \quad d(A, D), \quad CE, \quad d(E, E)$$
   for the points and line segments of the following diagram.

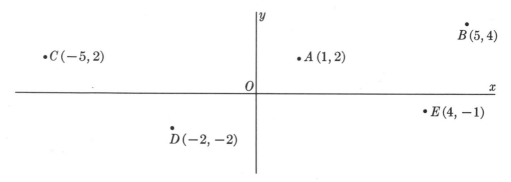

4. Verify the following for the points given in question (3).
   (a) $AB + BE \geq AE$ (b) $d(C, A) + d(A, B) \geq d(C, B)$
   (c) $DA + AB \geq DB$ (d) $d(E, A) + d(A, C) \geq d(E, C)$

5. Prove the theorem of this section using a diagram in which P is in quadrant IV and Q in quadrant II.

6. Prove that, for points P, Q, and R on a number line,
$$d(P, Q) + d(Q, R) \geq d(P, R).$$
   (Consider all possible cases.)

7. For points P and Q in the plane, prove that
   (a) $PQ > 0$ if $P \neq Q$,
   (b) $PQ = 0$ if and only if $P = Q$,
   (c) $PQ = QP$.

8. For what points P, Q, and R in the plane will $PQ + QR = PR$?

9. Use the result of question (8) to determine which of the following sets of points are collinear.
   (a) $P(3, -1)$, $Q(2, 5)$, $R(8, 3)$
   (b) $P(-1, 1)$, $Q(5, -1)$, $R(4, 3)$
   (c) $P(-1, 2)$, $Q(4, -2)$, $R(-3, 0)$

10. Determine which of the triangles PQR are right angled.
   (a) $P(1, 1)$, $Q(1, 4)$, $R(5, 4)$
   (b) $P(2, 3)$, $Q(-1, 2)$, $R(-3, -5)$
   (c) $P(-1, 2)$, $Q(5, 2)$, $R(1, -2)$

3.2. Line Segments in Three-Space

Theorem.   The distance $d(P, Q)$ between two points $P(x_1, y_1, z_1)$ and $Q(x_2, y_2, z_2)$ in space and the length of the line segment PQ is

$$d(P, Q) = PQ = \sqrt{(x_2 - x_1)^2 + (y_2 - y_1)^2 + (z_2 - z_1)^2}.$$

Proof: Let $P(x_1, y_1, z_1)$ and $Q(x_2, y_2, z_2)$ be arbitrary points in 3-space. In proceeding from point P to point Q, we move $x_2 - x_1$ units in the x direction, $y_2 - y_1$ units in the y direction, and $z_2 - z_1$ units in the z direction (these are shown as positive quantities in Figure 3.2 but of course any or all of them could be negative).

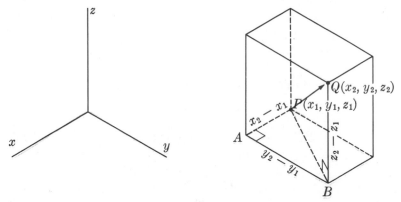

Figure 3.2

Line segment PA is parallel to the x-axis and has length $|x_2 - x_1|$; line segment AB is parallel to the y-axis and has length $|y_2 - y_1|$. Further, line segments PA and AB determine a plane parallel to the xy-plane and PB lies in this plane. From Section 3.1, line segment PB has length

$$PB = \sqrt{(x_2 - x_1)^2 + (y_2 - y_1)^2}\,.$$

Now line segment BQ is parallel to the z-axis and has length $|z_2 - z_1|$. This line segment is perpendicular to PB and so PB and BQ determine a plane which contains the right-angled triangle PBQ. Applying the theorem of Pythagoras, we obtain

$$PQ = \sqrt{PB^2 + BQ^2}$$
$$= \sqrt{(x_2 - x_1)^2 + (y_2 - y_1)^2 + (z_2 - z_1)^2}$$
$$= d(P, Q)\,.$$

This gives us a formula for the distance between two points P and Q in space, that is, the length of the line segment PQ.

Example. Let $P(2, 3, -1)$, $Q(-1, 0, 5,)$, and $R(-2, -1, 4)$ be three points in 3-space.

(a) Find PQ, QR, and PR.

(b) Verify that $PQ + QR \geq PR$.

Solution:

(a) $PQ = \sqrt{(-1 - 2)^2 + (0 - 3)^2 + (5 + 1)^2} = \sqrt{54} = 3\sqrt{6}.$
    $QR = \sqrt{(-2 + 1)^2 + (-1 - 0)^2 + (4 - 5)^2} = \sqrt{3}.$
    $PR = \sqrt{(-2 - 2)^2 + (-1 - 3)^2 + (4 + 1)^2} = \sqrt{57}.$

(b) $PQ \simeq 7.348$, $QR \simeq 1.732$, $PR \simeq 7.550$.
Therefore $PQ + QR > PR$.

EXERCISE 3.2

1. Find

   $d(A, B)$, OC, $d(D, C)$, AD, $d(B, B)$, AC, $d(E, D)$, $d(C, D)$, DA, CB

   for the points and line segments of the following diagram.

2. Verify that
   (a) $ED + DA \geq EA$
   (b) $d(O, C) + d(C, B) \geq d(O, B)$
   (c) $AD + DB \geq AB$
   (d) $d(C, D) + d(D, A) \geq d(C,A)$
   (e) $CE + ED \geq CD$
   (f) $d(E, D) + d(D, C) \geq d(E, C)$
   (g) $DC + CA \geq DA$
   (h) $d(A, E) + d(E, D) \geq d(A, D)$

   for the points and line segments in the diagram of question (1).

3. For points P and Q in 3-space, prove that
   (a) $PQ > 0$ if $P \neq Q$,
   (b) $PQ = 0$ if and only if $P = Q$,
   (c) $PQ = QP$.

4. For what points P, Q, and R in 3-space will $PQ + QR = PR$?

5. Use the result of question (4) to determine which of the following sets of points are collinear.
   (a) $P(-3, 1, 1)$, $Q(2, -3, 0)$, $R(-4, -1, 2)$
   (b) $P(-2, 1, 3)$, $Q(3, -1, 1)$, $R(10, -4, -4)$
   (c) $P(3, 1, -1)$, $Q(4, 0, -2)$, $R(3, -1, 0)$

6. Determine which of the following triangles PQR are right-angled.
   (a) $P(3, -1, 2)$, $Q(4, 3, -1)$, $R(3, 1, -4)$
   (b) $P(-1, -1, 3)$, $Q(4, -2, 5)$, $R(1, -3, -3)$
   (c) $P(3, -1, 0)$, $Q(4, 4, 1)$, $R(0, -2, 1)$

3.3. The Length of a Vector

In Section 2.3 it was pointed out that the two dimensional algebraic vector (a, b) could be represented geometrically in the plane by the directed line segment or arrow with initial point at the origin and terminal point at the point $P(a, b)$. Similarly, the three-dimensional vector (a, b, c) can be represented geometrically in 3-space by the line segment from the origin to the point $P(a, b, c)$.

Now the line segment from the origin to the point $P(a, b)$ has length $\sqrt{a^2 + b^2}$, and the line segment from the origin to the point $P(a, b, c)$ has length $\sqrt{a^2 + b^2 + c^2}$. We use these results to guide us in defining a length for the algebraic vectors (a, b) and (a, b, c).

DEFINITION. If $\mathbf{v} = (a, b)$, the length or magnitude $|\mathbf{v}|$ of $\mathbf{v}$ is defined to be

$$|\mathbf{v}| = \sqrt{a^2 + b^2}.$$

If $\mathbf{v} = (a, b, c)$, the length $|\mathbf{v}|$ of $\mathbf{v}$ is defined to be

$$|\mathbf{v}| = \sqrt{a^2 + b^2 + c^2}.$$

Example 1. Find the length of the vectors

(a) $\mathbf{u} = (3, -7)$,

(b) $\mathbf{v} = (-2, -3, -1)$.

Solution:

(a) $|\mathbf{u}| = \sqrt{3^2 + (-7)^2} = \sqrt{58}$.

(b) $|\mathbf{v}| = \sqrt{(-2)^2 + (-3)^2 + (-1)^2} = \sqrt{14}$.

Example 2.

(a) Find the length of the vector represented by the line segment from $P(-1, -1, 4)$ to $Q(3, -7, 1)$.

(b) Find the distance between the points $P(-1, -1, 4)$ and $Q(3, -7, 1)$.

Solution:

(a) Let

$$\mathbf{v} = \overrightarrow{PQ} \; ;$$

then

$$\mathbf{v} = (3 + 1, \ -7 + 1, \ 1 - 4) = (4, -6, -3)$$

and

$$|\mathbf{v}| = \sqrt{4^2 + (-6)^2 + (-3)^2} = \sqrt{61} \, .$$

(b) $d(P, Q) = \sqrt{(3 + 1)^2 + (-7 + 1)^2 + (1 - 4)^2}$

$$= \sqrt{4^2 + (-6)^2 + (-3)^2} = \sqrt{61} \, .$$

Example 2 merely emphasizes the relation between the defined length or magnitude of an algebraic two- or three-dimensional vector and the length of the corresponding line segments in 2-space or 3-space.

Example 3. Given $\mathbf{u} = 3\mathbf{e}_1 - 2\mathbf{e}_2 + \mathbf{e}_3$ and $\mathbf{v} = -\mathbf{e}_1 + \mathbf{e}_3$ in V_3, find

(a) $|\mathbf{u}|$,   (b) $|\mathbf{v}|$,   (c) $|\mathbf{u} + \mathbf{v}|$,   (d) $|2\mathbf{u} - 3\mathbf{v}|$.

Solution:

(a) $\mathbf{u} = 3\mathbf{e}_1 - 2\mathbf{e}_2 + \mathbf{e}_3 = (3, -2, 1)$.

$$|\mathbf{u}| = \sqrt{3^2 + (-2)^2 + 1^2} = \sqrt{14} \, .$$

(b) $\mathbf{v} = -\mathbf{e}_1 + \mathbf{e}_3 = (-1, 0, 1)$.

$$|\mathbf{v}| = \sqrt{(-1)^2 + 0^2 + 1^2} = \sqrt{2} \, .$$

(c) $\mathbf{u} + \mathbf{v} = (3, -2, 1) + (-1, 0, 1) = (2, -2, 2)$.

$$|\mathbf{u} + \mathbf{v}| = \sqrt{2^2 + (-2)^2 + 2^2} = \sqrt{12} = 2\sqrt{3} \, .$$

(d) $2\mathbf{u} - 3\mathbf{v} = 2(3, -2, 1) - 3(-1, 0, 1)$
$$= (6, -4, 2) + (3, 0, -3)$$
$$= (9, -4, -1).$$

$$|2\mathbf{u} - 3\mathbf{v}| = \sqrt{9^2 + (-4)^2 + (-1)^2} = \sqrt{98} = 7\sqrt{2}.$$

EXERCISE 3.3

1. Find the lengths of the following vectors.
   (a) $(0, 2)$ (b) $(0, 3, 0)$ (c) $(-6, 0)$ (d) $(0, 0, -4)$
   (e) $(1, 5)$ (f) $(1, 1, 2)$ (g) $(-3, 4)$ (h) $(-3, -3, 3)$
   (i) $(-2, -6)$ (j) $(4, -1, 6)$ (k) $(-5, -4)$ (l) $(\sqrt{2}, \sqrt{3}, \sqrt{4})$
   (m) $4\mathbf{e}_1 - 2\mathbf{e}_2$ (n) $-\mathbf{e}_1 - 3\mathbf{e}_2 + \mathbf{e}_3$
   (o) $2\mathbf{e}_1 - 3\mathbf{e}_2$ (p) $2\mathbf{e}_1 - 3\mathbf{e}_2 + \mathbf{e}_3$

2. Find the length of the vector $\overrightarrow{PQ}$ for each of the following P and Q.
   (a) $P(0, 0), Q(-2, 3)$ (b) $P(-1, 5), Q(3, -2)$
   (c) $P(-2, -3), Q(-5, -1)$ (d) $P(0, 0, 0), Q(-3, 1, 4)$
   (e) $P(-1, 2, 2), Q(3, 1, -4)$ (f) $P(-3, 1, -3), Q(4, 1, -7)$

3. If $\mathbf{u} = (3, 1, -4)$, $\mathbf{v} = 2\mathbf{e}_1 - \mathbf{e}_2 - \mathbf{e}_3$, and $\mathbf{w} = \mathbf{e}_1 + 4\mathbf{e}_2 - 2\mathbf{e}_3$, find the following.
   (a) $|\mathbf{u}|$ (b) $|\mathbf{v}|$ (c) $|\mathbf{w}|$ (d) $|\mathbf{u} + \mathbf{v}|$ (e) $|\mathbf{v} + \mathbf{w}|$
   (f) $|\mathbf{u} + \mathbf{w}|$ (g) $|\mathbf{u} + \mathbf{v} + \mathbf{w}|$ (h) $|2\mathbf{u} - 3\mathbf{v}|$ (i) $|3\mathbf{u} - \mathbf{v} - 2\mathbf{w}|$

4. Prove that $|k\mathbf{v}| = |k| |\mathbf{v}|$ if k is a real number. Explain the difference in the significance of the bars in the symbols $|k|$ and $|\mathbf{v}|$.

5. Prove that the length of a vector can equal 0 if and only if the vector is the zero vector.

3.4. Unit Vectors

The vector $\mathbf{u} = (\frac{1}{\sqrt{3}}, \frac{1}{\sqrt{3}}, \frac{1}{\sqrt{3}})$ has length

$$|\mathbf{u}| = \sqrt{\tfrac{1}{3} + \tfrac{1}{3} + \tfrac{1}{3}} = 1.$$

Such a vector is called a unit vector.

DEFINITION. A unit vector is a vector of length 1.

Example 1.
   (a) $\mathbf{e}_1$, $\mathbf{e}_2$, and $\mathbf{e}_3$ are unit vectors.
   (b) $\mathbf{u} = (\frac{3}{5}, -\frac{4}{5})$ is a unit vector since $|\mathbf{u}| = \sqrt{\frac{9}{25} + \frac{16}{25}} = 1$.
   (c) $\mathbf{v} = (\frac{1}{3}, -\frac{2}{3}, \frac{2}{3})$ is a unit vector since $|\mathbf{v}| = \sqrt{\frac{1}{9} + \frac{4}{9} + \frac{4}{9}} = 1$.

It should be obvious that every line segment in the plane joining the origin to a point on the circle whose equation is $x^2 + y^2 = 1$ will be a unit vector; that is, there is a unit vector in every direction in the plane (Figure 3.3).

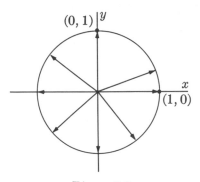

Figure 3.3

This fact means that we should be able to find a unit vector in the direction of an arbitrary vector (a, b).

This unit vector is found by using the result of question (4), Exercise 3.3.

$$|k\mathbf{v}| = |k||\mathbf{v}| ;$$

that is, the length of a scalar multiple of a vector is the length of the vector multiplied by the absolute value of the scalar.   For example,

$$|3\mathbf{v}| = 3|\mathbf{v}| ; \ |-5\mathbf{u}| = |-5||\mathbf{u}| = 5|\mathbf{u}|.$$

Now consider the vector $\mathbf{u} = (4, -3)$.   Its length is

$$|\mathbf{u}| = \sqrt{4^2 + (-3)^2} = 5,$$

so that $\frac{1}{5}\mathbf{u}$ and $-\frac{1}{5}\mathbf{u}$ will have length $\frac{1}{5}$ that of $\mathbf{u}$, that is, 1.

$$|\tfrac{1}{5}\mathbf{u}| = |(\tfrac{4}{5}, -\tfrac{3}{5})| = \sqrt{\tfrac{16}{25} + \tfrac{9}{25}} = 1$$

and

$$|-\tfrac{1}{5}\mathbf{u}| = |(-\tfrac{4}{5}, \tfrac{3}{5})| = \sqrt{\tfrac{16}{25} + \tfrac{9}{25}} = 1.$$

The same situation is found for three-dimensional vectors.   The line segments joining the origin to points on the sphere with centre the origin and radius 1 represent unit vectors so that there is a unit vector in every direction.

Example 2.   Find a unit vector in the direction of the vector $\mathbf{u} = (2, -1, 3)$.

Solution:

$$|\mathbf{u}| = \sqrt{4 + 1 + 9} = \sqrt{14}.$$

Thus $\frac{1}{\sqrt{14}}\mathbf{u}$ has length 1.

$$\frac{1}{\sqrt{14}}\mathbf{u} = (\tfrac{2}{\sqrt{14}}, \tfrac{-1}{\sqrt{14}}, \tfrac{3}{\sqrt{14}}).$$
$$|\tfrac{1}{\sqrt{14}}\mathbf{u}| = \sqrt{\tfrac{4}{14} + \tfrac{1}{14} + \tfrac{9}{14}} = 1.$$

$-\frac{1}{\sqrt{14}}\mathbf{u}$ also has length 1 and is collinear with $\mathbf{u}$.

We conclude that $\frac{\pm 1}{|\mathbf{v}|}\,\mathbf{v}$ are unit vectors collinear with $\mathbf{v}$.

EXERCISE 3.4

normalizing vectors

1. Find two unit vectors collinear with each of the following vectors.
   (a) $(1, 1)$ (b) $(-3, 1)$ (c) $(-2, -5)$ (d) $(\tfrac{1}{2}, -\tfrac{1}{2})$
   (e) $(1, 1, 2)$ (f) $(-1, 3, 1)$ (g) $(2, -2, 3)$ (h) $(-3, -3, 4)$

2. Find unit vectors parallel to $\overrightarrow{PQ}$ for the following P and Q.
   (a) $P(0, 2), Q(1, 3)$ (b) $P(-1, 4), Q(3, -2)$
   (c) $P(-2, -3), Q(-5, -2)$ (d) $P(0, 0, 2), Q(-3, 1, 4)$
   (e) $P(-1, 2, 2), Q(3, 1, -5)$ (f) $P(-3, 1, -3), Q(4, 1, 0)$

3. If $\mathbf{u} = (2, -1, 3)$, $\mathbf{v} = 2\mathbf{e}_1 - \mathbf{e}_2 - \mathbf{e}_3$, and $\mathbf{w} = \mathbf{u} + 3\mathbf{v}$, find unit vectors collinear with the following.
   (a) $\mathbf{u}$ (b) $\mathbf{u} + \mathbf{v}$ (c) $\mathbf{v} + \mathbf{w}$ (d) $\mathbf{u} + \mathbf{v} + \mathbf{w}$
   (e) $2\mathbf{u} - 3\mathbf{v}$ (f) $3\mathbf{u} + \mathbf{v} + \mathbf{w}$ (g) $\tfrac{1}{2}\mathbf{u} + \mathbf{v} - 3\mathbf{w}$

3.5. Inner or Dot Product

DEFINITION. If $\mathbf{u} = (a_1, a_2)$ and $\mathbf{v} = (b_1, b_2)$, we define the dot product or inner product $\mathbf{u} \cdot \mathbf{v}$ of $\mathbf{u}$ and $\mathbf{v}$ to be

$$\mathbf{u} \cdot \mathbf{v} = a_1 b_1 + a_2 b_2.$$

If $\mathbf{u} = (a_1, a_2, a_3)$ and $\mathbf{v} = (b_1, b_2, b_3)$, the dot product or inner product is defined similarly to be

$$\mathbf{u} \cdot \mathbf{v} = a_1 b_1 + a_2 b_2 + a_3 b_3.$$

Thus the inner product of two vectors is simply the sum of the products of corresponding components of the two vectors. The name "scalar product" is also often used for $\mathbf{u} \cdot \mathbf{v}$.

Note that the inner product of two vectors is a scalar (hence the name "scalar product") and not a vector; the set of two-dimensional (three-dimensional) vectors is not closed under this "multiplication". Of course the name "dot product" stems from the symbol $\mathbf{u} \cdot \mathbf{v}$ used to denote the product.

Example 1. Find $\mathbf{u} \cdot \mathbf{v}$ if
  (a) $\mathbf{u} = (3, -2)$, $\mathbf{v} = (-1, 7)$,
  (b) $\mathbf{u} = (3, -1, 5)$, $\mathbf{v} = (-1, -1, 2)$.

Solution:
  (a) $\mathbf{u} \cdot \mathbf{v} = (3, -2) \cdot (-1, 7) = 3(-1) + (-2)7 = -3 - 14 = -17$.
  (b) $\mathbf{u} \cdot \mathbf{v} = (3, -1, 5) \cdot (-1, -1, 2) = 3(-1) + (-1)(-1) + 5(2) = 8$.

Example 2. Find k so that $\mathbf{v} \cdot \mathbf{w} = 0$ if $\mathbf{v} = (3, -k, 2)$ and $\mathbf{w} = (-1, 4, 3)$.

Solution:
$$\mathbf{v} \cdot \mathbf{w} = (3, -k, 2) \cdot (-1, 4, 3) = -3 - 4k + 6 = 3 - 4k.$$
Therefore,
$$\mathbf{v} \cdot \mathbf{w} = 0 \text{ if } k = \tfrac{3}{4}.$$

Example 3. Find $\mathbf{v} \cdot \mathbf{v}$ if $\mathbf{v} = (-1, 3, -2)$.

Solution:
$$\mathbf{v} \cdot \mathbf{v} = (-1, 3, -2) \cdot (-1, 3, -2) = 1 + 9 + 4 = 14.$$

Example 4. If $\mathbf{u} = (3, -1)$, $\mathbf{v} = (2, -3)$, and $\mathbf{w} = (-1, 5)$, find
  (a) $\mathbf{u} \cdot (\mathbf{v} + \mathbf{w})$,
  (b) $\mathbf{u} \cdot \mathbf{v} + \mathbf{u} \cdot \mathbf{w}$.

Solution:
  (a)
$$\mathbf{v} + \mathbf{w} = (2, -3) + (-1, 5) = (1, 2).$$
$$\mathbf{u} \cdot (\mathbf{v} + \mathbf{w}) = (3, -1) \cdot (1, 2) = 3 - 2 = 1.$$
  (b)
$$\mathbf{u} \cdot \mathbf{v} = (3, -1) \cdot (2, -3) = 6 + 3 = 9.$$
$$\mathbf{u} \cdot \mathbf{w} = (3, -1) \cdot (-1, 5) = -3 - 5 = -8.$$
$$\mathbf{u} \cdot \mathbf{v} + \mathbf{u} \cdot \mathbf{w} = 1.$$

EXERCISE 3.5

1. Calculate $\mathbf{u} \cdot \mathbf{w}$ for the following pairs of vectors.
  (a) $\mathbf{u} = (1, 0)$, $\mathbf{w} = (3, 5)$.   (b) $\mathbf{u} = (0, 1)$, $\mathbf{w} = (3, 5)$
  (c) $\mathbf{u} = (1, -1)$, $\mathbf{w} = (-1, 1)$ (d) $\mathbf{u} = (3, 5)$, $\mathbf{w} = (-1, 4)$
  (e) $\mathbf{u} = (\tfrac{1}{2}, \tfrac{1}{4})$, $\mathbf{w} = (4, -2)$ (f) $\mathbf{u} = (a, b)$, $\mathbf{w} = (b, a)$
  (g) $\mathbf{u} = (a, b)$, $\mathbf{w} = (b, -a)$ (h) $\mathbf{u} = (\pi, \pi)$, $\mathbf{w} = (\tfrac{1}{\pi}, \tfrac{1}{\pi})$
  (i) $\mathbf{u} = (0, 0, 1)$, $\mathbf{w} = (0, 1, 0)$ (j) $\mathbf{u} = (-1, 0, 1)$, $\mathbf{w} = (1, 1, 1)$
  (k) $\mathbf{u} = (2, -1, 4)$, $\mathbf{w} = (3, 3, -1)$ (l) $\mathbf{u} = (-1, 5, -2)$, $\mathbf{w} = (-4, 2, -3)$
  (m) $\mathbf{u} = (-1, \tfrac{1}{2}, 3)$, $\mathbf{w} = (4, 4, -1)$ (n) $\mathbf{u} = (3, -\tfrac{1}{3}, -1)$, $\mathbf{w} = (\tfrac{1}{3}, 3, -1)$
  (o) $\mathbf{u} = (a, b, a)$, $\mathbf{w} = (b, a, b)$ (p) $\mathbf{u} = (a, a, b)$, $\mathbf{w} = (-a, b, -a)$

2. Find k so that
    (a) $(3, -k) \cdot (5, 4) = 0$,
    (c) $(-1, k, 2) \cdot (4, 1, -1) = 2$,
    (b) $(2, -4) \cdot (k, -3) = -7$,
    (d) $(-k, 3, -4) \cdot (2, -1, k) = 6$.

3. Find
    (a) $\mathbf{e}_1 \cdot \mathbf{e}_1$,
    (b) $\mathbf{e}_2 \cdot \mathbf{e}_2$,
    (c) $\mathbf{e}_3 \cdot \mathbf{e}_3$.

4. Find
    (a) $\mathbf{e}_1 \cdot \mathbf{e}_2$,
    (b) $\mathbf{e}_2 \cdot \mathbf{e}_3$,
    (c) $\mathbf{e}_3 \cdot \mathbf{e}_1$.

5. Find $\mathbf{u} \cdot \mathbf{u}$ if
    (a) $\mathbf{u} = (-3, 4)$,
    (b) $\mathbf{u} = (3, -2, 1)$,
    (c) $\mathbf{u} = (a, b, c)$.

6. Given $\mathbf{u} = (3, -2)$, $\mathbf{v} = (4, -7)$, and $\mathbf{w} = (-2, 3)$, find the following.
    (a) $\mathbf{u} \cdot (\mathbf{v} + \mathbf{w})$
    (b) $\mathbf{u} \cdot \mathbf{v} + \mathbf{u} \cdot \mathbf{w}$
    (c) $\mathbf{v} \cdot (\mathbf{u} + \mathbf{w})$
    (d) $\mathbf{v} \cdot \mathbf{u} + \mathbf{v} \cdot \mathbf{w}$
    (e) $\mathbf{u} \cdot 3\mathbf{v}$
    (f) $3(\mathbf{u} \cdot \mathbf{v})$
    (g) $3\mathbf{v} \cdot 4\mathbf{w}$
    (h) $12\mathbf{v} \cdot \mathbf{w}$
    (i) $-3\mathbf{u} \cdot -4\mathbf{v}$

7. Repeat question (6) if $\mathbf{u} = (4, -1, -1)$, $\mathbf{v} = (-3, 1, 5)$, and $\mathbf{w} = (4, -1, 2)$.

3.6. Properties of the Inner Product. I

In the next three sections, we consider some properties of the inner product. We state these properties and exemplify them and prove them for two-dimensional vectors. The proofs for three-dimensional vectors are left as exercises to the student.

Example 1.   Calculate $\mathbf{u} \cdot \mathbf{v}$ and $\mathbf{v} \cdot \mathbf{u}$ if
    (a) $\mathbf{u} = (3, -1)$, $\mathbf{v} = (4, -3)$,
    (b) $\mathbf{u} = (-2, 1, 4)$, $\mathbf{v} = (-2, -3, 6)$.

Solution:

(a)
$$\mathbf{u} \cdot \mathbf{v} = 3(4) + (-1)(-3) = 15.$$
$$\mathbf{v} \cdot \mathbf{u} = 4(3) + (-3)(-1) = 15.$$

Therefore,
$$\mathbf{u} \cdot \mathbf{v} = \mathbf{v} \cdot \mathbf{u} \text{ for these vectors } \mathbf{u} \text{ and } \mathbf{v}.$$

(b)
$$\mathbf{u} \cdot \mathbf{v} = (-2)(-2) + 1(-3) + 4(6) = 25.$$
$$\mathbf{v} \cdot \mathbf{u} = (-2)(-2) + (-3)(1) + 6(4) = 25.$$

Therefore,
$$\mathbf{u} \cdot \mathbf{v} = \mathbf{v} \cdot \mathbf{u} \text{ for these vectors } \mathbf{u} \text{ and } \mathbf{v}.$$

It should be evident that inner multiplication of real vectors involves multiplication of real numbers (the components), and that the order of the components in each product is thus immaterial, so that inner multiplication is commutative.

Property 1 $\qquad\qquad\qquad\qquad$ $\mathbf{u} \cdot \mathbf{v} = \mathbf{v} \cdot \mathbf{u}.$

Proof (in V_2): Let $\mathbf{u} = (a_1, a_2)$, $\mathbf{v} = (b_1, b_2)$.

$$\begin{aligned} \mathbf{u} \cdot \mathbf{v} &= a_1 b_1 + a_2 b_2 \\ &= b_1 a_1 + b_2 a_2 \\ &= \mathbf{v} \cdot \mathbf{u}. \end{aligned}$$

Therefore,

$$\mathbf{u} \cdot \mathbf{v} = \mathbf{v} \cdot \mathbf{u} \text{ for vectors } \mathbf{u} \text{ and } \mathbf{v} \text{ in } V_2.$$

Example 2. Calculate $\mathbf{u} \cdot (\mathbf{v} + \mathbf{w})$ and $\mathbf{u} \cdot \mathbf{v} + \mathbf{u} \cdot \mathbf{w}$ if
  (a) $\mathbf{u} = (3, -1)$, $\mathbf{v} = (-2, 5)$, $\mathbf{w} = (1, -4)$,
  (b) $\mathbf{u} = (3, -1, 2)$, $\mathbf{v} = (-2, 5, 3)$, $\mathbf{w} = (1, -4, -4)$.

Solution.
  (a) $\qquad\qquad$ $\mathbf{v} + \mathbf{w} = (-2, 5) + (1, -4) = (-1, 1).$

Therefore,

$$\mathbf{u} \cdot (\mathbf{v} + \mathbf{w}) = (3, -1) \cdot (-1, 1) = -3 - 1 = -4.$$

Also

$$\mathbf{u} \cdot \mathbf{v} = (3, -1) \cdot (-2, 5) = -6 - 5 = -11$$

and

$$\mathbf{u} \cdot \mathbf{w} = (3, -1) \cdot (1, -4) = 3 + 4 = 7.$$

Thus

$$\mathbf{u} \cdot \mathbf{v} + \mathbf{u} \cdot \mathbf{w} = -11 + 7 = -4.$$

Therefore,

$$\mathbf{u} \cdot (\mathbf{v} + \mathbf{w}) = \mathbf{u} \cdot \mathbf{v} + \mathbf{u} \cdot \mathbf{w} \text{ for these vectors } \mathbf{u},\, \mathbf{v},\, \text{and } \mathbf{w}.$$

  (b) $\qquad\qquad$ $\mathbf{v} + \mathbf{w} = (-2, 5, 3) + (1, -4, -4) = (-1, 1, -1).$

Therefore,

$$\mathbf{u} \cdot (\mathbf{v} + \mathbf{w}) = (3, -1, 2) \cdot (-1, 1, -1) = -3 - 1 - 2 = -6.$$

Also

$$\mathbf{u} \cdot \mathbf{v} = (3, -1, 2) \cdot (-2, 5, 3) = -6 - 5 + 6 = -5$$

and

$$\mathbf{u} \cdot \mathbf{w} = (3, -1, 2) \cdot (1, -4, -4) = 3 + 4 - 8 = -1.$$

Thus

$$\mathbf{u} \cdot \mathbf{v} + \mathbf{u} \cdot \mathbf{w} = -5 - 1 = -6.$$

Therefore,

$$\mathbf{u} \cdot (\mathbf{v} + \mathbf{w}) = \mathbf{u} \cdot \mathbf{v} + \mathbf{u} \cdot \mathbf{w} \text{ for these vectors } \mathbf{u},\, \mathbf{v},\, \text{and } \mathbf{w}.$$

These examples suggest that inner multiplication is distributive over vector addition.

Property 2 $\mathbf{u} \cdot (\mathbf{v} + \mathbf{w}) = \mathbf{u} \cdot \mathbf{v} + \mathbf{u} \cdot \mathbf{w}.$

Proof (in V_2): Let $\mathbf{u} = (a_1, a_2)$, $\mathbf{v} = (b_1, b_2)$, $\mathbf{w} = (c_1, c_2)$.

$$\mathbf{v} + \mathbf{w} = (b_1, b_2) + (c_1, c_2) = (b_1 + c_1, b_2 + c_2).$$

Therefore,

$$\begin{aligned}
\mathbf{u} \cdot (\mathbf{v} + \mathbf{w}) &= (a_1, a_2) \cdot (b_1 + c_1, b_2 + c_2) \\
&= a_1(b_1 + c_1) + a_2(b_2 + c_2) \\
&= a_1 b_1 + a_1 c_1 + a_2 b_2 + a_2 c_2.
\end{aligned}$$

Also

$$\mathbf{u} \cdot \mathbf{v} = (a_1, a_2) \cdot (b_1, b_2) = a_1 b_1 + a_2 b_2$$

and

$$\mathbf{u} \cdot \mathbf{w} = (a_1, a_2) \cdot (c_1, c_2) = a_1 c_1 + a_2 c_2.$$

Therefore,

$$\begin{aligned}
\mathbf{u} \cdot \mathbf{v} + \mathbf{u} \cdot \mathbf{w} &= (a_1 b_1 + a_2 b_2) + (a_1 c_1 + a_2 c_2) \\
&= a_1 b_1 + a_1 c_1 + a_2 b_2 + a_2 c_2.
\end{aligned}$$

Therefore,

$$\mathbf{u} \cdot (\mathbf{v} + \mathbf{w}) = \mathbf{u} \cdot \mathbf{v} + \mathbf{u} \cdot \mathbf{w} \text{ for vectors } \mathbf{u}, \mathbf{v}, \text{ and } \mathbf{w} \text{ in } V_2.$$

EXERCISE 3.6

1. Verify that $\mathbf{u} \cdot \mathbf{v} = \mathbf{v} \cdot \mathbf{u}$ for the following pairs of vectors.

    (a) $\mathbf{u} = (3, -1)$, $\mathbf{v} = (4, 2)$ (b) $\mathbf{u} = (6, -1)$, $\mathbf{v} = (-5, 7)$

    (c) $\mathbf{u} = (4, 2, -3)$, $\mathbf{v} = (1, -1, 4)$ (d) $\mathbf{u} = (3, -1, -2)$, $\mathbf{v} = (2, -5, 2)$

    (e) $\mathbf{u} = 2\mathbf{e}_1 - \mathbf{e}_2$, $\mathbf{v} = (3, 5)$ (f) $\mathbf{u} = -\mathbf{e}_1 - 3\mathbf{e}_2$, $\mathbf{v} = 4\mathbf{e}_1 + \mathbf{e}_2$

    (g) $\mathbf{u} = 3\mathbf{e}_1 - \mathbf{e}_2 + 5\mathbf{e}_3$, $\mathbf{v} = (4, 1, -1)$

    (h) $\mathbf{u} = -3\mathbf{e}_1 - \mathbf{e}_2 + 3\mathbf{e}_3$, $\mathbf{v} = 4\mathbf{e}_1 - 2\mathbf{e}_2 - 3\mathbf{e}_3$

    (i) $\mathbf{u} = (\frac{1}{2}, -\frac{3}{2}, \frac{1}{4})$, $\mathbf{v} = (\frac{3}{2}, -\frac{1}{3}, \frac{1}{2})$

2. Verify that $\mathbf{u} \cdot (\mathbf{v} + \mathbf{w}) = \mathbf{u} \cdot \mathbf{v} + \mathbf{u} \cdot \mathbf{w}$ for the following vectors.

    (a) $\mathbf{u} = (2, -1)$, $\mathbf{v} = (3, -2)$, $\mathbf{w} = (1, 4)$

    (b) $\mathbf{u} = (3, -4)$, $\mathbf{v} = (-1, 1)$, $\mathbf{w} = (5, 2)$

    (c) $\mathbf{u} = (2, -3, 3)$, $\mathbf{v} = (-1, 4, -1)$, $\mathbf{w} = (6, -3, 0)$

    (d) $\mathbf{u} = (-1, 5, 0)$, $\mathbf{v} = (4, -2, -3)$, $\mathbf{w} = (-5, 2, -1)$

3. Prove that

    $$\mathbf{u} \cdot \mathbf{v} = \mathbf{v} \cdot \mathbf{u}$$

    for vectors $\mathbf{u}$ and $\mathbf{v}$ in V_3.

4. Prove that

    $$\mathbf{u} \cdot (\mathbf{v} + \mathbf{w}) = \mathbf{u} \cdot \mathbf{v} + \mathbf{u} \cdot \mathbf{w}$$

    for vectors $\mathbf{u}$, $\mathbf{v}$, and $\mathbf{w}$ in V_3.

3.7. Properties of the Inner Product. II

Example 1.   Calculate $(5\mathbf{u}) \cdot \mathbf{v}$, $\mathbf{u} \cdot (5\mathbf{v})$, and $5(\mathbf{u} \cdot \mathbf{v})$ if
    (a) $\mathbf{u} = (3, -4)$, $\mathbf{v} = (-1, -3)$,
    (b) $\mathbf{u} = (2, -3, 5)$, $\mathbf{v} = (4, -1, -2)$.

Solution:
    (a)

$$5\mathbf{u} = 5(3, -4) = (15, -20).$$
$$(5\mathbf{u}) \cdot \mathbf{v} = (15, -20) \cdot (-1, -3) = -15 + 60 = 45.$$
$$5\mathbf{v} = 5(-1, -3) = (-5, -15).$$
$$\mathbf{u} \cdot 5\mathbf{v} = (3, -4) \cdot (-5, -15) = -15 + 60 = 45.$$
$$\mathbf{u} \cdot \mathbf{v} = (3, -4) \cdot (-1, -3) = -3 + 12 = 9.$$
$$5(\mathbf{u} \cdot \mathbf{v}) = 45.$$

Therefore $(5\mathbf{u}) \cdot \mathbf{v} = \mathbf{u} \cdot (5\mathbf{v}) = 5(\mathbf{u} \cdot \mathbf{v})$ for these vectors $\mathbf{u}$ and $\mathbf{v}$.

    (b)

$$5\mathbf{u} = 5(2, -3, 5) = (10, -15, 25).$$
$$(5\mathbf{u}) \cdot \mathbf{v} = (10, -15, 25) \cdot (4, -1, -2) = 40 + 15 - 50 = 5.$$
$$5\mathbf{v} = 5(4, -1, -2) = (20, -5, -10).$$
$$\mathbf{u} \cdot (5\mathbf{v}) = (2, -3, 5) \cdot (20, -5, -10) = 40 + 15 - 50 = 5.$$
$$\mathbf{u} \cdot \mathbf{v} = (2, -3, 5) \cdot (4, -1, -2) = 8 + 3 - 10 = 1.$$
$$5(\mathbf{u} \cdot \mathbf{v}) = 5.$$

Therefore $(5\mathbf{u}) \cdot \mathbf{v} = \mathbf{u} \cdot (5\mathbf{v}) = 5(\mathbf{u} \cdot \mathbf{v})$ for these vectors $\mathbf{u}$ and $\mathbf{v}$.

These examples illustrate the following property.

Property 3

$$(k\mathbf{u}) \cdot \mathbf{v} = \mathbf{u} \cdot (k\mathbf{v}) = k(\mathbf{u} \cdot \mathbf{v}) \text{ for any real number } k.$$

Proof (in V_2):   Let $\mathbf{u} = (a_1, a_2)$ and $\mathbf{v} = (b_1, b_2)$.
Then

$$k\mathbf{u} = k(a_1, a_2) = (ka_1, ka_2).$$
$$(k\mathbf{u}) \cdot \mathbf{v} = (ka_1, ka_2) \cdot (b_1, b_2)$$
$$= (ka_1)b_1 + (ka_2)b_2$$
$$= ka_1b_1 + ka_2b_2.$$
$$k\mathbf{v} = k(b_1, b_2) = (kb_1, kb_2).$$
$$\mathbf{u} \cdot (k\mathbf{v}) = (a_1, a_2) \cdot (kb_1, kb_2)$$
$$= a_1(kb_1) + a_2(kb_2)$$
$$= ka_1b_1 + ka_2b_2.$$
$$\mathbf{u} \cdot \mathbf{v} = (a_1, a_2) \cdot (b_1, b_2)$$
$$= a_1b_1 + a_2b_2.$$
$$k(\mathbf{u} \cdot \mathbf{v}) = k(a_1b_1 + a_2b_2) = ka_1b_1 + ka_2b_2.$$

Therefore $(k\mathbf{u}) \cdot \mathbf{v} = \mathbf{u} \cdot (k\mathbf{v}) = k(\mathbf{u} \cdot \mathbf{v})$ for vectors $\mathbf{u}$ and $\mathbf{v}$ in V_2.

Example 2. Calculate $\mathbf{v} \cdot \mathbf{v}$ and $|\mathbf{v}|^2$ for

   (a) $|\mathbf{v}| = (3, -1)$,

   (b) $|\mathbf{v}| = (-2, 5, 2)$.

Solution:

   (a)
$$\mathbf{v} \cdot \mathbf{v} = (3, -1) \cdot (3, -1) = 9 + 1 = 10.$$
$$|\mathbf{v}| = \sqrt{(3)^2 + (-1)^2} = \sqrt{10}.$$
$$|\mathbf{v}|^2 = 10.$$

Therefore, $\mathbf{v} \cdot \mathbf{v} = |\mathbf{v}|^2$ for this vector $\mathbf{v}$.

   (b)
$$\mathbf{v} \cdot \mathbf{v} = (-2, 5, 2) \cdot (-2, 5, 2) = 4 + 25 + 4 = 33.$$
$$|\mathbf{v}| = \sqrt{(-2)^2 + 5^2 + 2^2} = \sqrt{33}.$$
$$|\mathbf{v}|^2 = 33.$$

Therefore, $\mathbf{v} \cdot \mathbf{v} = |\mathbf{v}|^2$ for this vector $\mathbf{v}$.

These examples illustrate the following property.

Property 4 ✳ $\mathbf{v} \cdot \mathbf{v} = |\mathbf{v}|^2.$

Proof (in V_2): Let $\mathbf{v} = (a, b)$.

Then
$$\mathbf{v} \cdot \mathbf{v} = (a, b) \cdot (a, b) = a^2 + b^2.$$

Also
$$|\mathbf{v}| = \sqrt{a^2 + b^2}.$$
$$|\mathbf{v}|^2 = a^2 + b^2.$$

Therefore, $\mathbf{v} \cdot \mathbf{v} = |\mathbf{v}|^2$ for vectors $\mathbf{v}$ in V_2.

EXERCISE 3.7

1. Verify that $(2\mathbf{u}) \cdot \mathbf{v} = \mathbf{u} \cdot (2\mathbf{v}) = 2(\mathbf{u} \cdot \mathbf{v})$ for the following vectors.

   (a) $\mathbf{u} = (3, -4)$, $\mathbf{v} = (-6, 2)$ (b) $\mathbf{u} = (-1, 4)$, $\mathbf{v} = (5, 0)$

   (c) $\mathbf{u} = 2\mathbf{e}_1 - \mathbf{e}_2$, $\mathbf{v} = (5, -7)$ (d) $\mathbf{u} = \mathbf{e}_1 + 3\mathbf{e}_2$, $\mathbf{v} = -\mathbf{e}_1 + 5\mathbf{e}_2$

   (e) $\mathbf{u} = (1, 2, 1)$, $\mathbf{v} = (-3, 1, 4)$ (f) $\mathbf{u} = (-3, 1, -5)$, $\mathbf{v} = (-1, 0, 4)$

   (g) $\mathbf{u} = 3\mathbf{e}_1 + \mathbf{e}_2 + \mathbf{e}_3$, $\mathbf{v} = (4, -1, 3)$

   (h) $\mathbf{u} = 6\mathbf{e}_1 - \mathbf{e}_2 + 3\mathbf{e}_3$, $\mathbf{v} = 6\mathbf{e}_1 + 4\mathbf{e}_3$

2. Verify that $(-3\mathbf{u}) \cdot \mathbf{v} = \mathbf{u} \cdot (-3\mathbf{v}) = -3(\mathbf{u} \cdot \mathbf{v})$ for the vectors in question (1).

3. Verify that $\mathbf{v} \cdot \mathbf{v} = |\mathbf{v}|^2$ for the following vectors.

   (a) $\mathbf{v} = (5, -2)$ (b) $\mathbf{v} = -3\mathbf{e}_1 + \mathbf{e}_2$ (c) $\mathbf{v} = -4\mathbf{e}_1 + 5\mathbf{e}_2$

   (d) $\mathbf{v} = (-6, 3, 1)$ (e) $\mathbf{v} = -\mathbf{e}_1 + \mathbf{e}_2 - 3\mathbf{e}_3$ (f) $\mathbf{v} = 2\mathbf{e}_1 - \mathbf{e}_2 + 5\mathbf{e}_3$

4. Prove Property 3 for vectors in V_3.

5. Prove Property 4 for vectors in V_3.

6. Prove that $(\mathbf{u} + \mathbf{v}) \cdot (\mathbf{w} + \mathbf{x}) = \mathbf{u} \cdot \mathbf{w} + \mathbf{u} \cdot \mathbf{x} + \mathbf{v} \cdot \mathbf{w} + \mathbf{v} \cdot \mathbf{x}$.

7. Simplify   (a) $(2\mathbf{u} - 3\mathbf{v}) \cdot (\mathbf{u} + 4\mathbf{v})$,   (b) $(3\mathbf{u} - 4\mathbf{v}) \cdot (-2\mathbf{u} + 3\mathbf{v})$.

8. Evaluate the vectors in question 7(a) and (b) if $\mathbf{u}$ and $\mathbf{v}$ are vectors of lengths 2 and 3, respectively, and $\mathbf{u} \cdot \mathbf{v} = -6$.

3.8. Inner Product and the Cosine Law

The Cosine Law is an extension of the theorem of Pythagoras and states that in a triangle with sides and angles as shown in Figure 3.4, we have the relation

$$a^2 = b^2 + c^2 - 2bc \cos A .$$

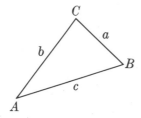

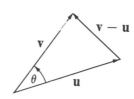

Figure 3.4   *Figure 3.5*

In this section we shall apply this law to the vector triangle shown in Figure 3.5 to prove the following result for vectors in V_2 (the proof for vectors in V_3 is left as an exercise).

Theorem. $\mathbf{u} \cdot \mathbf{v} = |\mathbf{u}| \, |\mathbf{v}| \cos \theta$,
where θ is the angle between the direction of vectors $\mathbf{u}$ and $\mathbf{v}$, $0 \leq \theta < \pi$.

Proof: Applying the cosine law to this triangle, in which the lengths of the sides are $|\mathbf{u}|$, $|\mathbf{v}|$, and $|\mathbf{v} - \mathbf{u}|$, yields

$$|\mathbf{v} - \mathbf{u}|^2 = |\mathbf{u}|^2 + |\mathbf{v}|^2 - 2|\mathbf{u}| \, |\mathbf{v}| \cos \theta .$$

Hence,

$$2|\mathbf{u}| \, |\mathbf{v}| \cos \theta = |\mathbf{u}|^2 + |\mathbf{v}|^2 - |\mathbf{v} - \mathbf{u}|^2 .$$

Now let

$$\mathbf{u} = (a_1, a_2) \text{ and } \mathbf{v} = (b_1, b_2) ,$$

so that

$$\mathbf{v} - \mathbf{u} = (b_1 - a_1, b_2 - a_2) .$$

Then

$$|\mathbf{u}|^2 = a_1^2 + a_2^2 ,$$
$$|\mathbf{v}|^2 = b_1^2 + b_2^2 ,$$

and

$$|\mathbf{v} - \mathbf{u}|^2 = (b_1 - a_1)^2 + (b_2 - a_2)^2 .$$

Hence,

$$2\,|\,\mathbf{u}\,|\,|\,\mathbf{v}\,|\cos\theta = a_1^2 + a_2^2 + b_1^2 + b_2^2$$
$$- (b_1^2 - 2a_1b_1 + a_1^2 + b_2^2 - 2b_2a_2 + a_2^2)$$
$$= 2a_1b_1 + 2a_2b_2\,.$$

Therefore,

$$|\,\mathbf{u}\,|\,|\,\mathbf{v}\,|\cos\theta = a_1b_1 + a_2b_2$$
$$= \mathbf{u}\cdot\mathbf{v}\,.$$

Thus the theorem is proved for vectors in V_2.

Example 1.   Verify the result of this theorem using the vectors
$$\mathbf{u} = (4, 0) \text{ and } \mathbf{v} = (0, 2)\,.$$

Solution: These vectors may be represented by the line segments joining the origin to the points $A\,(4, 0)$ and $B\,(0, 2)$, respectively, (Figure 3.6).   The angle θ between $\mathbf{u}$ and $\mathbf{v}$ is $\frac{\pi}{2}$.   Thus

$$|\,\mathbf{u}\,|\,|\,\mathbf{v}\,|\cos\theta = |\,\mathbf{u}\,|\,|\,\mathbf{v}\,|\cos\tfrac{\pi}{2} = 0$$

and

$$\mathbf{u}\cdot\mathbf{v} = (4, 0)\cdot(0, 2) = 0\,.$$

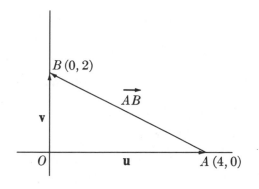

Figure 3.6   Figure 3.7

Example 2.   Verify the result of the theorem using the vectors

$$\mathbf{u} = (3, 3) \text{ and } \mathbf{v} = (0, 2)\,.$$

Solution: The vectors $\mathbf{u}$ and $\mathbf{v}$ are represented geometrically as shown in Figure 3.7. The angle θ between $\mathbf{u}$ and $\mathbf{v}$ is 45°.   Also $|\,\mathbf{u}\,| = 3\sqrt{2}$ and $|\,\mathbf{v}\,| = 2$.   Thus

$$|\,\mathbf{u}\,|\,|\,\mathbf{v}\,|\cos\theta = (3\sqrt{2})\,(2)\cos 45° = (3\sqrt{2})\,(2)\,(\tfrac{1}{\sqrt{2}}) = 6$$

and

$$\mathbf{u}\cdot\mathbf{v} = (3, 3)\cdot(2, 0) = 6\,.$$

EXERCISE 3.8

1. Verify that $\mathbf{u} \cdot \mathbf{v} = |\mathbf{u}|\,|\mathbf{v}| \cos \theta$ for the following pairs of vectors.

   (a) $(0, -3), (4, 0)$ (b) $(5, 0), (2, 0)$ (c) $(0, 4), (0, -4)$

   (d) $(3, 0), (-2, 0)$ (e) $(2, 5), (4, 10)$ (f) $(1, -3), (-2, 6)$

   (g) $(4, 4), (3, 0)$ (h) $(4, 4), (-3, 0)$ (i) $(4, 4), (0, 3)$

   (j) $(4, 4), (0, -3)$ (k) $(4, 4), (-4, 4)$ (l) $(4, 4), (4, -4)$

2. Repeat question (1) for the following pairs of vectors.

   (a) $(2, 0, 0), (0, 3, 0)$ (b) $(0, 3, 0), (0, -3, 0)$

   (c) $(2, 2, 0), (0, 0, 3)$ (d) $(2, 2, 0), (2, 2, 2\sqrt{2})$

   (e) $(3, 4, 0), (3, 4, 5)$ (f) $(5, -12, 0), (5, -12, 13)$

3. Prove the theorem of this section for vectors $\mathbf{u}$ and $\mathbf{v}$ in V_3.

3.9. Angle Between Vectors

Vectors in V_2 and V_3 may be represented geometrically by line segments with initial points at the origin. Two such line segments representing vectors $\mathbf{u}$ and $\mathbf{v}$ will determine a plane, and in that plane will determine an angle which is defined to be the angle between the algebraic vectors $\mathbf{u}$ and $\mathbf{v}$.

DEFINITION. The angle θ between the two- (three-) dimensional vectors $\mathbf{u}$ and $\mathbf{v}$ is the angle between the line segments with initial points at the origin that represent the two vectors.

From Section 3.8, we see that this angle may be determined from the equation

$$\mathbf{u} \cdot \mathbf{v} = |\mathbf{u}|\,|\mathbf{v}| \cos \theta .$$

Indeed, if $\mathbf{u}$ and $\mathbf{v}$ are nonzero vectors, we may write

$$\cos \theta = \frac{\mathbf{u} \cdot \mathbf{v}}{|\mathbf{u}|\,|\mathbf{v}|} .$$

Example 1. Find, to the nearest degree, the angle between the vectors

$$\mathbf{u} = (3, -1) \text{ and } \mathbf{v} = (3, 7) .$$

Solution:

$$\mathbf{u} \cdot \mathbf{v} = (3, -1) \cdot (3, 7) = 3\,(3) + (-1)\,(7) = 2 .$$
$$|\mathbf{u}| = \sqrt{9+1} = \sqrt{10}; \quad |\mathbf{v}| = \sqrt{9+49} = \sqrt{58} .$$

$$\cos \theta = \frac{2}{\sqrt{10}\sqrt{58}} \simeq .0834 \quad \text{(using logarithms)} .$$

Therefore, $\theta = 85°$ (to the nearest degree).

Example 2. Find, to the nearest degree, the angle between the vectors

$$\mathbf{u} = (3, -1, 2) \text{ and } \mathbf{v} = (2, 3, -4).$$

Solution:

$$\mathbf{u} \cdot \mathbf{v} = (3, -1, 2) \cdot (2, 3, -4) = 6 - 3 - 8 = -5.$$
$$|\mathbf{u}| = \sqrt{9 + 1 + 4} = \sqrt{14};$$
$$|\mathbf{v}| = \sqrt{4 + 9 + 16} = \sqrt{29}.$$

$$\cos \theta = \frac{-5}{\sqrt{14}\sqrt{29}} \simeq -0 \cdot 243 \quad \text{(using logarithms)}.$$

Thus, $\theta = 180° - 76° = 104°$ (to the nearest degree).

Example 3. Find the angle between the vectors $\mathbf{u} = (3, -4)$ and $\mathbf{v} = (4, 3)$.

Solution:

$$\mathbf{u} \cdot \mathbf{v} = (3, -4) \cdot (4, 3) = 12 - 12 = 0.$$
$$|\mathbf{u}| = \sqrt{9 + 16} = 5;$$
$$|\mathbf{v}| = \sqrt{16 + 9} = 5.$$

$$\cos \theta = \frac{0}{5(5)} = 0.$$

Hence, $\theta = 90°$. The angle between the vectors is, by definition, $90°$. The line segments with initial points at the origin that represent $\mathbf{u}$ and $\mathbf{v}$ are perpendicular.

DEFINITION. Two nonzero vectors $\mathbf{u}$ and $\mathbf{v}$ are perpendicular or orthogonal if the angle between them is $90°$.

It follows that two nonzero vectors $\mathbf{u}$ and $\mathbf{v}$ are orthogonal if and only if $\mathbf{u} \cdot \mathbf{v} = 0$. For, in that case,

$$\cos \theta = \frac{\mathbf{u} \cdot \mathbf{v}}{|\mathbf{u}| |\mathbf{v}|} = 0,$$

and so $\theta = 90°$.

Example 4. Find the value of k such that the vectors $\mathbf{u} = (3, 4, -2)$ and $\mathbf{v} = (5, -1, k)$ are orthogonal.

Solution: $\mathbf{u}$ and $\mathbf{v}$ are orthogonal if and only if $\mathbf{u} \cdot \mathbf{v} = 0$. But

$$\mathbf{u} \cdot \mathbf{v} = (3, 4, -2) \cdot (5, -1, k) = 15 - 4 - 2k.$$
$$\mathbf{u} \cdot \mathbf{v} = 0 \text{ if and only if } 11 - 2k = 0.$$
$$k = \tfrac{11}{2}.$$

Therefore, $(3, 4, -2)$ and $(5, -1, \tfrac{11}{2})$ are orthogonal.

Example 5.   Find $\angle A$ in $\triangle ABC$ with vertices $A(-3, 1)$, $B(2,\ 5)$, and $C(-5, 4)$.

Solution: The required $\angle A$ is the angle θ between the vectors $\overrightarrow{AB}$ and $\overrightarrow{AC}$ (Figure 3.8).

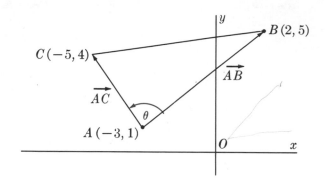

Figure 3.8

$$\overrightarrow{AB} = (2 - (-3), 5 - 1) = (5, 4).$$
$$\overrightarrow{AC} = (-5 - (-3), 4 - 1) = (-2, 3).$$
$$\overrightarrow{AB} \cdot \overrightarrow{AC} = (5, 4) \cdot (-2, 3) = -10 + 12 = 2.$$
$$|\overrightarrow{AB}| = \sqrt{25 + 16} = \sqrt{41}; \quad |\overrightarrow{AC}| = \sqrt{4 + 9} = \sqrt{13}.$$
$$\cos \theta = \frac{2}{\sqrt{41}\sqrt{13}} \simeq .0865 \quad \text{(using logarithms).}$$
$$\theta = 85° \quad \text{(to the nearest degree).}$$

Note that, from the diagram, this seems to be a reasonable answer. Triangles sketched in three dimensions may not provide as useful an indication to the validity of the result.   Note also that logarithms were used to obtain an approximation for $\frac{2}{\sqrt{41}\sqrt{13}}$.   The validity of this calculation can be checked by approximating

$$\frac{2}{\sqrt{41}\sqrt{13}} \simeq \frac{2}{6 \times 4} = \frac{1}{12} \simeq .08.$$

EXERCISE 3.9

1. Find the cosine of the angle between the following vectors **u** and **v**.
    (a) $(3, 4)$, $(-1, 5)$ (b) $(-5, 2)$, $(6, -3)$
    (c) $(4, 1)$, $(-7, 0)$ (d) $(3, -1, -1)$, $(4, 2, 1)$
    (e) $(3, -1, 0)$, $(4, 0, -3)$ (f) $(3, -2, -5)$, $(-5, 1, 1)$

2. Find to the nearest degree the angle between the following vectors **u** and **v**.
    (a) $(-1, 4)$, $(3, -1)$ (b) $(4, 0)$, $(-1, 3)$
    (c) $(3, -3)$, $(5, -2)$ (d) $(-1, 1, 4)$, $(3, 1, 0)$
    (e) $(0, 5, -2)$, $(-3, 1, 1)$ (f) $(4, -3, -1)$, $(2, 7, 0)$

3. Find to the nearest degree the angle the line segment PQ makes with the positive x-axis if P and Q are the following points.

(a) $P(3, 4), Q(7, 9)$ (b) $P(-5, 1), Q(7, 3)$

(c) $P(-1, -4), Q(-3, 1)$ (d) $P(1, 1, 4), Q(0, 6, -3)$

(e) $P(4, 4, -2), Q(-1, 5, 2)$ (f) $P(3, 0, -2), Q(5, 0, -2)$

4. Find, to the nearest degree,

(a) the angle the line segment from $P(4, -1)$ to $Q(5, -2)$ makes with the positive y-axis,

(b) the angle the line segment from $P(4, -1, 3)$ to $Q(5, 0, -3)$ makes with the positive y-axis,

(c) the angle the line segment from $P(2, -2, 1)$ to $Q(5, -3, 2)$ makes with the positive z-axis.

5. Find the angles of $\triangle PQR$ for $P(2, -1)$, $Q(3, 7)$, and $R(-3, 1)$.

6. Find the angles of $\triangle PQR$ for $P(3, -1, 1)$, $Q(-1, 7, 4)$, and $R(1, 1, 3)$.

7. For what values of k are the following pairs of vectors orthogonal?

(a) $(5, 7), (-2, 3k)$

(b) $6\mathbf{e}_1 - \mathbf{e}_2, k\mathbf{e}_1 + 3\mathbf{e}_2$

(c) $(4, -1, 3), (2, -k, 5)$

(d) $3\mathbf{e}_1 - \mathbf{e}_2 + 2k\mathbf{e}_3, 5\mathbf{e}_1 - 6\mathbf{e}_2 + \mathbf{e}_3$.

(e) $\overrightarrow{PQ}$ and $\overrightarrow{RS}$ for $P(-1, k)$, $Q(4, -3)$, $R(5, -2)$, and $S(0, -3)$.

(f) $\overrightarrow{PQ}$ and $\overrightarrow{RS}$ for $P(-3, -2, -2k)$, $Q(1, 5, -2)$, $R(0, 3, -1)$, and $S(2, 2, 5)$.

8. Is $\triangle PQR$ right-angled for $P(6, 5)$, $Q(1, 3)$, $R(3, -2)$?

9. Is $\triangle PQR$ right-angled for $P(-1, 3, 2)$, $Q(0, 3, 4)$, $R(2, 0, -1)$?

10. Find h and k so that $\mathbf{u} = (5, h, k)$ is orthogonal to both $\mathbf{v} = (1, 3, 2)$ and $\mathbf{w} = (-2, 1, 4)$.

11. Prove that the angle in a semicircle is a right angle. (Hint: in Figure 3.9 show that $\overrightarrow{BC} \cdot \overrightarrow{CA} = 0$.)

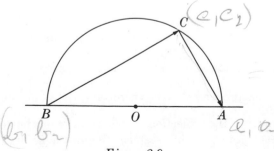

Figure 3.9

3.10. Projections

Consider $\triangle PQR$ shown in Figure 3.10.

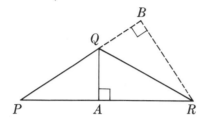
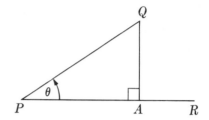

Figure 3.10   *Figure 3.11*

Let QA be constructed so that $QA \perp PR$.   Then we say that

(the length of) PA is the projection of PQ on PR.

Similarly,

(the length of) AR is the projection of QR on PR.

Finally, if we construct RB so that $RB \perp PQ$, we say that

(the length of) PB is the projection of PR on PQ produced.

In general, we may speak of the projection of any line segment PQ on a coterminal line segment PR; this will be PA where $QA \perp PR$ (Figure 3.11). Note that if θ is the angle between line segments PQ and PR we have

$$\text{projection of } PQ \text{ on } PR = PA = PQ \, |\cos \theta| \, .$$

We may now define the projection of vector **u** on vector **v**.

DEFINITION.   The projection of vector **u** on vector **v** is the projection of the line segment from the origin representing **u** on the line segment from the origin representing **v**.

The projection of vector **u** on vector **v** is a nonnegative scalar.

Example 1.   Find the projection of the vector $\mathbf{u} = (1, 4)$ on the vector $\mathbf{v} = (4, 3)$.

Solution: By definition, the projection of the vector **u** on the vector **v** will be the projection of line segment OP on line segment OQ for the points $P(1, 4)$ and $Q(4, 3)$ (see Figure 3.12).

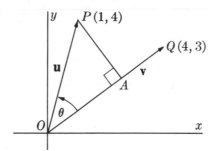

Figure 3.12

Now construct $PA \perp OQ$.   The required projection is $OA = OP \cos \theta$.

$$OP = |\mathbf{u}| = \sqrt{1 + 16} = \sqrt{17}$$

and θ is the angle between vectors $\mathbf{u}$ and $\mathbf{v}$, so that

$$\cos \theta = \frac{\mathbf{u} \cdot \mathbf{v}}{|\mathbf{u}||\mathbf{v}|} = \frac{(1, 4) \cdot (4, 3)}{\sqrt{17}\sqrt{25}} = \frac{16}{5\sqrt{17}} .$$

Thus

$$OA = \sqrt{17} \cdot \frac{16}{5\sqrt{17}} = \frac{16}{5} .$$

Theorem.   The projection of vector $\mathbf{u}$ on vector $\mathbf{v}$ is $\dfrac{|\mathbf{u} \cdot \mathbf{v}|}{|\mathbf{v}|}$.

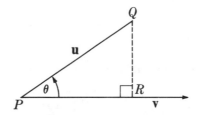

Figure 3.13

Proof: Choosing representatives of $\mathbf{u}$ and $\mathbf{v}$ that are coterminal and assuming angle θ is between the vectors (Figure 3.13), we may state the following.

$$\text{Projection of } \mathbf{u} \text{ on } \mathbf{v} = PR$$
$$= PQ \,|\cos \theta|$$
$$= |\mathbf{u}|\,|\cos \theta|$$
$$= |\mathbf{u}| \frac{|\mathbf{u} \cdot \mathbf{v}|}{|\mathbf{u}||\mathbf{v}|}$$
$$= \frac{|\mathbf{u} \cdot \mathbf{v}|}{|\mathbf{v}|} \quad \text{as required}.$$

Example 2.   We may now state immediately that, in Example 1, the projection of
$\mathbf{u} = (1, 4)$ on $\mathbf{v} = (4, 3)$ is

$$\frac{|\mathbf{u} \cdot \mathbf{v}|}{|\mathbf{v}|} = \frac{|(1, 4) \cdot (4, 3)|}{\sqrt{16 + 9}} = \frac{16}{5}.$$

Example 3.   Find the projection of vector $\mathbf{u} = (3, -1, 2)$ on vector $\mathbf{v} = (2, 5, -2)$.

Solution: The required projection is

$$\frac{|\mathbf{u} \cdot \mathbf{v}|}{|\mathbf{v}|} = \frac{|(3, -1, 2) \cdot (2, 5, -2)|}{\sqrt{4 + 25 + 4}}$$

$$= \frac{|-3|}{\sqrt{33}}.$$

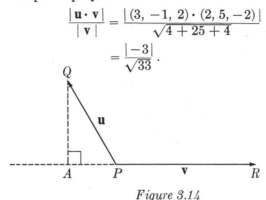

Figure 3.14

The fact that $\mathbf{u} \cdot \mathbf{v} = -3$ suggests a situation as shown in Figure 3.14.   The
projection PA is measured in the direction opposite to that of $\mathbf{v}$.   The angle
between $\mathbf{u}$ and $\mathbf{v}$ is greater than 90°.

EXERCISE 3.10

1. Find the projection of vector $\mathbf{u}$ on vector $\mathbf{v}$ for the following pairs of vectors
   $\mathbf{u}$ and $\mathbf{v}$.
   - (a) $\mathbf{u} = (3, 0)$, $\mathbf{v} = (2, 3)$
   - (b) $\mathbf{u} = (-1, 5)$, $\mathbf{v} = (4, 3)$
   - (c) $\mathbf{u} = (4, 5)$, $\mathbf{v} = (-5, 4)$
   - (d) $\mathbf{u} = (6, 1)$, $\mathbf{v} = (-1, 5)$
   - (e) $\mathbf{u} = 2\mathbf{e}_1 - 3\mathbf{e}_2$, $\mathbf{v} = (6, 2)$
   - (f) $\mathbf{u} = -3\mathbf{e}_1 - \mathbf{e}_2$, $\mathbf{v} = 2\mathbf{e}_1 + \mathbf{e}_2$
   - (g) $\mathbf{u} = (1, 1, -4)$, $\mathbf{v} = (2, -1, 3)$
   - (h) $\mathbf{u} = (4, 2, -1)$, $\mathbf{v} = (3, -1, 2)$
   - (i) $\mathbf{u} = (-4, 1, 3)$, $\mathbf{v} = (1, -2, 2)$
   - (j) $\mathbf{u} = (3, -3, 1)$, $\mathbf{v} = (2, -1, 4)$
   - (k) $\mathbf{u} = 3\mathbf{e}_1 - \mathbf{e}_2 - \mathbf{e}_3$, $\mathbf{v} = (-3, 1, 2)$
   - (l) $\mathbf{u} = \mathbf{e}_1 + 2\mathbf{e}_2 - \mathbf{e}_3$, $\mathbf{v} = 3\mathbf{e}_1 - \mathbf{e}_2 + 2\mathbf{e}_3$

2. Find the projection of vector $\overrightarrow{PQ}$ on vector $\overrightarrow{RS}$ for the following sets of points.
   - (a) $P(-3, 1)$, $Q(2, -5)$, $R(4, 2)$, $S(5, -3)$
   - (b) $P(-2, 1, 6)$, $Q(3, 1, -2)$, $R(-3, 1, 4)$, $S(2, -1, 2)$

3. When will the projection of $\mathbf{u}$ on $\mathbf{v}$ be zero?   *when they are orthogonal*

4. Is the projection of **u** on **v** (a) always, (b) ever, the same as the projection of **v** on **u**? In the event of a yes answer in (b), specify when.

3.11. Resolution of Vectors

Two plane vectors **u** and **v** can be added to produce a single plane vector **w**. Similarly, a plane vector **w** can be expressed in an infinite number of ways as the sum of two plane vectors **u** and **v**. The process of expressing **w** in the form **u** + **v** is called the resolution of a vector; the vectors **u** and **v** are called components of **w**.

The vector **w** = (a, b) can be expressed as the sum

$$\mathbf{w} = \mathbf{w_1} + \mathbf{w_2} = (a, 0) + (0, b) ;$$

here the components **w₁** and **w₂** of **w** are vectors collinear with the x- and y-axes, respectively. We may also use the symbols $\mathbf{w}_x$ and $\mathbf{w}_y$ for these components. This is an example of the most important case of the resolution of a vector, namely, its expression as the sum of two perpendicular vectors; in this case the two vectors are called rectangular components.

Example 1. Find rectangular components for the vector $(-2, \frac{5}{2})$.

Solution: One solution is $(-2, \frac{5}{2}) = (-2, 0) + (0, \frac{5}{2})$.

Suppose the vector **w** is resolved into rectangular components **w₁** and **w₂** with **w₁** collinear with the vector **u**; then **w₂** is collinear with vector **v** which is such that **u** · **v** = 0 (since **u** and **v** are perpendicular).

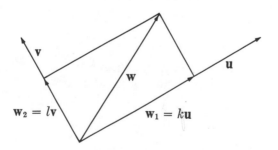

Figure 3.15

Then (Figure 3.15) we have

$$\mathbf{w_1} = k\mathbf{u} \quad (\mathbf{w_1} \text{ is in the direction of } \mathbf{u}),$$
$$\mathbf{w_2} = l\mathbf{v} \quad (\mathbf{w_2} \text{ is in the direction of } \mathbf{v}).$$

Therefore,

$$|\mathbf{w}|^2 = |\mathbf{w_1}|^2 + |\mathbf{w_2}|^2 \quad (\text{Theorem of Pythagoras}).$$

Example 2.   Find rectangular components $\mathbf{w}_1$ and $\mathbf{w}_2$ for the vector $\mathbf{w} = (3, 2)$ such that $\mathbf{w}_1$ is collinear with $\mathbf{u} = (1, 1)$.

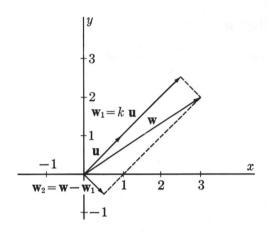

Solution:

    (i) $\mathbf{w} = (3, 2) = \mathbf{w}_1 + \mathbf{w}_2$.

    (ii) $\mathbf{w}_1 = k\mathbf{u}$

         $= k(1, 1)$

         $= (k, k)$.

   (iii) $\mathbf{w}_1 \cdot \mathbf{w}_2 = 0$.

From (i),

$$\begin{aligned}
\mathbf{w}_2 &= \mathbf{w} - \mathbf{w}_1 \\
&= (3, 2) - (k, k) \\
&= (3 - k, 2 - k).
\end{aligned}$$

From (iii),

$$\begin{aligned}
\mathbf{w}_1 \cdot \mathbf{w}_2 &= (k, k) \cdot (3 - k, 2 - k) \\
&= 3k - k^2 + 2k - k^2 \\
&= 5k - 2k^2 \\
&= 0.
\end{aligned}$$

Therefore,

$$k = 0 \text{ or } \tfrac{5}{2}.$$

Obviously, $k \neq 0$ and so $k = \tfrac{5}{2}$.   Therefore,

$$\mathbf{w}_1 = (\tfrac{5}{2}, \tfrac{5}{2}) \text{ and } \mathbf{w}_2 = (\tfrac{1}{2}, -\tfrac{1}{2})$$

are the required rectangular components.

    We may also solve this problem by finding $|\mathbf{w}_1|$ as the projection of $\mathbf{w}$ on $\mathbf{u}$.

We may extend this work on resolution of forces to three dimensions. In order to avoid many of the complications that arise, we shall confine our remarks to the resolution of a three-dimensional vector into components collinear with the vectors e_1, e_2, and e_3, that is, parallel to the co-ordinate axes. We may refer to such components of a vector w either by w_1, w_2, and w_3, or by w_x, w_y, and w_z. Note that these components are mutually orthogonal vectors.

Example 3. Resolve the vector $w = (3, -2, 5)$ into components collinear with e_1, e_2, and e_3.

Solution:

$$w = (3, -2, 5) = 3e_1 - 2e_2 + 5e_3 .$$

Therefore,

$$w_1 = 3e_1, \quad w_2 = -2e_2, \quad w_3 = 5e_3 .$$

Example 4. A force of 12 pounds is exerted on an object in the direction of the line segment joining $P(3, -1, 5)$ to $Q(7, 3, 7)$. Find the magnitude of the force parallel to each of the co-ordinate axes.

Solution: Let the force be represented by vector f. Then

$$f = k(7 - 3, 3 + 1, 7 - 5)$$
$$= k(4, 4, 2) .$$

Also

$$|f| = k\sqrt{16 + 16 + 4} = 6k .$$
$$6k = 12 \quad \text{and} \quad k = 2 .$$

Therefore,

$$f = 2(4, 4, 2)$$
$$= (8, 8, 4)$$
$$= 8e_1 + 8e_2 + 4e_3 .$$
$$f_x = 8e_1, \quad f_y = 8e_2, \quad f_z = 4e_3 .$$

The magnitudes of the forces parallel to the x-, y-, and z-axes are $8, 8$, and 4 pounds, respectively.

EXERCISE 3.11

1. Find rectangular components w_1 and w_2 parallel to the x- and y-axes, respectively, for the following vectors.
   (a) $(5, \frac{1}{2})$ (b) $(-4, 7)$ (c) $(6, -2)$ (d) $(-3, -4)$

2. The vector $(3, -7)$ is resolved into two rectangular components with equal magnitude; find this magnitude.

3. Repeat question (2) for the vectors   (a) $(-2, 6)$,   (b) $(-3, -5)$.

4. The vector $(4, -3)$ is resolved into two rectangular components w_1 and w_2 with $|w_1| = 2|w_2|$. Find $|w_2|$.

5. Find w_1 and w_2 such that
$$(3, -5) = w_1 + w_2 .$$

6. Find w_1 and w_2 such that
$$(3, -5) = w_1 + w_2 \quad \text{and} \quad w_1 \cdot w_2 = 0.$$

7. Find w_1 and w_2 such that
$$(3, -5) = w_1 + w_2 , \quad w_1 \cdot w_2 = 0 , \quad \text{and} \quad w_1 = k(1, 2) .$$

8. Find rectangular components for $w = (-3, 4)$, with one of the components parallel to $u = (-1, 2)$.

9. Resolve $w = (5, -1)$ into rectangular components, one of which is parallel to $u = (3, -2)$.

10. A boy is pulling a sled up a hill that has a rise of one foot in seven. The magnitude (pounds) and direction of the force exerted by the boy are represented by the vector $(9, 12)$. Find the force which draws the sled up the hill and the force which tends to lift the sled.

11. Cubesville is one mile due east of Squaresville. Its altitude is 264 feet greater than that of Squaresville and the towns are connected by a smooth-rising road. A disabled Stanley Steamer is being towed from Squaresville to Cubesville by a tow truck exerting a force whose magnitude and direction are represented by the vector $(2000, 1000)$. Find the force drawing the Stanley Steamer up the hill and the force tending to lift it.

12. State components w_x, w_y, and w_z for the following vectors w.
    (a) $(-1, 5, 3)$ (b) $(6, -4, 2)$ (c) $(-1, -6, 5)$

13. A force of 24 pounds is exerted on an object in the direction of the line segment joining point $P(4, -1, 3)$ to $Q(5, 3, -4)$. Find the magnitude of the force parallel to each of the co-ordinate axes.

14. Repeat question (13) if a force of 15 pounds is exerted in the direction of the line segment joining $P(5, -3, -2)$ to $Q(7, -1, 3)$.

15. Resolve vector $w = (3, -1, 5)$ into components collinear with
$$v_1 = (-2, 2, 0), \quad v_2 = (1, 1, 2), \quad v_3 = (1, 1, -1) .$$
Show that these components are mutually orthogonal vectors. *use the dot product*

3.12. Work

When a force is exerted over a certain distance, work is performed and the work done is given by the product

work = (magnitude of force in the direction of motion) (distance).

This concept may be considered in the light of our theory of algebraic vectors. Here, the force is expressed as an algebraic vector such as $\mathbf{w} = (a, b)$; such a vector has, of course, a magnitude and a direction. We consider that such a force is applied to an object and that the object moves a certain distance in a certain direction. The motion of the object can thus be expressed as a second vector $\mathbf{v} = (c, d)$.

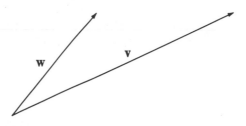

Figure 3.16

Figure 3.16 represents the force $\mathbf{w}$ acting on the object and the path $\mathbf{v}$ along which the object moves under the exertion of this force. Then,

(i) the magnitude of the force $\mathbf{w}$ in the direction of vector $\mathbf{v}$ is the projection of $\mathbf{w}$ on $\mathbf{v}$; that is, from Section 3.10,

$$\frac{|\mathbf{w} \cdot \mathbf{v}|}{|\mathbf{v}|};$$

(ii) the distance the object moves is the magnitude of vector $\mathbf{v}$, that is,

$$|\mathbf{v}|.$$

Therefore the work done by force $\mathbf{w}$ moving an object in the distance and direction represented by vector $\mathbf{v}$ is

$$\frac{|\mathbf{w} \cdot \mathbf{v}|}{|\mathbf{v}|} \times |\mathbf{v}| = |\mathbf{w} \cdot \mathbf{v}|.$$

Example 1. A force (in pounds) expressed by the vector $\mathbf{w} = (3, 7)$ moves an object a distance (in feet) and direction represented by the vector $\mathbf{v} = (2, 9)$. Find the work performed.

Solution:

$$\begin{aligned} \text{Work} &= |\mathbf{w} \cdot \mathbf{v}| \\ &= |(3, 7) \cdot (2, 9)| \\ &= 69. \end{aligned}$$

The work performed is 69 foot-pounds.

Example 2.   Find the work done if the force in Example 1 moves an object along vector $\mathbf{v} = (-2, -9)$.

Solution:

$$\text{Work} = |\mathbf{w} \cdot \mathbf{v}|$$
$$= (3, 7) \cdot (-2, -9) = 69 .$$

The negative sign of $\mathbf{w} \cdot \mathbf{v}$ indicates that we may consider that the work exerted in moving an object from point A to point B is the negative of the work exerted in moving an object from point B to point A, or that the work exerted in lowering an object a certain distance may be considered the negative of the amount of work required to raise the object the same distance.   Normally we consider that the work is the same in both cases, that is, we take the absolute value as the work performed.

Example 3.   A force of 10 pounds acting in a direction parallel to the line segment AB, with $A(1, 1, 2)$ and $B(2, 1, 5)$, is applied to an object as it moves on line segment PQ, with $P(3, -2, 4)$ and $Q(5, 1, -3)$.   Find the work done.   (Assume that the unit of measurement in the co-ordinate system is the foot.)

Solution: We must first find the vector $\mathbf{w}$ describing this force.   The force is parallel to line segment AB, and hence is parallel to vector

$$\overrightarrow{AB} = (2 - 1, 1 - 1, 5 - 2) = (1, 0, 3) .$$

Therefore,

$$\mathbf{w} = k(1, 0, 3)$$

and

$$|\mathbf{w}| = k\sqrt{10} .$$
$$k\sqrt{10} = 10 .$$
$$k = \sqrt{10} .$$

Therefore,

$$\mathbf{w} = \sqrt{10}(1, 0, 3) = (\sqrt{10}, 0, 3\sqrt{10}) .$$

Secondly, we find the vector $\mathbf{v}$ over which this force is exerted.

$$\mathbf{v} = \overrightarrow{PQ} = (5 - 3, 1 + 2, -3 - 4) = (2, 3, -7).$$

Then

$$|\mathbf{w} \cdot \mathbf{v}| = |(\sqrt{10}, 0, 3\sqrt{10}) \cdot (2, 3, -7)|$$
$$= |2\sqrt{10} - 21\sqrt{10}|$$
$$= 19\sqrt{10} ,$$

so that the work done is $19\sqrt{10}$ foot-pounds.

EXERCISE 3.12

1. Find the work done by force **w** exerted on an object moving along vector **v** if **w** and **v** are the following.

(a) $\mathbf{w} = (5, 2)$, $\mathbf{v} = (3, -2)$ (b) $\mathbf{w} = (5, 2)$, $\mathbf{v} = (-3, 2)$

(c) $\mathbf{w} = (\frac{1}{2}, \frac{2}{3})$, $\mathbf{v} = (6, -6)$ (d) $\mathbf{w} = (-3, 0)$, $\mathbf{v} = (0, 2)$

(e) $\mathbf{w} = (1, 1, 3)$, $\mathbf{v} = (3, 2, 4)$ (f) $\mathbf{w} = (-3, 1, 4)$, $\mathbf{v} = (2, -2, 3)$

2. Explain the answer in question (1d).

3. A force of 5 pounds acting in the direction of line segment AB, with $A(2, 5)$, and $B(5, 9)$, is exerted on an object moving from point $P(-2, 1)$ to point $Q(3, 7)$ (distance in feet). Find the work done.

4. A force of 19 pounds acting in the direction of line segment EF, with $E(3, 1, 1)$ and $F(-2, -1, 4)$, is exerted on an object moving along PQ, with $P(3, -1, 4)$ and $Q(-2, 5, -1)$ (distance in feet). Find the work done in moving from P to Q.

5. Find the work done by the tow truck in question (11), Exercise 3.11, in towing the Stanley Steamer from Squaresville to Cubesville.

Chapter Summary

Definition of distance $d(P, Q)$ between two points P and Q · Length of line segment PQ · Line segments in 3-space · Length of a vector; unit vector · Inner product (dot product, scalar product)

Properties of the inner product:

$$\mathbf{u} \cdot \mathbf{v} = \mathbf{v} \cdot \mathbf{u}.$$
$$\mathbf{u} \cdot (\mathbf{v} + \mathbf{w}) = \mathbf{u} \cdot \mathbf{v} + \mathbf{u} \cdot \mathbf{w}.$$
$$(k\mathbf{u}) \cdot \mathbf{v} = k(\mathbf{u} \cdot \mathbf{v}) = \mathbf{u} \cdot (k\mathbf{v}).$$
$$\mathbf{v} \cdot \mathbf{v} = |\mathbf{v}|^2.$$

Angle between two vectors:

$$\mathbf{u} \cdot \mathbf{v} = |\mathbf{u}| |\mathbf{v}| \cos \theta.$$

Orthogonal vectors · Projections · Resolution of vectors · Work

REVIEW EXERCISE 3

1. Use the distance formula to determine which of the following sets of points are collinear.

(a) $P(3, -1, 1)$, $Q(3, -2, 1)$, $R(-2, 1, 2)$

(b) $P(2, -1, -1)$, $Q(-5, -3, 1)$, $R(-1, -5, -1)$

(c) $P(3, 4, -1)$, $Q(-1, 2, 3)$, $R(1, 0, -7)$

2. Use the distance formula to determine which of the following triangles PQR are right-angled.
   (a) $P(-1,3,2)$, $Q(3,-2,4)$, $R(5,-2,0)$
   (b) $P(1,0,2)$, $Q(0,3,2)$, $R(-3,1,0)$
   (c) $P(3,1,1)$, $Q(-4,1,5)$, $R(0,3,12)$

3. Rework questions (1) and (2) using vectors.

4. Find the length of the following vectors.
   (a) $(5,-2)$ (b) $(-3,1,1)$ (c) $(4,1,-2)$
   (d) $\overrightarrow{PQ}$; $P(6,-1)$, $Q(-3,2)$ (e) $\overrightarrow{PQ}$; $P(-3,1,-1)$, $Q(-5,-1,4)$

5. Find unit vectors collinear with the vectors in question (4).

6. If $\mathbf{u} = (-1,5,2)$, $\mathbf{v} = -3\mathbf{e}_1 - 2\mathbf{e}_2 + \mathbf{e}_3$, and $\mathbf{w} = \mathbf{e}_1 - 4\mathbf{e}_2 + 2\mathbf{e}_3$, find
   (a) $|\mathbf{u}|$,   (b) $|\mathbf{u}+\mathbf{v}|$,   (c) $|\mathbf{v}-\mathbf{w}|$,   (d) $|2\mathbf{u}-\mathbf{v}+3\mathbf{w}|$.

7. For the vectors of question (6), calculate the following.
   (a) $\mathbf{u}\cdot\mathbf{v}$ (b) $\mathbf{v}\cdot\mathbf{w}$ (c) $\mathbf{w}\cdot\mathbf{u}$ (d) $\mathbf{u}\cdot(\mathbf{v}+\mathbf{w})$
   (e) $\mathbf{u}\cdot\mathbf{v}+\mathbf{u}\cdot\mathbf{w}$ (f) $\mathbf{u}\cdot(\mathbf{v}-\mathbf{w})$ (g) $\mathbf{u}\cdot\mathbf{u}+\mathbf{v}\cdot\mathbf{v}+\mathbf{w}\cdot\mathbf{w}$
   (h) $\mathbf{u}\cdot\mathbf{v}-\mathbf{u}\cdot\mathbf{w}$ (i) $(-4\mathbf{u})\cdot\mathbf{w}$ (j) $(3\mathbf{u}-\mathbf{v})\cdot(2\mathbf{v}+\mathbf{w})$

8. For the vectors of question (6), find the cosine of the angle between
   (a) $\mathbf{u}$ and $\mathbf{v}$,   (b) $\mathbf{v}$ and $\mathbf{w}$,   (c) $\mathbf{w}$ and $\mathbf{u}$.

9. Use vectors to determine the angles of the following triangles PQR.
   (a) $P(-1,1)$, $Q(3,-1)$, $R(2,4)$ (b) $P(0,0,1)$, $Q(4,-2,3)$, $R(3,3,2)$

10. Find to the nearest degree the angle between $\overrightarrow{PQ}$ and the positive x-axis.
    (a) $P(-1,4)$, $Q(3,7)$ (b) $P(2,2,5)$, $Q(-1,5,4)$

11. Find the projection of vector $\mathbf{u}$ on vector $\mathbf{v}$ for the following vectors.
    (a) $\mathbf{u} = (5,-2)$, $\mathbf{v} = (4,7)$ (b) $\mathbf{u} = (-1,2,1)$, $\mathbf{v} = (3,-4,4)$

12. Find the work done by force $\mathbf{w}$ exerted on an object moving along vector $\mathbf{v}$ for the following.
    (a) $\mathbf{w} = (3,1)$, $\mathbf{v} = (2,-6)$ (b) $\mathbf{w} = (2,1,0)$, $\mathbf{v} = (-3,1,4)$

13. A force of 6 pounds acting in the direction of line segment AB is exerted on an object moving from point P to point Q (distance in feet). Find the work done for the following situations.
    (a) $A(4,2)$, $B(-3,6)$, $P(2,3)$, $Q(5,7)$
    (b) $A(1,1,3)$, $B(3,-4,2)$, $P(1,5,-3)$, $Q(3,4,6)$

14. A force of 9 pounds is exerted on an object in the direction of the line segment joining point $P(-3,5,1)$ to point $Q(4,3,2)$. Find the magnitude of the components of the force parallel to the co-ordinate axes.

15. Find the components of the vector $\mathbf{w} = (3,3,7)$ collinear with the vectors
$$\mathbf{v}_1 = (1,-3,0),\ \mathbf{v}_2 = (3,1,0),\ \text{and}\ \mathbf{v}_3 = (0,0,4).$$

Chapter 4

LINES IN TWO- AND THREE-SPACE

4.1. The Vector Equation of a Line

Let a line l be determined by two points A and B and let P be an arbitrary point on the line. Then $\overrightarrow{AP} = k\overrightarrow{AB}$, $k \in Re$, and we have the following possibilities.

Value of k	Position of P if $\overrightarrow{AP} = k\overrightarrow{AB}$
0	at A (Figure 4.1 (a))
1	at B (Figure 4.1 (b))
$0 < k < 1$	between A and B (Figure 4.1 (c))
$k > 1$	B between A and P (Figure 4.1 (d))
$k < 0$	A between P and B (Figure 4.1 (e))

Then $\overrightarrow{AP} = k\,\overrightarrow{AB}$ represents the following geometric figures.

(i)   a point on line AB if $k =$ any specific real number
(ii)   line segment AB for $\{k \,|\, 0 \leq k \leq 1,\ k \in Re\}$
(iii) ray AB for $\{k \,|\, k \geq 0,\ k \in Re\}$
(iv) ray BA for $\{k \,|\, k \leq 1,\ k \in Re\}$
(v)   line AB for $\{k \,|\, k \in Re\}$

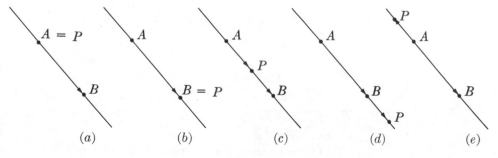

Figure 4.1

If it is understood that the domain of k is Re, we may refer to $\overrightarrow{AP} = k\,\overrightarrow{AB}$ as a vector representation or equation for the line l determined by the points A and B.

Example 1. Determine k so that P is the midpoint of line segment AB.

Solution: $\overrightarrow{AP} = \tfrac{1}{2}\overrightarrow{AB}$ if P is the midpoint of AB; therefore $k = \tfrac{1}{2}$.

Example 2. If $\overrightarrow{AP} = -\tfrac{2}{3}\overrightarrow{AB}$, locate P relative to A and B.

Solution: $k < 0$ and so A lies between P and B; also $3\,|\,\overrightarrow{AP}\,| = 2\,|\,\overrightarrow{AB}\,|$, so that if $|\,\overrightarrow{AB}\,|$ is three units, then $|\,\overrightarrow{AP}\,|$ is two units.

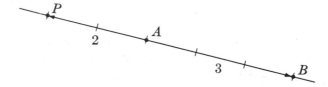

The vector equation $\overrightarrow{AP} = k\,\overrightarrow{AB}$, $k \in Re$, is the equation of the line l determined by two distinct points A and B without regard to a standard co-ordinate system. The vectors involved all lie along the line l and are expressed relative to the two fixed points A and B. We proceed to locate the line l with respect to the frame of reference of a standard co-ordinate system and to find an equation for l with respect to this frame of reference.

Our first step is to consider a frame of reference consisting of a single point O. With respect to such a fixed point, any point P on the line l will have a position vector $\overrightarrow{OP}$ represented by the line segment from O to P; similarly, the fixed points A and B, which determine the line l, will have position vectors $\overrightarrow{OA}$ and $\overrightarrow{OB}$, respectively (Figure 4.2).

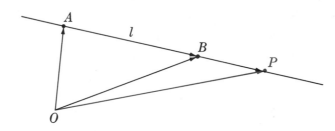

Figure 4.2

Now

$$\begin{aligned}
\overrightarrow{OP} &= \overrightarrow{OA} + \overrightarrow{AP} \\
&= \overrightarrow{OA} + k\,\overrightarrow{AB}, \qquad k \in Re, \\
&= \overrightarrow{OA} + k(\overrightarrow{OB} - \overrightarrow{OA}), \qquad \text{since } \overrightarrow{OA} + \overrightarrow{AB} = \overrightarrow{OB} \\
&= (1 - k)\overrightarrow{OA} + k\,\overrightarrow{OB}.
\end{aligned}$$

Then

$$\overrightarrow{OP} = (1 - k)\overrightarrow{OA} + k\overrightarrow{OB}, \qquad k \in Re,$$

is called the positional vector equation of line l in terms of the position vectors $\overrightarrow{OA}$ and $\overrightarrow{OB}$ of the points A and B determining l. If we denote vector $\overrightarrow{OP}$ by $\mathbf{r}$, $\overrightarrow{OA}$ by $\mathbf{r_1}$, and $\overrightarrow{OB}$ by $\mathbf{r_2}$, this equation becomes

$$\mathbf{r} = (1 - k)\,\mathbf{r_1} + k\,\mathbf{r_2}.$$

A slightly different form of the vector equation of line l is developed in question (7), Exercise 4.1. This second form will be used in some of the later developments.

By restricting k to subsets of Re, we get vector equations for various parts of line l.

Domain of k	$\mathbf{r} = (1 - k)\mathbf{r_1} + k\mathbf{r_2}$ represents
0	P at A
1	P at B
$0 \leq k \leq 1$	line segment AB
$k \geq 0$	ray AB
$k \leq 1$	ray BA
Re	line l

Note that if A and B have position vectors $\mathbf{r_1}$ and $\mathbf{r_2}$, respectively, then

$$\mathbf{r} = (1 - k)\mathbf{r_1} + k\mathbf{r_2}$$

is the position vector of point P such that $\overrightarrow{AP} = k\overrightarrow{AB}$.

Example 3. Interpret the equation $\mathbf{r} = \frac{2}{3}\mathbf{r_1} + \frac{1}{3}\mathbf{r_2}$.

Solution: $\mathbf{r}$ is the position vector of a point P on the line AB such that $\overrightarrow{AP} = k\overrightarrow{AB} = \frac{1}{3}\overrightarrow{AB}$; thus the equation represents a point P that divides line segment AB in the ratio $1:2$.

Example 4. What figure does the equation $\mathbf{r} = (1 - k)\mathbf{r_1} + k\mathbf{r_2}$, $0 \leq k \leq \frac{1}{2}$, represent?

Solution: This equation represents the line segment joining A to the midpoint of line segment AB.

In our development thus far, we have placed no restrictions on the location of the point O and the line l; they may be in 2-space or in 3-space and the vector equation

$$\mathbf{r} = (1 - k)\mathbf{r_1} + k\mathbf{r_2}$$

will be the same in either situation. In either case, the point O and the line l determine a plane if O is not on l.

In succeeding sections we shall interpret the vector equation of a line relative to a Cartesian co-ordinate system first in the plane and then in 3-space.

EXERCISE 4.1

1. If $\overrightarrow{AP} = k\overrightarrow{AB}$, determine P relative to points A and B for the following real values of k (include a diagram).

   (a) $\frac{1}{3}$ (b) 2 (c) -1 (d) $\frac{5}{4}$

   (e) $-\frac{3}{2}$ (f) $\sqrt{2}$ (g) $0 \leq k \leq 1$ (h) $k > \frac{1}{2}$

   (i) $k = \{0, 1, 2\}$ (j) $2k < 1$ (k) $k < 0$ or $k > 1$ (l) $k \in I$

2. Determine k if $\overrightarrow{AP} = k\overrightarrow{AB}$ in the following situations.

   (a) P divides line segment AB in the ratio $2 : 3$.

   (b) P is twice as far from A as from B.

   (c) P is twice as far from B as from A.

3. If $\mathbf{r}$, $\mathbf{r}_1$, and $\mathbf{r}_2$ are position vectors of P, A, and B, relative to a point O, interpret the following equations (include a diagram).

   (a) $\mathbf{r} = \frac{1}{2}\mathbf{r}_1 + \frac{1}{2}\mathbf{r}_2$ (b) $\mathbf{r} = \frac{1}{3}\mathbf{r}_1 + \frac{2}{3}\mathbf{r}_2$

   (c) $\mathbf{r} = \frac{1}{5}\mathbf{r}_1 + \frac{4}{5}\mathbf{r}_2$ (d) $\mathbf{r} = -\mathbf{r}_1 + 2\mathbf{r}_2$

   (e) $\mathbf{r} = -\frac{1}{2}\mathbf{r}_1 + \frac{3}{2}\mathbf{r}_2$ (f) $\mathbf{r} = 3\mathbf{r}_1 - 2\mathbf{r}_2$

4. Interpret the equation $\mathbf{r} = (1 - k)\mathbf{r}_1 + k\mathbf{r}_2$ for the following sets of real values for k.

   (a) $\frac{1}{3} \leq k \leq \frac{2}{3}$ (b) $\frac{2}{3} \leq k \leq 1$

   (c) $-1 \leq k \leq 0$ (d) $1 \leq k \leq 2$

   (e) $-1 \leq k \leq \frac{1}{2}$ (f) $-\frac{1}{2} \leq k \leq \frac{3}{2}$

5. Prove that if points A and B have position vectors $\mathbf{r}_1$ and $\mathbf{r}_2$, respectively, then point P which divides line segment AB in the ratio $p : q$ ($p > 0$, $q > 0$) has position vector

$$\mathbf{r} = \frac{q\mathbf{r}_1 + p\mathbf{r}_2}{p + q}.$$

6. Interpret the result in question (5) in the case that p or q or both are negative numbers.

7. A line l is determined by a point A on the line and a vector $\mathbf{s}$ collinear with the line. Show that the line has vector equation

$$\mathbf{r} = \mathbf{r}_1 + k\mathbf{s},$$

where $\mathbf{r}_1$ and $\mathbf{r}$ are position vectors, with respect to a fixed point O, of point A and an arbitrary point P on l.

8. Rewrite the equations of the points in question (3) in the form $\mathbf{r} = \mathbf{r}_1 + k\mathbf{s}$, where $\mathbf{s} = \mathbf{r}_2 - \mathbf{r}_1$.

4.2. Parametric Equations of a Line in Two-Space

We have developed the positional vector equation
$$\mathbf{r} = (1 - k)\mathbf{r}_1 + k\mathbf{r}_2, \quad k \in Re,$$
for the line determined by two points A and B. $\mathbf{r}_1$ and $\mathbf{r}_2$ are position vectors, with respect to a fixed point O, of the fixed points A and B, and $\mathbf{r}$ is the position vector of an arbitrary point P on the line, the position of P on the line depending on the real value assigned to k.

We now introduce a Cartesian co-ordinate system in the plane of O and the line l by selecting two mutually perpendicular lines through point O and labelling them as the x- and y-axes in the usual manner (Figure 4.3).

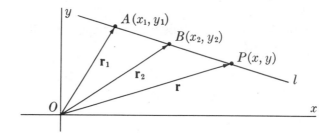

Figure 4.3

The point A has co-ordinates (x_1, y_1) relative to this co-ordinate system and the position vector $\mathbf{r}_1$ is the algebraic vector (x_1, y_1); similarly, B has co-ordinates (x_2, y_2) and P has co-ordinates (x, y). Thus

$$\mathbf{r}_1 = (x_1, y_1), \quad \mathbf{r}_2 = (x_2, y_2), \quad \mathbf{r} = (x, y),$$

and the vector equation for line l can be written

$$(x, y) = (1 - k)(x_1, y_1) + k(x_2, y_2).$$

Example 1. Find the vector equation of the line l determined by the points $A(4, 3)$ and $B(-2, 9)$.

Solution: The vector equation of l is

$$(x, y) = (1 - k)(4, 3) + k(-2, 9).$$

Now the vector equation

$$(x, y) = (1 - k)(x_1, y_1) + k(x_2, y_2)$$

can be written

$$(x, y) = [(1 - k)x_1, \ (1 - k)y_1] + (kx_2, ky_2)$$
$$= [(1 - k)x_1 + kx_2, \ (1 - k)y_1 + ky_2]$$

by our rules for multiplication of algebraic vectors by a scalar and for addition of algebraic vectors. Identifying components in these two vectors (2-dimensional vectors are equal if and only if corresponding components are equal) yields the two equations

$$\left. \begin{array}{l} x = (1 - k)x_1 + kx_2 \\ y = (1 - k)y_1 + ky_2 \end{array} \right\} \quad k \in Re .$$

These are the parametric equations of the line determined by the points $A(x_1, y_1)$ and $B(x_2, y_2)$; the equations are given in terms of the parameter k. Note that a line in 2-space has a *pair* of parametric equations.

Also note that every point on the line determined by the points $A(x_1, y_1)$ and $B(x_2, y_2)$ has co-ordinates $(\alpha x_1 + \beta x_2, \alpha y_1 + \beta y_2)$, where $\alpha + \beta = 1$.

Another useful form for the parametric equations of the line l is developed in question (7), Exercise 4.2.

Example 2. Find the parametric equations of the line l determined by the points $A(4, 3)$ and $B(-2, 9)$ (see Example 1).

Solution: The parametric equations of l are

$$x = (1 - k)(4) + k(-2) = 4 - 6k,$$
$$y = (1 - k)(3) + k(9) = 3 + 6k .$$

We may find these by direct substitution in the parametric equations

$$x = (1 - k)x_1 + kx_2,$$
$$y = (1 - k)y_1 + ky_2,$$

or by writing the vector equation of the required line in the form

$$(x, y) = (1 - k)(4, 3) + k(-2, 9)$$

as in Example 1, and then combining on the right side

$$(x, y) = [(1 - k)(4) + k(-2), \ (1 - k)(3) + k(9)],$$

and equating corresponding components.

Of course, any restriction of k to a subset of Re in the parametric equations

$$x = (1 - k)x_1 + kx_2$$
$$y = (1 - k)y_1 + ky_2$$

yields the parametric equations of a part of the line (a point, a set of points, a line segment, a ray, etc.) determined by $A(x_1, y_1)$ and $B(x_2, y_2)$.

Example 3.   Find the midpoint of the line segment AB of the preceding examples.

Solution: The parametric equations of line AB are

$$x = 4 - 6k, \quad y = 3 + 6k \,.$$

The midpoint of the line segment AB is the point corresponding to the value $\frac{1}{2}$ of k; its co-ordinates are then

$$4 - 6(\tfrac{1}{2}) \text{ and } 3 + 6(\tfrac{1}{2}) \,.$$

The required point has co-ordinates $(1, 6)$.

Example 4.   Check that point $P(1, 6)$ is the midpoint of line segment AB determined by $A(4, 3)$ and $B(-2, 9)$.

Solution: We need only show that $\overrightarrow{AP} = \overrightarrow{PB}$.

$$\overrightarrow{AP} = \overrightarrow{OP} - \overrightarrow{OA} = (1, 6) - (4, 3) = (-3, 3) \,.$$
$$\overrightarrow{PB} = \overrightarrow{OB} - \overrightarrow{OP} = (-2, 9) - (1, 6) = (-3, 3) \,.$$

Therefore, P is the midpoint of line segment AB.

Example 5.   Locate the point with co-ordinates $(-2x_1 + 3x_2, -2y_1 + 3y_2)$.

Solution: The equations
$$x = (1 - 3)x_1 + 3x_2$$
$$y = (1 - 3)y_1 + 3y_2$$

are the equations of the part of the line l determined by $A(x_1, y_1)$ and $B(x_2, y_2)$ corresponding to the single value 3 of k.   This is the single point C such that $\overrightarrow{AC} = 3\,\overrightarrow{AB}$.   Thus P is on l on the side of B opposite to that of A and a distance from B that is twice that of B from A (Figure 4.4).

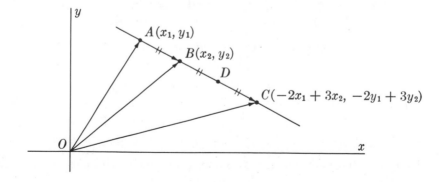

Figure 4.4

Example 6.   Determine the figure with parametric equations

$$x = (1 - k)x_1 + kx_2$$
$$y = (1 - k)y_1 + ky_2$$

$1 \le k \le 3, \ k \in Re.$

Solution: These are the parametric equations of the line segment BC shown in Figure 4.4.

Note that if k had been restricted to I in this example, with $1 \le k \le 3$, the parametric equations would have determined only the three points B, D, and C.

EXERCISE 4.2

1. Give vector equations and parametric equations (with respect to a Cartesian co-ordinate system) for lines determined by the pairs of points with the given co-ordinates (include a diagram).

   (a) $(1, 1)$ and $(5, 2)$ (b) $(3, 7)$ and $(-4, 2)$
   (c) $(6, 6)$ and $(0, 0)$ (d) $(-1, 0)$ and $(0, 7)$
   (e) $(3, -3)$ and $(0, 5)$ (f) $(-2, 3)$ and $(-4, 7)$
   (g) $(-2, 4)$ and $(-5, -6)$ (h) $(-3, -1)$ and $(-7, -2)$
   (i) $(4, \frac{1}{3})$ and $(-\frac{1}{2}, 0)$ (j) $(5, \sqrt{2})$ and $(\sqrt{3}, \ 6)$

2. Find the midpoints of the line segments determined by the pairs of points in question (1).

3. Find the co-ordinates of the point P dividing line segment AB, determined by $A(-5, 2)$ and $B(9, 5)$, in the following ratios.

   (a) $1 : 2$ (b) $3 : 5$ (c) $-1 : 2$ (d) $2 : -1$

4. Locate the following points with respect to the points $A(x_1, y_1)$ and $B(x_2, y_2)$ (include a diagram).

   (a) $(\frac{1}{3}x_1 + \frac{2}{3}x_2, \frac{1}{3}y_1 + \frac{2}{3}y_2)$ (b) $(2x_1 - x_2, 2y_1 - y_2)$
   (c) $(\frac{4}{3}x_1 - \frac{1}{3}x_2, \frac{4}{3}y_1 - \frac{1}{3}y_2)$ (d) $(-4x_1 + 5x_2, -4y_1 + 5y_2).$

5. Determine the figure with parametric equations
   $$x = (1 - k)(4) + k(-3), \qquad y = (1 - k)(-5) + k(6)$$
   for the following sets of values for k (use a diagram).

   (a) Re (b) 0 (c) 1 (d) $\frac{1}{2}$ (e) 2 (f) $\{0, 1, 2\}$
   (g) $\{-1, 0, 1\}$ (h) $\{-1 \le k \le 1, \ k \in Re\}$ (i) $\{k \ge 0, \ k \in Re\}$
   (j) $\{k \le 0, \ k \in Re\}$ (k) $\{k \ge 1, \ k \in Re\} \cup \{k \le 0, \ k \in Re\}.$

6. Determine the co-ordinates of two points on the line with parametric equations
   $$x = 5 - 3t, \ y = 4 + 7t.$$
   Is the point $(14, -17)$ on this line?   Is the point $(-\frac{1}{2}, \frac{27}{2})$?

7. Show that the vector equation $\mathbf{r} = \mathbf{r_1} + k\mathbf{s}$ of line l developed in question (7), Exercise 4.1 gives rise to the parametric equations
$$x = x_1 + ka, \qquad y = y_1 + kb, \qquad k \in Re,$$
if point A on l has co-ordinates (x_1, y_1) and vector $\mathbf{s}$, collinear with l, is $\mathbf{s} = (a, b)$ with respect to the chosen co-ordinate system.

8. Write vector and parametric equations of the form given in question (7) for line l if A has co-ordinates $(2, 3)$ and $\mathbf{s}$ is the given vector.
   (a) $\mathbf{s} = (3, 5)$ (b) $\mathbf{s} = (-2, 1)$ (c) $\mathbf{s} = (0, -5)$ (d) $\mathbf{s} = (-4, 0)$
   (e) $\mathbf{s} = \overrightarrow{AB}$ with $B(4, 9)$ (f) $\mathbf{s} = \overrightarrow{AB}$ with $B = (-5, -1)$

9. State the co-ordinates of the points corresponding to parameter values 0 and 1 on the lines with the following equations.   State also the vector (a, b) collinear with each line.
   (a) $x = 3 + 2k, y = 4 - 3k$ (b) $x = -1 - 2k, y = 3 - k$
   (c) $x = 4k, y = 1 - 2k$ (d) $x = 3, y = -2 + 5k$
   (e) $x = k, y = -2k$ (f) $x = 4 - k, y = -1$

10. Describe the location of the line l with parametric equations
$$x = 4 - 2t, y = 3 \,.$$

11. Describe the location of the line with parametric equations
$$x = -3, y = 5 + 3t \,.$$

12. Find the parametric equations of the line through the origin and the point (x_1, y_1).

13. Find the parametric equations of the lines through point $A(x_1, y_1)$ and
   (a) parallel to the x-axis,   (b) parallel to the y-axis.

14. The vector equation of line l is
$$(x, y) = (1 - k)(1, 2) + k(-2, 3) \,.$$
   On this line, points A, B, C, and D correspond to the parametric values 0, 1, 2, and 3, respectively.   Show that
$$\overrightarrow{AC} = 2\overrightarrow{AB}, \qquad \overrightarrow{AD} = 3\overrightarrow{AB}, \qquad \overrightarrow{AC} = \tfrac{2}{3}\overrightarrow{AD} \,.$$

15. If the vector equation of line l is
$$(x, y) = (1 - k)(x_1, y_1) + k(x_2, y_2),$$
   and if points A, B, and P correspond to the values $0, 1$, and t of the parameter k, respectively, prove that
$$\overrightarrow{AP} = t\overrightarrow{AB} \,.$$

16. If points R, S, and T correspond to the parametric values 0, t_1, and t_2, respectively, for the line in question (15), prove that
$$\overrightarrow{RT} = \frac{t_2}{t_1}\,\overrightarrow{RS}, \quad \text{if} \quad t_1 \neq 0 \,.$$

4.3. The Linear Equation of a Line in Two-Space

A line l in 2-space determines a unique line l' through the origin and perpendicular to l (Figure 4.5); l' is called the normal axis of l.   The direction of the normal axis l' (and hence of l) is known when a point $M(a, b)$, different from the origin, is known to lie on the normal axis.   In this case, l' is collinear with vector $\overrightarrow{OM} = (a, b)$.

A particular line l in 2-space is thus determined by

(i) a point $P_1(x_1, y_1)$ on l

and

(ii) a point $M(a, b)$ on the normal axis l'.

We obtain an equation for l by noting that, if $P(x, y)$ is any point on l different from P_1, then the vector $\overrightarrow{P_1P}$ is perpendicular to vector $\overrightarrow{OM}$.

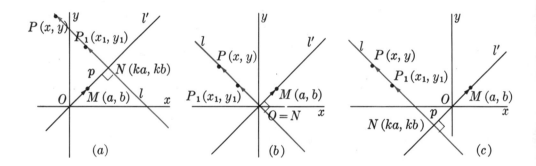

(a) (b) (c)

Figure 4.5

Theorem.   Let line l in 2-space be determined by

(i) point $P_1(x_1, y_1)$ on l,

(ii) point $M(a, b)$ on l', the normal axis of l.

Then l has the equation

$$ax + by = ax_1 + by_1.$$

Proof: Let $P(x, y)$ be any point on l different from P_1.   Then

$$\overrightarrow{P_1P} = (x - x_1, y - y_1)$$

is perpendicular to vector $\overrightarrow{OM} = (a, b)$.   But $\overrightarrow{OM} \perp \overrightarrow{P_1P}$ if and only if

$$(x - x_1, y - y_1) = 0 \, ;$$

that is,

$$ax - ax_1 + by - by_1 = 0 \, ,$$

or

$$ax + by = ax_1 + by_1.$$

Thus the co-ordinates of every point P on l satisfy this equation, which is therefore the equation of line l.

This equation is the one that has been studied earlier, the linear equation

$$ax + by = c.$$

Example 1.   Find the equation of line l if l passes through $P_1(5, 7)$ and its normal axis l' lies on $M(-3, 1)$.

Solution:

First Method (from first principles):   Let $P(x, y)$ be any point on l distinct from P_1. Then $\overrightarrow{OM} = (-3, 1)$, $\overrightarrow{P_1P} = (x - 5, y - 7)$, and $\overrightarrow{OM} \perp \overrightarrow{P_1P}$. Therefore,

$$(-3, 1) \cdot (x - 5, y - 7) = 0$$

and hence

$$-3x + y = -8$$

is the required equation.

Second Method: Since $\overrightarrow{OM} = (-3, 1)$ is collinear with the normal axis, the equation of l is of the form

$$-3x + y = c,$$

where

$$c = (-3)(5) + 1(7)$$
$$= -8,$$

since $P_1(5, 7)$ lies on l.   This gives us the same equation as obtained by the first method.

It is sometimes useful to take the point of intersection N of line l and its normal axis l' as the point P_1 on l (Figure 4.5).   Point N will have co-ordinates (ka, kb) for some real number k, since $\overrightarrow{ON} = k\overrightarrow{OM}$. Then, if $P(x, y)$ is any different point on l, we have $\overrightarrow{NP} \perp \overrightarrow{OM}$ so that

$$(a, b) \cdot (x - ka, y - kb) = 0,$$

or

$$ax + by = k(a^2 + b^2).$$

Example 2.   Find the point of intersection of the line l with equation $2x - 5y = 12$ and its normal axis l'.

Solution: We note first that l' passes through point $M(2, -5)$, and secondly, that the point of intersection N of l and l' has co-ordinates $(2k, -5k)$, where k is such that

$$2x - 5y = k(2^2 + (-5)^2)$$
$$= 12.$$
$$29k = 12 \text{ and } k = \tfrac{12}{29}.$$

The point of intersection is $N(\tfrac{24}{29}, -\tfrac{60}{29})$.

When we know the co-ordinates (ka, kb) of the point of intersection N of l and l', we can immediately find the perpendicular distance p from the origin to line l. This distance can be considered as

(i) the length of vector $\overrightarrow{ON} = (ka, kb)$,

or

(ii) the length of line segment ON.

The required distance is $|k|\sqrt{a^2 + b^2}$.

Example 3. Find the distance p from the origin to the line l with equation $2x - 5y = 12$ (see Example 2).

Solution: We found that $k = \frac{12}{29}$; the required distance p is

$$\frac{12}{29}\sqrt{2^2 + (-5)^2} = \frac{12}{29}\sqrt{29}.$$

The general linear equation

$$ax + by = c, \qquad a, b, c \in Re$$

may be rewritten in the form

$$ax + by = \left(\frac{c}{a^2 + b^2}\right)(a^2 + b^2),$$

so that

$$ax + by = k(a^2 + b^2), \qquad \text{where } k = \frac{c}{a^2 + b^2}.$$

Note that, when the equation is written in this form,

(i) point $M(a, b)$ lies on the normal axis l' of l (why?);

(ii) if l and l' intersect in point N, then $\overrightarrow{ON} = k\overrightarrow{OM}$ and so N has co-ordinates (ka, kb);

(iii) the (perpendicular) distance p from the origin to line l is

$$p = |\overrightarrow{ON}| = |k|\sqrt{a^2 + b^2}.$$

Example 4. Find the equations of the lines perpendicular to the vector $(4, 1)$ and 7 units distance from the origin (two answers).

Solution: The equations of the lines are of the form

$$4x + y = c.$$

If we write this equation as

$$4x + y = \frac{c}{17}(17),$$

then the distance from the origin to the line is $\frac{|c|}{\sqrt{17}}$. Therefore,

$$\frac{|c|}{\sqrt{17}} = 7$$

and so $c = 7\sqrt{17}$ or $-7\sqrt{17}$. The required equations are

$$4x + y = 7\sqrt{17} \qquad \text{and} \qquad 4x + y = -7\sqrt{17}.$$

Example 5.   If line l has equation $5x + 3y = 7$, find
   (a) a vector perpendicular to the direction of l,
   (b) a point on the normal axis l',
   (c) the point of intersection N of l and l',
   (d) the distance from O to l.

Solution:
   (a) Vector $(5, 3)$ is perpendicular to the direction of l.
   (b) Point $M\,(5, 3)$ lies on l'.
   (c) Writing $5x + 3y = \frac{7}{34}(34)$, where $34 = 5^2 + 3^2$, we see that the point of intersection N of l and l' is such that $\overrightarrow{ON} = \frac{7}{34}\overrightarrow{OM}$; thus N has co-ordinates $(\frac{35}{34}, \frac{21}{34})$.
   (d) The distance from O to l is $\frac{7}{34}\sqrt{34}$ or $\frac{7}{\sqrt{34}}$. This may be checked by using the distance formula to find the length of line segment ON.

Example 6.   Find the distance from the point $Q\,(7, 4)$ to the line l whose equation is $3x + 5y = 19$.

Solution: The point $M\,(3, 5)$ lies on the normal axis l' and the point $P_1(3, 2)$ lies on l, since $3\,(3) + 5\,(2) = 19$. Thus we may sketch the location of l (Figure 4.6.)

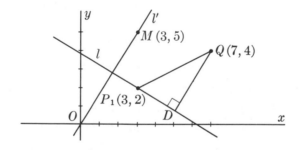

Figure 4.6

The required distance QD is the projection of vector $\overrightarrow{P_1Q}$ on a vector perpendicular to the direction of l; we may take $\overrightarrow{OM} = (3, 5)$ as this vector.

$$\overrightarrow{P_1Q} = (7 - 3, 4 - 2) = (4, 2)\,.$$

Therefore,   required distance $= \dfrac{|\,\overrightarrow{P_1Q} \cdot \overrightarrow{OM}\,|}{|\,\overrightarrow{OM}\,|}$

$$= \dfrac{|\,(4, 2) \cdot (3, 5)\,|}{\sqrt{34}}$$

$$= \tfrac{22}{\sqrt{34}} = \tfrac{11}{17}\sqrt{34}\,.$$

Note that we could have used the point of intersection N of l and l' (or any other point on l) instead of P_1.

EXERCISE 4.3

1. Find the equation of line l through point P_1 if its normal axis lies on point M; use two methods in (a)-(f). Locate the line in the plane in each case.
   (a) $M(1,1)$, $P_1(5,5)$ (b) $M(3,3)$, $P_1(-1,0)$
   (c) $M(-1,4)$, $P_1(2,-8)$ (d) $M(-1,2)$, $P_1(4,3)$
   (e) $M(-3,1)$, $P_1(9,-3)$ (f) $M(-2,-3)$, $P_1(-4,7)$
   (g) $M(3,0)$, $P_1(10,0)$ (h) $M(0,4)$, $P_1(0,9)$
   (i) $M(\frac{1}{2},\frac{1}{3})$, $P_1(3,2)$ (j) $M(-2,-5)$, $P_1(4,-1)$
   (k) $M(3,7)$, $P_1(0,0)$ (l) $M(-2,5)$, $P_1(0,5)$

2. Find the equation of l if l and l' intersect in the following points N.
   (a) $N(3,5)$ (b) $N(-3,7)$ (c) $N(-2,-7)$ (d) $N(0,4)$ (e) $N(0,0)$

3. Find the equations of the lines perpendicular to the given vector and at the given distance from the origin.
   (a) $(3,4)$, 5   (b) $(-2,7)$, 3   (c) $(4,-6)$, 10

4. Find the intersection of line l and its normal axis l', and sketch the lines l with the following equations.
   (a) $3x + 4y = 13$ (b) $3x = 7$
   (c) $2x - 5y = 9$ (d) $-3x + 7y = 3$
   (e) $2y = -5$ (f) $4x - 6y = -3$
   (g) $-3x + 2y = 13$ (h) $-x - 5y = -3$

5. Find the distance from the origin to line l in question (4).

6. Find the distance from point Q to the line whose equation is given.
   (a) $Q(3,-7)$, $2x - y = 5$ (b) $Q(-3,-1)$, $x + 5y = -8$
   (c) $Q(-1,6)$, $5x - 3y = -2$ (d) $Q(2,5)$, $-2x + 7y = 3$

7. Prove that the distance from the origin to the line with equation $ax + by = c$ is
$$\frac{|c|}{\sqrt{a^2 + b^2}}.$$

8. Prove that the distance from the point $P_1(x_1, y_1)$ to the line with equation $ax + by = c$ is
$$\frac{|ax_1 + by_1 - c|}{\sqrt{a^2 + b^2}}.$$

9. Prove that the origin lies between the points $A(a,b)$ and $B(ka,kb)$ whenever $k < 0$.

10. Show that the equation of line l can be written in the form
$$x \cos \omega + y \sin \omega = p$$
where ω is the angle that the normal axis l' makes with the positive x-axis $(0° \leq \omega \leq 360°)$ and p is the distance from O to l.

4.4. Direction Numbers · Symmetric Equations of a Line in Two-Space

We have seen that a line l in the plane is determined by two points P_1 and P_2 or by a point P_1 and the direction of the normal axis l'. The line l is also determined by a point $P_1(x_1, y_1)$ and the direction of the line l itself, given by the angle α that l makes with the positive x-axis $(0° \leq \alpha \leq 180°)$.

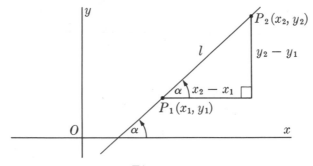

Figure 4.7

Now suppose (Figure 4.7) that we were able to stand at the point $P_1(x_1, y_1)$ on line l. If we walked a directed distance $x_2 - x_1$ units parallel to the x-axis, and then $y_2 - y_1$ units parallel to the y-axis, we would reach the point $P_2(x_2, y_2)$ on line l. In this sense, the ordered pair of real numbers $(x_2 - x_1, y_2 - y_1)$ determines the *direction* of the line l. For this reason, such an ordered pair of real numbers is called a set of direction numbers for the line l.

Every ordered pair of real numbers (a, b) will thus determine the direction of an infinite family of parallel lines (Figure 4.8).

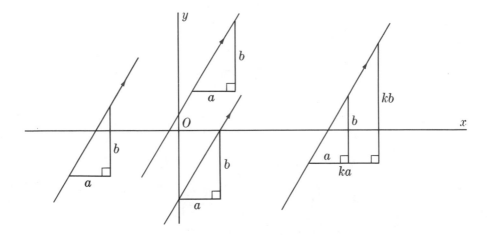

Figure 4.8

An application of the properties of similar triangles shows that any ordered pair (ka, kb), $k \neq 0$, determines the same infinite family of parallel lines. Thus if l has direction numbers $(3, 5)$, then l will also have direction numbers $(6, 10)$, $(9, 15)$, $(-3, -5)$, and, in general, $(3k, 5k)$.

Example 1. Find a general expression for the direction numbers of the line l through points $P_1(2, -5)$ and $P_2(3, 7)$.

Solution: Since $(x_2 - x_1, y_2 - y_1)$ is a set of direction numbers, then $(3 - 2, 7+5)$, or $(1, 12)$ is a set of direction numbers for l. This means that if we start at $P_1(2, -5)$ and move one unit parallel to the x-axis, then 12 units parallel to the y-axis, we will reach point P_2.

The general expression for the set of direction numbers of this line l is $(k, 12k)$, for $k \neq 0$. If we start at $P_1(2, -5)$ and move k units parallel to the x-axis, then $12k$ units parallel to the y-axis, we shall arrive at a point on line l.

We have now encountered another interpretation for an ordered pair of real numbers.

(1) (a, b) can be interpreted as the co-ordinates of a point A in the plane.

(2) (a, b) can be interpreted as the vector $\overrightarrow{OA}$.

(3) (a, b) can be interpreted as the direction of a family of parallel lines (having the direction of vector $\overrightarrow{OA}$), that is, as direction numbers for the family of parallel lines.

It should be clear from the context which interpretation is being used.

In Section 4.2 we determined the parametric equations

$$x = (1 - k)x_1 + kx_2$$
$$y = (1 - k)y_1 + ky_2$$

of the line l determined by two points $P_1(x_1, y_1)$ and $P_2(x_2, y_2)$.

These equations may be rewritten as

$$x - x_1 = k(x_2 - x_1),$$
$$y - y_1 = k(y_2 - y_1),$$

and, by the elimination of k, combined into the single equation

$$\frac{x - x_1}{x_2 - x_1} = \frac{y - y_1}{y_2 - y_1}, \quad \text{provided } x_1 \neq x_2, \; y_1 \neq y_2.$$

This is a symmetric equation of the line l in 2-space. Of course,

$$\frac{x - x_2}{x_2 - x_1} = \frac{y - y_2}{y_2 - y_1}$$

is also a symmetric equation for this line.

Example 2.   Find a symmetric equation of the line l through the points $P_1(3, 5)$ and $P_2(7, 10)$.

Solution: A symmetric equation of l is

$$\frac{x - 3}{7 - 3} = \frac{y - 5}{10 - 5} \quad \text{or} \quad \frac{x - 7}{7 - 3} = \frac{y - 10}{10 - 5} \, ;$$

that is,

$$\frac{x - 3}{4} = \frac{y - 5}{5} \quad \text{or} \quad \frac{x - 7}{4} = \frac{y - 10}{5} \, .$$

Setting each ratio in the left equation equal to the parameter k yields the parametric equations

$$x = 3 + 4k, \quad y = 5 + 5k \, .$$

(From the right equation we get $x = 7 + 4h$, $y = 10 + 5h$.)   Finally, multiplying both members of the symmetric equation by 20 yields

$$5(x - 3) = 4(y - 5) \quad \text{or} \quad 5(x - 7) = 4(y - 10),$$

that is, $5x - 4y = -5$, the linear equation of l.

Example 3.   Find a symmetric equation of the line l through the points $P_1(3, 5)$ and $P_2(7, 5)$.

Solution: Line l does not have a symmetric equation because $y_2 - y_1 = 0$. Parametric equations and a linear equation may be determined.

The symmetric equation of l may be modified by noting that the denominators form a set of direction numbers for l.   Also, since

$$\frac{x - x_1}{k(x_2 - x_1)} = \frac{y - y_1}{k(y_2 - y_1)} \quad \text{for } k \neq 0,$$

any set of direction numbers may be used in the equation; that is, if l has direction numbers (a, b) and if l lies on $P_1(x_1, y_1)$, then l has equation

$$\frac{x - x_1}{a} = \frac{y - y_1}{b} \, .$$

Example 4.   Find the linear equation of line l if it has direction parallel to vector $\mathbf{v} = (3, -2)$ and lies on the point $Q(2, 7)$.

Solution: The line l has direction numbers $(3, -2)$; its equation is

$$\frac{x - 2}{3} = \frac{y - 7}{-2} \, .$$

This equation may be written as $2x + 3y = 25$.

EXERCISE 4.4

1. Find (i) direction numbers (ii) a symmetric equation for the following lines.
   (a) line l through $P_1(3, 3)$ and $P_2(7, 9)$
   (b) line l through $P_1(-2, 5)$ and $P_2(8, 0)$
   (c) line l through $P_1(-3, -2)$ and $P_2(0, 7)$
   (d) line l through $P_1(-1, -2)$ and $P_2(-3, -4)$
   (e) line l with equation $3x + 7y = 10$
   (f) line l with equation $-2x + 9y = 18$
   (g) line l with equation $4x - 3y = 12$
   (h) line l with equations $x = 4 + 3t$, $y = 6 - 2t$
   (i) line l with equations $x = -3 - t$, $y = 4$
   (j) line l with equations $x = -2$, $y = 1 - 3t$
   (k) line l through $P_1(5, 2)$ if its normal axis lies on $A(3, -4)$

2. Find the equations of the lines l through $A(1, -5)$ with direction numbers
   (a) $(5, -1)$,   (b) $(3, 7)$,   (c) $(-4, -3)$,   (d) $(5, 0)$.

3. Find the equation of line l through $P_1(-2, 3)$ if its normal axis has equation $3x - 5y = 7$.

4. What can be said about line l if its direction numbers are
   (a) $(k, 0)$,   (b) $(0, k)$,
   for $k \in Re$, $k \neq 0$?

4.5. Direction Cosines and Angles for a Line in Two-Space

The symmetric equation

$$\frac{x - x_1}{x_2 - x_1} = \frac{y - y_1}{y_2 - y_1}, \qquad x_2 \neq x_1, \ y_2 \neq y_1,$$

may be modified as

$$\frac{x - x_1}{\dfrac{x_2 - x_1}{d}} = \frac{y - y_1}{\dfrac{y_2 - y_1}{d}}$$

with $d = \sqrt{(x_2 - x_1)^2 + (y_2 - y_1)^2}$.

Now if α is the angle between line l and the positive x-axis $(0° \leq \alpha \leq 180°)$, and β is the angle between l and the positive y-axis $(-90° \leq \beta \leq 90°)$, we see from Figure 4.9 that

$$\cos \alpha = \frac{x_2 - x_1}{d} \quad \text{and} \quad \cos \beta = \frac{y_2 - y_1}{d}.$$

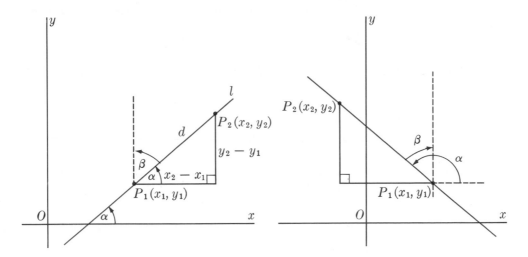

Figure 4.9

The equation of l can then be written in the form

$$\frac{x - x_1}{\cos \alpha} = \frac{y - y_1}{\cos \beta}.$$

α and β are called the direction angles of l, and $\cos \alpha$ and $\cos \beta$ are called the direction cosines of l.

Since $\cos \alpha$ and $\cos \beta$ can be either positive or negative, there are four possible patterns of signs for $(\cos \alpha, \cos \beta)$.

$$(+, +), \quad (-, +), \quad (-, -), \quad '(+, -).$$

Now the line through point P with direction cosines $(-s, -t)$ has direction opposite to that of the line through P with direction cosines $(+s, +t)$. We do not distinguish between these lines. Nor do we distinguish between the lines through P with direction cosines $(-s, t)$ and $(s, -t)$.

The x-axis divides the plane into two half-planes, the upper half-plane, where y is positive, and the lower half-plane, where y is negative.

In order to specify a unique pair of direction angles for a line l, we shall adopt the following convention. We call that portion of l lying in the upper half-plane (assuming that l is not parallel to the x-axis) *the upper portion of* l. With the usual convention that angles measured in a counterclockwise direction are positive and angles measured in a clockwise direction are negative, we define α as the angle from the positive direction of the x-axis to the upper portion of l, and β as the angle from the upper portion of l to the positive direction of the y-axis. If l is parallel to the x-axis, $\alpha = 0°$ and $\beta = 90°$.

With this convention, $0 \le \alpha < 180°$, $-90° < \beta \le 90°$, $\alpha + \beta = 90°$, and *cos β is always positive.* It follows, from the equation in the preceding sentence, that

$$\cos^2\alpha + \cos^2\beta = \cos^2\alpha + \sin^2\alpha = 1 ;$$

that is, the sum of the squares of the direction cosines of l is unity.

Of course, the set of direction cosines $(\cos \alpha, \cos \beta)$ is also a set of direction numbers for l since

$$\cos \alpha = \frac{1}{d}(x_2 - x_1) \quad \text{and} \quad \cos \beta = \frac{1}{d}(y_2 - y_1) .$$

It is also possible to obtain the direction cosines of a line l from a set of direction numbers (Figure 4.10); if l has direction numbers (a, b), then

$$\cos \alpha = \frac{a}{\sqrt{a^2 + b^2}} \quad \text{and} \quad \cos \beta = \frac{b}{\sqrt{a^2 + b^2}} .$$

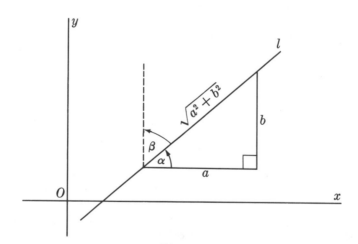

Figure 4.10

Example 1. Find the direction cosines and direction angles, to the nearest degree, of line l through points $P_1(5, -4)$ and $P_2(-1, 7)$ (Figure 4.11).

Solution: l has direction numbers $(-1 - 5, 7 + 4)$ or $(-6, 11)$. Therefore,

$$\cos \alpha = \frac{-6}{\sqrt{157}} \quad \text{and} \quad \cos \beta = \frac{11}{\sqrt{157}}, \quad \text{by our convention,}$$

$$\simeq -.479 . \qquad \simeq .878 .$$

$$\alpha = 119° . \qquad \beta = -29° .$$

$$\alpha + \beta = 90° .$$

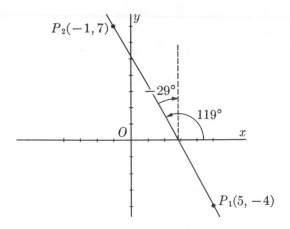

Figure 4.11

Example 2. Find the direction angles, to the nearest degree, of l if its direction cosines, without regard to our convention on signs, are

(a) $(\frac{1}{2}, -\frac{\sqrt{3}}{2})$, (b) $(-\frac{2}{3}, -\frac{\sqrt{5}}{3})$.

Solution:

(a) We take $\cos \alpha = -\frac{1}{2}$ and $\cos \beta = \frac{\sqrt{3}}{2}$ by our convention.

$\cos \alpha = -\frac{1}{2}.$ $\alpha = 120°.$

$\cos \beta = \frac{\sqrt{3}}{2}.$ $\beta = -30°.$

$\alpha + \beta = 90°.$

(b) We take $\cos \alpha = \frac{2}{3}$ and $\cos \beta = \frac{\sqrt{5}}{3}$ by our convention.

$\cos \alpha = 0.667.$ $\alpha = 48°.$

$\cos \beta = 0.745.$ $\beta = 42°.$

$\alpha + \beta = 90°.$

Since the normal axis l' of l is collinear with the vector (a, b) if l has equation $ax + by = c$, then l' has direction numbers (a, b). Similarly, l then has direction parallel to the vector $(-b, a)$, since

$$(a, b) \cdot (-b, a) = 0,$$

so that l has direction numbers $(-b, a)$.

Example 3. Find the direction cosines and a symmetric equation of the line l whose equation is $-2x + 5y = 10$.

Solution:

(a) The normal axis l' has direction numbers $(-2, 5)$; thus, the line l has direction numbers $(5, 2)$, since $(-2, 5) \cdot (5, 2) = 0$. Therefore,

$$\cos \alpha = \frac{5}{\sqrt{29}} \quad \text{and} \quad \cos \beta = \frac{2}{\sqrt{29}}.$$

(b) In order to write a symmetric equation of line l, we need the co-ordinates of a point on l. These are easily determined; for example, $(5, 0)$ and $(0, 2)$ are the co-ordinates of points on l. Then

$$\frac{x - 5}{5} = \frac{y - 0}{2} \quad \text{and} \quad \frac{x - 0}{5} = \frac{y - 2}{2}$$

are symmetric equations for l.

EXERCISE 4.5

1. Find (a) the direction cosines, (b) the direction angles of the lines in question (1), Exercise 4.4.

2. Find the equations of lines l through $A(2, 3)$ with direction angles
    (a) $45°, 45°$, (b) $120°, -30°$, (c) $165°, -75°$.

3. Find the direction angles, to the nearest degree, of the lines l whose direction cosines, without regard to our convention on signs, are given as
    (a) $\frac{3}{4}, \frac{\sqrt{7}}{4}$, (b) $-\frac{1}{3}, \frac{2\sqrt{2}}{3}$, (c) $\frac{3}{5}, -\frac{4}{5}$, (d) $-\frac{5}{13}, -\frac{12}{13}$.

4. Find the equation of line l if its distance from the origin is 5 units and its normal axis makes an angle of $30°$ with the positive x-axis.

4.6. Equations of the Line in Three-Space

The line l determined by two points A and B with position vectors $\mathbf{r}_1$ and $\mathbf{r}_2$ with respect to a fixed point O, has vector equation

$$\mathbf{r} = (1 - k)\mathbf{r}_1 + k\mathbf{r}_2, \quad k \in Re .$$

Now we introduce a three-dimensional Cartesian co-ordinate system by selecting three mutually perpendicular lines through point O and labelling them as the x-, y-, and z-axes in the usual manner (Figure 4.12).

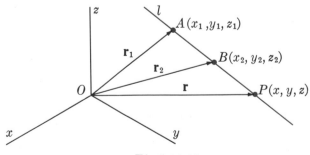

Figure 4.12

Then point A will have co-ordinates (x_1, y_1, z_1) relative to this co-ordinate system and position vector $\mathbf{r}_1$ will be the algebraic vector (x_1, y_1, z_1); thus we will have

$$\mathbf{r}_1 = (x_1, y_1, z_1), \quad \mathbf{r}_2 = (x_2, y_2, z_2), \quad \mathbf{r} = (x, y, z).$$

Our vector equation for line l can then be written

$$(x, y, z) = (1 - k)(x_1, y_1, z_1) + k(x_2, y_2, z_2).$$

Example 1. Find the vector equation of the line l determined by the points

$$A(-5, 3, 1) \quad \text{and} \quad B(2, 7, -4).$$

Solution: The vector equation of l is

$$(x, y, z) = (1 - k)(-5, 3, 1) + k(2, 7, -4).$$

Now the vector equation

$$(x, y, z) = (1 - k)(x_1, y_1, z_1) + k(x_2, y_2, z_2)$$

can be written

$$(x, y, z) = [(1 - k)x_1, \ (1 - k)y_1, \ (1 - k)z_1] + (kx_2, \ ky_2, \ kz_2)$$
$$= [(1 - k)x_1 + kx_2, \ (1 - k)y_1 + ky_2, \ (1 - k)z_1 + kz_2].$$

Identifying components in these two vectors yields

$$\left. \begin{array}{l} x = (1 - k)x_1 + kx_2 \\ y = (1 - k)y_1 + ky_2 \\ z = (1 - k)z_1 + kz_2 \end{array} \right\} \quad k \in Re.$$

These equations are parametric equations of the line l in 3-space determined by the points $A(x_1, y_1, z_1)$ and $B(x_2, y_2, z_2)$. A line in 3-space is represented by a set of three parametric equations.

Again we note that any point on the line determined by points $A(x_1, y_1, z_1)$ and $B(x_2, y_2, z_2)$ has co-ordinates $(\alpha x_1 + \beta x_2, \ \alpha y_1 + \beta y_2, \ \alpha z_1 + \beta z_2)$, where $\alpha + \beta = 1$.

Example 2. Find parametric equations of the line l determined by the points $A(-5, 3, 1)$ and $B(2, 7, -4)$ (see Example 1).

Solution: Parametric equations of l are

$$x = (1 - k)(-5) + k(2) = -5 + 7k,$$
$$y = (1 - k)(3) + k(7) = 3 + 4k,$$
$$z = (1 - k)(1) + k(-4) = 1 - 5k.$$

As in the corresponding situation in 2-space, any restriction on k in the vector equation or parametric equations of l will yield the equation or equations of a part of l (point, subset of points, line segment, ray, etc.).

Recall also that any particular value of the parameter k determines a point P on l such that $\overrightarrow{AP} = k\,\overrightarrow{AB}$.

Example 3.   Find the point that divides the line segment AB in the ratio $2:1$ for the points $A(2, 2, -5)$ and $B(-1, 4, 3)$.

Solution: If point P_1 divides line segment AB in the ratio $2:1$, then $\overrightarrow{AP_1} = \frac{2}{3}\overrightarrow{AB}$. Now any point P on the line determined by A and B has co-ordinates

$$x = (1 - k)\,(2) + k(-1) = 2 - 3k\,,$$
$$y = (1 - k)\,(2) + k(4) = 2 + 2k\,,$$
$$z = (1 - k)\,(-5) + k(3) = -5 + 8k\,,$$

and P_1 is the point corresponding to the value $\frac{2}{3}$ of k.   Thus P_1 has co-ordinates

$$[2 - 3(\tfrac{2}{3})\,,\ \ 2 + 2(\tfrac{2}{3})\,,\ \ -5 + 8(\tfrac{2}{3})]\ \ \text{or}\ \ (0, \tfrac{10}{3}, \tfrac{1}{3})\,.$$

The parametric equations of the line l determined by the points $A(x_1, y_1, z_1)$ and $B(x_2, y_2, z_2)$ may be rewritten as

$$x - x_1 = k(x_2 - x_1)\,,\ \ y - y_1 = k(y_2 - y_1),\ \ z - z_1 = k(z_2 - z_1)\,,$$

and, by the elimination of k, combined into the equations

$$\frac{x - x_1}{x_2 - x_1} = \frac{y - y_1}{y_2 - y_1} = \frac{z - z_1}{z_2 - z_1}\,,\qquad \text{provided } x_1 \neq x_2,\, y_1 \neq y_2,\, z_1 \neq z_2.$$

These are symmetric equations of the line l in 3-space.   (There are essentially two distinct equations involved in this expression; any two of the equations

$$\frac{x - x_1}{x_2 - x_1} = \frac{y - y_1}{y_2 - y_1}\,,\qquad \frac{x - x_1}{x_2 - x_1} = \frac{z - z_1}{z_2 - z_1}\,,\qquad \frac{y - y_1}{y_2 - y_1} = \frac{z - z_1}{z_2 - z_1}$$

will determine the third.)

Example 4.   Find symmetric equations of the line l determined by the points $A(3, -5, 7)$ and $B(-1, -1, 5)$.

Solution: Symmetric equations of l are

$$\frac{x - 3}{-1 - 3} = \frac{y - (-5)}{-1 - (-5)} = \frac{z - 7}{5 - 7}\,;$$

that is,

$$\frac{x - 3}{-4} = \frac{y + 5}{4} = \frac{z - 7}{-2}\,.$$

(Note that $\dfrac{x+1}{4} = \dfrac{y+1}{-4} = \dfrac{z-5}{2}$ are also symmetric equations of l.)

Parametric equations of l can be found by setting the common ratios equal to k.

$$\frac{x-3}{-4} = \frac{y+5}{4} = \frac{z-7}{-2} = k .$$

Hence

$$x = 3 - 4k ,$$
$$y = -5 + 4k ,$$
$$z = 7 - 2k .$$

(Note that $x = -1 + 4k$, $y = -1 - 4k$, $z = 5 + 2k$ are also parametric equations for l.)

Example 5. Find symmetric equations of the line l that passes through the points $A(-3, 1, 7)$ and $B(-4, 1, 5)$.

Solution: It is impossible to write symmetric equations for line l since $y_2 - y_1 = 0$. However, it is possible to obtain parametric equations in the usual way.

EXERCISE 4.6

1. Find vector, parametric, and symmetric (where possible) equations of the line l determined by the following pairs of points.
    (a) $A(1, 1, 1)$, $B(5, 5, 5)$
    (b) $A(1, 0, 4)$, $B(5, 3, 9)$
    (c) $A(4, 2, 1)$, $B(1, 2, 4)$
    (d) $A(-1, 3, 5)$, $B(7, 7, -3)$
    (e) $A(-4, 1, 7)$, $B(-1, 5, 2)$
    (f) $A(4, -3, -3)$, $B(6, 7, -3)$
    (g) $A(5, -1, 3)$, $B(-2, -1, 3)$
    (h) $A(-6, 2, 1)$, $B(-1, -1, -7)$
    (i) $A(-3, 1, 6)$, $B(-3, 6, 6)$
    (j) $A(0, 0, 1)$, $B(0, 1, 0)$

2. Find the midpoints of the line segments AB determined by the points in question (1).

3. Find the co-ordinates of the point P dividing line segment AB, determined by $A(3, -1, -2)$ and $B(-1, 5, 6)$, in the ratio,
    (a) $1:3$,
    (b) $2:5$,
    (c) $-3:2$,
    (d) $5:-1$.

4. Locate the following points relative to the points $A(x_1, y_1, z_1)$ and $B(x_2, y_2, z_2)$.
    (a) $(\frac{1}{2}x_1 + \frac{1}{2}x_2,\ \frac{1}{2}y_1 + \frac{1}{2}y_2,\ \frac{1}{2}z_1 + \frac{1}{2}z_2)$
    (b) $(\frac{1}{5}x_1 + \frac{4}{5}x_2,\ \frac{1}{5}y_1 + \frac{4}{5}y_2,\ \frac{1}{5}z_1 + \frac{4}{5}z_2)$
    (c) $(-x_1 + 2x_2,\ -y_1 + 2y_2,\ -z_1 + 2z_2)$
    (d) $(-3x_1 + 4x_2,\ -3y_1 + 4y_2,\ -3z_1 + 4z_2)$
    (e) $(2x_1 - x_2,\ 2y_1 - y_2,\ 2z_1 - z_2)$
    (f) $(5x_1 - 4x_2,\ 5y_1 - 4y_2,\ 5z_1 - 4z_2)$

5. Determine the figure with parametric equations

$$x = (1 - k)(-2) + k(4)$$
$$y = (1 - k)(3) + k(-3)$$
$$z = (1 - k)(1) + k(2)$$

for the following sets of values for k.

(a) Re (b) 0   (c) 1   (d) $\frac{1}{2}$ (e) 3

(f) $\{0, 1, \frac{1}{2}\}$ (g) $\{-1, 0, 1\}$

(h) $\{0 \leq k \leq 1, \ k \in Re\}$ (i) $\{k \geq 0, \ k \in Re\}$

(j) $\{k \leq 0, \ k \in Re\}$ (k) $\{k \geq 1, \ k \in Re\} \cup \{k \leq 0, \ k \in Re\}$

6. Describe the location of the lines l with the following parametric equations

(a) $x = 3$ (b) $x = 3 + 2t$ (c) $x = 3 - 2t$

    $y = 4 - t$ $y = 4$ $y = 4 + 3t$

    $z = -1$ $z = -2$ $z = 2$

7. Find parametric equations of the lines through the point $A(x_1, y_1, z_1)$ and

(a) parallel to the x-axis,

(b) parallel to the y-axis,

(c) parallel to the z-axis.

8. Let the vector equation of line l be $\mathbf{r} = \mathbf{r}_1 + k\mathbf{s}$, where $\mathbf{r}_1$ is the position vector of point P_1 on l, $\mathbf{r}$ is that of an arbitrary point P on l, and $\mathbf{s}$ is a vector parallel to l. If $\mathbf{r}_1 = (x_1, y_1, z_1)$ and $\mathbf{s} = (s_1, s_2, s_3)$, find the corresponding parametric equations of l.

9. Using question (8), find the parametric equations of line l through $P_1(-2, 5, 3)$ if $\mathbf{s}$ is the vector

(a) $(-3, 1, -4)$,   (b) $(4, 0, -7)$,   (c) $(0, -2, 1)$.

10. Sketch the parallelogram with the origin and the points $A(x_1, y_1, z_1)$, $B(x_2, y_2, z_2)$ as three of its vertices. Find the equations of the line through A parallel to line OB and those of the line through B parallel to OA. Verify that their point of intersection is $C(x_1 + x_2, y_1 + y_2, z_1 + z_2)$.

11. Sketch the parallelopiped (a parallelopiped is a three-dimensional figure with six faces each of which is a parallelogram) with the origin and the points $A(x_1, y_1, z_1)$, $B(x_2, y_2, z_2)$, and $C(x_3, y_3, z_3)$ as four adjacent vertices. Find the co-ordinates of the other four vertices, A' opposite to A, B' opposite to B, C' opposite to C, and O' opposite to O.

12. Find the co-ordinates of the midpoints of the diagonals AA', BB' CC' and OO' of the parallelopiped in question (11). What conclusion can you make?

4.7. Direction Numbers, Cosines, and Angles of Lines in Three-Space

The work of Sections 4.4 and 4.5 on direction numbers, cosines, and angles of lines in 2-space extends easily to lines in 3-space.

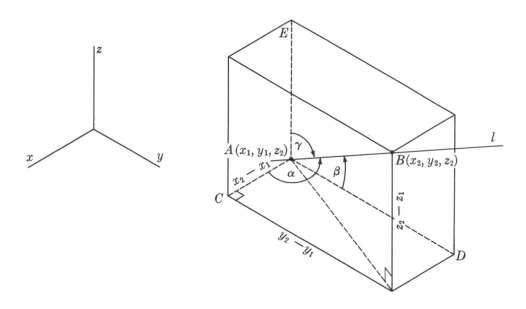

Figure 4.13

The ordered set of numbers $(x_2 - x_1, y_2 - y_1, z_2 - z_1)$ is a set of direction numbers for the line l through $A(x_1, y_1, z_1)$, $B(x_2, y_2, z_2)$ (see Figure 4.13); they determine the direction of line l in the sense that, if we start at any point P in 3-space and travel $x_2 - x_1$ units parallel to the x-axis, $y_2 - y_1$ units parallel to the y-axis, and $z_2 - z_1$ units parallel to the z-axis, we reach a point Q such that PQ is parallel to AB. As in the 2-dimensional case, the ordered set

$$[k(x_2 - x_1), \; k(y_2 - y_1), \; k(z_2 - z_1)]$$

is a set of direction numbers for l for any nonzero real number k.

Example 1. Find the direction numbers of the line l through points $A(3, -2, -5)$ and $B(4, 2, -1)$.

Solution: The ordered set

$$(4 - 3, 2 - (-2), -1 - (-5)) \quad \text{or} \quad (1, 4, 4)$$

is a set of direction numbers for l, as is $(k, 4k, 4k)$, for any nonzero real number k.

Note now that an ordered triple (a, b, c) of real numbers can be interpreted as

(1) the co-ordinates of a point A in 3-space,

(2) vector $\overrightarrow{OA}$,

(3) the direction numbers of a family of parallel lines in 3-space (having the direction of vector $\overrightarrow{OA}$).

Again, the specific interpretation in any situation should be determined by the context.

Noting that the denominators in the symmetric equations

$$\frac{x - x_1}{x_2 - x_1} = \frac{y - y_1}{y_2 - y_1} = \frac{z - z_1}{z_2 - z_1}$$

for the line l form a set of direction numbers for the line l, and that these equations may be written

$$\frac{x - x_1}{k(x_2 - x_1)} = \frac{y - y_1}{k(y_2 - y_1)} = \frac{z - z_1}{k(z_2 - z_1)}, \quad \text{for } k \neq 0,$$

we see that, in symmetric equations of the form

$$\frac{x - x_1}{a} = \frac{y - y_1}{b} = \frac{z - z_1}{c},$$

(a, b, c) is a set of direction numbers of the line l through $A(x_1, y_1, z_1)$.

Example 2.   Find symmetric equations of the line l through the point $A(3, 3, -4)$ with direction numbers $(3, -2, 5)$.

Solution: Symmetric equations of l are

$$\frac{x - 3}{3} = \frac{y - 3}{-2} = \frac{z + 4}{5}.$$

The equations of line l through $A(x_1, y_1, z_1)$ and $B(x_2, y_2, z_2)$ may also be written

$$\frac{\dfrac{x - x_1}{x_2 - x_1}}{d} = \frac{\dfrac{y - y_1}{y_2 - y_1}}{d} = \frac{\dfrac{z - z_1}{z_2 - z_1}}{d},$$

where d is the length of line segment AB. By referring to Figure 4.13, we see that

$$\frac{x_2 - x_1}{d} = \cos \alpha \quad \text{(from } \triangle ABC, \text{ rt.-angled at } C),$$

$$\frac{y_2 - y_1}{d} = \cos \beta \quad \text{(from } \triangle ABD, \text{ rt.-angled at } D),$$

$$\frac{z_2 - z_1}{d} = \cos \gamma \quad \text{(from } \triangle ABE, \text{ rt.-angled at } E),$$

where α, β, and γ are the angles line l (determined by the directed line segment AB) makes with the positive direction of the x-, y-, and z-axes, respectively. Note especially that in general, α, β, and γ lie in three different planes. Angles α, β, γ are called the direction angles of l, and $\cos\alpha$, $\cos\beta$, $\cos\gamma$, the direction cosines of l.

Example 3. Find the direction cosines and direction angles, to the nearest degree, of line l through points $P_1(5, 2, 3)$ and $P_2(8, 4, 5)$.

Solution:

$$P_1P_2 = \sqrt{(8-5)^2 + (4-2)^2 + (5-3)^2} = \sqrt{17}\,.$$

$$x_2 - x_1 = 8 - 5 = 3\,, \qquad y_2 - y_1 = 4 - 2 = 2\,, \qquad z_2 - z_1 = 5 - 3 = 2\,,$$

$$\cos\alpha = \tfrac{3}{\sqrt{17}}\,, \qquad\qquad \cos\beta = \tfrac{2}{\sqrt{17}}\,, \qquad\qquad \cos\gamma = \tfrac{2}{\sqrt{17}}\,,$$

$$\alpha = 44°\,. \qquad\qquad\qquad \beta = 61°\,. \qquad\qquad\qquad \gamma = 61°\,.$$

If (a, b, c) is a set of direction numbers for line l, then (see question (4), Exercise 4.7) its direction cosines are

$$\cos\alpha = \frac{a}{d}\,, \qquad \cos\beta = \frac{b}{d}\,, \qquad \cos\gamma = \frac{c}{d}\,, \qquad \text{with } d = \sqrt{a^2 + b^2 + c^2}\,,$$

so that

$$\cos^2\alpha + \cos^2\beta + \cos^2\gamma = 1\,.$$

Now there are eight possible patterns of signs for the direction cosines of line l.

$$
\begin{array}{cc}
(+,\ +,\ +) & (-,\ +,\ +) \\
(+,\ +,\ -) & (-,\ +,\ -) \\
(+,\ -,\ +) & (-,\ -,\ +) \\
(+,\ -,\ -) & (-,\ -,\ -)
\end{array}
$$

However, if l has direction cosines $\cos\alpha$, $\cos\beta$, and $\cos\gamma$, then $-\cos\alpha$, $-\cos\beta$, and $-\cos\gamma$ are the direction cosines of the line in the direction opposite to that of l. As we pointed out in our discussion for 2-space, we do not distinguish between these lines.

We now establish a convention for the choice of sign.

The xy-plane divides 3-space into two halves: an upper half, where z is positive, and a lower half, where z is negative. A line l, not parallel to the xy-plane, has an upper portion, that part of l lying in the upper half of 3-space, and a lower portion, that part lying in the lower half. We then define γ as the angle between the upper portion of l and the positive direction of the z-axis, α as the angle between the upper portion of l and the positive direction of the x-axis, and β as the angle between the upper portion of l and the positive direction of the y-axis. Then $\cos\gamma$ is always positive. We choose γ as the first quadrant angle and α and β as first or second quadrant angles. We make no attempt to assign directions to these angles; such an attempt would be not only difficult in 3-space but fruitless as well, since $\cos\theta = \cos(-\theta)$.

If l is parallel to the xy-plane, we define γ as $90°$, α in the same way as for 2-space and β as the *unsigned* angle between the upper portion of l and the positive direction of the y-axis. In this case, we define the upper portion of l as that part of l directly above or below the upper portion of l', where l' is the line parallel to l and lying in the xy-plane.

Example 4. Find the direction angles of line l if its direction cosines, without regard to our convention on signs, are given as $-\frac{1}{3}, \frac{2}{3}, -\frac{2}{3}$.

Solution: We must take the negative of these direction numbers to get one of our accepted patterns for direction cosines; we take

$$\cos \alpha = \tfrac{1}{3} \qquad\qquad \cos \beta = -\tfrac{2}{3} \qquad\qquad \cos \gamma = \tfrac{2}{3}$$
$$\simeq 0.333. \qquad\qquad \simeq -0.667. \qquad\qquad \simeq 0.667.$$
$$\alpha = 71°. \qquad\qquad \beta = 132°. \qquad\qquad \gamma = 48°.$$

EXERCISE 4.7

1. Find the direction numbers, cosines, and angles (to the nearest degree) of the following lines.
   (a) Line l through $A(2, 5, 2)$ and $B(3, 6, 3)$
   (b) Line l through $A(0, 0, 4)$ and $B(5, 1, 5)$
   (c) Line l through $A(3, -2, 5)$ and $B(4, -2, 6)$
   (d) Line l through $A(0, 0, 1)$ and $B(1, 0, 0)$
   (e) Line l with equations $\dfrac{x-3}{4} = \dfrac{y+2}{-1} = \dfrac{z-3}{5}$
   (f) Line l with equations $\dfrac{x+2}{-5} = \dfrac{y}{-4} = \dfrac{z+1}{3}$
   (g) Line l with equations $\dfrac{2x-3}{4} = \dfrac{3y+2}{-1} = \dfrac{z-3}{2}$
   (h) Line l with equations $x = 4 - 3t,\ y = -2 + t,\ z = 4t$
   (i) Line l with equations $x = 3 - 2t,\ y = -6,\ z = 2 + 3t$
   (j) Line l with equations $x = 5 + 3t,\ y = 1 - 2t,\ z = 3$

2. What can be said about the line l if its direction numbers are
   (a) $(0, 0, k)$? \qquad (b) $(0, k, 0)$? \qquad (c) $(k, 0, 0)$?

3. Find the equations of the following lines.
   (a) l through $A(1, 1, 5)$ with direction numbers $(4, 3, -1)$
   (b) l through $A(-3, 1, 3)$ with direction numbers $(-1, 2, -4)$
   (c) l through $A(4, 2, 4)$ with direction numbers $(3, 0, -2)$
   (d) l through $A(-1, 5, 2)$ with direction numbers $(0, 3, 0)$
   (e) l through $A(4, 1, 7)$ with direction cosines $(\tfrac{1}{3}, -\tfrac{2}{3}, \tfrac{2}{3})$
   (f) l through $A(2, -1, 8)$ with direction cosines $(\tfrac{1}{\sqrt{5}}, \tfrac{2}{\sqrt{5}}, 0)$

(g) l through $A(4, 1, 0)$ with direction angles $45°, 45°, 90°$

(h) l through $A(-2, 1, 2)$ with direction angles $60°, 120°, 45°$

4. Show that if (a, b, c) is a set of direction numbers for line l, then its direction cosines, without regard to our convention on signs, are given by

$$\cos \alpha = \frac{a}{d}, \qquad \cos \beta = \frac{b}{d}, \qquad \cos \gamma = \frac{c}{d}, \qquad \text{where } d = \sqrt{a^2 + b^2 + c^2}.$$

Chapter Summary

Vector equation of a line · Positional vector equation of a line · Parametric equations of a line in 2-space (from the vector equation) · The linear equation of a line in 2-space · Direction angles, cosines, and numbers of lines in 2-space · Equations of a line in 3-space · Direction angles, cosines, and numbers of lines in 3-space

REVIEW EXERCISE 4

1. If $\overrightarrow{AP} = k\overrightarrow{AB}$, determine P relative to points A and B for the following real values of k (include a diagram).

(a) $\frac{3}{4}$ (b) $-\frac{4}{3}$ (c) $\frac{1}{2} \le k \le 1$ (d) $k \le -1$

2. In question (1), determine k if

(a) P divides line segment AB in the ratio $1:4$,

(b) P is three times as far from B as from A.

3. If $\mathbf{r}$, $\mathbf{r}_1$, and $\mathbf{r}_2$ are position vectors of points P, A, and B with respect to a fixed point O, interpret the equation

$$\mathbf{r} = (1 - k)\mathbf{r}_1 + k\mathbf{r}_2$$

for the following sets of real values for k.

(a) $k = \{0, 1\}$ (b) $k \ge 1$ (c) $-1 \le k \le 1$

4. Give vector and parametric equations for lines determined by pairs of points with the following co-ordinates (include a diagram).

(a) $(4, 1)$ and $(3, 4)$ (b) $(-2, 1)$ and $(3, -2)$

(c) $(5, 0)$ and $(0, 2)$ (d) $(-3, -4)$ and $(-2, 0)$

5. Describe the figure with parametric equations

$$x = (1 - k)(-3) + k(4)$$
$$y = (1 - k)(5)$$

for the following sets of real values of k.

(a) $k = \{0, 1\}$ (b) $k \ge 0$ (c) $k \in Re$

6. Write vector and parametric equations for the line l passing through point A and collinear with the vector $\mathbf{s}$ for the following.
   (a) $A(2, -1)$, $\mathbf{s} = (3, -1)$ (b) $A(5, 0)$, $\mathbf{s} = (-2, -3)$

7. The normal axis of line l lies on point M; l lies on point Q. Find the linear equation of l in the following cases.
   (a) $M(2, 3)$, $Q(4, -1)$ (b) $M(3, 0)$, $Q(-2, -3)$
   (c) $M(5, -2)$, $Q(0, 0)$ (d) $M(4, 4)$, $Q(3, 3)$

8. Find the equation of line l if l and its normal axis intersect in the following points.
   (a) $N(5, 2)$ (b) $N(-3, 1)$ (c) $N(-4, -3)$

9. Find the intersection of line l and its normal axis l', and sketch the lines l with the following equations.
   (a) $x + 4y = 9$ (b) $2x = 7$
   (c) $3x - 2y = -4$ (d) $-x + 3y = -6$

10. Find the distance from the origin to line l in question (9).

11. Find the distance from point $R(-1, 5)$ to line l in question (9).

12. Find (i) direction numbers, (ii) direction cosines, (iii) direction angles, (iv) symmetric equations of the following lines.
    (a) Line l through $P_1(-3, 4)$ and $P_2(4, -3)$
    (b) Line l with equation $6x - 4y = 24$
    (c) Line l with parametric equations $x = 5 - 2k$, $y = -3 + k$
    (d) Line l through $P_1(5, -2)$ if its normal axis lies on $M(3, 4)$

13. Find vector, parametric, and symmetric equations (where possible) of the lines l determined by the following pairs of points.
    (a) $A(3, -2, 3)$, $B(4, 0, -2)$ (b) $A(5, 2, -1)$, $B(5, 2, 6)$
    (c) $A(-1, 3, -2)$, $B(5, -3, -3)$ (d) $A(2, 1, 7)$, $B(-6, 1, -4)$

14. Find the midpoints of the line segments AB determined by the points in question (13).

15. Find the direction numbers, cosines, and angles, to the nearest degree, of the lines in question (13).

16. Find the direction numbers, cosines, and angles, to the nearest degree, of the following lines.
    (a) Line l with equations $\dfrac{2x - 5}{3} = \dfrac{y + 2}{-7} = \dfrac{z - 6}{3}$
    (b) Line l with parametric equations $x = 3 - 5t$, $y = 4 - t$, $z = -3$

17. Find the equations of the following lines.
    (a) l through $A(4, 1, -2)$ with direction numbers $(5, 1, -4)$
    (b) l through $A(-2, 3, -1)$ with direction cosines $(\frac{3}{5}, 0, \frac{4}{5})$
    (c) l through $A(5, -1, 2)$ with direction angles $60°, 45°, 120°$

Chapter **5**

PLANES

5.1. The Vector Equation of the Plane

Let a plane I be determined by three noncollinear points A, B, and C, and let P be an arbitrary point on the plane (Figure 5.1). Let PD be parallel to AC and PE be parallel to AB. Then, $\overrightarrow{AD} = k\,\overrightarrow{AB}$ and $\overrightarrow{AE} = m\,\overrightarrow{AC}$ and

$$\overrightarrow{AP} = \overrightarrow{AD} + \overrightarrow{AE},$$

so that

$$\overrightarrow{AP} = k\,\overrightarrow{AB} + m\,\overrightarrow{AC}, \quad k,m \in Re$$

is a vector representation or equation of the plane I determined by the noncollinear points A, B, and C.

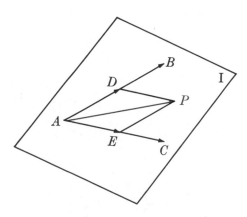

Figure 5.1

Now choose a point O in 3-space. With regard to this point, any point P will have a position vector $\overrightarrow{OP}$ represented by the line segment from O to P; similarly, points A, B, and C will have position vectors $\overrightarrow{OA}$, $\overrightarrow{OB}$, and $\overrightarrow{OC}$, respectively (Figure 5.2).

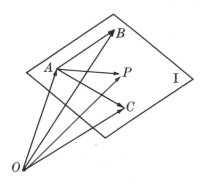

Figure 5.2

Then,

$$\overrightarrow{OP} = \overrightarrow{OA} + \overrightarrow{AP}$$
$$= \overrightarrow{OA} + k\,\overrightarrow{AB} + m\,\overrightarrow{AC} \quad (k,m \in Re)$$
$$= \overrightarrow{OA} + k(\overrightarrow{OB} - \overrightarrow{OA}) + m(\overrightarrow{OC} - \overrightarrow{OA}),$$

so that

$$\overrightarrow{OP} = (1 - k - m)\overrightarrow{OA} + k\,\overrightarrow{OB} + m\,\overrightarrow{OC}, \quad k,m \in Re\,,$$

is the positional vector equation of the plane I in terms of the position vectors $\overrightarrow{OA}, \overrightarrow{OB}$, and $\overrightarrow{OC}$ of the points A, B, and C determining I. If we denote vector $\overrightarrow{OP}$ by $\mathbf{r}$, $\overrightarrow{OA}$ by $\mathbf{r}_1$, $\overrightarrow{OB}$ by $\mathbf{r}_2$, and $\overrightarrow{OC}$ by $\mathbf{r}_3$, this equation becomes

$$\mathbf{r} = (1 - k - m)\mathbf{r}_1 + k\,\mathbf{r}_2 + m\,\mathbf{r}_3\,.$$

Example.   Interpret the equation $\mathbf{r} = \frac{1}{3}\mathbf{r}_1 + \frac{1}{3}\mathbf{r}_2 + \frac{1}{3}\mathbf{r}_3$.

Solution: $\mathbf{r}$ is the position vector of a point P on the plane ABC determined by points A, B, and C with position vectors $\mathbf{r}_1, \mathbf{r}_2$, and $\mathbf{r}_3$; P is such that

$$\overrightarrow{AP} = k\,\overrightarrow{AB} + m\,\overrightarrow{AC} \quad \text{with } k = m = \tfrac{1}{3} \text{ (Figure 5.3)}.$$

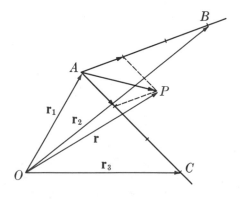

Figure 5.3

If, in the development of the positional vector equation of the plane determined by the noncollinear points A, B, and C, we let $\mathbf{s} = \overrightarrow{AB}$ and $\mathbf{t} = \overrightarrow{AC}$, we obtain

$$\mathbf{r} = \mathbf{r}_1 + k\mathbf{s} + m\mathbf{t}.$$

This equation is another useful form of the vector equation of a plane.

EXERCISE 5.1

1. If noncollinear points A, B, and C have position vectors $\mathbf{r}_1$, $\mathbf{r}_2$, and $\mathbf{r}_3$, locate points P with the position vectors given below.   (Use a diagram.)
   (a) $\mathbf{r} = \frac{1}{2}\mathbf{r}_1 + \frac{1}{4}\mathbf{r}_2 + \frac{1}{4}\mathbf{r}_3$ (b) $\mathbf{r} = \frac{1}{3}\mathbf{r}_1 + \frac{2}{3}\mathbf{r}_2$
   (c) $\mathbf{r} = \frac{4}{5}\mathbf{r}_1 + \frac{1}{5}\mathbf{r}_3$ (d) $\mathbf{r} = 3\mathbf{r}_1 - \mathbf{r}_2 - \mathbf{r}_3$
   (e) $\mathbf{r} = 4\mathbf{r}_1 - 2\mathbf{r}_2 - \mathbf{r}_3$ (f) $\mathbf{r} = \mathbf{r}_1 + 2\mathbf{r}_2 - 2\mathbf{r}_3$
   (g) $\mathbf{r} = \frac{1}{3}\mathbf{r}_1 + \frac{1}{4}\mathbf{r}_2 + \frac{5}{12}\mathbf{r}_3$ (h) $\mathbf{r} = \frac{3}{2}\mathbf{r}_1 - \mathbf{r}_2 + \frac{1}{2}\mathbf{r}_3$

2. Find k and m in the following equations so that $\mathbf{r}$ is the position vector of a point coplanar with A, B, and C.
   (a) $\mathbf{r} = \frac{1}{3}\mathbf{r}_1 + \frac{1}{6}\mathbf{r}_2 + m\mathbf{r}_3$ (b) $\mathbf{r} = 2\mathbf{r}_1 + k\mathbf{r}_2 + 3\mathbf{r}_3$
   (c) $\mathbf{r} = -2\mathbf{r}_1 + k\mathbf{r}_2 + m\mathbf{r}_3$ (d) $\mathbf{r} = 4\mathbf{r}_1 + k\mathbf{r}_2 - m\mathbf{r}_3$

3. Describe the region determined by equation
   $$\mathbf{r} = (1 - k - m)\mathbf{r}_1 + k\mathbf{r}_2 + m\mathbf{r}_3$$
   if (a) $0 \leq k \leq 1$, $0 \leq m \leq 1$, $k, m \in Re$,
   (b) $0 \leq k \leq 1$, $k, m \in Re$,
   (c) $0 \leq m \leq 1$, $k, m \in Re$,
   (d) $0 \leq k \leq 1$, $-1 \leq m \leq 0$, $k, m \in Re$,
   (e) $-1 \leq k \leq 0$, $-1 \leq m \leq 0$, $k, m \in Re$,
   (f) $k \geq 0$, $m \leq 0$, $k, m \in Re$.

5.2. The Parametric Equations of a Plane

We now have the vector equation

$$\mathbf{r} = (1 - k - m)\mathbf{r}_1 + k\mathbf{r}_2 + m\mathbf{r}_3, \qquad k, m \in Re,$$

for the plane I determined by three noncollinear points A, B, and C with position vectors $\mathbf{r}_1$, $\mathbf{r}_2$, and $\mathbf{r}_3$, with respect to a fixed point O. $\mathbf{r}$ is then the position vector of an arbitrary point P on the plane (depending on the real values assigned to the parameters k and m).

Suppose now that we introduce a three-dimensional Cartesian co-ordinate system in the usual way with origin at O (Figure 5.4).

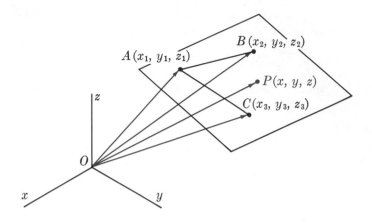

Figure 5.4

Then, point A will have co-ordinates (x_1, y_1, z_1) relative to this co-ordinate system, and its position vector $\mathbf{r}_1$ will be the algebraic vector (x_1, y_1, z_1); thus, for $A, \mathbf{r}_1 = (x_1, y_1, z_1)$, for $B, \mathbf{r}_2 = (x_2, y_2, z_2)$, for $C, \mathbf{r}_3 = (x_3, y_3, z_3)$, for $P, \mathbf{r} = (x, y, z)$. The vector equation for the plane I may be written

$$(x, \, y, \, z) = (1 - k - m)(x_1, \, y_1, \, z_1) + k(x_2, \, y_2, \, z_2) + m(x_3, \, y_3, \, z_3) \, .$$

Example 1. Find the vector equation of the plane I determined by the points $A(-5, 3, 1)$, $B(2, 7, -4)$, and $C(5, 0, -2)$.

Solution: The vector equation may be written

$$(x, \, y, \, z) = (1 - k - m)(-5, \, 3, \, 1) + k(2, \, 7, \, -4) + m(5, \, 0, \, \, -2) \, .$$

This equation may be written in the form

$$
\begin{aligned}
(x, & y, z) \\
&= [-5(1 - k - m), 3(1 - k - m), (1 - k - m)] + (2k, 7k, -4k) + (5m, 0, -2m) \\
&= (-5 + 7k + 10m, 3 + 4k - 3m, 1 - 5k - 3m) \, .
\end{aligned}
$$

In general, the vector equation

$$(x, \, y, \, z) = (1 - k - m)(x_1, \, y_1, \, z_1) + k(x_2, \, y_2, \, z_2) + m(x_3, \, y_3, \, z_3)$$

may be written in the form

$$
\begin{aligned}
(x, y, z) &= [(1 - k - m)x_1, (1 - k - m)y_1, (1 - k - m)z_1] + (kx_2, ky_2, kz_2) \\
&\quad + (mx_3, my_3, mz_3) \\
&= [(1 - k - m)x_1 + kx_2 + mx_3, (1 - k - m)y_1 + ky_2 + my_3, \\
&\quad (1 - k - m)z_1 + kz_2 + mz_3] \, .
\end{aligned}
$$

Identifying corresponding components in these two vectors yields

$$x = (1 - k - m)\,x_1 + kx_2 + mx_3\,,$$
$$y = (1 - k - m)\,y_1 + ky_2 + my_3\,,$$
$$z = (1 - k - m)\,z_1 + kz_2 + mz_3\,, \qquad k,\,m \in Re\,.$$

These are the parametric equations of the plane determined by the three non-collinear points $A\,(x_1, y_1, z_1)$, $B\,(x_2, y_2, z_2)$, and $C\,(x_3, y_3, z_3)$. Note that the equations involve two parameters, k and m. Also note that every point on the plane has co-ordinates

$$(\alpha x_1 + \beta x_2 + \gamma x_3,\ \alpha y_1 + \beta y_2 + \gamma y_3,\ \alpha z_1 + \beta z_2 + \gamma z_3)\,,$$

where $\alpha + \beta + \gamma = 1$.

Example 2. Find the parametric equations of the plane I determined by the points $A\,(-5, 3, 1)$, $B\,(2, 7, -4)$, and $C\,(5, 0, -2)$ (see Example 1).

Solution: Identifying vector components from the vector equation of Example 1 yields the parametric equations of the plane

$$x = -5 + 7k + 10m\,,$$
$$y = 3 + 4k - 3m\,,$$
$$z = 1 - 5k - 3m\,.$$

These can also be obtained by direct substitution in the parametric equations for the plane.

It should be pointed out that any restrictions on k and m in the parametric equations of the plane will give the equations of a *part* of the plane (a point, a line, a region, etc.).

EXERCISE 5.2

1. Find vector and parametric equations of the planes determined by the following sets of points.
   (a) $A\,(0, 0, 0)$, $B\,(1, 4, 9)$, $C\,(2, 2, 5)$
   (b) $A\,(0, 0, 0)$, $B\,(-1, -3, -1)$, $C\,(2, 5, -4)$
   (c) $A\,(1, 0, 0)$, $B\,(0, 1, 0)$, $C\,(0, 0, 1)$
   (d) $A\,(0, 0, 3)$, $B\,(0, -2, 0)$, $C\,(5, 0, 0)$
   (e) $A\,(5, 0, 0)$, $B\,(3, 2, -1)$, $C\,(4, 4, 0)$
   (f) $A\,(-1, 3, -1)$, $B\,(0, 2, 0)$, $C\,(3, -1, 2)$
   (g) $A\,(2, 4, 3)$, $B\,(2, -1, 5)$, $C\,(2, 0, 6)$

2. Describe the location of the planes with the following parametric equations.

(a) $x = -5$
$y = 4 + k + m$
$z = 1 - 2k - m$

(b) $x = 4 - k + 2m$
$y = 3$
$z = -2 + k - m$

(c) $x = -2 + 3k - 4m$
$y = 3 - 2k - m$
$z = 0$

3. Find the parametric equations of the planes through the point $A(x_1, y_1, z_1)$ and

(a) parallel to the yz-plane,
(b) parallel to the xz-plane,
(c) parallel to the xy-plane.

4. Describe the figure with parametric equations
$$x = (1 - k - m)(4) + k(-3) + m,$$
$$y = (1 - k - m)(-2) + k(5) + m(2),$$
$$z = (1 - k - m)(3) + k(-1) + m(-1),$$
if $k, m \in Re$ and $0 \le k \le 1$, $0 \le m \le 1$.

5.3. The Linear Equation of the Plane

We may obtain the linear equation of the plane in 3-space by making the following observation. A plane I in 3-space (Figure 5.5) determines a unique line l through the origin and perpendicular to I; we call this line the normal axis of I. The normal axis has the direction of vector $\overrightarrow{OM}$ joining the origin O to point $M(a, b, c)$ on l.

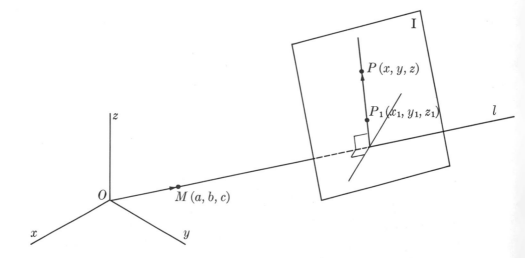

Figure 5.5

A particular plane in 3-space is thus determined when we know a point $P_1(x_1, y_1, z_1)$ on the plane and the direction of the normal axis. (This is known when we know a point $M(a, b, c)$ on the normal axis.) We obtain an equation for the plane by noting that, if $P(x, y, z)$ is any point on the plane, $P \neq P_1$, then vector $\overrightarrow{P_1P}$ is perpendicular to vector $\overrightarrow{OM}$.

Theorem. Let plane I be determined by

(i) point $P_1(x_1, y_1, z_1)$ on I ,

(ii) point $M(a, b, c)$ on l, the normal axis of I .

Then I has the equation

$$ax + by + cz = ax_1 + by_1 + cz_1 .$$

Proof: Let $P(x, y, z)$ be any point on I, $P \neq P_1$. Then

$$\overrightarrow{P_1P} = (x - x_1, y - y_1, z - z_1)$$

is perpendicular to

$$\overrightarrow{OM} = (a, b, c) .$$

But $\overrightarrow{OM} \perp \overrightarrow{P_1P}$ if and only if

$$\overrightarrow{OM} \cdot \overrightarrow{P_1P} = 0 .$$

$$(a, b, c) \cdot (x - x_1, y - y_1, z - z_1) = 0 ;$$

that is,

$$ax - ax_1 + by - by_1 + cz - cz_1 = 0 ,$$

or

$$ax + by + cz = ax_1 + by_1 + cz_1 .$$

Note that the equation of a plane is of the form

$$ax + by + cz = d , \quad a, b, c, d \in Re ,$$

where (a, b, c) is a vector perpendicular to the plane.

Example 1. Find the equation of the plane perpendicular to the vector $\mathbf{v} = (2, -3, -3)$ and containing the point $P_1(1, 1, 2)$.

Solution:

First Method: Let $P(x, y, z)$ be any point on the plane, $P \neq P_1$. Then $\overrightarrow{P_1P} = (x - 1, y - 1, z - 2)$ is perpendicular to $\mathbf{v} = (2, -3, -3)$.

$$(2, -3, -3) \cdot (x - 1, y - 1, z - 2) = 0 ;$$

that is,

$$2x - 2 - 3y + 3 - 3z + 6 = 0$$

or

$$2x - 3y - 3z = -7 .$$

Second Method: Since the vector $\mathbf{v} = (2, -3, -3)$ is perpendicular to the plane, the plane has an equation of the form

$$2x - 3y - 3z = d\,.$$

Since $P_1(1, 1, 2)$ lies on the plane, we have

$$2\,(1) - 3\,(1) - 3\,(2) = d\,.$$

Thus,
$$d = -7\,.$$

The required equation is $2x - 3y - 3z = -7$, as before.

It is sometimes useful to choose as the point P_1 on the plane I the point N of intersection of the plane and its normal axis (Figure 5.6). N will have co-ordinates (ka, kb, kc), since $\overrightarrow{ON} = k\overrightarrow{OM}$ for some real number k. Then, if $P(x, y, z)$ is any different point on I,

$$\overrightarrow{P_1P} = (x - ka, y - kb, z - kc)$$
and
$$\overrightarrow{OM} \perp \overrightarrow{P_1P}$$
so that
$$(a, b, c) \cdot (x - ka, y - kb, z - kc) = 0\,,$$

and this equation yields
$$ax + by + cz = k\,(a^2 + b^2 + c^2)$$

as an alternative form of the equation of the plane.

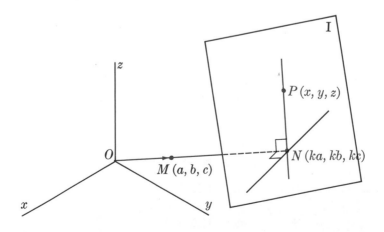

Figure 5.6

When the equation of the plane is written in this form, we can obtain immediately the normal intercept p of the plane, that is, the perpendicular distance from the origin to the plane, or the distance cut off on the normal axis by the plane. This distance is the length of vector $\overrightarrow{ON}$ (equivalently the length of line segment ON), so that

$$p = |\overrightarrow{ON}| = |k|\sqrt{a^2 + b^2 + c^2}.$$

Example 2.   Find the equation of the plane perpendicular to the vector $(2, -1, 3)$ and with normal intercept 5 (two answers).

Solution: We may write the equation of the plane in the form

$$2x - y + 3z = k(4 + 1 + 9)$$
$$= 14k.$$

This plane has normal intercept $|k|\sqrt{14}$ and so

$$|k|\sqrt{14} = 5.$$
$$k\sqrt{14} = 5 \quad \text{or} \quad -5.$$
$$14k = 5\sqrt{14} \quad \text{or} \quad -5\sqrt{14}.$$

The required equations are $2x - y + 3z = 5\sqrt{14}$ and $2x - y + 3z = -5\sqrt{14}$.

Example 3.   The plane I has equation $2x + y - 5z = 16$; find

(a) a vector perpendicular to I,

(b) a point on the normal axis l of I,

(c) the point of intersection of l and I,

(d) the distance from O to I.

Solution:

(a) Vector $(2, 1, -5)$ is perpendicular to I.

(b) Point $M(2, 1, -5)$ lies on the normal axis l.

(c) Writing $2x + y - 5z = 16$ in the form $ax + by + cz = k(a^2 + b^2 + c^2)$, we obtain

$$2x + y - 5z = \tfrac{16}{30}(2^2 + 1^2 + (-5)^2),$$

so that $k = \tfrac{8}{15}$. Then the point of intersection N of I and l is such that $\overrightarrow{ON} = \tfrac{8}{15}\overrightarrow{OM}$; thus N has co-ordinates $(\tfrac{16}{15}, \tfrac{8}{15}, -\tfrac{8}{3})$.

(d) The distance from O to I is $|k|\sqrt{a^2 + b^2 + c^2}$, that is, in this example, $\tfrac{8}{15}\sqrt{30}$.

Example 4. Find the distance from the point $Q(4, -1, 7)$ to the plane I, whose equation is

$$2x + y - 5z = 16.$$

Solution:

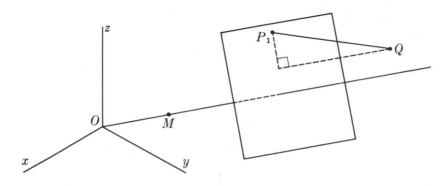

If P_1 is a point on I, the required distance is the projection of the vector $\overrightarrow{QP_1}$ on a vector perpendicular to I; $\overrightarrow{OM} = (2, 1, -5)$ is such a vector.

It is a simple matter to find the co-ordinates of a point P_1 on I; assign y and z arbitrary values and solve for x. If $y = z = 0$, then $x = 8$, so that $(8, 0, 0)$ may be taken as co-ordinates for P_1. Then $\overrightarrow{QP_1} = (4, 1, -7)$ and

$$\text{required distance} = \text{projection of } \overrightarrow{QP_1} \text{ on } \overrightarrow{OM}$$
$$= \frac{|(4, 1, -7) \cdot (2, 1, -5)|}{|(2, 1, -5)|}$$
$$= \frac{44}{\sqrt{30}}.$$

EXERCISE 5.3

1. Find the equations of the planes perpendicular to the given vectors **v** and passing through the given points P_1.
   - (a) $\mathbf{v} = (5, 5, 1)$, $P_1(1, 1, 5)$
   - (b) $\mathbf{v} = (0, 1, 2)$, $P_1(3, -1, 4)$
   - (c) $\mathbf{v} = (5, 2, 0)$, $P_1(-3, 1, 5)$
   - (d) $\mathbf{v} = (2, 0, 0)$, $P_1(3, 3, 1)$
   - (e) $\mathbf{v} = (4, 2, -1)$, $P_1(1, 0, 1)$
   - (f) $\mathbf{v} = (-3, -2, 2)$, $P_1(5, 0, 2)$
   - (g) $\mathbf{v} = (3, 3, -4)$, $P_1(0, 0, 0)$
   - (h) $\mathbf{v} = (4, 0, 0)$, $P_1(0, 0, 0)$
   - (i) $\mathbf{v} = (3, 5, -2)$, $P_1(1, 1, 1)$
   - (j) $\mathbf{v} = (0, -1, 0)$, $P_1(5, 0, 4)$

2. Find the equations of the planes perpendicular to the following vectors and with the given normal intercepts (two solutions for each).
   - (a) $(0, 2, 0)$, 4
   - (b) $(-3, 0, 0)$, 2
   - (c) $(5, 0, -3)$, 3
   - (d) $(0, 5, -2)$, $\frac{1}{2}$
   - (e) $(3, -3, 1)$, $\sqrt{3}$
   - (f) $(2, -3, -5)$, π

3. Find the equations of the planes which meet their normal axes in the following points.

   (a) $(2, 2, 3)$ (b) $(-4, 3, 0)$ (c) $(4, -1, -3)$

4. Find the points of intersection with their normal axes of the planes with the following equations.

   (a) $2x - 3y + z = 0$ (b) $x + 3y + 4z = 5$ (c) $-x + 3y + z = 10$
   (d) $5x - y - z = 16$ (e) $-2x + 3y - z = 24$ (f) $3x - y + 4z = -16$

5. Find the distance from the origin to the planes in question (4).

6. Prove that the distance from the origin to the plane whose equation is $ax + by + cz = d$ is

$$\frac{|d|}{\sqrt{a^2 + b^2 + c^2}}.$$

7. Find the distance from the following points Q to the plane whose equation is given.

   (a) $Q(4, 0, 0)$, $3x - 2y + z = 0$ (b) $Q(1, 1, 0)$, $2x - 3y + z = 6$
   (c) $Q(-1, 2, 4)$, $2x + 5y - 3z = 30$ (d) $Q(2, 2, -3)$, $x + 4y - z = 16$
   (e) $Q(0, 4, -3)$, $-x - 2y + 3z = 12$ (f) $Q(-1, 5, -1)$, $2x - 3y - 4z = 24$

8. Prove that the distance from the point $Q(x_1, y_1, z_1)$ to the plane whose equation is $ax + by + cz = d$ is

$$\frac{|ax_1 + by_1 + cz_1 - d|}{\sqrt{a^2 + b^2 + c^2}}.$$

9. Using the formula

$$\frac{|ax_1 + by_1 + cz_1 - d|}{\sqrt{a^2 + b^2 + c^2}}$$

   for the distance from the point $Q(x_1, y_1, z_1)$ to the plane with equation $ax + by + cz = d$, verify your answers in questions (6) and (7).

5.4. Sketching Planes in Three-Space

Recall that, through any three distinct noncollinear points, there is a unique plane. To graph $ax + by + cz = d$, we find three distinct noncollinear points whose co-ordinates satisfy the given equation and use the triangle formed by the line segments joining these points to indicate the entire plane they determine.

Example 1. Graph the equation $x + 2y + 3z = 6$.

Solution: All we need do is find three noncollinear points on the locus. In this example, we can proceed by finding the points where the locus meets the co-ordinate axes. We proceed as follows.

(i) Let $y = z = 0$ in the given equation; this leaves $x = 6$, and thus $(6, 0, 0)$ is a point on the locus which is also on the x-axis, and hence is the point of intersection with the x-axis.

(ii) Let $x = z = 0$; this leaves $2y = 6$ or $y = 3$, and so $(0, 3, 0)$ is the point of intersection with the y-axis.

(iii) Let $x = y = 0$; this leaves $3z = 6$ or $z = 2$ and so $(0, 0, 2)$ is the point of intersection with the z-axis.

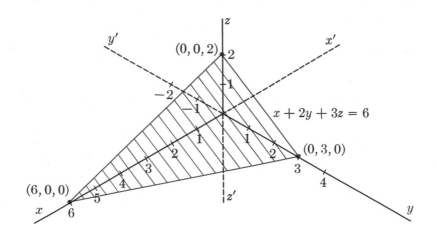

Figure 5.7

These three points cannot be collinear (why not?), and the triangle joining them may be used to represent the plane of the given equation (Figure 5.7).

Example 2. Draw the graph of the equation $x + 2y + 3z = 0$.

Solution: Note that here the constant term is zero; this means that $(0, 0, 0)$ is a point of the locus; that is, the plane passes through the origin. In this case, there is only one point of intersection with the axes. Here we need to find two additional points. These may be determined by assigning values to, say, y and z, and solving for x.

(i) Let $y = -3$, $z = 2$; then $x = 0$.

(ii) Let $y = 0$, $z = 2$; then $x = -6$.

Then $(0, -3, 2)$ and $(-6, 0, 2)$ together with $(0, 0, 0)$ are three points which determine the plane (Figure 5.8).

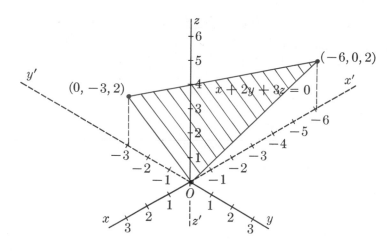

Figure 5.8

Example 3.   Sketch the plane whose equation is $x + 2y = 4$.

Solution: Note that this equation does not contain a term in z (or contains the term $0z$ if you prefer); hence, z is unrestricted in value, and if (x_1, y_1) is a number pair such that $x_1 + 2y_1 = 4$, then (x_1, y_1, z), *for any* z, will represent a point on the required plane.   The plane is parallel to the z-axis and intersects the xy-co-ordinate plane in the line $x + 2y = 4$, $z = 0$ (Figure 5.9).

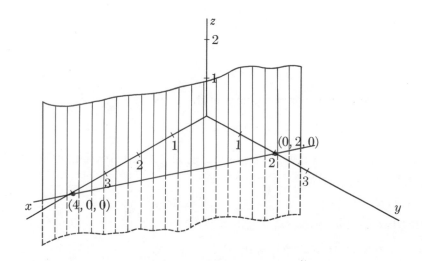

Figure 5.9

EXERCISE 5.4

1. Draw triangles representing the graphs of the following equations.

   (a) $4x + y + 3z = 12$ (b) $3x - y + z = 6$

   (c) $2x - y - 2z - 4 = 0$ (d) $x = 5$

   (e) $3z - 5 = 0$ (f) $6x + y - z - 6 = 0$

   (g) $3x - 2y - z + 6 = 0$ (h) $x + y = 4$

   (i) $y - z = 6$ (j) $x + 2z - 8 = 0$

2. Use vectors to prove that the plane whose equation is $x + 2y = 4$ is parallel to the z-axis.

3. Prove that the plane whose equation is $by + cz = d$ is parallel to the x-axis.

5.5. Systems of One and Two Linear Equations in x, y, and z

In the next chapter, we shall consider the problem of finding the solution of a system of linear equations. In Sections 5.5, 5.6, and 5.7, we merely point out the possible representations in 3-space of systems of linear equations of the form $ax + by + cz = d$ and their solution sets.

One Equation

We have already seen that a single equation of the form

$$ax + by + cz = d$$

represents a plane in 3-space perpendicular to the vector (a, b, c). The solution set of the single equation is the infinite set of triples (x_1, y_1, z_1) of real numbers such that

$$ax_1 + by_1 + cz_1 = d \ ;$$

these are the co-ordinates of the points in the plane.

Two Equations

A system of two linear equations in x, y, and z representing planes may have the following representations in 3-space.

   (i) a single plane

   (ii) two distinct parallel planes ~~ratio of A:B:C's otherwise~~

   (iii) two distinct intersecting planes

These three possibilities are illustrated in Figure 5.10.

In the first situation, the equations must have the form

$$ax + by + cz = d$$

and

$$kax + kby + kcz = kd, \quad k \neq 0.$$

These equations are equivalent; the solution set consists of an infinite number of triples (x_1, y_1, z_1) of real numbers such that

$$ax_1 + by_1 + cz_1 = d.$$

In the second situation, the planes would both be perpendicular to the same vector (the normal axis to both planes), and so would have equations of the form

$$ax + by + cz = d,$$
$$kax + kby + kcz = e, \quad \text{where } k \neq 0 \text{ and } e \neq kd.$$

In this case, the solution set is the null set, since any triple (x_1, y_1, z_1) of real numbers such that

$$ax_1 + by_1 + cz_1 = d$$

would be such that

$$kax_1 + kby_1 + kcz_1 = kd \neq e$$

and so would not satisfy the second equation.

In the third situation, the planes would not be perpendicular to the same vector, and so would have equations of the form

$$a_1x + b_1y + c_1z = d_1,$$
$$a_2x + b_2y + c_2z = d_2,$$

with $(a_1, b_1, c_1) \neq k(a_2, b_2, c_2)$.   In this case, the two planes intersect in a line, and so the solution set of the system of two equations is the infinite set of triples (x_1, y_1, z_1) of real numbers representing points on this line of intersection.

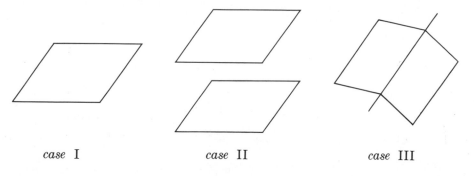

case I   *case* II   *case* III

Figure 5.10

Example 1.   Describe the solution sets of the following systems of equations.

(a) $x - 2y + z = 3$ (b) $x - 2y + z = 3$ (c) $x - 2y + z = 3$

$\ \ 4x - 8y + 4z = 12$ $\ \ x - 2y + z = 8$ $\ \ x - 2y + 2z = 3$

Solution:

(a) The two equations are equivalent; their solution set is the infinite set of triples (x_1, y_1, z_1) of real numbers such that $x_1 - 2y_1 + z_1 = 3$. These are the co-ordinates of the points on the plane whose equation is $x - 2y + z = 3$.

(b) The two equations represent distinct planes perpendicular to the vector $(1, -2, 1)$; these planes are parallel and do not intersect. The solution set of the system of equations is the null set.

(c) The equations represent planes perpendicular to the vectors $(1, -2, 1)$ and $(1, -2, 2)$, respectively; these vectors are not collinear, and so the planes are not parallel. The planes intersect in a line and the solution set of the system of equations is the infinite set of triples (x_1, y_1, z_1) representing points on that line. These triples satisfy the two equations simultaneously; thus,

$$x_1 - 2y_1 + z_1 = 3 \,,$$
$$x_1 - 2y_1 + 2z_1 = 3 \,.$$

The result in the last part of Example 1 indicates another way of representing the equations of a line in space.   The line l may be represented algebraically by a pair of linear equations representing planes intersecting in that line.

Example 2.   Find a system of two linear equations representing planes intersecting in the line

$$\frac{x - 2}{3} = \frac{y + 1}{2} = \frac{z - 1}{-4} \,.$$

Solution: We may write these equations as

$$\frac{x - 2}{3} = \frac{y + 1}{2} \quad \text{and} \quad \frac{y + 1}{2} = \frac{z - 1}{-4} \,,$$

that is, as the system

$$2x - 3y = 7 \,,$$
$$2y + z = -1 \,.$$

This is only one such system; there will be an infinite number of systems since each line is the intersection of an infinite number of pairs of planes.

EXERCISE 5.5

Sketch systems of planes represented by the following systems of equations (diagrams such as in Figure 5.10), and describe the solution sets of the systems.

1. $x + 3y - 2z = 4$

2. $2x - 3y = 6$

3. $-x - y + 3z = 2$
   $2x + 2y - 6z = -4$

4. $x + 3y = 2$
   $x + 3y = 3$

5. $x + 3y = 2$
   $y + 3z = 2$

6. $x + y - 3z = 2$
   $4x + y - z = -3$

7. $x + y - 2z = 5$
   $2x + 2y - 4z = 5$

8. $x - y + 2z = 1$
   $4x + 2y - z = 0$

9. $x + 2z = 1$
   $2y - z = 0$

10. $x = 5$
    $3y - 2z = 0$

5.6. Systems of Three Linear Equations in x, y, and z

A system of three linear equations in x, y, and z representing planes may have the following geometric representations in 3-space.

(i)   a single plane

(ii) two distinct parallel planes

(iii) three distinct parallel planes

(iv) three distinct planes intersecting in pairs in a set of three parallel lines

(v)   two distinct planes intersecting in a line

(vi) two parallel planes and a third plane intersecting them in a pair of parallel lines

(vii) three distinct planes intersecting in a straight line

(viii) three distinct planes intersecting in a single point

From examining the above situations, we see that the solution sets of systems of three linear equations (geometrically, the sets of points common to three planes) can represent a plane ((i) above), a line ((v) and (vii) above), a point ((viii) above), or the null set ((ii), (iii), (iv), and (vi) above). These possibilities are illustrated in Figure 5.11. (The number of the diagram corresponds to that of the case listed above.)

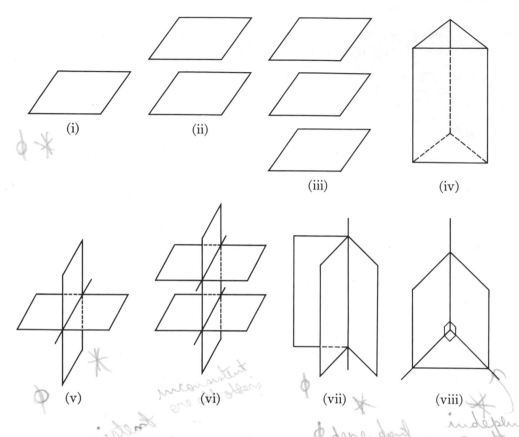

Figure 5.11

Example.   Describe the solution sets of the following systems of equations.

(a) $-x + y + 3z = 2$
    $2x - 2y - 6z = -4$
    $-3x + 3y + 9z = 6$

(b) $-x + y + 3z = 2$
    $2x - 2y - 6z = -4$
    $-x + y + 3z = 4$

(c) $-x + y + 3z = 2$
    $-x + y + 3z = 4$
    $2x - 2y - 6z = 10$

(d) $x = 0$
    $y = 0$
    $x + y = 4$

(e) $-x + y + 3z = 2$
    $2x - 2y - 6z = -4$
    $x - 3y + 5z = 6$

(f) $-x + y + 3z = 2$
    $-x + y + 3z = 4$
    $x - 3y + 5z = 6$

(g) $-x + y + 3z = 2$
    $x - 3y + 5z = 6$
    $-2y + 8z = 8$

(h) $x = 0$
    $y = 0$
    $z = 0$

Solution:

(a) The three equations are equivalent equations; they each represent the same plane. The solution set consists of an infinite number of triples of real numbers representing points on that plane. See (i) above.

(b) The first two equations represent the same plane (equivalent equations); the third equation represents a plane parallel to the first. The solution set is the null set. See (ii) above.

(c) The three equations represent three distinct parallel planes; the solution set is the null set. See (iii) above.

(d) The first equation represents the yz-co-ordinate plane; the second represents the xz-co-ordinate plane; the third equation represents a plane parallel to the z-axis. The three planes meet in pairs in parallel lines; the solution set of the system is the null set. See (iv) above.

(e) The first two equations represent the same plane (equivalent equations); the third equation represents a plane which is not parallel to the first, since $(1, -3, 5) \neq k(-1, 1, 3)$. The two planes intersect in a line; the solution set consists of all triples of real numbers representing points on that line. See (v) above.

(f) The first two equations represent distinct parallel planes; the third represents a plane not parallel to these, which therefore intersects them in two parallel lines. The solution set is the null set. See (vi) above.

(g) The first two equations represent distinct nonparallel planes which intersect in a line l; the third equation is formed by adding corresponding members of the first two equations. Hence, any triple of real numbers that satisfies the first two equations will also satisfy the third. The third equation must then represent a plane through the line of intersection l. The solution set is the infinite set of triples of real numbers representing points on the line l. See (vii) above.

(h) The three equations represent, respectively, the yz-, xz-, and xy-co-ordinate planes. These planes intersect in a single point, the origin. The solution set of the system of equations consists of the single point $(0, 0, 0)$. See (viii) above.

EXERCISE 5.6

Sketch the systems of planes represented by the following systems of equations (diagrams such as in Figure 5.11), and describe the solution sets of the systems.

1. $-x + y - 2z = 0$
    $x - y + 2z = 0$
    $3x - y + 4z = -3$

2. $x - 3y + 2z = 2$
    $3x - 9y + 6z = 6$
    $-2x + 6y - 4z = -4$

3. $x - 3y + 2z = 2$
   $3x - 2y + z = -1$
   $-2x + 6y - 4z = -4$

4. $x - 3y + 2z = 2$
   $-2x + 6y - 4z = 4$
   $3x - 2y + z = -1$

5. $4x - y - z = 2$
   $2x + y + 2z = 4$
   $4x + 2y + 4z = 8$

6. $y = 0$
   $z = 0$
   $y + z = 4$

7. $2x + y + z = 5$
   $3x + 2y + z = 7$
   $5x + 3y + 2z = 12$

8. $x = 3$
   $y = 4$
   $x + y = 12$

9. $x = 3$
   $y = 4$
   $x + y = 7$

10. $3x - 2y - z = -4$
    $-x - 2y + z = -2$
    $2x + 3y - z = 5$
    (Hint: Try $(1, 2, 3)$ as a solution.)

11. $x - y - z = -1$
    $4x + 2y + z = 11$
    $-3x - 3y - 2z = -12$
    (Hint: Try $(2, 0, 3)$ as a solution)

12. $2x - y - z = -3$
    $x + 2y - z = -1$
    $3x + y - 2z = -4$
    (Hint: Try $(1, 1, 4)$ as a solution.)

5.7. Systems of More Than Three Linear Equations in x, y, and z

We shall not attempt to spell out here all the various possibilities of geometric representations of systems of four, five, etc., linear equations in x, y, and z. Some of the possibilities will be considered in Exercise 5.7.

We emphasize that, if the system is represented geometrically by a set of planes that have no common point, then the system has no solution.   The solution set is the null set.   If the planes have a single point in common, the system has a unique solution.   The only other possibility is that the planes have an infinite number of points in common; the corresponding system of equations has an infinite number of elements in its solution set.

EXERCISE 5.7

1. Use diagrams to indicate the planes represented by systems of four linear equations in x, y, and z if the systems have
   (a) no solution,
   (b) a unique solution,
   (c) an infinite number of solutions.

   List as many situations as possible.   (Hint: four identical planes for (c), two pairs of equivalent parallel planes in (a), etc.)

2. Write a system of equations corresponding to each diagram in question (1).

Chapter Summary

Vector equation of a plane · Parametric equations of a plane (from the vector equation) · The linear equation of the plane · Sketching planes in 3-space · Systems of linear equations in x, y, and z

REVIEW EXERCISE 5

1. If noncollinear points A, B, and C have position vectors $\mathbf{r}_1$, $\mathbf{r}_2$, and $\mathbf{r}_3$, locate points P with the following position vectors (use a diagram).

   (a) $\mathbf{r} = \frac{1}{3}\mathbf{r}_1 + \frac{1}{3}\mathbf{r}_2 + \frac{1}{3}\mathbf{r}_3$

   (b) $\mathbf{r} = \mathbf{r}_1 - 2\mathbf{r}_2 + 2\mathbf{r}_3$

   (c) $\mathbf{r} = \frac{1}{2}\mathbf{r}_1 + \frac{1}{2}\mathbf{r}_3$

   (d) $\mathbf{r} = \frac{4}{3}\mathbf{r}_1 - \mathbf{r}_2 + \frac{2}{3}\mathbf{r}_3$

2. Describe the region with equation

   $$\mathbf{r} = (1 - k - m)\mathbf{r}_1 + k\mathbf{r}_2 + m\mathbf{r}_3$$

   if (a) $0 \le k \le 1$, $0 \le m \le 1$, $k, m \in Re$,

   (b) $-1 \le k \le 0$, $0 \le m \le 1$, $k, m \in Re$.

3. Find vector and parametric equations of the planes determined by the following sets of points.

   (a) $A\,(0,0,0)$, $B\,(3,2,-1)$, $C\,(4,-1,1)$

   (b) $A\,(1,2,-1)$, $B\,(3,-1,4)$, $C\,(-2,1,5)$

   (c) $A\,(-3,1,4)$, $B\,(6,-1,-1)$, $C\,(-3,5,0)$

   (d) $A\,(5,-2,0)$, $B\,(-3,0,0)$, $C\,(4,0,-1)$

4. Describe the location of the planes with the following parametric equations.

   (a) $x = -2$, $y = 4 + k + m$, $z = 3 - 2k - m$, $k, m \in Re$

   (b) $x = -2 + 3k - 4m$, $y = 0$, $z = 3 - m - 2k$, $k, m \in Re$ ·

5. Find the equations of the planes perpendicular to the given vectors $\mathbf{v}$ and passing through the given points Q.

   (a) $\mathbf{v} = (1,1,5)$, $Q\,(-2,1,3)$

   (b) $\mathbf{v} = (4,-1,0)$, $Q\,(2,2,5)$

   (c) $\mathbf{v} = (-1,3,-1)$, $Q\,(2,-1,5)$

   (d) $\mathbf{v} = (2,0,5)$, $Q\,(3,-1,4)$

6. Find the equations of the planes perpendicular to the following vectors and with the given normal intercepts (two solutions for each).

   (a) $(5,1,2)$, 3

   (b) $(2,-1,-1)$, $\sqrt{3}$

7. (a) Find the intersection of the plane with equation

   $$x - 3y + 2z = 6$$

   and its normal axis.

   (b) Find the distance from the origin to this plane.

   (c) Sketch the plane in part (a).

8. Find the distance from the point $Q(3, -1, -1)$ to the planes whose equations are

(a) $3x + y - 4z = 24$,

(b) $6x - y - 2z - 12 = 0$,

(c) $x + 3y = 6$,

(d) $x = 2$.

9. Sketch the planes in question (8).

10. Sketch the systems of planes represented by the following systems of equations, and describe the solution sets of the systems.

(a) $3x - y + 2z = 6$

(b) $x - 3y - z = 6$
$3x - 4y + 6z = 12$

(c) $x + y - 2z = 4$
$3x + y - 6z = 12$
$3x + 3y - 6z = 4$

(d) $x + y - 2z = 4$
$3x + y - 6z = 12$
$3x + 3y - 6z = 12$

(e) $x = 0$
$y = 0$
$x + y = 2$

(f) $y = 3$
$z = -2$
$y - z = 5$

Chapter **6**

SYSTEMS OF LINEAR EQUATIONS

6.1. Solution of Independent Systems

We shall use the following classification of systems of linear equations according to their solution sets.

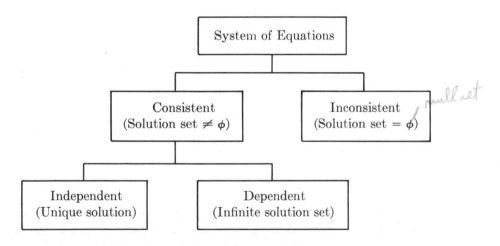

We recall that our *modus operandi* in solving an independent system of equations has been to replace the given system by an equivalent system (one that has the same solution set) a number of times until an equivalent system of the form

$$x = a, \quad y = b, \quad z = c, \quad \text{etc.}$$

is obtained. This system then yields the desired solution set. In this section, we shall review this approach for independent systems, and in the next sections, we shall consider some inconsistent and dependent systems. Notice the orderly approach used in the examples.

161

Example 1. Solve the system of equations

$$2x - 3y = 5, \tag{1}$$
$$5x + 2y = -3. \tag{2}$$

Solution: Multiply both members of equation (1) by 5 and both members of equation (2) by 2. (We shall indicate this procedure hereafter by writing (1) $\times$ 5 and (2) $\times$ 2.)

(1) $\times$ 5 $10x - 15y = 25.$ \hfill (3)

(2) $\times$ 2 $10x + 4y = -6.$ \hfill (4)

Now the system of equations (3) and (4) is equivalent to the system (1) and (2). So is the system consisting of equation (3) and a new equation, (5), obtained by subtracting the members of equation (4) from the corresponding members of equation (3) (this operation is indicated hereafter by the notation (3) − (4)).

$$10x - 15y = 25. \tag{3}$$
$$10x + 4y = -6. \tag{4}$$

(3) − (4) $-19y = 31.$ \hfill (5)

We call the system (3), (5), an equivalent reduced system of equations. From (5), we may read off the value of y, namely, $-\frac{31}{19}$. Knowing the value of y, we may find the corresponding value of x by substitution in (3). (It is usually simpler to substitute in one of the original equations.)

$$10x - 15\left(-\tfrac{31}{19}\right) = 25.$$
$$10x = \tfrac{10}{19}.$$
$$x = \tfrac{1}{19}.$$

Thus

$$x = \tfrac{1}{19}, \qquad y = -\tfrac{31}{19}$$

is a system of equations equivalent to the original one and its solution is obvious. These values may be checked by substitution in one of the original equations, usually one from which a variable has been eliminated. Here, we choose equation (2).

$$5\left(\tfrac{1}{19}\right) + 2\left(-\tfrac{31}{19}\right) = -\tfrac{57}{19} = -3.$$

The solution set consists of the single ordered pair $\left\{\left(\tfrac{1}{19}, -\tfrac{31}{19}\right)\right\}$.

Example 2. Solve the system of equations

$$2x + 5y - 3z = 2, \tag{1}$$
$$3x - 2y + 4z = 1, \tag{2}$$
$$-5x - 3y + 2z = 3. \tag{3}$$

Solution:

   Step 1

$$2x + 5y - 3z = 2. \tag{1}$$

(2) $\times$ 2
$$6x - 4y + 8z = 2. \tag{4}$$

(3) $\times$ 2
$$-10x - 6y + 4z = 6. \tag{5}$$

   Step 2

$$2x + 5y - 3z = 2. \tag{1}$$

(4) $-$ 3 $\times$ (1)
$$-19y + 17z = -4. \tag{6}$$

(5) $+$ 5 $\times$ (1)
$$19y - 11z = 16. \tag{7}$$

   Step 3

$$2x + 5y - 3z = 2. \tag{1}$$

$$-19y + 17z = -4. \tag{6}$$

(6) $+$ (7)
$$6z = 12. \tag{8}$$

Note that we have now reached an equivalent reduced system (1), (6), (8). From (8),

$$z = 2.$$

From (6),

$$-19y + 17\,(2) = -4.$$
$$y = 2.$$

From (1),

$$2x + 5\,(2) - 3\,(2) = 2.$$
$$x = -1.$$

Then

$$x = -1, \quad y = 2, \quad z = 2$$

is a system equivalent to the original and its solution is obvious.   We may check by substitution in equation (2)

$$3\,(-1) - 2\,(2) + 4\,(2) = 1.$$

The solution set consists of a single ordered triple $\{(-1, 2, 2)\}$.

EXERCISE 6.1

Use the method of this section to replace each of the following systems by an equivalent reduced system, and use the latter system to obtain the solution of the original system.

1. $x + y = 8$
   $2x + y = 1$

2. $2x - 3y = -4$
   $2x + y = 4$

3. $x + 2 = y$
   $2x + y = 11$

4. $3x - 5y = -7$
   $2x - 5y = -8$

5. $4x - 5y = -2$
   $2x + 7y = 14$

6. $6x + 7y = 27$
   $5x + 2y = 11$

7. $2x + 5y = 6$

    $5x - 2y = \frac{1}{2}$

8. $y = \frac{x}{2} - 3$

    $3x - 2y = 7$

9. $\frac{4}{3}x + \frac{1}{5}y = 7$

    $\frac{2}{3}x + \frac{5}{4}y = -\frac{9}{4}$

10. $x + y - z = -5$
    $x + y + z = 9$
    $x - y + z = -1$

11. $x + 2y + z = 1$
    $2x - 3y - z = 6$
    $3x + 5y + 4z = 5$

12. $2x - y + z = 5$
    $x + 2y + z = 12$
    $3x + y - 2z = 1$

13. $4x - 2y + 3z = 16$
    $7x - 5y + 4z = 15$
    $2x + 3y + 2z = 21$

14. $2a + 6b - c = -7$
    $11a - b + 15c = -25$
    $5a - 3b + 11c = -13$

15. $l - m + 2n = 5$
    $2l + m - 4n = 0$
    $3l + 2m + 2n = 3$

16. $\dfrac{1}{x} + \dfrac{1}{y} = 4$

    $\dfrac{1}{x} - \dfrac{1}{y} = 8$

17. $\dfrac{2}{3x} + \dfrac{3}{2y} = 5$

    $\dfrac{3}{2x} + \dfrac{2}{3y} = \dfrac{35}{6}$

18. $2x + y - z = 0$

    $3x + 4y - 2z = 0$

    $4x - y + 3z = 0$

19. $\dfrac{3}{x} + \dfrac{2}{y} = 6$

    $\dfrac{4}{x} - \dfrac{1}{y} = -2$

20. $\dfrac{1}{5x} - \dfrac{2}{3y} = 6$

    $\dfrac{3}{5x} + \dfrac{5}{3y} = -1$

21. $3x - y + 2z = 0$

    $3x - 4y + z = 0$

    $2x - 6y + 3z = 0$

6.2. Inconsistent Systems

In Section 6.1, we considered systems of two equations in two variables and of three equations in three variables. The systems studied there were independent; that is, they had a unique solution. In this section, we shall consider some systems which we will find are inconsistent. Some of these will consist of m equations in n variables with $m \neq n$.

It will be noted that our approach in discussing these systems is exactly the same as that used in Section 6.1. We replace the given system of equations by an equivalent reduced system from which we may read off the unique solution (as in Section 6.1), or observe that there is no solution (the system is inconsistent).

Example 1. Examine the system of equations

$$x + 3y = 7, \tag{1}$$
$$x + 3y = -2; \tag{2}$$

that is, find the solution set if it exists, or label the system inconsistent if it does not.

Solution: The equivalent reduced system is

pair of parallel lines

$$x + 3y = 7, \tag{1}$$

$(2) - (1)$ $0y = -9. \tag{3}$

Now there is no real number y for which $0y = -9$; this system is inconsistent.

Example 2.   Examine the system of equations

$$x + 2y - z = 5,$$ (1)
$$3x + 9y - z = 8,$$ (2)
$$2x + 10y + 2z = -2.$$ (3)

Solution:

$$x + 2y - z = 5.$$ (1)

$(2) - 3 \times (1)$ $\qquad\qquad 3y + 2z = -7.$ (4)

$(3) - 2 \times (1)$ $\qquad\qquad 6y + 4z = -12.$ (5)

Then (1), (4), (5) is an equivalent system.

$$x + 2y - z = 5.$$ (1)
$$3y + 2z = -7.$$ (4)

$(5) - 2 \times (4)$ $\qquad\qquad 0z = 2.$ (6)

Now (1), (4), (6) is a reduced system equivalent to the original; it has no solution since there is no real number z such that $0z = 2$.   The original system is inconsistent.

Example 3.   Examine the system

$$x + 3y = 1,$$ (1)
$$3x + y = 5,$$ (2)
$$5x - y = -3.$$ (3)

Solution:

$$x + 3y = 1.$$ (1)

$(2) - 3 \times (1)$ $\qquad\qquad -8y = 2.$ (4)

$(3) - 5 \times (1)$ $\qquad\qquad -16y = -8.$ (5)

Then (1), (4), (5) is an equivalent system.

$$x + 3y = 1.$$ (1)
$$-8y = 2.$$ (4)

$(5) - 2 \times (4)$ $\qquad\qquad 0y = -12.$ (6)

System (1), (4), (6) is the reduced system equivalent to the original.   We can see that this system has no solution; thus the original system is inconsistent.

EXERCISE 6.2

Examine the following systems of equations. Replace each by an equivalent reduced system from which a solution can be read or the system can be recognized as inconsistent.

1. $3x - 2y = 7$
   $6x - 5y = 3$

2. $3x - 2y = 7$
   $6x - 4y = 3$

3. $x + 4y = 6$
   $-2x - 8y = 7$

4. $x + 2y - 3z = -1$
   $3x - y + z = 3$
   $5x + 3y - 5z = 4$

5. $x + 2y - 3z = -1$
   $3x - y + z = 3$
   $2x + y + z = 5$

6. $2x - y + z = 3$
   $3x + 2y - z = 5$
   $x - 4y + 3z = -2$

7. $x - 3y = 6$
   $2x + y = 3$
   $3x - 2y = 8$

8. $x - 3y = 5$
   $2x + y = 3$
   $3x - 2y = 8$

9. $2x + 3y = 5$
   $3x - 2y = -2$
   $-4x + 7y = 6$

10. $x + 3y - 2z = 7$
    $2x - y - z = 3$
    $3x + 2y - 3z = -5$
    $5x - y - 2z = 2$

11. $x + 2y - z = 3$
    $2x + y - 4z = 5$
    $x + 4y - 2z = -2$
    $2x - y - 3z = -3$

12. $x + 2y - z = 3$
    $2x - y + 3z = -1$
    $x - 4y + 2z = -2$
    $2x + 5y = 4$

13. $x + 2y = 4$
    $3x - y = 7$
    $2x - 3y = 3$
    $5x + y = 3$

14. $x + 2y = 4$
    $3x - y = 7$
    $2x - 3y = 3$
    $5x + 3y = 15$

15. $x + y = 7$
    $3x - 2y = 5$
    $2x + 3y = -1$
    $4x - y = 6$

6.3. Dependent Systems

In this section, we shall repeat the technique of Sections 6.1 and 6.2 with consistent systems of equations which we find are dependent. A study of the examples will show the situation that arises with such a system and also the way of indicating the infinite number of solutions possible.

Example 1. Examine the system of equations

$$2x + y = 4, \tag{1}$$
$$4x + 2y = 8. \tag{2}$$

Solution:

$$2x + y = 4. \tag{1}$$
$(2) - 2 \times (1)$
$$0y = 0. \tag{3}$$

This reduced system is equivalent to the original system. Obviously $0y = 0$ is true for all real numbers y. Let y have the real value k; then from (1),

$$2x + k = 4 \,.$$
$$x = \frac{4 - k}{2} \,.$$

The system has an infinite number of solutions; the solution set is

$$\left\{ \left(\frac{4 - k}{2} , \, k \right) \middle| k \in Re \right\} .$$

Particular solutions may be obtained by assigning real values to k; such solutions are $(2, 0)$, $(\frac{3}{2}, 1)$, $(1, 2)$, $(\frac{1}{2}, 3)$, etc. The system is a dependent one.

Example 2. Examine the system of equations

3 intersecting planes

$$x + 3y - 2z = 4 \,, \tag{1}$$
$$4x - y + z = -1 \,, \tag{2}$$
$$3x - 4y + 3z = -5 \,. \tag{3}$$

Solution:

$$x + 3y - 2z = 4 \,. \tag{1}$$
$(2) - 4 \times (1)$
$$-13y + 9z = -17 \,. \tag{4}$$
$(3) - 3 \times (1)$
$$-13y + 9z = -17 \,. \tag{5}$$

Then

$$x + 3y - 2z = 4 \,. \tag{1}$$
$$-13y + 9z = -17 \,. \tag{4}$$
$(5) - (4)$
$$0z = 0 \,. \tag{6}$$

(1), (4), (6) is an equivalent reduced system. Again $0z = 0$ is true for all real numbers z; assigning the real value k to z produces, from (4),

$$-13y + 9k = -17 \,.$$
$$y = \frac{9k + 17}{13} \,.$$

From (1),

$$x + 3 \left(\frac{9k + 17}{13} \right) - 2k = 4 \,.$$
$$x = \frac{1 - k}{13} \,.$$

The solution set is

$$\left\{ \left(\frac{1 - k}{13}, \, \frac{9k + 17}{13} , \, k \right) \middle| k \in Re \right\} .$$

Specific solutions include $(\frac{1}{13}, \frac{17}{13}, 0)$, $(0, 2, 1)$, $(\frac{2}{13}, \frac{8}{13}, -1)$, etc. The system is a dependent one.

Example 3.   Examine the system

$$-9y + 17z = -6.\tag{1}$$

Solution: Whenever a real value is assigned to z, (1) determines a corresponding real value for y; the ordered pairs (y, z) are solutions of (1). The solution set is

$$\left\{\left(\frac{6 + 17k}{9}, k\right)\,\middle|\,k \in Re\right\}.$$

Specific solutions include $(\frac{2}{3}, 0)$, $(\frac{23}{9}, 1)$, etc.   The system is a dependent one.

Example 4.   Examine the system

$$2x + y - 3z = 4,\tag{1}$$
$$5x - 2y + z = 7.\tag{2}$$

Solution:

(1) × 5	$10x + 5y - 15z = 20.$	(3)
(2) × 2	$10x - 4y + 2z = 14.$	(4)

(3), (4) is an equivalent system, as is (3), (5).

	$10x + 5y - 15z = 20.$	(3)
(4) − (3)	$-9y + 17z = -6.$	(5)

We can go no further in eliminating variables from our system of equations, and this is our equivalent reduced system. Thus we look for solutions to this last system.   From Example 3, the solution set of equation (5) is

$$\left\{\left(\frac{6 + 17k}{9}, k\right)\,\middle|\,k \in Re\right\}.$$

Replacing z by k and y by $\dfrac{6 + 17k}{9}$ in (1) yields

$$2x + \frac{6 + 17k}{9} - 3k = 4,$$

or

$$x = \frac{5k + 15}{9}.$$

The solution set of the original system is

$$\left\{\left(\frac{5k + 15}{9}, \frac{6 + 17k}{9}, k\right)\,\middle|\,k \in Re\right\}.$$

Specific solutions include $(\frac{5}{3}, \frac{2}{3}, 0)$, etc.   The system is a dependent one.

Example 5. Examine the system

$$-13y + 11z - 7w = -17 \,. \tag{1}$$

Solution: Whenever arbitrary real values k and l are assigned to z and w, (1) determines a corresponding real value for y; the ordered triples (y, z, w) are solutions of (1). The solution set is

$$\left\{ \left(\frac{17 + 11k - 7l}{13}, k, l \right) \,\middle|\, k, l \in Re \right\} \,.$$

Specific solutions include $(\frac{17}{13}, 0, 0)$, $(\frac{28}{13}, 1, 0)$, $(\frac{10}{13}, 0, 1)$, etc. The system is a dependent one.

Example 6. Examine the system

$$x + 4y - 3z + 2w = 5 \,, \tag{1}$$
$$3x - y + 2z - w = -2 \,. \tag{2}$$

Solution: The system

$$x + 4y - 3z + 2w = 5 \,, \tag{1}$$
$$(2) - 3 \times (1) \qquad -13y + 11z - 7w = -17 \,, \tag{3}$$

is an equivalent one, and no further elimination of variables is possible; it is a reduced system and we must look for solutions of this system. From Example 5, the solution set of (3) is

$$\left\{ \left(\frac{17 + 11k - 7l}{13}, k, l \right) \,\middle|\, k, l \in Re \right\} \,.$$

Replacing w by l, z by k, and y by $\dfrac{17 + 11k - 7l}{13}$ in (1) yields

$$x + 4 \left(\frac{17 + 11k - 7l}{13} \right) - 3k + 2l = 5 \,.$$

$$x = \frac{-3 - 5k + 2l}{13} \,.$$

The solution set is

$$\left\{ \left(\frac{-3 - 5k + 2l}{13}, \frac{17 + 11k - 7l}{13}, k, l \right) \,\middle|\, k, l \in Re \right\} \,.$$

Specific solutions include $(-\frac{3}{13}, \frac{17}{13}, 0, 0)$, $(-\frac{6}{13}, \frac{21}{13}, 1, 1)$, etc. The system is a dependent one.

EXERCISE 6.3

Examine the following systems of equations. State whether they are consistent (independent or dependent) or inconsistent. If a unique solution exists, state the solution. In the case of a dependent system, state the solution set and four specific solutions.

1. $x - 3y = 4$

2. $3x + 2y = -3$

3. $x + 2y - z = 3$

4. $2x - y + 3z = -1$

5. $x + y - z + w = 5$

6. $x - 3y + 2z - w = -2$

7. $x + 2y = 3$
$2x - y = 2$

8. $x + 2y = 3$
$3x + 6y = 6$

9. $x + 2y = 3$
$3x + 6y = 9$

10. $x - 2y - 2z = 6$
$3x - 4y + z = -1$
$5x - 8y - 3z = 12$

11. $x - 2y - 2z = 6$
$3x - 4y + z = -1$
$5x - 8y - 3z = 11$

12. $x - 2y - 2z = 6$
$3x - 4y + z = -1$
$2x - 5y + 3z = -10$

13. $x - 2y + z = 3$
$2x - y + 3z = 6$

14. $2x + 3y - z = 5$
$x + 5y - 3z = -2$

15. $3x - 2y + 4z = 2$
$5x - y - 2z = -3$

16. $x + 2y - z + 2w = 6$
$3x - y - 2z + 3w = 9$

17. $2x - 3y - z + 5w = 7$
$3x - 2y + 5z - w = -2$

18. $2x + 3y - z - w = 4$
$4x + y - 3z + 2w = -1$

19. $x - y + z + 2w - 3t = 2$
$2x + 3y - z + w - 4t = 5$

Find the general solution and four specific integral solutions (if possible) for the following systems.

20. $2x + 5y = 4$

21. $x + y - 2z = 3$
$2x - y + 3z = 5$

22. $3x + y - 2z = 4$
$2x - y + 4z = 2$

6.4. Systems of Homogeneous Equations

The systems that we have been considering thus far have been mainly systems of linear nonhomogeneous equations. A linear homogeneous equation in x and y is one of the form

$$3x + 2y = 0 ;$$

a linear homogeneous equation in x, y, and z is one of the form

$$3x + 2y - z = 0 .$$

A linear homogeneous equation in certain variables involves only first powers of these variables; the constant term is 0. The equations

$$3x + 2y = 5 \quad \text{and} \quad 3x + 2y - z = -2$$

are linear nonhomogeneous equations.

A system of linear homogeneous equations, such as

(i) $x - 3y = 0,$ (ii) $2x + y - z = 0,$ (iii) $x + 2y - z = 0,$
      $2x + y = 0,$ $3x - y + 4z = 0,$ $3x - y + 5z = 0,$
                                                                                      $4x + y + 2z = 0,$

is never inconsistent because $(0, 0)$ is a solution of (i), and $(0, 0, 0)$ is a solution of (ii) and (iii).   The only question we are concerned with in such a system is whether it is independent or dependent.   This is determined using the technique of the preceding sections.

Example 1.   Examine the system

$$x - 3y = 0, \tag{1}$$
$$2x + y = 0. \tag{2}$$

Solution:

$$x - 3y = 0. \tag{1}$$
(2) $- 2 \times$ (1) $$7y = 0. \tag{3}$$

The only real value of y for which $7y = 0$ is 0.   Replacement of y by this value in (1) yields

$$x - 3(0) = 0.$$
$$x = 0.$$

Thus $(0, 0)$ is the only solution; the system is independent.

Example 2.   Examine the system

$$x - 3y = 0, \tag{1}$$
$$-3x + 9y = 0. \tag{2}$$

Solution:

$$x - 3y = 0. \tag{1}$$
(2) $+ 3 \times$ (1) $$0y = 0. \tag{3}$$

Now $0y = 0$ for all real values of y.   Replacing y by k in (1) yields

$$x - 3k = 0,$$
$$x = 3k.$$

The solution set is

$$\{ (3k, k) \mid k \in Re \}.$$

Note that this set includes the particular solution $(0, 0)$.   The system is dependent.

Example 3.   Examine the system

$$x + 3y - 5z = 0, \tag{1}$$
$$2x + y - 6z = 0. \tag{2}$$

Solution:

$$x + 3y - 5z = 0. \tag{1}$$
(2) − 2 × (1)
$$-5y + 4z = 0. \tag{3}$$

(1), (3) is an equivalent reduced system.   Now in (3), any real value k may be assigned to z and a corresponding real value obtained for y.

$$-5y + 4k = 0.$$
$$y = \tfrac{4}{5}k.$$

Replacing z by k and y by $\tfrac{4}{5}k$ in (1) yields

$$x + 3\left(\frac{4k}{5}\right) - 5k = 0.$$
$$x = \tfrac{13}{5}k.$$

The solution set of the original system is

$$\{ (\tfrac{13}{5}k, \tfrac{4}{5}k, k) \mid k \in Re \}.$$

Note that this includes the solution $(0, 0, 0)$.   The system is dependent.

Example 4.   Examine the system

$$x - 3y + 2z = 0, \tag{1}$$
$$3x + y - 4z = 0, \tag{2}$$
$$5x + y - 3z = 0. \tag{3}$$

Solution:

$$x - 3y + 2z = 0. \tag{1}$$
(2) − 3 × (1)
$$10y - 10z = 0. \tag{4}$$
(3) − 5 × (1)
$$16y - 13z = 0. \tag{5}$$

(1), (4), (5) is an equivalent system.

$$x - 3y + 2z = 0. \tag{1}$$
$\tfrac{1}{10}$ × (4)
$$y - z = 0. \tag{6}$$
(5) − 16 × (6)
$$3z = 0. \tag{7}$$

From this equivalent reduced system, we see that the only solution is $(0, 0, 0)$; the original system is independent.

Example 5.   Examine the system

$$x - 3y + 2z = 0, \qquad (1)$$
$$2x - 6y + 4z = 0, \qquad (2)$$
$$-3x + 9y - 6z = 0. \qquad (3)$$

Solution:

$$x - 3y + 2z = 0. \qquad (1)$$

$(2) - 2 \times (1)$ $\qquad\qquad\qquad 0y + 0z = 0. \qquad (4)$

$(3) + 3 \times (1)$ $\qquad\qquad\qquad\quad 0z = 0. \qquad (5)$

(1), (4), (5) is an equivalent reduced system.   From (5), we see that z is an arbitrary real number, say l; from (4), we see that y is also arbitrary, say k.   Replacing y by k and z by l in (1) yields

$$x - 3k + 2l = 0.$$
$$x = 3k - 2l.$$

The solution set is

$$\{ (3k - 2l, k, l) \mid k, l \in Re \}.$$

The system is dependent.

EXERCISE 6.4

Examine the following systems of homogeneous equations.   Classify them as independent or dependent, and in each case give the solution set.

1. $x - 5y = 0$

2. $3x - 2y + z = 0$

3. $x - 2y - z + 3w = 0$

4. $x + 5y = 0$
    $3x - 2y = 0$

5. $x + 3y = 0$
    $3x + 9y = 0$

6. $x - 2y = 0$
    $3x + y = 0$

7. $x - 2y + z = 0$
    $3x - 6y + z = 0$

8. $x - 2y + z = 0$
    $3x - 6y + 3z = 0$

9. $x - 4y - 3z = 0$
    $3x - y + 2z = 0$

10. $x + y - 3z = 0$
    $3x - y + z = 0$
    $4x + 3y - z = 0$

11. $x + 2y - z = 0$
    $3x - y + z = 0$
    $-x - 9y + 5z = 0$

12. $x + 2y - z = 0$
    $-3x - 6y + 3z = 0$
    $2x + 4y - 2z = 0$

13. $x + 2y - z + 3w = 0$
    $3x - y + 4z - 5w = 0$

14. $2x - y + 3z - w = 0$
    $5x - 2y + 2z + w = 0$

15. $2x - y - z + 2w = 0$
    $6x - 3y - 3z + 6w = 0$

16. $3x + 2y - z + w = 0$
    $6x + 4y - 2z + w = 0$

17. $x - 3y - 2z + w = 0$
    $3x - y + 2z - 2w = 0$
    $4x - 3y + z - 3w = 0$

18. $3x - 2y + z + w = 0$
    $2x + 5y - 3z - w = 0$
    $3x + 4y - z + 4w = 0$

6.5. The Augmented Matrix of a System of Equations. Equivalent Matrices

By a real matrix we shall mean simply a rectangular array of real numbers. Then

(i) $\begin{bmatrix} 2 & -1 \\ 3 & 2 \end{bmatrix}$ (ii) $\begin{bmatrix} 3 & \frac{1}{2} & -7 \\ 5 & 0 & 1 \end{bmatrix}$ (iii) $\begin{bmatrix} 0 & \pi & -2 \\ 3 & 1 & \sqrt{2} \\ 4 & 0 & 7 \end{bmatrix}$

(iv) $[3 \ -5]$ (v) $[1 \ \ 0 \ -4]$ (vi) $\begin{bmatrix} 2 \\ 1 \\ 3 \end{bmatrix}$

are called matrices. We enclose the rectangular array of real numbers in square brackets. Matrix (i) contains two rows (across) and two columns (up and down) of real numbers. We call it a 2×2 matrix. Matrix (ii) is a 2×3 matrix (two rows, three columns), and (iii) is a 3×3 matrix (three rows, three columns). Matrices (iv) and (v) are also called row vectors, and matrix (vi) is also called a column vector. In a sense, we can consider matrices as extensions of these row and column vectors. At this point, we stress that a matrix is not a number but simply an array of numbers. Matrices and their properties are studied at greater length in Chapters 9 and 10 of Relations, Transformations and Statistics.

We may associate two matrices with every system of m linear equations in n variables. First, we take the array of coefficients of the variables; this gives us the matrix of coefficients of the system. For example, associated with the system

$$2x - 3y = 5\,,$$
$$4x + y = 6\,,$$

we have

$$\begin{bmatrix} 2 & -3 \\ 4 & 1 \end{bmatrix}$$

as the matrix of coefficents. Now adjoin the constant terms of the system (when written on the right side of the equations) to the coefficients of the variables. The resulting array is called the augmented matrix of the system. For the above system, the augmented matrix is

$$\begin{bmatrix} 2 & -3 & 5 \\ 4 & 1 & 6 \end{bmatrix}.$$

Example 1. Write (a) the matrix of coefficients and (b) the augmented matrix of the system

$$3x - 2y + z = 5\,,$$
$$4x - 2y + 3z = 0\,.$$

Solution:

  (a) The matrix of coefficients is

$$\begin{bmatrix} 3 & -2 & 1 \\ 4 & -2 & 3 \end{bmatrix}.$$

  (b) The augmented matrix is

$$\begin{bmatrix} 3 & -2 & 1 & 5 \\ 4 & -2 & 3 & 0 \end{bmatrix}.$$

Example 2. Write (a) the matrix of coefficients and (b) the augmented matrix of the system

$$2x - y + z = 0,$$
$$4x + 3y - z = 0,$$
$$x + 2y - 5z = 0.$$

Solution:

  (a) The matrix of coefficients is

$$\begin{bmatrix} 2 & -1 & 1 \\ 4 & 3 & -1 \\ 1 & 2 & -5 \end{bmatrix}.$$

  (b) The augmented matrix is

$$\begin{bmatrix} 2 & -1 & 1 & 0 \\ 4 & 3 & -1 & 0 \\ 1 & 2 & -5 & 0 \end{bmatrix}.$$

DEFINITION.   Two matrices are row equivalent if each can be obtained from the other by a sequence of operations of the following types.

   Type 1: The interchange of two rows

   Type 2: The multiplication of a row by a nonzero real number

   Type 3: The addition to the elements of one row of a multiple of the corresponding elements of another row

Note that these are the same types of operations that we performed in changing a given system of equations to an equivalent reduced system.

Example 3.   Find the matrices equivalent to

$$\begin{bmatrix} 2 & -1 \\ 2 & 5 \end{bmatrix},$$

by

  (a) interchanging the two rows,

  (b) multiplying row (2) by 5,

  (c) adding 3 × row (1) to row (2).

Solution:

(a) $\begin{bmatrix} 2 & -1 \\ 3 & 5 \end{bmatrix}$ $\xrightarrow{\text{Interchange rows.}}$ $\begin{bmatrix} 3 & 5 \\ 2 & -1 \end{bmatrix}$.

(b) $\begin{bmatrix} 2 & -1 \\ 3 & 5 \end{bmatrix}$ $\xrightarrow{\text{Multiply row (2) × (5).}}$ $\begin{bmatrix} 2 & -1 \\ 15 & 25 \end{bmatrix}$.

(c) $\begin{bmatrix} 2 & -1 \\ 3 & 5 \end{bmatrix}$ $\xrightarrow{\text{Add 3 × row (1) to row (2).}}$ $\begin{bmatrix} 2 & -1 \\ 3+6 & 5-3 \end{bmatrix}$ $=$ $\begin{bmatrix} 2 & -1 \\ 9 & 2 \end{bmatrix}$.

Example 4. Find the matrix equivalent to

$$\begin{bmatrix} 5 & -1 \\ 2 & 4 \end{bmatrix}$$

by performing *successively* the following operations.

  (i) Multiply row (2) by $\frac{1}{2}$.

  (ii) Add (-5) × row (2) to row (1).

  (iii) Interchange rows.

Solution:

$\begin{bmatrix} 5 & -1 \\ 2 & 4 \end{bmatrix}$ $\xrightarrow{\text{Multiply row (2) × } \frac{1}{2}.}$ $\begin{bmatrix} 5 & -1 \\ 1 & 2 \end{bmatrix}$

$\xrightarrow{\text{Add } (-5) \times \text{row (2) to row (1).}}$ $\begin{bmatrix} 0 & -11 \\ 1 & 2 \end{bmatrix}$

$\xrightarrow{\text{Interchange rows.}}$ $\begin{bmatrix} 1 & 2 \\ 0 & -11 \end{bmatrix}$

Note that the matrices $\begin{bmatrix} 5 & -1 \\ 2 & 4 \end{bmatrix}$ and $\begin{bmatrix} 1 & 2 \\ 0 & -11 \end{bmatrix}$ are equivalent according to the definition.

EXERCISE 6.5

1. Write the matrix of coefficients and the augmented matrix for each of the systems of equations in Exercise 6.3.

2. (a) Write the augmented matrix of the system

$$3x - 2y = 7,$$
$$5x + 2y = 4.$$

   (b) Perform the following operations successively on the matrix from (a).

(i) Interchange two rows.

(ii) Add 4 × row (1) to row (2).

(iii) Multiply row (1) by 6.

Perform successively the following operations to find a matrix equivalent to the given matrix in questions (3) to (11).

(a) Add 3 × row (2) to row (1).

(b) Interchange rows.

(c) Multiply row (2) by 3.

3. $\begin{bmatrix} 2 & -1 \\ 5 & 0 \end{bmatrix}$

4. $\begin{bmatrix} 3 & -3 \\ 1 & 1 \end{bmatrix}$

5. $\begin{bmatrix} 1 & 0 \\ 0 & 1 \end{bmatrix}$

6. $\begin{bmatrix} 4 & 2 & -1 \\ 0 & 1 & 3 \end{bmatrix}$

7. $\begin{bmatrix} 2 & 1 & -2 \\ 4 & 1 & 6 \end{bmatrix}$

8. $\begin{bmatrix} 1 & 1 & 1 \\ 1 & 1 & 1 \end{bmatrix}$

9. $\begin{bmatrix} 3 & -1 & 5 & 0 \\ 2 & 1 & 5 & 2 \end{bmatrix}$

10. $\begin{bmatrix} -3 & 1 & 1 & 2 \\ 0 & 4 & 1 & 5 \end{bmatrix}$

11. $\begin{bmatrix} -1 & 3 & 3 & -4 \\ 2 & 0 & 1 & 3 \end{bmatrix}$

Perform successively the following operations to find a matrix equivalent to the given matrix in question (12) to (14).

(a) Interchange rows (1) and (3).

(b) Multiply row (2) by 2.

(c) Add 3 × row (2) to row (3).

(d) Interchange rows (1) and (2).

12. $\begin{bmatrix} 3 & -1 & 4 \\ 5 & 1 & 2 \\ 0 & 1 & 5 \end{bmatrix}$

13. $\begin{bmatrix} 2 & -1 & 6 \\ 1 & 1 & 2 \\ 5 & 3 & 1 \end{bmatrix}$

14. $\begin{bmatrix} 1 & 3 & -2 & 1 \\ 4 & 1 & 1 & -3 \\ 0 & 1 & 5 & 2 \end{bmatrix}$

Perform successively the following operations to find a matrix equivalent to the augmented matrix in question (15) to (20).

(a) Add (−1) × row (3) to row (1).

(b) Interchange rows (2) and (3).

(c) Multiply row (2) by 4.

(d) Add $\frac{1}{2}$ × row (1) to row (2).

15. $3x - 2y = 7$
    $x + 4y = -1$
    $2x - y = 3$

16. $x - 2y = -3$
    $3x + y = 5$
    $x - y = -1$

17. $x - y = -2$
    $2x + y + 3z = 5$
    $x + 3y - 2z = -1$

18. $x + 5y = 3$
    $-2x + y = -1$
    $3x - 2y = 0$

19. $6x - y = 3$
    $3x + y = -4$
    $2x - 3y = 3$

20. $x + y + 2z = -2$
    $3x - y + 3z = 5$
    $4x - 2y + 5z = -1$

6.6. Row-Reduced Echelon Forms of a Matrix

Example 1.   Perform the following operations successively on the matrix

$$\begin{bmatrix} 3 & -1 & 2 \\ 1 & 5 & -3 \\ -2 & 4 & 1 \end{bmatrix}.$$

   (i) Interchange rows (1) and (2).

   (ii) Add $(-3) \times$ row (1) to row (2).

   (iii) Add $2 \times$ row (1) to row (3).

Solution:

$$\begin{bmatrix} 3 & -1 & 2 \\ 1 & 5 & -3 \\ -2 & 4 & 1 \end{bmatrix} \xrightarrow{\text{Interchange rows (1) and (2).}} \begin{bmatrix} 1 & 5 & -3 \\ 3 & -1 & 2 \\ -2 & 4 & 1 \end{bmatrix}$$

$$\xrightarrow{\text{Add } (-3) \times \text{ row (1) to row (2).}} \begin{bmatrix} 1 & 5 & -3 \\ 0 & -16 & 11 \\ -2 & 4 & 1 \end{bmatrix}$$

$$\xrightarrow{\text{Add } 2 \times \text{ row (1) to row (3).}} \begin{bmatrix} 1 & 5 & -3 \\ 0 & -16 & 11 \\ 0 & 14 & -5 \end{bmatrix}$$

Note that in our resulting equivalent matrix, the first entry in row (1) is 1 and the first entries in the other rows are 0.

Example 2.   Continue with Example 1 by performing successively the following additional operations.

   (i) Multiply row (2) by $-\frac{1}{16}$.

   (ii) Add $(-14) \times$ row (2) to row (3).

Solution:

$$\begin{bmatrix} 1 & 5 & -3 \\ 0 & -16 & 11 \\ 0 & 14 & -5 \end{bmatrix} \xrightarrow{\text{Multiply row (2) by} -\frac{1}{16}.} \begin{bmatrix} 1 & 5 & -3 \\ 0 & 1 & -\frac{11}{16} \\ 0 & 14 & -5 \end{bmatrix}$$

$$\xrightarrow{\text{Add } (-14) \times \text{ row (2) to row (3).}} \begin{bmatrix} 1 & 5 & -3 \\ 0 & 1 & -\frac{11}{16} \\ 0 & 0 & \frac{37}{8} \end{bmatrix}$$

Note that in this matrix, which is equivalent to the original matrix of Example 1, the first nonzero entry in rows (1) and (2) is 1.

Example 3.   Continue the above example by multiplying row (3) by $\frac{8}{37}$.

Solution:

$$\begin{bmatrix} 1 & 5 & -3 \\ 0 & 1 & -\frac{11}{16} \\ 0 & 0 & \frac{37}{8} \end{bmatrix} \xrightarrow{\text{Multiply row (3) by } \frac{8}{37}.} \begin{bmatrix} 1 & 5 & -3 \\ 0 & 1 & -\frac{11}{16} \\ 0 & 0 & 1 \end{bmatrix}$$

The matrix

$$\begin{bmatrix} 1 & 5 & -3 \\ 0 & 1 & -\frac{11}{16} \\ 0 & 0 & 1 \end{bmatrix}$$

is equivalent to the original matrix

$$\begin{bmatrix} 3 & -1 & 2 \\ 1 & 5 & -3 \\ -2 & 4 & 1 \end{bmatrix}$$

and is called a row-reduced echelon form of this matrix.

A row-reduced echelon form of a matrix is an equivalent matrix in which

   (i)   the first nonzero entry in each row is 1,

   (ii)   each row contains more initial zero terms than the preceding rows.

The following matrices are in row-reduced echelon form.

$$\begin{bmatrix} 1 & -3 \\ 0 & 1 \end{bmatrix} \qquad \begin{bmatrix} 1 & -3 & 5 \\ 0 & 0 & 1 \end{bmatrix}$$

$$\begin{bmatrix} 1 & 5 \\ 0 & 1 \\ 0 & 0 \end{bmatrix} \qquad \begin{bmatrix} 1 & 3 & -1 \\ 0 & 1 & 4 \\ 0 & 0 & 1 \end{bmatrix} \qquad \begin{bmatrix} 1 & 5 & 2 \\ 0 & 0 & 1 \\ 0 & 0 & 0 \end{bmatrix}$$

$$\begin{bmatrix} 1 & 0 & 2 & 5 \\ 0 & 0 & 1 & 3 \\ 0 & 0 & 0 & 1 \\ 0 & 0 & 0 & 0 \end{bmatrix}$$

Example 4.   Find a row-reduced echelon form for the matrix

$$\begin{bmatrix} 5 & 7 \\ 4 & 3 \end{bmatrix}.$$

Solution: We may obtain a 1 as the first nonzero entry by multiplying row (1) by $\frac{1}{5}$.   We may accomplish the same result, however, by adding $(-1) \times$ row (2) to row (1).   In this way we avoid introducing fractions unnecessarily.

$$\begin{bmatrix} 5 & 7 \\ 4 & 3 \end{bmatrix} \xrightarrow[\text{Add } (-1) \times \text{row (2) to row (1).}]{} \begin{bmatrix} 1 & 4 \\ 4 & 3 \end{bmatrix}$$

$$\xrightarrow[\text{Add } (-4) \times \text{row (1) to rows (2).}]{} \begin{bmatrix} 1 & 4 \\ 0 & -13 \end{bmatrix}$$

$$\xrightarrow[\text{Multiply row (2) by } -\frac{1}{13}.]{} \begin{bmatrix} 1 & 4 \\ 0 & 1 \end{bmatrix}.$$

Then $\begin{bmatrix} 1 & 4 \\ 0 & 1 \end{bmatrix}$ is a row-reduced echelon form of $\begin{bmatrix} 5 & 7 \\ 4 & 3 \end{bmatrix}.$

Example 5.   Find a row-reduced echelon form for the matrix

$$\begin{bmatrix} 2 & -1 & 5 \\ 3 & 2 & 6 \end{bmatrix}.$$

Solution:

$$\begin{bmatrix} 2 & -1 & 5 \\ 3 & 2 & 6 \end{bmatrix} \xrightarrow[\text{Add } (-1) \times \text{row (1) to row (2).}]{} \begin{bmatrix} 2 & -1 & 5 \\ 1 & 3 & 1 \end{bmatrix}$$

$$\xrightarrow[\text{Interchange rows (1) and (2).}]{} \begin{bmatrix} 1 & 3 & 1 \\ 2 & -1 & 5 \end{bmatrix}$$

$$\xrightarrow[\text{Add } (-2) \times \text{row (1) to row (2).}]{} \begin{bmatrix} 1 & 3 & 1 \\ 0 & -7 & 3 \end{bmatrix}$$

$$\xrightarrow[\text{Multiply row (2) by } -\frac{1}{7}.]{} \begin{bmatrix} 1 & 3 & 1 \\ 0 & 1 & -\frac{3}{7} \end{bmatrix}$$

This is a matrix of the required form.

Example 6.   Find a row-reduced echelon form for the matrix

$$\begin{bmatrix} 1 & -2 & 1 & 3 \\ 2 & 3 & -1 & 4 \\ 4 & -1 & 1 & 12 \end{bmatrix}.$$

Solution:

$$\begin{bmatrix} 1 & -2 & 1 & 3 \\ 2 & 3 & -1 & 4 \\ 4 & -1 & 1 & 12 \end{bmatrix} \xrightarrow[\text{Add } (-2) \times \text{row (1) to row (2).}]{} \begin{bmatrix} 1 & -2 & 1 & 3 \\ 0 & 7 & -3 & -2 \\ 4 & -1 & 1 & 12 \end{bmatrix}$$

$$\xrightarrow[\text{Add } (-4) \times \text{row (1) to row (3).}]{} \begin{bmatrix} 1 & -2 & 1 & 3 \\ 0 & 7 & -3 & -2 \\ 0 & 7 & -3 & 0 \end{bmatrix}$$

$$\xrightarrow[\text{Add } (-1) \times \text{row (2) to row (3).}]{} \begin{bmatrix} 1 & -2 & 1 & 3 \\ 0 & 7 & -3 & -2 \\ 0 & 0 & 0 & 2 \end{bmatrix}$$

Multiply row (2) by $\frac{1}{7}$.
$$\begin{bmatrix} 1 & -2 & 1 & 3 \\ 0 & 1 & -\frac{3}{7} & -\frac{2}{7} \\ 0 & 0 & 0 & 2 \end{bmatrix}$$

Multiply row (3) by $\frac{1}{2}$.
$$\begin{bmatrix} 1 & -2 & 1 & 3 \\ 0 & 1 & -\frac{3}{7} & -\frac{2}{7} \\ 0 & 0 & 0 & 1 \end{bmatrix}$$

This matrix is one of the required form.

It should be pointed out that a row-reduced echelon form of a given matrix is not unique; different sequences of operations may produce different forms. However, these forms will all have the same pattern of initial 1's and 0's in the rows in common. They also will all be equivalent matrices.

Example 7.   Find a row-reduced echelon form of the matrix

$$\begin{bmatrix} 5 & 7 \\ 4 & 3 \end{bmatrix}$$

by using a different sequence of operations from that used in Example 4.

Solution:

$$\begin{bmatrix} 5 & 7 \\ 4 & 3 \end{bmatrix}$$ Multiply row (1) by $\frac{1}{5}$.
$$\begin{bmatrix} 1 & \frac{7}{5} \\ 4 & 3 \end{bmatrix}$$

Add $(-4) \times$ row (1) to row (2).
$$\begin{bmatrix} 1 & \frac{7}{5} \\ 0 & -1\frac{3}{5} \end{bmatrix}$$

Multiply row (2) by $-\frac{5}{13}$.
$$\begin{bmatrix} 1 & \frac{7}{5} \\ 0 & 1 \end{bmatrix}$$

This is a row-reduced echelon form different from that obtained previously, but the two are equivalent matrices.

Any other row-reduced echelon of the matrix in Example 6 will be of the form

$$\begin{bmatrix} 1 & * & * & * \\ 0 & 1 & * & * \\ 0 & 0 & 0 & 1 \end{bmatrix}.$$

EXERCISE 6.6

Find row-reduced echelon forms for the following matrices.

1. $\begin{bmatrix} 1 & 3 \\ 3 & 18 \end{bmatrix}$ 2. $\begin{bmatrix} 2 & 3 \\ 5 & -2 \end{bmatrix}$ 3. $\begin{bmatrix} 1 & 3 \\ 3 & 9 \end{bmatrix}$

4. $\begin{bmatrix} 1 & 3 & -1 \\ 2 & 4 & 5 \end{bmatrix}$ 5. $\begin{bmatrix} 3 & -1 & 2 \\ -1 & 4 & 7 \end{bmatrix}$ 6. $\begin{bmatrix} 2 & -1 & 6 \\ 5 & 2 & 4 \end{bmatrix}$

7. $\begin{bmatrix} 1 & 3 \\ -1 & 4 \\ 6 & 2 \end{bmatrix}$ 8. $\begin{bmatrix} 3 & 2 \\ -4 & 1 \\ 2 & 3 \end{bmatrix}$ 9. $\begin{bmatrix} -2 & 5 \\ 3 & -4 \\ 3 & 6 \end{bmatrix}$

10. $\begin{bmatrix} 1 & -1 & 5 \\ 3 & 1 & 4 \\ -2 & 5 & 2 \end{bmatrix}$ 11. $\begin{bmatrix} 3 & -2 & 4 \\ 2 & 5 & -1 \\ 4 & -9 & 9 \end{bmatrix}$ 12. $\begin{bmatrix} -2 & 3 & 5 \\ 2 & -3 & -5 \\ 5 & 2 & -1 \end{bmatrix}$

13. $\begin{bmatrix} 1 & 3 & -1 & 2 \\ 4 & 2 & -3 & 1 \\ -2 & 6 & 3 & 0 \end{bmatrix}$ 14. $\begin{bmatrix} 2 & -3 & -3 & 0 \\ 4 & 1 & -5 & 2 \\ -3 & 6 & 1 & -1 \end{bmatrix}$ 15. $\begin{bmatrix} 3 & 3 & 0 & 1 \\ -2 & 4 & 1 & -2 \\ 1 & 7 & 1 & -3 \end{bmatrix}$

Find row-reduced echelon forms for the augmented matrices of the following systems of equations.

16. $2x + 5y = 3$
$3x - y = 7$

17. $3x - 2y = 1$
$x + 4y = -3$
$2x - y = 5$

18. $2x + y - 3z = 1$
$4x - 2y + z = -3$
$-3x + y - 4z = 0$

19. $6x - y = 2$
$2x + y = 1$

20. $3x + 2y = -1$
$2x + 5y = 2$
$-x + 2y = -3$

21. $x + 3y - z = 1$
$4x - y + 3z = 0$
$2x - 2y - 3z = -4$

6.7. Application of the Row-Reduced Echelon Form

In this section, we will see that a row-reduced echelon form of the augmented matrix of a system of equations is the augmented matrix of an equivalent reduced system of equations. Further, we shall see how the solution of a system of equations (or the recognition of inconsistency) can be read from the row-reduced echelon matrix.

Example 1.

(a) Write the augmented matrix of the system

$$3x - 2y = 5,$$
$$5x + 3y = 8.$$

(b) Find a row-reduced echelon form of the augmented matrix.

(c) Apply the operations used in (b) to the system of equations to produce an equivalent reduced system of equations.

Solution:

(a) The augmented matrix is

$$\begin{bmatrix} 3 & -2 & 5 \\ 5 & 3 & 8 \end{bmatrix}.$$

We perform (b) and (c) in columns.

(b) Augmented matrix   (c) Original System

$$\begin{bmatrix} 3 & -2 & 5 \\ 5 & 3 & 8 \end{bmatrix}$$

$3x - 2y = 5.$ (1)
$5x + 3y = 8.$ (2)

Step 1.

Multiply row (2) × 3.
$$\begin{bmatrix} 3 & -2 & 5 \\ 15 & 9 & 24 \end{bmatrix}$$

(2) × 3

$3x - 2y = 5.$ (1)
$15x + 9y = 24.$ (3)

Step 2.

Add (-5) × row (1) to row (2).
$$\begin{bmatrix} 3 & -2 & 5 \\ 0 & 19 & -1 \end{bmatrix}$$

(3) − 5 × (1)

$3x - 2y = 5.$ (1)
$0x + 19y = -1.$ (4)

Step 3.

Multiply row (1) × $\frac{1}{3}$ and row (2) × $\frac{1}{19}$.
$$\begin{bmatrix} 1 & -\frac{2}{3} & \frac{5}{3} \\ 0 & 1 & \frac{-1}{19} \end{bmatrix}$$

(1) × $\frac{1}{3}$
(4) × $\frac{1}{19}$

$x - \frac{2}{3}y = \frac{5}{3}.$ (5)
$y = \frac{-1}{19}.$ (6)

We have now reached an equivalent reduced system of equations and a row-reduced echelon form of the augmented matrix. The solution of the original system can now be obtained quite easily.

The result of Example 1 should convince us of the truth of the following assertion.

The same operations applied to the augmented matrix of a system of equations to reduce it to row-reduced echelon form will change the system to an equivalent reduced system.

The following example shows how the row-reduced echelon form can be used to read the solution of a system of equations.

Example 2. The following matrices are row-reduced echelon forms of the augmented matrices of certain systems of equations. Write corresponding equivalent reduced systems of equations and examine their solutions.

(a) $\begin{bmatrix} 1 & 4 & -2 \\ 0 & 1 & 5 \end{bmatrix}$ (b) $\begin{bmatrix} 1 & 4 & -2 \\ 0 & 1 & 0 \end{bmatrix}$

(c) $\begin{bmatrix} 1 & 4 & -2 \\ 0 & 0 & 1 \end{bmatrix}$ (d) $\begin{bmatrix} 1 & 4 & -2 \\ 0 & 0 & 0 \end{bmatrix}$

Solution:

(a)

$$x + 4y = -2 .$$
$$y = 5 .$$

The solution set is $\{(-22, 5)\}$. The system is independent.

(b)

$$x + 4y = -2 .$$
$$y = 0 .$$

The solution set is $\{(-2, 0)\}$. The system is independent.

(c)

$$x + 4y = -2 .$$
$$0y = 1 .$$

The solution set is ϕ; the system is inconsistent.

(d)

$$x + 4y = -2 .$$
$$0y = 0 .$$

Here y is an arbitrary real number. Let $y = k$, $k \in Re$, and

$$x = -4k - 2 .$$

The solution set is $\{(-4k - 2, k) \mid k \in Re\}$. The system is dependent.

The next examples combine the above results to show how a system of equations can be examined by using a row-reduced echelon form of the augmented matrix.

Example 3. Find a row-reduced echelon form of the augmented matrix of the system

$$x + 3y - 2z = -4 ,$$
$$3x - y + 4z = 7 ,$$
$$5x - 5y + 10z = 18 ,$$

and use this form to investigate the solution of the system.

Solution: The augmented matrix is

$$\begin{bmatrix} 1 & 3 & -2 & -4 \\ 3 & -1 & 4 & 7 \\ 5 & -5 & 10 & 18 \end{bmatrix}.$$

A row-reduced echelon form for it is found as follows.

$$\begin{bmatrix} 1 & 3 & -2 & -4 \\ 3 & -1 & 4 & 7 \\ 5 & -5 & 10 & 18 \end{bmatrix} \xrightarrow{\text{Add } (-3) \times \text{ row (1) to row (2).}} \begin{bmatrix} 1 & 3 & -2 & -4 \\ 0 & -10 & 10 & 19 \\ 5 & -5 & 10 & 18 \end{bmatrix}$$

$$\xrightarrow{\text{Add } (-5) \times \text{ row (1) to row (3).}} \begin{bmatrix} 1 & 3 & -2 & -4 \\ 0 & -10 & 10 & 19 \\ 0 & -20 & 20 & 38 \end{bmatrix}$$

$$\xrightarrow{\text{Add } (-2) \times \text{ row (2) to row (3).}} \begin{bmatrix} 1 & 3 & -2 & -4 \\ 0 & -10 & 10 & 19 \\ 0 & 0 & 0 & 0 \end{bmatrix}$$

$$\xrightarrow{\text{Multiply row (2) } \times -\frac{1}{10}.} \begin{bmatrix} 1 & 3 & -2 & -4 \\ 0 & 1 & -1 & -\frac{19}{10} \\ 0 & 0 & 0 & 0 \end{bmatrix}.$$

This matrix is a row-reduced echelon form of the augmented matrix; it corresponds to the system of equations

$$x + 3y - 2z = -4,$$
$$y - z = -\frac{19}{10},$$
$$0z = 0.$$

Then, z is an arbitrary real number.

$$z = k.$$
$$y = k - \frac{19}{10}.$$
$$x = -3\left(k - \frac{19}{10}\right) + 2k - 4 = -k + \frac{17}{10}.$$

The solution set is $\left\{\left(-k + \frac{17}{10}, \ k - \frac{19}{10}, \ k\right) \middle| k \in Re\right\}$.   The system is dependent.

Example 4.   Examine the system

$$x + 2y - z = 3,$$
$$4x + 3y - 2z = -1,$$
$$-x + 3y - z = 4.$$

Solution: A row-reduced echelon form of the augmented matrix is found as follows.

$$\begin{bmatrix} 1 & 2 & -1 & 3 \\ 4 & 3 & -2 & -1 \\ -1 & 3 & -1 & 4 \end{bmatrix}$$ Add $(-4) \times$ row (1) to row (2). $\longrightarrow$ $$\begin{bmatrix} 1 & 2 & -1 & 3 \\ 0 & -5 & 2 & -13 \\ -1 & 3 & -1 & 4 \end{bmatrix}$$

Add $1 \times$ row (1) to row (3). $\longrightarrow$ $$\begin{bmatrix} 1 & 2 & -1 & 3 \\ 0 & -5 & 2 & -13 \\ 0 & 5 & -2 & 7 \end{bmatrix}$$

Add $1 \times$ row (2) to row (3). $\longrightarrow$ $$\begin{bmatrix} 1 & 2 & -1 & 3 \\ 0 & -5 & 2 & -13 \\ 0 & 0 & 0 & -6 \end{bmatrix}$$

Multiply row (2) $\times -\frac{1}{5}$ and row (3) $\times -\frac{1}{6}$. $\longrightarrow$ $$\begin{bmatrix} 1 & 2 & -1 & 3 \\ 0 & 1 & -\frac{2}{5} & \frac{13}{5} \\ 0 & 0 & 0 & 1 \end{bmatrix}$$

This row-reduced echelon form corresponds to the equivalent reduced system

$$x + 2y - z = 3,$$
$$y - \tfrac{2}{5}z = \tfrac{13}{5},$$
$$0z = 1,$$

from which we see that the original system has no solution; the system is inconsistent.

EXERCISE 6.7

Write systems of equations corresponding to the following matrices and examine their solution.

1. $[1 \quad 5]$

2. $[1 \quad 3 \quad -2]$

3. $\begin{bmatrix} 1 & 2 & -1 \\ 0 & 1 & 6 \end{bmatrix}$

4. $\begin{bmatrix} 1 & 0 & 4 \\ 0 & 1 & -3 \end{bmatrix}$

5. $\begin{bmatrix} 1 & 3 & -1 \\ 0 & 1 & 0 \end{bmatrix}$

6. $\begin{bmatrix} 1 & 0 & 5 \\ 0 & 0 & 4 \end{bmatrix}$

7. $\begin{bmatrix} 1 & 3 & -2 \\ 0 & 0 & 0 \end{bmatrix}$

8. $\begin{bmatrix} 1 & 3 & 0 \\ 0 & 1 & 0 \end{bmatrix}$

9. $\begin{bmatrix} 1 & 5 & 0 \\ 0 & 0 & 0 \end{bmatrix}$

10. $\begin{bmatrix} 1 & 2 & -3 & 1 \\ 0 & 0 & 1 & 2 \end{bmatrix}$

11. $\begin{bmatrix} 1 & -1 & 5 & 2 \\ 0 & 1 & 1 & 4 \end{bmatrix}$

12. $\begin{bmatrix} 1 & 3 & -2 & 0 \\ 0 & 0 & 0 & 4 \end{bmatrix}$

13. $\begin{bmatrix} 1 & 1 & -4 & 3 \\ 0 & 0 & 0 & 0 \end{bmatrix}$

14. $\begin{bmatrix} 1 & 2 & -1 & 5 \\ 0 & 1 & 3 & 1 \\ 0 & 0 & 1 & 2 \end{bmatrix}$

15. $\begin{bmatrix} 1 & 3 & 3 & 2 \\ 0 & 1 & 4 & -1 \\ 0 & 0 & 0 & 1 \end{bmatrix}$

16. $\begin{bmatrix} 1 & 2 & -1 & 5 \\ 0 & 0 & 1 & 4 \\ 0 & 0 & 0 & 1 \end{bmatrix}$ 17. $\begin{bmatrix} 1 & 2 & -1 & 5 \\ 0 & 0 & 1 & 4 \\ 0 & 0 & 0 & 0 \end{bmatrix}$ 18. $\begin{bmatrix} 1 & 3 & 1 & 4 \\ 0 & 1 & 5 & 2 \\ 0 & 0 & 0 & 0 \end{bmatrix}$

Use the method of Section 6.7 to investigate the following systems of equations.

19. $3x - 2y = 4$
    $4x + y = 7$

20. $2x - 5y = 7$
    $4x - 10y = 17$

21. $3x - y = 4$
    $-6x + 2y = -8$

22. $x + 2y - z = 7$
    $3x - y + z = -3$

23. $x - y + 2z = 5$
    $3x - y + 3z = 10$

24. $2x - y = 5$
    $3x + 2y = -2$
    $x - 4y = 12$

25. $x + 3y - 2z = 7$
    $2x - y - z = 4$
    $5x - 2y + 3z = -3$

26. $x - 2y + z = -2$
    $x + 3y = 6$
    $3x - y + 2z = 4$

27. $2x + 3y - z = 5$
    $4x - 5y + 5z = -3$
    $3x - y + 2z = 1$

6.8. Interpretation of Solutions of Systems of Equations

A system of equations in the variables x and y may have no solution (system inconsistent), a unique solution (system independent), or an infinite solution set (system dependent). In the latter case, the general solution is a set of ordered pairs $\{(x, y)\}$ in which each co-ordinate can be expressed in terms of an arbitrary parameter or real number k.

Example 1.   Examine the solution set of the system

$$x - 3y = 5 ,$$
$$2x - 6y = 10 .$$

Solution: The augmented matrix is

$$\begin{bmatrix} 1 & -3 & 5 \\ 2 & -6 & 10 \end{bmatrix} .$$

Then

$$\begin{bmatrix} 1 & -3 & 5 \\ 2 & -6 & 10 \end{bmatrix} \xrightarrow{\text{Add } (-2) \times \text{ row (1) to row (2).}} \begin{bmatrix} 1 & -3 & 5 \\ 0 & 0 & 0 \end{bmatrix} ;$$

this row-reduced echelon form corresponds to the system

$$x - 3y = 5 ,$$
$$0y = 0 .$$

Then y is arbitrary;

$$y = k , \quad k \in Re ,$$

and

$$x = 3k + 5 .$$

The solution of the system may be written

$$\{(x, y) \mid x = 3k + 5,\ y = k,\ k \in Re\}\,.$$

The system is dependent.

Now we have seen that the parametric equations

$$x = 3k + 5\,,$$
$$y = k\,, \qquad\qquad k \in Re\,,$$

represent a line in two dimensions (Section 4.2). This confirms what we already know, that is, that the geometric interpretation of the solution set in Example 1 is a line in the plane. The system represents two identical lines.

The following examples concern systems of equations in the variables x, y, and z. Again, the system may have no solution, a unique solution, or an infinite solution set. We examine the parametric equations that arise in the latter case.

Example 2.   Examine the system

$$x + y + 2z = -3\,,$$
$$x + 4y + 7z = -13\,,$$
$$2x - y - z = 4\,.$$

Solution: The augmented matrix is

$$\begin{bmatrix} 1 & 1 & 2 & -3 \\ 1 & 4 & 7 & -13 \\ 2 & -1 & -1 & 4 \end{bmatrix}.$$

Then

$$\begin{bmatrix} 1 & 1 & 2 & -3 \\ 1 & 4 & 7 & -13 \\ 2 & -1 & -1 & 4 \end{bmatrix}$$

Add $(-1) \times$ row (1) to row (2).
$$\begin{bmatrix} 1 & 1 & 2 & -3 \\ 0 & 3 & 5 & -10 \\ 2 & -1 & -1 & 4 \end{bmatrix}$$

Add $(-2) \times$ row (1) to row (3).
$$\begin{bmatrix} 1 & 1 & 2 & -3 \\ 0 & 3 & 5 & -10 \\ 0 & -3 & -5 & 10 \end{bmatrix}$$

Add $1 \times$ row (2) to row (3).
$$\begin{bmatrix} 1 & 1 & 2 & -3 \\ 0 & 3 & 5 & -10 \\ 0 & 0 & 0 & 0 \end{bmatrix}$$

Multiply row (2) $\times \frac{1}{3}$.
$$\begin{bmatrix} 1 & 1 & 2 & -3 \\ 0 & 1 & \frac{5}{3} & -\frac{10}{3} \\ 0 & 0 & 0 & 0 \end{bmatrix}.$$

The row-reduced echelon matrix corresponds to the system

$$x + y + 2z = -3,$$
$$y + \tfrac{5}{3}z = -\tfrac{10}{3},$$
$$0z = 0.$$

Then z is an arbitrary real number;

$$z = k, \quad k \in Re,$$
$$y = -\tfrac{5}{3}k - \tfrac{10}{3},$$
$$x = \tfrac{5}{3}k + \tfrac{10}{3} - 2k - 3 = -\tfrac{1}{3}k + \tfrac{1}{3}.$$

The solution set is $\{(x, y, z)\}$ with

$$x = -\tfrac{1}{3}k + \tfrac{1}{3}, \quad y = -\tfrac{5}{3}k - \tfrac{10}{3}, \quad z = k, \quad k \in Re.$$

We have seen (Section 4.6) that these are the parametric equations of a line in 3-space. This again confirms what we concluded before; the geometric interpretation of the solution set is a line in 3-space. The system represents three planes intersecting in a line.

Example 3. Examine the system

$$x + y - 2z = 5,$$
$$2x + 2y - 4z = 10.$$

Solution: The augmented matrix

$$\begin{bmatrix} 1 & 1 & -2 & 5 \\ 2 & 2 & -4 & 10 \end{bmatrix}$$

is equivalent to the row echelon form

$$\begin{bmatrix} 1 & 1 & -2 & 5 \\ 0 & 0 & 0 & 0 \end{bmatrix},$$

which corresponds to the system

$$x + y - 2z = 5,$$
$$0y + 0z = 0.$$

Here y and z are arbitrary real numbers, $y = k$, $z = l$, and

$$x = -k + 2l + 5.$$

The solution set is $\{(x, y, z)\}$ with

$$x = -k + 2l + 5,$$
$$y = k,$$
$$z = l, \qquad k, l \in Re.$$

Again we have seen (Section 5.2) that these are the parametric equations of a plane in 3-space. This system of equations represents two planes intersecting in a plane, that is, two identical planes.

EXERCISE 6.8

Examine the systems of equations represented in questions (1) to (27) of Exercise 6.7. Select the dependent systems, write the general solutions in parametric form, and identify the corresponding geometric figure (line or plane).

6.9. Systems of Three Equations in Three Variables

In this section, we will again look at systems of three equations in three variables but from a different point of view. Such a system involves equations of the form

$$ax + by + cz = d .$$

We know that this equation is that of a plane in 3-space with normal vector

$$\mathbf{u} = (a, b, c) .$$

We have considered the possible geometric interpretations of such systems in Section 5.6. We have seen that such a system is independent only if two of the equations represent planes intersecting in a line (nonparallel planes) and the third equation represents a plane intersecting this line in a point (the line is not in the plane and not parallel to the plane).

Now two planes are parallel if and only if their normal vectors are parallel. Thus,

$$x + 2y + 3z = 6 \quad \text{with normal vector } \mathbf{u} = (1, 2, 3)$$

and

$$2x + 4y + 6z = 7 \quad \text{with normal vector } \mathbf{v} = (2, 4, 6)$$

represent parallel planes, since $\mathbf{v} = 2\mathbf{u}$, whereas

$$x - y + 3z = 2 \quad \text{with normal vector } \mathbf{u} = (1, -1, 3)$$

and

$$2x - 2y + 4z = -3 \quad \text{with normal vector } \mathbf{v} = (2, -2, 4)$$

do not, since $\mathbf{v} \neq k\mathbf{u}$.

The line of intersection l of two nonparallel planes I and II, is perpendicular to the plane determined by the normal vectors $\mathbf{u}$ and $\mathbf{v}$ to the planes.

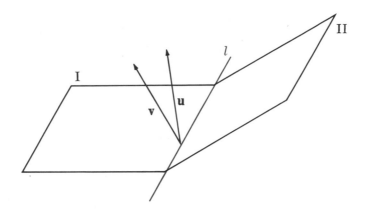

The condition that a third equation does not represent a plane containing the line l or parallel to the line l is that the normal vector $\mathbf{w}$ of this plane does not lie in the plane determined by $\mathbf{u}$ and $\mathbf{v}$; that is, $\mathbf{w}$ is not a linear combination of $\mathbf{u}$ and $\mathbf{v}$.

Example 1.   Use the above considerations to determine whether the following system is independent.

(1)	$x - 2y + 2z = 5$.	$\mathbf{u} = (1, -2, 2)$.
(2)	$3x - y + z = -2$.	$\mathbf{v} = (3, -1, 1)$.
(3)	$4x - 2y + z = 3$.	$\mathbf{w} = (4, -2, 1)$.

Solution: The normal vectors to the three planes involved are given.   Obviously, $\mathbf{u} \neq k\mathbf{v}$, so that (1) and (2) represent nonparallel planes intersecting in a line. The question now is whether we can find k and m such that

$$\mathbf{w} = k\mathbf{u} + m\mathbf{v} ,$$

that is,

$$(4, -2, 1) = k(1, -2, 2) + m(3, -1, 1)$$

$$= (k + 3m, -2k - m, 2k + m) .$$

This is possible if and only if

$$k + 3m = 4 ,$$

$$-2k - m = -2 ,$$

$$2k + m = 1 ,$$

has a solution (k, m).

The augmented matrix of the system is

$$\begin{bmatrix} 1 & 3 & 4 \\ -2 & -1 & -2 \\ 2 & 1 & 1 \end{bmatrix}$$

and this matrix is equivalent to the row-reduced echelon form

$$\begin{bmatrix} 1 & 3 & 4 \\ 0 & 1 & \frac{6}{5} \\ 0 & 0 & 1 \end{bmatrix}.$$

An examination of the corresponding system of equations shows that no solution (k, m) is possible. Thus, **u**, **v**, and **w** are noncoplanar vectors, and the original system is independent.

The student will recognize, of course, that the time spent in determining this fact could have just as profitably been spent in obtaining the solution.

Example 2. Determine whether the following system is independent.

(1) $\qquad\qquad x + y + 3z = -2.\qquad$ **u** $= (1, 1, 3).$

(2) $\qquad\qquad x - 4y - 7z = 6.\qquad$ **v** $= (1, -4, -7).$

(3) $\qquad\qquad 4x - y + 2z = 5.\qquad$ **w** $= (4, -1, 2).$

Solution: **u** and **v** are noncollinear and hence determine a plane. This system is independent if and only if real numbers k and m do not exist such that

$$\mathbf{w} = k\mathbf{u} + m\mathbf{v};$$

that is,

$$(4, -1, 2) = k(1, 1, 3) + m(1, -4, -7)$$
$$= (k + m, k - 4m, 3k - 7m),$$

or

$$k + m = 4,$$
$$k - 4m = -1,$$
$$3k - 7m = 2.$$

The augmented matrix is equivalent to

$$\begin{bmatrix} 1 & 1 & 4 \\ 0 & 1 & 1 \\ 0 & 0 & 0 \end{bmatrix}$$

and the corresponding system has solution $(3, 1)$; therefore

$$\mathbf{w} = 3\mathbf{u} + \mathbf{v}$$

and so the original system is not independent.

Again, this method tells us nothing further about the solution, that is, whether the system is inconsistent or dependent, and does not give us the solution in the latter case.

Example 3. Determine whether the following system is independent.

(1) $x - y - 2z = 3$. $\mathbf{u} = (1, -1, -2)$.

(2) $5x - 2y + 3z = -4$. $\mathbf{v} = (5, -2, 3)$.

(3) $3x - 3y - 6z = 7$. $\mathbf{w} = (3, -3, -6)$.

Solution: Since $\mathbf{w} = 3\mathbf{u}$, we see that the planes represented by (1) and (3) are parallel planes and so the system of equations is not independent.

EXERCISE 6.9

Use the technique of Section 6.9 to determine if the following systems are independent.

1. $x - y - 2z = 7$
$3x + 2y - z = -3$
$x - 2y + z = 5$

2. $2x - 3y + z = 0$
$5x - y + 3z = -2$
$x - 2y - z = 5$

3. $3x - y - z = -3$
$2x + y - 2z = 5$
$7x + y - 5z = 6$

4. $x - y + 3z = -2$
$2x - y + z = 5$
$3x - y - z = 12$

5. $3x - y - z = 2$
$x - 2y + 3z = -1$
$2x + y - 4z = 5$

6. $x - y + 2z = -1$
$2x - 2y + 4z = 3$
$3x - 3y + 6z = 0$

7. $3x - y - 2z = 5$
$x + y + 2z = -2$
$x - 3y - 6z = 7$

8. $2x - 3y - z = 3$
$x - y + z = 5$
$-4x + 6y + 2z = 7$

9. $x - 3y - z = 2$
$2x + y - z = 0$
$3x - y + 2z = 2$

10. $2x - y - z = 3$
$x - 2y - 2z = -1$
$3x - 3y - 3z = 0$

Chapter Summary

Solution of systems of equations · consistent (independent and dependent) and inconsistent systems · equivalent reduced systems

Systems of homogenous equations

The matrix of coefficients and the augmented matrix of a system of equations · equivalent matrices

Row-reduced echelon form and application to the solution of a system of equations

Interpretation of solutions of systems of equations

REVIEW EXERCISE 6

1. Replace each of the following systems by an equivalent reduced system and use the latter to obtain the solution (if existent) of the original system.

(a) $x + y = 7$
    $3x - y = 2$

(b) $5x - 2y = 7$
    $3x + 4y = -3$

(c) $3x - 2y = 7$
    $6x - 4y = 21$

(d) $x - 3y = -3$
    $-2x + 6y = 6$

(e) $2x + 3y = 10$
    $x - 4y = 7$

(f) $x + 2y = 6$
    $3x + 6y = 12$

(g) $x + 3y - 2z = 6$
    $2x - y - z = -3$
    $3x + 2y - 4z = 10$

(h) $x - 2y + z = -4$
    $3x - 4y + 2z = 3$
    $4x - 6y + 3z = 6$

(i) $6x - y - z = -2$
    $2x + 3y + z = 4$
    $2x - 7y - 3z = -10$

(j) $3x + y - 2z = 3$
    $x + 4y = -1$
    $3y - 2z = 6$

2. Examine the following systems of equations. State whether they are consistent (independent or dependent) or inconsistent. If a solution exists, state the solution set.

(a) $6x - y = 7$

(b) $x - 3y + 2z = 6$

(c) $6x - y + 2z = 7$
    $2x + 3y - z = 3$

(d) $3x + 2y - 4z = 12$
    $2x - y + 3z = 3$

(e) $x - 2y - z = 4$
    $2x - 4y - 2z = 7$

(f) $3x - y - z = -2$
    $-9x + 3y - 2z = 6$

(g) $x + 2y - z - 3w = 4$
    $2x - y - z + 2w = 7$

(h) $3x - y - 2z + 5w = -2$
    $6x - 2y + 3z - w = 5$

3. Examine the following systems of equations. Classify them as independent or dependent; in each case, give the solution set.

(a) $3x + 4y = 0$

(b) $x + 3y + 3z = 0$

(c) $2x - 3y = 0$
    $x + 4y = 0$

(d) $3x - 4y = 0$
    $-9x + 12y = 0$

(e) $3x - 2y - z = 0$
    $2x + 4y - z = 0$

(f) $x + 2y - 6z = 0$
    $2x + 4y + 3z = 0$

(g) $x + 3y - 2z = 0$
    $3x - y + 4z = 0$
    $x + 6y - z = 0$

(h) $3x - y - 2z = 0$
    $x + 2y - 4z = 0$
    $x - 5y + 6z = 0$

(i) $x + 3y = 0$
    $2x - y = 0$
    $3x + y = 0$

(j) $x - 3y - z = 0$
    $2x - y - z = 0$
    $-x + 3y - 2z = 0$

(k) $x + y - 3z + 2w = 0$
    $3x - y + z - 2w = 0$

(l) $6x - y - z + 2w = 0$
    $3x + 2y - z + w = 0$

4. Are any of the systems in question (3) inconsistent? If not, why not?

5. Write the matrices of coefficients and the augmented matrices for the systems in question (1).

6. Find row-reduced echelon forms for the following matrices.

(a) $\begin{bmatrix} 1 & 2 \\ -7 & 6 \end{bmatrix}$

(b) $\begin{bmatrix} 3 & 2 \\ -4 & 6 \end{bmatrix}$

(c) $\begin{bmatrix} -3 & 4 \\ 4 & 6 \end{bmatrix}$

(d) $\begin{bmatrix} 1 & 2 & -5 \\ 3 & -1 & 6 \end{bmatrix}$

(e) $\begin{bmatrix} 4 & -2 & 5 \\ 1 & 7 & 3 \\ 5 & 2 & 9 \end{bmatrix}$

(f) $\begin{bmatrix} 3 & 2 & 5 \\ -1 & -1 & -1 \\ 2 & 1 & 3 \end{bmatrix}$

(g) $\begin{bmatrix} 3 & -2 \\ 5 & 2 \\ 1 & 4 \end{bmatrix}$

(h) $\begin{bmatrix} 2 & -1 & 4 \\ 3 & 3 & 1 \\ 1 & 5 & -3 \end{bmatrix}$

(i) $\begin{bmatrix} 1 & 3 & -2 \\ 4 & 1 & 5 \\ 6 & 2 & 1 \\ 3 & -4 & 5 \end{bmatrix}$

(j) $\begin{bmatrix} 3 & -1 & -1 & 2 \\ 4 & 1 & 5 & 3 \\ -1 & 6 & 3 & 0 \\ 2 & 1 & 1 & 6 \end{bmatrix}$

7. Use the row-reduced echelon form of the augmented matrix of each of the following systems of equations to investigate the solution of the system.

(a) $4x - y = 6$
    $3x + 2y = -4$

(b) $3x + 2y = 2$
    $-6 + 4y = 4$

(c) $-x + 3y = 2$
    $3x - 9y = -6$

(d) $x + 3y - 2z = 4$
    $3x - y - z = -2$

(e) $x - 2y + z = -1$
     $2x - 4y + 3z = 3$

(f) $x - 2y = 6$
     $3x - y = 4$
     $-2x + 3y = -1$

(g) $x - 3y + z = 1$
     $2x - y - z = -4$
     $6x - y + 3z = -1$

(h) $x - 2y - 2z = -1$
     $4x - y + 3z = 4$
     $x + 5y + 9z = 7$

(i) $3x - 2y + z = 0$
     $-x + 3y - z = 0$
     $4x + 2y = 0$

(j) $2x - y + 3z = 0$
     $x + y - 5z = 0$
     $3x - y = 7$

8. Select the dependent systems of question (7), write their solutions in parametric form, and identify the corresponding geometric figure (line or plane).

Chapter 7

THE ALGEBRA OF SETS

7.1. Sets and Subsets

The term set is regarded as one of the basic undefined ideas of mathematics. In geometry, the terms point, line, and plane were undefined and their properties were established by means of the axioms. We did find it useful, however, to have some intuitive idea of what we understood by a point, a line, or a plane. In the same way, we find it useful to establish an intuitive idea of what we mean by a set by using what we might call a "pseudo-definition".

A *set* is a collection of objects from a specified universe.

A set is *well-defined* if each member of the universe is either in the set or not in the set.

We should note that our "definition" lacks one of the attributes of a proper definition since the words set and collection are, for all practical purposes, synonymous. We are really using the word set to define itself.

It is important in set theory to have the universe or universal set (U) of any discussion clearly determined. If we are asked for $\{x \mid 1 < x < 2\}$, we cannot give any sensible answer since the universe (in this case, the replacement set for the variable x) has not been specified. If $U = I$, there is no member of the set of integers which satisfies the inequalities and so

$$\{x \in I \mid 1 < x < 2\} = \phi \quad \text{(the empty set or null set)}.$$

If $U = Ra$, there is an infinite number of rational numbers which satisfy the inequalities and our solution set is the set of all rationals between 1 and 2.

In many instances, the universe may be obvious from the context and so not be specifically stated. In $\{x \mid x + 1 = 5\}$, if we understand that the universe is a particular set of numbers, we may omit any specific statement to that effect.

So frequently are certain sets of numbers used that special symbols are used to designate these sets. We first give the symbols used in this text, followed by a description of the symbol, and finally symbols that may be used in some other texts.

$$N = \{\text{all natural numbers}\} = \{1, 2, 3, \cdots\}$$

$$W = \{\text{all whole numbers}\} = \{0, 1, 2, 3, \cdots\} = N_0$$

$$I = \{\text{all integers}\} = \{\cdots, -2, -1, 0, +1, +2, \cdots\} = Z$$

$$I^+ = \{\text{all positive integers}\} = Z^+$$

$$I^- = \{\text{all negative integers}\} = Z^-$$

$$Ra = \{\text{all rationals}\} = Q$$

$$Re = \{\text{all real numbers}\} = R = \Re$$

$$C = \{\text{all complex numbers}\} = \mathfrak{C}$$

If a set A has the property that every element of A is also an element of B, then A is a *subset* of B. This is written as

$$A \subseteq B \quad (A \text{ is contained in or is equal to } B)$$

or

$$B \supseteq A \quad (B \text{ contains } A \text{ or is equal to } A).$$

If every element of A is an element of B but some element of B is not an element of A, then A is a *proper subset* of B. This is written as $A \subset B$ or $B \supset A$. We note that any set is a subset of the universe $(A \subseteq U)$. If A is not identical with U, then $A \subset U$.

We also consider the empty set ϕ to be a subset of every set.

If x is an element of (belongs to) a set A, we write $x \in A$. If x is not an element of A, we write $x \notin A$.

While our work in this chapter will deal mainly with finite sets, there are some properties of infinite sets which may be of interest. The natural numbers can be put into a one-to-one correspondence with a subset of the integers, the positive integers,

$$1 \to +1, \quad 2 \to +2, \quad \cdots, \quad n \to +n, \quad \cdots.$$

Because of the similar properties of N and I^+, we could say that $N \subset I$.

It is also possible, however, to put the set of all integers into a 1-1 correspondence with the set of natural numbers.

$$\cdots, \quad -n, \cdots, -3, -2, -1, \quad 0, +1, +2, +3, \cdots, +n, \cdots$$
$$\cdots, \quad \downarrow \quad \cdots, \quad \downarrow \quad \downarrow \quad \downarrow \quad \downarrow \quad \downarrow \quad \downarrow \quad \downarrow \quad \cdots, \quad \downarrow \quad \cdots$$
$$\cdots, 2n+1, \cdots, \quad 7, \quad 5, \quad 3, \quad 1, \quad 2, \quad 4, \quad 6, \cdots, \quad 2n, \cdots$$

We may, therefore, define an *infinite set* as a set that can be put into a 1-1 correspondence with a proper subset of itself. In this way, the set I is an infinite set and, in a similar manner, we can show that N, W, Ra, Re, C, are infinite sets.

EXERCISE 7.1

1. If $U = I$, state which of the following are sets in this universe.
   (a) {all prime integers}
   (b) $\{+1, +3, +5, +7, +9\}$
   (c) $\{(1, 2), (1, 3), (2, 5), (3, -7), (-3, -5)\}$
   (d) $\{x \in I \mid 2x - 1 > 3\}$
   (e) $\{y \mid y = \dfrac{x}{2} + 3,\ x \text{ is an even integer}\}$
   (f) $\{y \mid y = \dfrac{x}{2} + 3,\ x \in I\}$

2. Let U be the set of positive integers less than 5.
   (a) Form a new universe V of ordered pairs (x, y), where $x \in U$ and $y \in U$. How many elements are in V?
   (b) W is the set of ordered pairs (x, y) such that $x \in U$, $y \in U$, and $x \neq y$. How many elements are in W?
   (c) Are the following statements true?
$$V \subset U. \qquad W \subset U. \qquad W \subset V.$$

3. $A = \{1, 2\}$, $B = \{\{1, 2, 3\}, \{4, 5\}, 6\}$, $C = \{\{2\}, \{1, 2\}\}$
   State whether the following are true or false.
   (a) $2 \in A, 2 \in B, 2 \in C$ \qquad (b) $A \in B, A \in C$

4. Form sets A, B, C, such that $A \in B$, $B \in C$, and $A \not\subset C$.

5. Prove that N and Ra are infinite sets.

7.2. Operations on Sets

In this section we will assume that all sets in a particular discussion are sets from the same universe and, unless it is necessary, we will not specify the universe.

The *union* of the sets A and B, symbolized by $A \cup B$ (read "A union B" or "A cup B"), is the set of all elements that are members of either A or B.

Note that here the word "or" is used in the inclusive sense; that is, in A or B means in either A or B or both.

Example 1. If $A = \{a, b, c, d\}$, $B = \{b, c, d, e, f\}$, then

$$A \cup B = \{a, b, c, d, e, f\}.$$

The *intersection* of the sets A and B, symbolized by $A \cap B$ (read "A intersection B" or "A cap B"), is the set of all elements that are members of both A and B. In Example 1, $A \cap B = \{b, c, d\}$.

Example 2.   If $X = \{1, 3, 5\}$, $Y = \{$all even integers$\}$, then

$$X \cap Y = \phi.$$

In this case the sets X and Y are said to be *disjoint*.

The operations of union and intersection are *binary operations* on sets since they form a new set from two given sets belonging to the universe.   In this respect, and in other ways, they may be regarded as analagous to the arithmetical operations of addition and multiplication.

On the other hand the operation of complementation, which we consider next, is a *unary operation* since it forms a new set from *one* given set belonging to the universe.

The *complement* of a set T is that set of elements in U which are not members of T.   The complement of T is written as T' (read T prime).

Example 3.   If $U = \{1, 2, 3, \cdots, 10\}$ and $A = \{2, 4, 6, 8, 10\}$, then

$$A' = \{1, 3, 5, 7, 9\}.$$

Example 4.   If $U = \{1, 2, 3, \cdots, 20\}$ and
$$A = \{x \in U \mid x \text{ is a prime number}\},$$
$$B = \{2, 5, 8, 11, 14, 17, 20\},$$
$$C = \{x \in U \mid x \text{ is even}\},$$

state the elements of the sets

$$A \cap B, \quad A \cup C, \quad A', \quad B', \quad C', \quad (A \cup C)', \quad A' \cap C'.$$

Solution:

$$A \cap B = \{2, 5, 11, 17\}$$
$$A \cup C = \{2, 3, 4, 5, 6, 7, 8, 10, 11, 12, 13, 14, 16, 17, 18, 19, 20\}$$
$$A' = \{1, 4, 6, 8, 9, 10, 12, 14, 15, 16, 18, 20\}$$
$$B' = \{1, 3, 4, 6, 7, 9, 10, 12, 13, 15, 16, 18, 19\}$$
$$C' = \{1, 3, 5, \cdots, 19\}$$
$$(A \cup C)' = \{1, 9, 15\}$$
$$A' \cap C' = \{1, 9, 15\}$$

EXERCISE 7.2

1. If $A = \{a, b, c, d\}$, $B = \{c, d, e\}$, $C = \{e, f, g, h\}$, state the elements of the sets
   $$A \cup C, \quad B \cap A, \quad B \cap C, \quad B \cap (A \cup C), \quad (B \cap A) \cup (B \cap C).$$

2. If $U = \{\frac{1}{2}, \frac{1}{3}, \frac{1}{4}, \cdots, \frac{1}{10}\}$, $A = \{\frac{1}{2}, \frac{1}{5}, \frac{1}{8}\}$, $B = \{\frac{1}{2}, \frac{1}{4}, \frac{1}{6}, \frac{1}{8}, \frac{1}{10}\}$, $C = \{\frac{1}{3}, \frac{1}{5}, \frac{1}{7}, \frac{1}{9}\}$, state the elements of the sets

$A \cap C$, $C \cap A$, $A \cup B$, $B \cup A$, A', B', C', $(A \cup B)'$, $A' \cap B'$, $A' \cap B$, $A' \cap (A \cup B)$.

3. If $U = \{x \in I \mid -5 < x < 5\}$ and $P = \{x \in I \mid -2 < x < 3\}$, state the elements of the sets

$$P', \quad P' \cap P, \quad P' \cup P, \quad P \cap U, \quad P \cup U.$$

4. If $X = \{-3, -2, -1, 0, 1, 2, 3\}$, $Y = \{-5, -4, -3, -2, -1\}$, $Z = \{-2, -1, 0, 1, 2\}$, show that

(a) $X \cap (Y \cap Z) = (X \cap Y) \cap Z$,

(b) $X \cup (Y \cup Z) = (X \cup Y) \cup Z$,

(c) $X \cup (Y \cap Z) = (X \cup Y) \cap (X \cup Z)$,

(d) $X \cap (Y \cup Z) = (X \cap Y) \cup (X \cap Z)$.

5. If $U = \{1, 2, 3, \cdots, 10\}$, $A = \{x \in U \mid x \text{ is a prime}\}$, $B = \{x \in U \mid x \text{ is odd}\}$, show that

(a) $A' \cap B' = (A \cup B)'$,

(b) $A' \cup B' = (A \cap B)'$.

6. If $U = I^+$, $P = \{x \in I^+ \mid x \text{ is a prime}\}$, $Q = \{x \in I^+ \mid x \text{ is even}\}$, describe the sets or list the elements of the sets

$$P', \quad Q', \quad P \cap Q, \quad P \cup Q.$$

7. If $A = \{(x, y) \mid x + 2y = 3, x, y \in Re\}$, $B = \{(x, y) \mid x + y = 1, x, y \in Re\}$, state the elements of $A \cap B$.

8. If $X = \{(x, y) \mid x + 2y = 3, x, y, \in Re\}$, $Y = \{(x, y) \mid 3x + 6y = 7, x, y \in Re\}$, state the elements of $X \cap Y$.

7.3. Laws of Intersection and Union

A useful device to assist our consideration of relationships that may exist between the subsets of a given universe is a Venn diagram. The universal set is represented by the set of points inside and on the boundary of a simple closed curve (usually a rectangle) and a set A in U by the points inside and on the boundary of a second simple closed curve (usually a circle) inside the rectangle. In Figure 7.1, U and A are both labelled but, in future, we will assume that the set of points inside and on the rectangle represent the universe under discussion and will omit the label U.

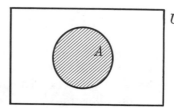

Figure 7.1

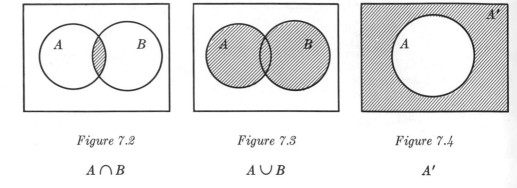

Figure 7.2   Figure 7.3   Figure 7.4

$A \cap B$ $A \cup B$ A'

The intersection $A \cap B$ of two sets A and B is respresented by the common region enclosed by the two intersecting circles as in the shaded part of Figure 7.2.

The union $A \cup B$ of two sets is represented by the sets of points A or B or both as in the shaded part of Figure 7.3.

The complement A' of a set is represented by the set of all points U but not in A as in the shaded part of Figure 7.4.   (Note that the circle is *not* part of A'.)

If $A \cap B = \varnothing$, then A and B are *disjoint* and in the Venn diagram the circles enclosing the sets A and B do not intersect as in Figure 7.5.

If $A \subset B$, the circle enclosing the set A will be completely contained in the circle enclosing the set B as in Figure 7.6.

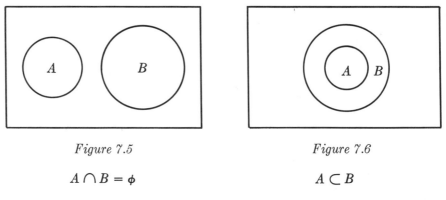

Figure 7.5   Figure 7.6

$A \cap B = \phi$ $A \subset B$

Using these six Venn diagrams as a basis, we can produce a geometrical interpretation for any expression involving sets and set operations.   It should be noted, however, that Venn diagrams *do not prove* the truth of a relationship between sets; they only illustrate its plausibility.   Also, the use of Venn diagrams to illustrate relationships between more than three sets becomes very complicated and it is difficult to see clearly the relationship being studied.

From Figures 7.2 and 7.3 it is immediately obvious that

(i) $A \cap B = B \cap A$ and   (ii) $A \cup B = B \cup A$.

Thus each of the operations of set intersection and set union is a *commutative* operation.   The analogy between the set operations $\cap$ and $\cup$ and the arithmetical operations $\times$ and $+$ is apparent.   Arithmetically, if a and b are numbers, then

$$a \times b = b \times a \quad \text{and} \quad a + b = b + a.$$

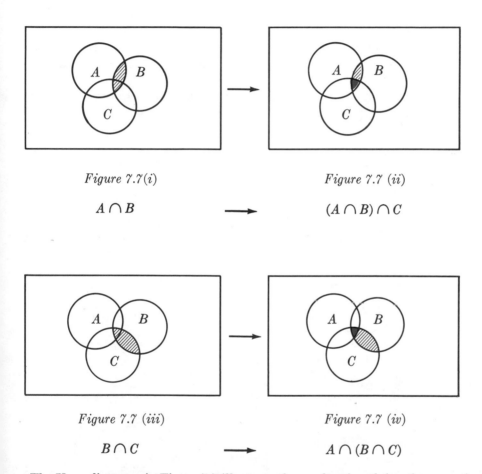

Figure 7.7(*i*)

$A \cap B$

Figure 7.7 (*ii*)

$(A \cap B) \cap C$

Figure 7.7 (*iii*)

$B \cap C$

Figure 7.7 (*iv*)

$A \cap (B \cap C)$

The Venn diagrams in Figure 7.7 illustrate the results of applying the operation of set intersection to three sets A, B, and C.

In Figure 7.7 (*i*), the shaded region represents the set $A \cap B$.   The doubly-shaded region in Figure 7.7 (*ii*) represents the result of the operation of intersection of the new set $A \cap B$ and the set C, that is, $(A \cap B) \cap C$.

In Figures 7.7 (*iii*) and 7.7 (*iv*), the set $B \cap C$ is formed first and again the doubly-shaded region in Figure 7.7 (*iv*) represents the set $A \cap (B \cap C)$.

Since the doubly-shaded regions in Figures 7.7 (*ii*) and 7.7 (*iv*) are the same, we may conclude that

$$(A \cap B) \cap C = A \cap (B \cap C).$$

This result was also shown in a special case in question (4a) of Exercise 7.2. It would appear to be true in all cases that the operation of set intersection is *associative*. Again we may compare the associative law of set intersection with the associative law of multiplication in arithmetic, where

$$(a \times b) \times c = a \times (b \times c).$$

Generally in arithmetic the use of the associative law permits the omission of parentheses and we simply write $a \times b \times c$. Similarly, for set intersection, we may write $A \cap B \cap C$.

In the same way, we may demonstrate with Venn diagrams in Figures 7.8 (*i*), (*ii*), (*iii*), (*iv*), that the operation of union is associative.

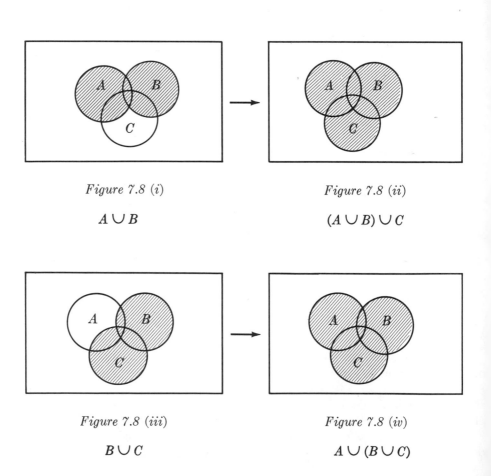

Figure 7.8 (i)

$A \cup B$

Figure 7.8 (ii)

$(A \cup B) \cup C$

Figure 7.8 (iii)

$B \cup C$

Figure 7.8 (iv)

$A \cup (B \cup C)$

$$(A \cup B) \cup C = A \cup (B \cup C) = A \cup B \cup C$$

which we may compare with

$$(a + b) + c = a + (b + c) = a + b + c$$

for the addition of numbers.

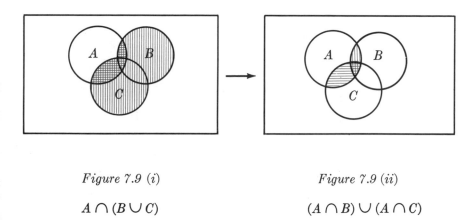

Figure 7.9 (i)   Figure 7.9 (ii)

$A \cap (B \cup C)$ $(A \cap B) \cup (A \cap C)$

In Figure 7.9 (i), the vertically-shaded region represents the set $B \cup C$; the horizontally-shaded region represents the intersection of A with $B \cup C$. or $A \cap (B \cup C)$.

In Figure 7.9 (ii), the vertically-shaded region represents the set $A \cap B$ and the horizontally-shaded region, the set $A \cap C$. The union of these two sets is the set $(A \cap B) \cup (A \cap C)$ and we see that this is the same region as $A \cap (B \cup C)$. The Venn diagrams illustrate the *distributive law* of intersection over union.

$$A \cap (B \cup C) = (A \cap B) \cup (A \cap C).$$

We may compare this with the arithmetical distributive law of multiplication over addition.

$$a(b + c) = ab + ac.$$

In Exercise 7.3, question (1) asks for the illustration, by means of Venn diagrams, of the distributive law of union over intersection.

$$A \cup (B \cap C) = (A \cup B) \cap (A \cup C).$$

Here we see that the arithmetical analogy is false.   In arithmetic, addition is not distributive over multiplication.

$$a + (b \times c) \neq (a + b) \times (a + c).$$

We see, therefore, that the arithmetical analogy, while it is useful in certain cases, should be used with great caution. The two systems are not *isomorphic*. That is, briefly and rather loosely, they do not have exactly the same structure.

Example 1. Illustrate, by means of a Venn diagram, that

$$\text{if } A \subseteq B, \text{ then } A \cap B = A.$$

Solution:

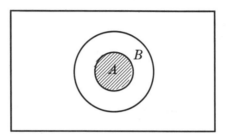

$A \cap B$ is the shaded region. $A \cap B = A$ if $A \subseteq B$.

Example 2. Illustrate, by means of Venn diagrams, that

$$(A \cap B) \cup [(A \cup C) \cap (B \cup C)] = (A \cap B) \cup C.$$

Solution:

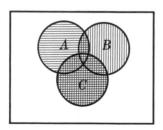 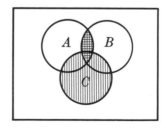 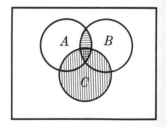

$(A \cup C) \cap (B \cup C)$ $(A \cap B) \cup [(A \cup C) \cap (B \cup C)]$ $(A \cap B) \cup C$

is   is   is

the doubly-shaded region.   all the shaded region.   all the shaded region.

Therefore

$$(A \cap B) \cup [(A \cup C) \cap (B \cup C)] = (A \cap B) \cup C.$$

EXERCISE 7.3

Illustrate the following identities by means of Venn diagrams.

1. $A \cup (B \cap C) = (A \cup B) \cap (A \cup C)$
2. If $A \subseteq B$, then $A \cup B = B$.
3. $A \cap U = A$.
4. $A \cup U = U$.
5. $A \cap (A \cup B) = A$.
6. $A \cup (A \cap B) = A$.
7. $(A \cap B) \cup (A \cap C) = A \cap (B \cup C)$.
8. $(A \cup B) \cap (A \cap B) = A \cap B$.
9. $(A \cup B) \cup (A \cap B) = A \cup B$.
10. $(A \cap B) \cup (A \cap C) \cup (B \cap C) = (A \cup B) \cap (B \cup C) \cap (A \cup C)$.

7.4. Laws of Complementation

In this section we will make use of Venn diagrams to illustrate various laws of complementation and combinations of these laws with the laws of intersection and union.

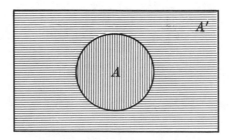

Figure 7.10

$$A \cap A' = \phi \quad \text{and} \quad A \cup A' = U$$

In Figure 7.10, the region which represents the set A is shaded vertically and the region which represents A', the complement of A, is shaded horizontally.

We note from the definition in Section 7.1 that the points on the circle are in A and not in A'. We see that there are no elements common to both A and A'. This, of course, is obvious from the definition of A'. Hence

$$A \cap A' = \phi.$$

Also, from Figure 7.10, we see that the union of A and A' includes all elements of the universe and hence

$$A \cup A' = U.$$

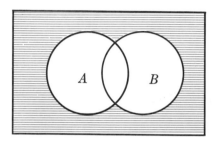

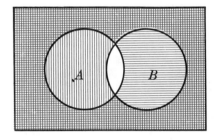

Figure 7.11 (i)   *Figure 7.11 (ii)*

$(A \cup B)'$ $A' \cap B'$

In Figure 7.11 (*i*), the unshaded region represents the set $A \cup B$, and therefore the shaded region will represent $(A \cup B)'$.

In Figure 7.11 (*ii*), the vertically-shaded region represents the set B', and the horizontally-shaded region represents the set A'. The doubly-shaded region, therefore, represents the set $A' \cap B'$. We note that the doubly-shaded region in Figure 7.11 (*ii*) is the same region as the shaded region in Figure 7.11 (*i*). The Venn diagrams illustrate the law that the complement of a union is the intersection of the complements.

$$(A \cup B)' = A' \cap B'.$$

In Exercise 7.4, question (1), we are asked to use Venn diagrams to illustrate the law that the complement of an intersection is the union of the complements.

$$(A \cap B)' = A' \cup B'.$$

These two laws are known as the De Morgan Laws.

Example 1.   Use a Venn diagram to illustrate that

$$A \cap (A' \cup B) = A \cap B.$$

Solution:

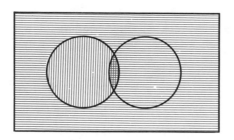

(A' ∪ B)   A $A \cap (A' \cup B) = A \cap B$

Example 2.   Use Venn diagrams to illustrate that $(A \cap B')' \cap B = B$.

Solution:

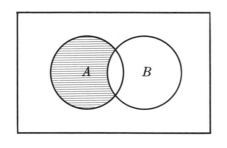

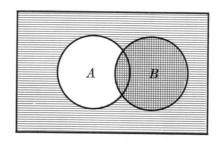

$A \cap B'$ $(A \cap B')' \cap B = B$

EXERCISE 7.4

Illustrate the following identities by means of Venn diagrams.

1. $(A \cap B)' = A' \cup B'$.
2. $(A \cap B \cap C)' = A' \cup B' \cup C'$.
3. $(A \cap B')' \cup B = A' \cup B$.
4. $(A \cup B')' \cap B = A' \cap B$.
5. $(A')' = A$.
6. $A' \cup (A \cap B) = A' \cup B$.
7. $A' \cap (A \cup B) = A' \cap B$.
8. $(A \cap B') \cup (A' \cap B)' = A \cup B'$.

7.5. Algebra of Sets

The following equations, most of which we have illustrated by Venn diagrams in the previous sections or exercises, are *identities* for any sets A, B, and C in a common universe U.

(1) (a) $A \cap B = B \cap A$.   (b) $A \cup B = B \cup A$.

(2) (a) $(A \cap B) \cap C = A \cap (B \cap C)$.   (b) $(A \cup B) \cup C = A \cup (B \cup C)$.

(3) (a) $A \cap (B \cup C) = (A \cap B) \cup (A \cap C)$.   (b) $A \cup (B \cap C) = (A \cup B) \cap (A \cup C)$.

(4) (a) $A \cap \phi = \phi$.   (b) $A \cup \phi = A$.

(5) (a) $A \cap U = A$.   (b) $A \cup U = U$.

(6) (a) $A \cap A' = \phi$.   (b) $A \cup A' = U$.

(7) (a) $A \cap A = A$.   (b) $A \cup A = A$.

(8) (a) $A \cap (A \cup B) = A$.   (b) $A \cup (A \cap B) = A$.

(9) (a) $(A \cap B)' = A' \cup B'$.   (b) $(A \cup B)' = A' \cap B'$.

(10) (a) $U' = \phi$.   (b) $\phi' = U$.

(11) $(A')' = A$.

(12) $A \subseteq B$ if and only if $A \cap B = A$, and $A \subseteq B$ if and only if $A \cup B = B$.

We may accept these identities as the basic axioms of an algebra of sets and prove more complex results by using them. While we have demonstrated the plausibility of each of these results by using Venn diagrams, we must remember that such a demonstration is not a rigorous proof. We may in fact prove these "axioms" in terms of the verbal definitions of the symbols and operations by using logical connectives and a process called set inclusion. (See Section 7.6).

If we examine closely the (a) and (b) equations in Identities (1) to (10), we notice important similarities in form. These illustrate the very important *Principle of Duality* in Set Theory. This principle states that any established result involving sets and complements and the operations of union and intersection gives a corresponding dual result by replacing U by ϕ and $\cup$ by $\cap$, and vice versa. For example, in Identity (3),

(a) $A \cap (B \cup C) = (A \cap B) \cup (A \cap C)$

(b) $A \cup (B \cap C) = (A \cup B) \cap (A \cup C)$

or in Identity (6),

(a) $A \cap A' = \phi$

(b) $A \cup A' = U$

We may note also that the analogies to the laws of an algebraic field, as in the real number system, are true only for (1), (2), (3(a)), (4), and (5(a)) when $+$ is the analogue of $\cup$, $\times$ of $\cap$, 0 of ϕ, and 1 of U. For example,

$$A \cap \phi = \phi \longleftrightarrow a \times 0 = 0,$$

and

$$A \cup \phi = A \longleftrightarrow a + 0 = a.$$

The very important differences from the algebra of a field should also be noted; for example, contrast $A \cap A = A$ with $a \times a = a^2$.

Using the basic identities, more complex identities, which have previously been illustrated by Venn diagrams, may now be proved algebraically. In the first example we shall quote the axiom numbers as authorities for reference but these would normally be omitted.

Example 1.   Prove that

$$(A \cap B') \cup (A' \cap B)' = A \cup B'.$$

Solution 1:

$$
\begin{aligned}
(A \cap B') \cup (A' \cap B)' &= (A \cap B') \cup (A \cup B') && \text{(9(a)) and (11)} \\
&= [(A \cap B') \cup A] \cup B' && \text{(2(b))} \\
&= A \cup B'. && \text{(8(b))}
\end{aligned}
$$

Solution 2:

$$
\begin{aligned}
(A \cap B') \cup (A' \cap B)' &= (A \cap B') \cup (A \cup B') && \text{(9(a)) and (11)} \\
&= A \cup B'. && \text{(12) and } (A \cap B' \subseteq A \cup B')
\end{aligned}
$$

It should be noted that other methods of solution are possible   As in geometry and most branches of mathematics, alternative solutions are often, and indeed usually, possible.

Example 2.   Simplify the set expression

$$[A \cap (B \cup A')] \cup B.$$

Solution:

$$
\begin{aligned}
[A \cap (B \cup A')] \cup B &= [(A \cap B) \cup (A \cap A')] \cup B && \text{(3(a))} \\
&= [(A \cap B) \cup \phi] \cup B && \text{(6(a))} \\
&= (A \cap B) \cup B && \text{(4(b))} \\
&= B. && \text{(8(b))}
\end{aligned}
$$

Some of the steps in the above solution may be omitted after facility in working with the basic identities has been attained.

EXERCISE 7.5

Prove the following set identities.

1. $(S \cap U)' \cup S' = S'$.

2. $(\phi \cap A) \cup B = B$.

3. $A' \cup (A \cap B) = A' \cup B$.

4. $X \cap Y \cap X' = \phi$.

5. $(A \cap B')' \cup B = A' \cup B$.

6. $(P \cup Q') \cap (P' \cap Q)' = P \cup Q'$.

7. $(M' \cap \phi)' \cap M = M$.

8. State and prove the dual identities in questions (1) to (7).

Simplify the following set expressions.

9. $A \cup A' \cup B$.

10. $(P \cap U)' \cap P$.

11. $(P \cup U)' \cup P$.

12. $(A \cap B) \cup (A' \cup B)$.

13. $[M \cap (N \cup M')] \cup N$.

14. $(A \cap U) \cup A'$.

15. $(A \cup \phi) \cap A'$.

16. $(A \cap B) \cup B \cup [(A \cap B) \cap (C \cup D)]$.

7.6. The Fundamental Identities

As was stated in Section 7.5, the fundamental identities may be regarded as axioms or we may prove them in terms of the verbal definitions of the symbols and operations using logical connectives and a process called set inclusion.

In using the process of set inclusion we select any arbitrary element x of a set A and if we can prove that x must then be an element of a set B, then $A \subseteq B$. Similarly, if $y \in B$ enables us to prove that $y \in A$, then $B \subseteq A$. If $A \subseteq B$ and $B \subseteq A$, then $A = B$.

By our definitions we know that if $x \in A \cap B$, then $x \in A$ *and* $x \in B$; also if $y \in A \cup B$, then $y \in A$ *or* $y \in B$. The logical connectives used here are the words *and* and *or*. We remember that *or* is interpreted as the inclusive alternative; y belongs to A or to B or to both.

If $x \in A'$, then $x \notin A$ also follows from the definition of the complement of a given set. The logical connective used here is the word *not*.

Fundamental Identity (11) (Section 7.5) is one of the simpler ones to prove and so we will discuss it first.

Example 1. Prove that
$$(A')' = A .$$

Solution: If
$$x \in (A')', \quad \text{then} \quad x \notin A' . \tag{1}$$

Since
$$x \notin A', \quad \text{then} \quad x \in A . \tag{2}$$

Hence
$$(A')' \subseteq A . \tag{3}$$

If
$$x \in A, \quad \text{then} \quad x \notin A' . \tag{4}$$

Since
$$x \notin A', \quad \text{then} \quad x \in (A')' . \tag{5}$$

Hence
$$A \subseteq (A')' . \tag{6}$$

Therefore
$$(A')' = A . \tag{7}$$

In lines (1) and (2), we use the definition of complement. In line (3), we use the logical law that, if x is an element of $(A')'$ implies that x must then be an element of A, then $(A')'$ is a subset of A. A similar argument is used in lines (4) to (6). Since lines (1) to (6) show that every element of $(A')'$ is an element of A and also that every element of A is an element of $(A')'$, then A and $(A')'$ must be the same set.

Example 2. Prove that
$$A \cap (B \cup C) = (A \cap B) \cup (A \cap C) .$$

Solution: If
$$x \in A \cap (B \cup C) ,$$

then
$$x \in A \qquad \text{and} \quad x \in B \cup C .$$

That is,
$$x \in A \qquad \text{and} \quad x \in B \text{ or } C .$$
$$x \in A \text{ and } B \quad \text{or} \quad x \in A \text{ and } C .$$
$$x \in A \cap B \quad \text{or} \quad x \in A \cap C .$$

Thus
$$x \in (A \cap B) \cup (A \cap C) .$$

Hence
$$A \cap (B \cup C) \subseteq (A \cap B) \cup (A \cap C) .$$

If
$$x \in (A \cap B) \cup (A \cap C) ,$$

then
$$x \in A \text{ and } B \quad \text{or} \quad x \in A \text{ and } C .$$

That is,

$$x \in A \quad \text{and} \quad x \in B \text{ or } C.$$
$$x \in A \quad \text{and} \quad x \in B \cup C.$$

Thus

$$x \in A \cap (B \cup C).$$

Hence

$$(A \cap B) \cup (A \cap C) \subseteq A \cap (B \cup C).$$

Therefore

$$A \cap (B \cup C) = (A \cap B) \cup (A \cap C).$$

Example 3. Prove that

$$A \cup (A \cap B) = A.$$

In this case we will assume that if $A \subseteq B$, then $A \cup B = B$ (Fundamental Identity (12)).

Solution: If

$$x \in A \cap B,$$

then

$$x \in A \text{ and } B;$$

that is,

$$x \in A.$$

Hence

$$(A \cap B) \subseteq A.$$

Therefore

$$(A \cap B) \cup A = A. \tag{12}$$

Example 4. Prove that

$$\phi' = U.$$

In this case we must remember that all elements are elements of the universe under discussion and no $x \in \phi$.

Solution: If

$$x \in \phi',$$

then

$$x \notin \phi.$$

Thus

$$x \in U.$$

Therefore

$$\phi' \subseteq U.$$

If

$$x \in U,$$

then

$$x \notin \phi.$$

Thus
$$x \in \phi'.$$

Hence
$$U \subseteq \phi'.$$

Therefore
$$\phi' = U.$$

EXERCISE 7.6

1. Using the method of set inclusion prove each of the fundamental identities in Section 7.5 (page 210).

7.7. Cartesian Product

We recall that the set
$$\{(x, y) \mid x \in S, \, y \in T\}$$

is the set of all ordered pairs (x, y) that can be formed by choosing x from a set S and y from a set T.

Example 1. If $S = \{0, 1, 2\}$ and $T = \{4, 5\}$, then
$$\{(x, y) \mid x \in S, \, y \in T\}$$

is the set of ordered pairs
$$\{(0, 4), (0, 5), (1, 4), (1, 5), (2, 4), (2, 5)\}.$$

This set of ordered pairs is called the Cartesian product set $S \times T$ (read S cross T). We note that the Cartesian product set $T \times S$ or $\{(x, y) \mid x \in T, \, y \in S\}$ is *not* the same set of ordered pairs although it will contain the same number of elements. The set S contains three members and the set T, two members. Both $S \times T$ and $T \times S$ contain six members, each member being an ordered pair of numbers.
$$T \times S = \{(4, 0), (5, 0), (4, 1), (5, 1), (4, 2), (5, 2)\}.$$

We know from Cartesian plane geometry that there is a one-to-one correspondence between the elements of the set $Re \times Re$ or $\{(x, y) \mid x \in Re, \, y \in Re\}$ and the points of the Cartesian plane.

From this example, it would appear that if a set A contains r elements and a set B contains s elements, then the set $A \times B$ will contain rs elements. A lattice representation of $A \times B$ can be formed easily if A and B are finite sets with a reasonably small number of elements.

Example 2.   Find the number of elements in $A \times B$ if $A = \{1, 2, 3, 4\}$ and $B = \{a, b, c\}$.

Solution: ·

$\begin{smallmatrix} & B \\ A & \end{smallmatrix}$	a	b	c
1	$(1, a)$	$(1, b)$	$(1, c)$
2	$(2, a)$	$(2, b)$	$(2, c)$
3	$(3, a)$	$(3, b)$	$(3, c)$
4	$(4, a)$	$(4, b)$	$(4, c)$

From this we see that $A \times B$ contains 12 elements. A contains 4 elements, B contains 3 elements, and $A \times B$ contains 4×3 elements.

Another way of observing the number of elements in $A \times B$ is by means of a tree diagram.

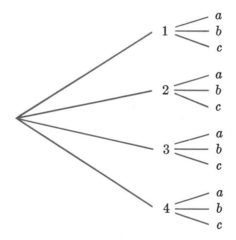

We note that the first member of each ordered pair has associated with it each element of the second set as a second member of an ordered pair.   In the example, A contains 4 elements; each of these elements is paired in turn with each element of the set B and thus three ordered pairs are formed with each of the 4 elements of A as a first member.   The total number of elements is, therefore, $4 \times 3 = 12$.

If $A = \{2, 3, 5\}$, the Cartesian product set $A \times A$ will contain $3 \times 3 = 9$ elements.   If we are asked for the subset of $A \times A$ which has as elements the ordered pairs which pair only *distinct* elements of A, the elements $(2, 2)$, $(3, 3)$, and $(5, 5)$ are not needed.   From the first member 2, we can form two ordered pairs $(2, 3)$ and $(2, 5)$, and similarly for each of the three first members.   The number of elements in the subset is $3 \times 2 = 6$.   There are 3 choices for the first member and, for *each* of these choices, there are 2 members for the second choice.

EXERCISE 7.7

1. If $A = \{a, b, c, d\}$ and $B = \{r, s\}$, list the elements of $A \times B$ and $B \times A$.

2. If $P = \{1, 2, 3, 4, 5\}$, list the elements of $P \times P$.

3. If $P = \{1, 2, 3, 4, 5\}$, list the elements of the subset of $P \times P$ that consists of all ordered pairs in $P \times P$ in which the first member is not equal to the second member.

4. In questions (2) and (3), state the number of elements in the sets listed.

5. Find

$$\{(x, y) \mid x \in S, \ y \in T\}$$

if

(a) $S = \{-2, -1, 0, 1, 2\}$, $T = \{0, 1\}$;

(b) $S = \{1, 2, 3\}$, $T = \{0\}$;

(c) $S = \{0\}$, $T = \{y \in N \mid y < 10\}$;

(d) $S = \{x \in N \mid x < 12 \text{ and } x \text{ is prime}\}$, $T = \{x \in N \mid 4x \le 12\}$.

6. In question (5), state the number of elements in S, in T, and in $S \times T$.

7. How many elements are in $A \times B$ if $A = \{0, 1, 2, 3\}$ and $B = \phi$?

8. How many elements are in $\phi \times \phi$?

9. If $A = \{-1, 0, 1\}$, $B = \{1, 2\}$, $C = \{0, 1\}$, list the elements in $A \times B \times C$ and $B \times A \times C$.

7.8. Number of Elements in A∪B

If $A = \{1, 2, 3, 4, 5\}$ and $B = \{3, 4, 5, 6\}$, then $A \cap B = \{3, 4, 5\}$ and $A \cup B = \{1, 2, 3, 4, 5, 6\}$. We see that the number of elements in A is 5, in B is 4, in $A \cap B$ is 3, and in $A \cup B$ is 6. We will represent the number of elements in a given set as $n(A)$. In the example given, $n(A) = 5, n(B) = 4, n(A \cap B) = 3$, $n(A \cup B) = 6$.

We notice that $n(A \cup B)$ is *not* equal to $n(A) + n(B)$ but, in this example,

$$n(A \cup B) = n(A) + n(B) - n(A \cap B). \tag{1}$$

In general if we add the number of elements in A to the number of elements in B, we include the common elements in $A \cap B$ twice. In the example, the elements 3, 4, and 5 appear in both A and B, that is, in $A \cap B$, and are counted twice in adding the number of elements of A to the number of elements of B. In $A \cup B$ the common elements are counted once only and so the result in (1) is true in general.

Example 1. If $A = \{a, b, c, d, e, f\}$ and $B = \{e, f, g, h\}$, find the number of elements in $A \cap B$ and in $A \cup B$.

Solution:

$$A \cap B = \{e, f\}$$
$$n(A \cap B) = 2 .$$
$$n(A \cup B) = n(A) + n(B) - n(A \cap B)$$
$$= 6 + 4 - 2$$
$$= 8 .$$

EXERCISE 7.8

1. In each of the following examples, state the values of $n(A \times B)$, $n(A \cap B)$, and $n(A \cup B)$.
   (a) $A = \{-2, -1, 0, 1, 2\}$, $B = \{0, 1, 2, 3, 4\}$
   (b) $A = \{a, b, c, d\}$, $B = \{e, f, g\}$
   (c) $A = \{1, 2, 3, 4, 5\}$, $B = \{2, 3, 4\}$
   (d) $A = \{x \in N \mid x \leq 12, x \text{ is prime}\}$, $B = \{x \in N \mid x \leq 12, x \text{ is even}\}$
   (e) $A = \{x \in N \mid x < 10\}$, $B = \phi$

2. If P and Q are disjoint sets, give a formula for $n(P \cup Q)$ and $n(P \cap Q)$.

3. If $T \subset S$, what is the value of $n(T \cap S)$ and $n(T \cup S)$?

4. If $n(A \cup B) = n(A)$, what is the relationship between sets A and B?

5. If $n(R \cup S) = n(R) + n(S)$, what is the value of $n(R \cap S)$?

6. If $A = \{1, 2, 3\}$, $B = \{2, 3, 4\}$, $C = \{3, 5\}$, state the value of $n(A \cup B \cup C)$.

7.9. A×B×C and A∪B∪C

The ideas of the previous two sections can be extended to include more than two sets.　For example,

$$A \times B \times C = \{(x, y, z) \mid x \in A, y \in B, z \in C\} .$$

The set $A \times B \times C$ is a set of ordered triples, the first member of each triple being an element of set A, the second member, an element of set B, and the third member, an element of set C.　Again there is a one-to-one correspondence between the elements of the set $\{(x, y, z) \mid x, y, z \in Re\}$ and the points of Cartesian three-dimensional space.

The set

$$A \times B \times C \times D = \{(x, y, z, w) \mid x \in A, y \in B, z \in C, w \in D\}$$

extends the idea to four sets. Is there a correspondence between the set
$\{(x, y, z, w) \mid x, y, z, w \in Re\}$ and the points in any geometrical space?

Example 1. $A = \{1, 2, 3\}, B = \{2, 3\}, C = \{3, 4\}.$
$A \times B \times C = \{(1, 2, 3), (1, 2, 4), (1, 3, 3), (1, 3, 4), (2, 2, 3), (2, 2, 4),$
$\qquad\qquad (2, 3, 3), (2, 3, 4), (3, 2, 3), (3, 2, 4), (3, 3, 3), (3, 3, 4)\}.$

In this example, $n(A) = 3$, $n(B) = 2$, $n(C) = 2$ and $n(A \times B \times C) = 3 \times 2 \times 2 = 12$. Again, a tree diagram may prove helpful in setting up the ordered triples.

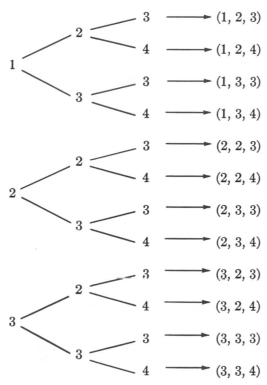

We know that if $n(A) = r \cdot n(B) = s$, then $n(A \times B) = rs$.
It would appear that there is a natural extension of this to any number of sets and that if

$$n(A_1) = a_1, \qquad n(A_2) = a_2, \qquad \cdots, \qquad n(A_n) = a_n,$$

then

$$n(A_1 \times A_2 \times \cdots \times A_n) = a_1 a_2 \cdots a_n$$

Returning to the example where $n(A) = 3$, $n(B) = 2$, and $n(C) = 2$, we see that $n(A \times B) = 6$ as found in Section 7.7. Each of these 6 ordered pairs can, in turn, be paired with one element of C to produce one element of $A \times B \times C$. The 6 ordered pairs of $A \times B$ produce 6 ordered triples with the element 3 of C and a further 6 ordered triples with the element 4 of C. The total number of elements in $A \times B \times C$ is, therefore, $6 \times 2 = 12$.

Knowing that $n(A \cup B) = n(A) + n(B) - n(A \cap B)$ and using the identities established in the algebra of sets, we can calculate the number of elements in $A \cup B \cup C$.

$$\begin{aligned}
n(A \cup B \cup C) &= n[A \cup (B \cup C)] \\
&= n(A) + n(B \cup C) - n[A \cap (B \cup C)] \\
&= n(A) + n(B) + n(C) - n(B \cap C) - n[(A \cap B) \cup (A \cap C)] \\
&= n(A) + n(B) + n(C) - n(B \cap C) - \\
&\quad [n(A \cap B) + n(A \cap C) - n((A \cap B) \cap (A \cap C))] \\
&= n(A) + n(B) + n(C) - n(B \cap C) - n(A \cap B) - n(A \cap C) \\
&\quad + n(A \cap B \cap C).
\end{aligned}$$

Note that in the last line we have used the result that

$$(A \cap B) \cap (A \cap C) = A \cap A \cap B \cap C = A \cap B \cap C.$$

This formula appears to be rather complicated but, by examining a Venn diagram, we should be able to interpret it more easily.

In the Venn diagram, we have indicated by the letters, p, q, r, s, t, u, w, the number of elements in each of the subsets of $A \cup B \cup C$. We see that

$$\begin{aligned}
n(A \cup B \cup C) &= p + q + r + s + t + u + w \\
n(A) &= p + s + t + w, \\
n(B) &= q + s + u + w, \\
n(C) &= r + t + u + w.
\end{aligned}$$

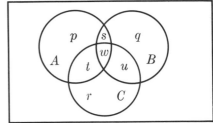

Thus

$$\begin{aligned}
n(A) + n(B) + n(C) &= p + q + r + 2s + 2t + 2u + 3w \\
&= n(A \cup B \cup C) + s + t + u + 2w. \\
n(A \cap B) &= s + w, \\
n(B \cap C) &= u + w, \\
n(A \cap C) &= t + w, \\
n(A \cap B \cap C) &= w \\
n(A \cap B) + n(B \cap C) + n(A \cap C) &= s + t + u + 3w.
\end{aligned}$$

Therefore

$$n(A \cup B \cup C) = n(A) + n(B) + n(C) - (s + t + u) - 2w$$
$$= n(A) + n(B) + n(C) - (s + t + u + 3w) + w$$
$$= n(A) + n(B) + n(C) - n(A \cap B) - n(B \cap C)$$
$$- n(A \cap C) + n(A \cap B \cap C).$$

Example 2. If $A = \{1, 2, 3, 4, 5\}$, $B = \{3, 4, 5, 6\}$, $C = \{5, 6, 7,\}$ find

$$n(A \times B \times C) \quad \text{and} \quad n(A \cup B \cup C).$$

Solution:

$$n(A \times B \times C) = 5 \times 4 \times 3 = 60.$$
$$n(A \cup B \cup C) = n(A) + n(B) + n(C) - n(A \cap B) - n(B \cap C) - n(A \cap C)$$
$$+ n(A \cap B \cap C)$$
$$= 5 + 4 + 3 - 3 - 2 - 1 + 1$$
$$= 7.$$

EXERCISE 7.9

1. If $A = \{a, b, c, d\}$, $B = \{b, c, d, e\}$, $C = \{c, d, e, f, g\}$, find the number of elements in $A \times B \times C$ and in $A \cup B \cup C$.

2. For the following sets P, Q, R, find $n(P \times Q \times R)$ and $n(P \cup Q \cup R)$.
    (a) $P = \{-2, -1, 0, 1, 2\}$, $Q = \{0, 1, 2, 3\}$, $R = \{2, 3\}$
    (b) $P = \{1, 2, 3\}$, $Q = \{1, 2, 3, 4\}$, $R = \{1, 2, 3, 4, 5\}$
    (c) $P = \{a, b, c\}$, $Q = \{d, e, f\}$, $R = \{g, h\}$
    (d) $P = \{1, 2, 3, 4\}$, $Q = \{0\}$, $R = \{0, 1, 2\}$
    (e) $P = \{0, 5, 10\}$, $Q = \{10\}$, $R = \phi$

3. If $A = \{1, 2, 3, 4\}$, what is the value of $n(A \times A \times A)$ and $n(A \cup A \cup A)$?

4. If $n(A) = 2$, $n(B) = 3$, $n(C) = 5$, and $A \subset B \subset C$, find the value of $n(A \cup B \cup C)$.

5. If $A = \{1, 2, 3, 4\}$, find the number of elements in the subset of $A \times A \times A$ that has three distinct members in each ordered triple.

6. If $n(A) = 8$, find (i) $n(A \times A \times A)$ and (ii) the number of elements in $A \times A \times A$ that have three distinct members in each ordered triple.

7. If P, Q, and R are disjoint sets, state a formula for $n(P \cup Q \cup R)$.

8. If $n(A) = 6$, what is the value of $n(A \times A \times A)$ and $n(A \cup A \cup A)$?

9. If $A = \{0, 1, 2\}$, $B = \{-1, 0\}$, $C = \{2, 3\}$, $D = \{1, 2, 3\}$, calculate the value of $n(A \cup B \cup C \cup D)$.

7.10. Statistics of Attributes

One interesting application of the previous two sections is in checking or analysing certain statistical data.   In many cases a Venn diagram may be sufficient to solve the problem, while in other cases the formulae developed in Section 7.9 may have to be used.

Example 1.   In a certain high school there are 187 students in Grade 13.   Of these students

> 99 study mathematics,
> 70 study physics,
> 61 study chemistry,
> 46 study both mathematics and physics,
> 22 study both physics and chemistry,
> 43 study both mathematics and chemistry,
> 21 study mathematics, chemistry, and physics.

How many students study at least one of these subjects?

Solution: Let

$$M = \{\text{students of mathematics}\},$$
$$P = \{\text{students of physics}\},$$
$$C = \{\text{students of chemistry}\}.$$

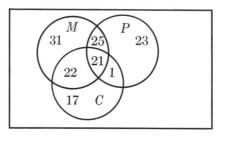

Since 21 students study all three subjects, we can enter in the number 21 in the section representing $M \cap P \cap C$ in the Venn diagram.

46 students study mathematics and physics; so that will be the number in $M \cap P$.   21 of these, however, are already entered in $M \cap P \cap C$ leaving 25 to be entered in the remaining portion of $M \cap P$, that is, in $M \cap P \cap C'$.   Similarly, the numbers 22 and 1 can be entered in $M \cap C \cap P'$ and $C \cap P \cap M'$, respectively.

On examining the diagram, we see that we have now accounted for 68 students who study mathematics along with either or both of physics and chemistry.   Since there are 99 mathematics students in all, the remaining 31 must study mathematics only and that number can be entered in the section representing $M \cap P' \cap C'$. Similarly the numbers 17 and 23 can be entered in the sections representing $C \cap M' \cap P'$ and $P \cap C' \cap M'$, respectively.

When we now total the numbers in the seven regions, we obtain a total of 140 students who study at least one of the three subjects.   Therefore

$$M \cup P \cup C = 140 \,.$$

Alternatively, from the given data we know that

$$n(M) = 99, n(P) = 70, n(C) = 61,$$
$$n(M \cap P) = 46, n(P \cap C) = 22, n(M \cap C) = 43,$$
$$n(M \cap P \cap C) = 21.$$

Therefore

$$
\begin{aligned}
n(M \cup P \cup C) &= n(M) + n(P) + n(C) - n(M \cap P) - n(P \cap C) \\
&\quad - n(M \cap C) + n(M \cap P \cap C) \\
&= 99 + 70 + 61 - 46 - 22 - 43 + 21 \\
&= 251 - 111 \\
&= 140.
\end{aligned}
$$

Therefore 140 students study at least one of the subjects.

Example 2. In a certain factory the following data were compiled from a survey of employees.

> 64 were Canadian born.
> 37 were married.
> 49 were male.
> 33 of the Canadians were married.
> 21 of the males were married.
> 30 of the Canadian born were male.
> 14 were married Canadian born males.

Analyse the consistency of the data.

Solution: Let

$$A = \{\text{Canadian born}\},$$
$$B = \{\text{married}\},$$
$$C = \{\text{males}\}.$$

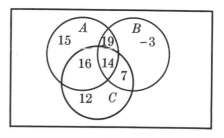

When we enter the numbers in the various regions of the Venn diagram, we see that $n(B \cap A' \cap C') = -3$. This is impossible since it symbolizes the statement that the number of non-Canadian married females is -3. We conclude, therefore, that the data are inconsistent and that the compiler was in error.

EXERCISE 7.10

1. In a survey of 82 people the following information was obtained: 41 of those interviewed were male, 42 had voted Liberal at the last election, 38 were married, 12 of the males were married, 21 of the males had voted Liberal, 10 of the Liberal voters were married, and 4 of the Liberal voters were married males. How many unmarried females had not voted Liberal?

2. In an advertisement, a firm which produced three products A, B, and C stated that, of 10,000 families surveyed,

> 6974 used product A,
> 5417 used product B,
> 7246 used product C,
> 2950 used both A and B,
> 4623 used both A and C,
> 3545 used both B and C, and
> 1720 used all three products.

Why should the firm be prosecuted for fraudulent advertising?

3. Data obtained from a survey of 200 students were reported as follows.

> 114 studied Mathematics.
> 100 studied History.
> 67 studied French.
> 48 studied Mathematics and History.
> 41 studied Mathematics and French.
> 37 studied History and French.
> 17 studied all three.

How many students studied

(a) exactly two of these subjects?

(b) exactly one of these subjects?

(c) none of these subjects?

4. From 600 scientists interviewed, the following data were obtained.

> 339 had studied physics.
> 345 had studied chemistry.
> 315 had studied biology.
> 151 had studied physics and chemistry.
> 157 had studied physics and biology.
> 175 had studied chemistry and biology.

Assuming that all 600 had studied at least one of these subjects, how many had studied all three?

5. Of 1200 students in Dudgeon High School, 900 attended the first football game. The team lost 54-0 and only 400 attended the second game.

(a) What is the minimum number that could have seen both games?

(b) If 250 attended both games, how many did not attend either game?

6. A dime, a nickel, and a quarter were tossed together 100 times and turned up heads 54, 47, and 49 times, respectively. The dime and nickel were heads together 25 times; the dime and quarter were heads together 27 times; the nickel and quarter were heads together 22 times. If all 3 were tails 11 times, how many times were all 3 heads?

Chapter Summary

$x \in A$ x is an element of set A.

$A \subseteq B$ A is a subset of B.

$A \cap B$ The set of all elements in both A and B

$A \cup B$ The set of all elements in A or B or both

A' The complement of A

Fundamental Identities

(1) (a) $A \cap B = B \cap A$.   (b) $A \cup B = B \cup A$.

(2) (a) $(A \cap B) \cap C = A \cap (B \cap C)$.   (b) $(A \cup B) \cup C = A \cup (B \cup C)$.

(3) (a) $A \cap (B \cup C) = (A \cap B) \cup (A \cap C)$.   (b) $A \cup (B \cap C) = (A \cup B) \cap (A \cup C)$.

(4) (a) $A \cap \phi = \phi$.   (b) $A \cup \phi = A$.

(5) (a) $A \cap U = A$.   (b) $A \cup U = U$.

(6) (a) $A \cap A' = \phi$.   (b) $A \cup A' = U$.

(7) (a) $A \cap A = A$.   (b) $A \cup A = A$.

(8) (a) $A \cap (A \cup B) = A$.   (b) $A \cup (A \cap B) = A$.

(9) (a) $(A \cap B)' = A' \cup B'$.   (b) $(A \cup B)' = A' \cap B'$.

(10) (a) $U' = \phi$.   (b) $\phi' = U$.

(11) $(A')' = A$.

(12) $A \subseteq B$ iff $A \cap B = A$ and $A \subseteq B$ iff $A \cup B = B$.

$$S \times T = \{(x, y) \mid x \in S, y \in T\}.$$
$$n(S \times T) = n(S) \times n(T).$$
$$n(S \cup T) = n(S) + n(T) - n(S \cap T).$$
$$n(S \cup T \cup R) = n(S) + n(T) + n(R) - n(S \cap T) - n(S \cap R)$$
$$- n(R \cap T) + n(S \cap T \cap R).$$

REVIEW EXERCISE 7

1. If $A = \{2, 3, 5, 7, 11, 13\}$, $B = \{1, 3, 5, 7, 11, 13\}$, list the elements of the sets $A \cap B$, $A \cup B$. List the elements of set $C = \{x \in B \mid x \text{ is a prime}\}$.

2. If $U = \{x \in N \mid x < 20\}$, $A = \{x \in U \mid x \text{ is a prime}\}$, $B = \{x \in U \mid x \text{ is odd}\}$, list the elements of

$$A \cap B, \quad A \cup B, \quad A', \quad B', \quad (A \cap B)', \quad (A \cup B)', \quad A \cap B'.$$

3. Construct Venn diagrams to illustrate the following sets.

    (a) $A \cap B'$ (b) $A' \cap B$

    (c) $A \cap B$ when $A \subseteq B$ (d) $A \cup B$ when $A \subseteq B$

   (e) $A \cup A' \cup B$ (f) $(A \cap B) \cap (A' \cap B)$

   (g) $(P \cap Q')' \cup Q$ (h) $A \cap B \cap C'$

   (i) $(P \cap Q) \cup R$ (j) $A' \cap B' \cap C'$

4. Use the fundamental identities to simplify the following set expressions.

   (a) $A \cup A' \cup B$ (b) $(C \cap D) \cup (C' \cap D)$

   (c) $(P \cup Q) \cap P'$ (d) $[(C \cap \phi) \cup C]'$

   (e) $(R \cup S) \cup R \cup [(R \cup S) \cap (P \cup Q)]$

5. $A = \{1, 2, 3, 4\}$, $B = \{1, 2, 3, 4, 5, 6\}$, $C = \{5, 6, 7\}$

   (a) State which of the following are true.

       (i) $A \subseteq B$.   (ii) $C \subseteq B$.   (iii) $A \cap B = A$.

       (iv) $A \cap B = \phi$.   (v) $A \cap C = \phi$.   (vi) $A \cup C = B$.

   (b) Draw a Venn diagram to illustrate the relationship between the sets A, B, and C.

6. If $A = \{1, 2, 3, 4\}$, $B = \{1, 2, 3, 4, 5, 6\}$, $C = \{5, 6, 7\}$, find the value of each of the following.

   (a) $n(A \times C)$ (b) $n(A \times B \times C)$

   (c) $n(A \cap B)$ (d) $n(A \cup C)$

   (e) $n(B \cap C)$ (f) $n(A \cup B \cup C)$

7. If $A = \{1, 2, 3, 4\}$, find the number of elements in the subset of $A \times A$ for which the first and second members of each ordered pair are unlike.

Supplementary.

8. Prove, by using set inclusion, that

   (a) $A \cup A' \cup B = U$,   (b) $(P \cap Q') \cup Q = P \cup Q$,

   (c) $X \cap Y \cap X' = \phi$,   (d) $(M' \cap \phi)' \cap M = M$.

9. In a class of 36 students, each of whom must study French or Latin, 31 study French and 15 study both French and Latin. How many study Latin?

10. A display was given by the gymnastic club of a certain school. 94 visitors attended on the first day, 123 on the second day, and 122 on the third day. 47 attended on both the first and second days, 38 on both the first and third days, and 45 on both the second and third days. If 22 visitors attended on all three days, how many different visitors saw the display?

Chapter 8

ARRANGEMENTS AND SUBSETS

8.1. Arrangements of a Set

If two sets A and B contain r elements and s elements, respectively, we know from Chapter 7 that the Cartesian product set $A \times B$ contains rs elements. This could be reworded to state that, if a certain act can be performed in r different ways and if, for each of these ways, a second act can be performed in s different ways, then the two acts can be performed successively in rs different ways.

Consider the set of five elements $A = \{a, b, c, d, e\}$. The number of elements in the subset of $A \times A \times A$, in which no two of the members in each ordered triple are like, is $5 \times 4 \times 3$ or 60. We can arrive at this by considering that we have 3 spaces ☐☐☐ to fill for each element of $A \times A \times A$. The first space can be filled with any one of the five letters. For each of these ways the second space can be filled with any one of the four remaining letters. Hence the first two spaces can be filled in $5 \times 4 = 20$ different ways. For *each* of these ways, the third space can be filled with any of the three remaining letters. The three spaces can, therefore, be filled in $5 \times 4 \times 3$ or 60 different ways.

In this case we have sixty 3-arrangements of five objects. We note that the set $A \times A \times A$ contains $5 \times 5 \times 5$ or 125 elements, each of which is an ordered triple, and also includes ordered triples with two or three like letters.

This can be extended to include arrangements of any finite number of elements from any finite set.

DEFINITION. An r-arrangement of n objects is an *ordered* selection of r of the objects ($r \in W$, $n \in N$).

The number of r-arrangements may be deduced in the same way as we found the number of 3-arrangements of five objects.

n	$n-1$	$n-2$	$\cdots$	$n-(r-1)$

We may select the first object in n different ways. For *each* of these ways, the second object can be selected from any one of the remaining $(n-1)$ objects.

The first two objects can, therefore, be selected in $n(n-1)$ different ways and, for *each* of these ways, the third object can be selected in $(n-2)$ different ways. The first three objects can be selected in $n(n-1)(n-2)$ ways. Continuing this procedure, the rth object can be selected in $n-(r-1)$ different ways $(r \leq n)$. The r objects can be selected in $n(n-1)(n-2)\cdots(n-r+1)$ different ways.

Therefore, the number of r-arrangements of n objects is

$$n(n-1)(n-2)\cdots(n-r+1)\qquad(r \leq n).$$

Various symbols are used to indicate the number of r-arrangements of n objects taken r at a time. The one we shall use in this text is $n_{(r)}$. Others used are $P(n, r)$, $P\binom{n}{r}$, and $_nP_r$. The number of arrangements of five objects taken three at a time is $5_{(3)}$ or $5 \times 4 \times 3$.

Example 1. Find the number of 4-arrangements of six objects.

Solution: Number of 4-arrangements $= 6_{(4)}$
$$= 6 \times 5 \times 4 \times 3$$
$$= 360 .$$

Example 2. How many different licence plates, each containing five digits, can be made using the ten digits 0 to 9 if
    (a) the first digit cannot be 0 and repetition of digits is not allowed?
    (b) the first digit cannot be 0 but repetitions are allowed?

In how many arrangements in (b) do repetitions actually occur?

Solution:

    (a) Since the first digit cannot be 0, there are nine choices for the first digit. The other digits form 4-arrangements of the nine remaining digits. Therefore

$$\text{number of licence plates} = 9 \times 9_{(4)}$$
$$= 9 \times 9 \times 8 \times 7 \times 6$$
$$= 27{,}216 .$$

    (b) If repetitions are allowed, there are ten choices for each digit after the first. Therefore

$$\text{number of licence plates} = 9 \times 10^4$$
$$= 9 \times 10{,}000$$
$$= 90{,}000 .$$

The number of arrangements in which repetitions occur is

$$90{,}000 - 27{,}216$$
$$= 62{,}784 .$$

Example 3. How many arrangements of all of the letters of the word *numbers* are possible if

(a) there is no restriction?

(b) the letter *s* must be last?

(c) the vowels must be together?

Solution:

(a) Number of arrangements with no restrictions

$$= 7_{(7)}$$
$$= 7 \times 6 \times 5 \times 4 \times 3 \times 2 \times 1$$
$$= 5040 .$$

(b) Since *s* must be placed last, the other six letters may be arranged in $6_{(6)}$ ways. Therefore

number of arrangements with *s* last

$$= 6_{(6)}$$
$$= 6 \times 5 \times 4 \times 3 \times 2 \times 1$$
$$= 720 .$$

(c) Since the vowels must be together, they can be considered as one object. Therefore the number of arrangements is $6_{(6)}$. But for *each* of these arrangements the *u* and *e* may be interchanged without altering the position of the other letters. Therefore

total number of arrangements with vowels together

$$- 2 \times 6_{(6)}$$
$$= 2 \times 720$$
$$= 1440 .$$

EXERCISE 8.1

1. Find the value of
   (i) $4_{(2)}$,   (ii) $16_{(2)}$,   (iii) $7_{(4)}$,
   (iv) $15_{(3)}$,   (v) $5_{(5)}$,   (vi) $6_{(4)}$.

2. Find the number of 3-arrangements of eight objects.

3. Find the number of 2-arrangements of seven objects.

4. Find the number of 5-arrangements of five objects.

5. Find the number of 6-arrangements of six objects.

6. How many three-digit numbers can be made from the digits 1, 2, 3, 4, 5 if repetitions are not allowed?

7. How many three-digit numbers can be made from the digits 0, 1, 2, 3, 4, if repetitions are not allowed?

8. How many three-digit numbers can be made from the digits 0, 1, 2, 3, 4, if repetitions are allowed?

9. If there are five possible routes by which a driver can travel from Toronto to Ottawa and three possible routes from Ottawa to Montreal, how many different ways are there to travel from Toronto to Montreal via Ottawa?

10. If a dime, a nickel, and a quarter are tossed together, in how many different ways can they fall?

11. In how many ways can eight boys be arranged in a row if
    (a) there is no restriction?
    (b) two boys, John and Jim, must be together?
    (c) John and Jim must be kept apart?

12. How many batting orders are possible for a baseball team of nine players if the pitcher must bat in ninth position?

13. How many possible signals can be made using five different signal flags arranged one above the other?

14. In how many ways can a chairman, a vice-chairman, and a secretary be chosen from a committee of nine members?

15. There are four routes between two towns. In how many ways can a driver travel by one route and return by a different route?

16. In how many ways can the letters of the word *factor* be arranged if
    (a) there is no restriction?
    (b) the first letter must be a consonant?
    (c) the second and fifth letters must be vowels?

17. The dial of a combination lock has one hundred different numbers on it. The lock is opened by dialing three different numbers in a particular order. How many different combinations can be produced?

18. There are ten teams in a hockey league. How many games are in the schedule if each team must play each of the other teams once at home and once away from home?   90

19. There are six teams in another hockey league. Each team must play each of the other teams seven times on home ice and seven times away from home. How many games are played each season?

8.2. Factorials

In Section 8.1 we have seen that the number of 3-arrangements of five objects is

$$5_{(3)} = 5 \times 4 \times 3,$$

and that the number of 5-arrangements of five objects is

$$5_{(5)} = 5 \times 4 \times 3 \times 2 \times 1.$$

In the latter case we have the product of all the natural numbers from 1 to 5 inclusive.   Such a product is written as 5! and read as "five factorial".   We may understand that

$$n_{(n)} = n! = n(n-1)(n-2)\cdots(3)(2)(1)$$

is the product of all the natural numbers from 1 to n inclusive.   (Note that we must assume that n is a natural number.)

Probably the most rigorous way to define factorial notation is by a recursive definition,

$$0! = 1, \quad 1 \times 0 = 1$$
$$(n+1)! = n!(n+1) \quad (n \geq 0).$$

It may appear strange to define 0! as 1, but the reason for this definition will appear later.

From the recursive definition, we obtain

$$1! = 0!(1) = 1,$$
$$2! = 1!(2) = 1 \times 2,$$
$$3! = 2!(3) = 1 \times 2 \times 3,$$
$$4! = 3!(4) = 1 \times 2 \times 3 \times 4,$$

and so on, in agreement with our more intuitive concept of the product of all the natural numbers from 1 to n inclusive.

The number of r-arrangements of n elements may be expressed in terms of factorials.   We know that

$$5_{(3)} = 5 \times 4 \times 3 = \frac{5 \times 4 \times 3 \times 2 \times 1}{2 \times 1}$$
$$= \frac{5!}{2!}.$$

$$16_{(4)} = 16 \times 15 \times 14 \times 13$$
$$= \frac{16 \times 15 \times 14 \times 13 \times 12!}{12!}$$
$$= \frac{16!}{12!}.$$

Similarly,

$$n_{(r)} = n(n-1)(n-2)\cdots(n-r+1)$$
$$= \frac{n(n-1)(n-2)\cdots(n-r+1)(n-r)!}{(n-r)!}.$$

Therefore

$$n_{(r)} = \frac{n!}{(n-r)!}.$$

Note: This implies that

$$n_{(n)} = \frac{n!}{(n-n)!}$$
$$= \frac{n!}{0!}.$$

But we know that

$$n_{(n)} = n!.$$

That is,

$$\frac{n!}{0!} = n!.$$

This will only be true if $0!$ is equal to 1, which agrees with the definition that $0! = 1$.   With any other definition we would lose consistency.

Example 1.   Evaluate $\dfrac{52!}{50!}$

Solution:

$$\frac{52!}{50!} = \frac{52\cdot51\cdot50!}{50!}$$
$$= 52\cdot51$$
$$= 2652.$$

Example 2.   Solve for n in $\dfrac{(n+2)!}{n!} = 56.$

Solution:

$$\frac{(n+2)!}{n!} = 56.$$
$$\frac{(n+2)(n+1)n!}{n!} = 56.$$
$$(n+2)(n+1) = 56.$$
$$n^2 + 3n + 2 = 56.$$
$$n^2 + 3n - 54 = 0.$$
$$(n+9)(n-6) = 0.$$

Therefore

$$n = 6 \quad (n \in N).$$

State why $n = -9$ can't be

Example 3.   Prove that $(n+1)_{(r+1)} = (n+1)n_{(r)}$.

Solution:

$$(n+1)_{(r+1)} = \frac{(n+1)!}{(n+1-r-1)!}$$

$$= \frac{(n+1)n!}{(n-r)!}$$

$$= (n+1)\frac{n!}{(n-r)!}$$

$$= (n+1)n_{(r)}.$$

Therefore

$$(n+1)_{(r+1)} = (n+1)n_{(r)}.$$

EXERCISE 8.2

In each of the following questions,

$$n, r \in N, \quad n \geq r.$$

1. Find the value of each of the following.

    (a) $\dfrac{8!}{6!}$ (b) $\dfrac{6!}{3!3!}$ (c) $\dfrac{20!}{19!}$

    (d) $\dfrac{8!}{5!3!}$ (e) $\dfrac{7!}{5!2!} + \dfrac{7!}{3!4!}$ (f) $\dfrac{20!}{17!3!}$

2. Express each of the following as a single factorial expression.

    (a) $(n+1)n!$ (b) $\dfrac{(n+7)!}{n+7}$ (c) $(n-r+1)(n-r)!$ ~~one longer~~

3. Simplify the following as far as possible.

    (a) $\dfrac{(n+5)!}{(n+3)!}$ (b) $\dfrac{n!}{(n-1)!}$

    (c) $\dfrac{(n+1)!}{n!}$ (d) $\dfrac{(n-r+1)!}{(n-r)!}$

    (e) $\dfrac{(n-r)!}{(n-r-1)!}$ (f) $\dfrac{(n-r+1)!}{(n-r-1)!}$ $(n-r)(n-r-1)$

4. Solve the following equations.

    (a) $\dfrac{(n+5)!}{(n+4)!} = 7.$ (b) $\dfrac{(n+2)!}{n!} = 20.$

    (c) $n_{(2)} = 30.$ (d) $\dfrac{n!}{2(n-2)!} = 6.$

    (e) $\dfrac{(n+1)!}{(n-1)!} = 12.$ (f) $\dfrac{(n-1)!}{(n-3)!} = 42.$

5. Prove that $n_{(r+1)} = (n-r)n_{(r)}$.

8.3. Arrangements with Like Elements

How many six-digit numbers can be made using the digits 1, 1, 1, 2, 2, 3? If the digits were all different, we know that the number of numbers would be 6!. In this case, however, certain of the digits are alike and interchanging the positions of the three 1's or the two 2's among themselves without altering the positions of the other digits would not produce another number. The number of arrangements must be less than 6!. Our problem is to discover the number of distinct arrangements possible. To do this we imagine some means of distinguishing among the like objects. We may, for instance, temporarily label the 1's and 2's with distinctive subscripts 1_1, 1_2, 1_3, 2_1, 2_2. In this case $1_1\,1_2\,1_3\,2_2\,3\,2_1$ would be a different arrangement from $1_2\,1_1\,1_3\,2_2\,3\,2_1$. The three 1's can then be rearranged among themselves in 3! ways without altering the position of the other digits. Similarly, the two 2's can be rearranged in 2! ways without altering the positions of the other digits. We shall assume that there are x arrangements of the six digits taken all at a time with three alike of one kind (the 1's) and two alike of another (the 2's).

Let the number of arrangements be x. If the three 1's were unlike, then, for *each* of these x arrangements, the 1's could be rearranged among themselves in 3! ways without altering the positions of the other digits.

Therefore the number of arrangements with unlike 1's would be $x \cdot 3!$. Similarly, if the two 2's were unlike, they could be rearranged in 2! ways without altering the positions of the other digits.

Therefore the number of arrangements with unlike 1's and 2's would be $x \cdot 3! \cdot 2!$.

But if the 1's and 2's were unlike, the number of arrangements would be 6!. Hence

$$x \cdot 3! \cdot 2! = 6!.$$

$$x = \frac{6!}{3!\,2!}$$

$$= 60.$$

Therefore the number of six-digit numbers is 60.

This process can obviously be extended to arrangements of any number of objects taken *all* at a time with certain of the objects alike.

To Find the Number of Arrangements of n Objects When Some Are Alike

To find the number of arrangements of n objects taken all at a time with n_1 alike of one kind, n_2 alike of a second, $\cdots$, n_r alike of an rth kind ($n \geq n_1 + n_2 + \cdots + n_r$), we proceed as follows.

Let the number of arrangements be x. If the n_1 like objects were unlike, then, for each of these x arrangements, the n_1 like objects could be rearranged among themselves in $n_1!$ ways without altering the positions of the other objects.

Therefore the number of arrangements would be $x \cdot n_1!$.

Similarly, if the n_2 like objects were unlike, each of these $x \cdot n_1!$ arrangements would give rise to $n_2!$ arrangements.

Therefore the number of arrangements would be $x \cdot n_1! \cdot n_2!$.

Similarly, if all the objects were unlike, the number of arrangements would be

$$x \cdot n_1! \cdot n_2! \cdots n_r!.$$

But if all n objects were unlike, the number of arrangements would be $n!$.   Hence

$$x \cdot n_1! \cdot n_2! \cdots n_r! = n!.$$

$$x = \frac{n!}{n_1! \, n_2! \cdots n_r!} \quad (n \geq n_1 + n_2 + \cdots + n_r).$$

Therefore the number of n-arrangements of n objects, if n_1 are alike of one kind, n_2 alike of a second, $\cdots$, n_r alike of an rth kind, is

$$\frac{n!}{n_1! \cdot n_2! \cdots n_r!}.$$

Example 1.   Find the number of ways of arranging the letters of the word Tennessee taken all at a time (a) if there is no restriction, (b) if the first two letters must be e.

Solution:

(a) $$\text{Number of arrangements} = \frac{9!}{4!2!2!}$$
$$= 3780.$$

(b)   Place two e's in the first two positions.   Therefore

$$\text{number of arrangements} = 1 \times \frac{7!}{2!2!2!}$$
$$= 630.$$

Example 2.   A man wished to travel from one point in a city to a second point which is five blocks south and six blocks east of his starting point.   In how many ways can he make the journey if he always travels either south or east?

Solution: If we consider a south-going route past one block as being represented by the letter S and an east-going route past one block as being represented by the letter E, then the problem is equivalent to the number of arrangements of eleven letters, five of which are S and six of which are E. Therefore

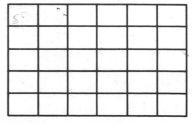

$$\text{number of routes} = \frac{11!}{6!5!} = \frac{11 \times 10 \times 9 \times 8 \times 7}{5 \times 4 \times 3 \times 2 \times 1} = 462.$$

Example 3. How many five-digit numbers can be formed from the digits 1, 2, 3, 4, 5, if the odd digits must always appear in ascending order?

Solution: Since the order of the odd digits cannot be altered, they may be considered as like digits.   Hence

$$\text{number of numbers} = \frac{5!}{3!}$$

$$= 20 .$$

EXERCISE 8.3

1. Evaluate the following.

   (a) $\dfrac{6!}{3!2!}$ (b) $\dfrac{8!}{3!5!}$ (c) $\dfrac{10!}{6!2!}$ (d) $\dfrac{12!}{7!4!}$

2. Find the number of arrangements of all the letters of each of the following.
   (a) Ottawa   (b) Toronto   (c) subset
   (d) algebra   (e) Mississippi   (f) element

3. In how many ways can all the letters of the word *factor* be arranged if the consonants must always appear in the order *f, c, t, r*?

4. How many six-digit numbers may be formed from the digits 1, 1, 1, 2, 3, 4?

5. Find the number of arrangements of all the letters of the word *parallel*.   In how many of the arrangements will the three *l*'s be together?

6. How many numbers greater than 3,000,000 can be formed from the digits 1, 2, 3, 3, 3, 4, 4?

7. How many numbers can be formed using all of the digits 1, 2, 2, 3, 3, 3, 4, if the odd digits must always occupy the odd positions?

8. How many possible routes may a person travel in order to go from one point in a city to a second point which is six blocks south and three blocks east, if he travels always in a southerly or easterly direction?

9. In the arrangements of all of the letters of the word *Toronto*, how many
   (a) start with the letter *o*?
   (b) start with two *o*'s?
   (c) start with one *o* with the second letter other than *o*?
   (d) start with three *o*'s?
   (e) start with two *o*'s with the third letter other than *o*?

10. In the arrangements of all of the letters of the word *Ottawa*, how many
    (a) start with *t*, with the second letter other than *t*?
    (b) start with *ta*?

11. How many numbers can be formed using all of the digits from 1 to 7 if the odd digits must always be in descending order and the even digits in ascending order?

12. How many odd numbers can be formed using all of the digits 1, 3, 4, 4, 5, 5?

8.4. Subsets of a Set

Consider the set $A = \{a, b, c, d, e\}$. One subset ϕ contains no elements; one subset, A itself, contains all five elements. It is also fairly obvious that there will be five different subsets each consisting of one element, $\{a\}, \{b\}, \{c\}, \{d\}, \{e\}$. However, the number of subsets each consisting of 2 or 3 or 4 elements of A is not so obvious. Since $n(A) = 5$, it is possible, in this case, to write out all of the subsets consisting of, say, three elements of A. These subsets are $\{a, b, c\}$, $\{a, b, d\}$, $\{a, b, e\}$, $\{a, c, d\}$, $\{a, c, e\}$, $\{a, d, e\}$, $\{b, c, d\}$, $\{b, c, e\}$, $\{b, d, e\}$, $\{c, d, e\}$. However, even with just these ten possible subsets, it requires care and is time consuming to have to list all of them in order to find the required number of subsets. It would be rather tedious to find the number of 40-element subsets of a set of one hundred elements in this way!

Returning to our example of the number of 3-element subsets (usually simply called 3-subsets) of a given set of five elements. The subset $\{a, b, c\}$ gives rise to 3! arrangements of its elements all three at a time. This is true for each of the 3-subsets of A, and if we let the number of 3-subsets be x, the number of 3-arrangements of the five elements of A is $x(3!)$. However, we know that the total number of 3-arrangements of five elements is $5_{(3)}$. Hence

$$x(3!) = 5_{(3)}.$$

$$x = \frac{5_{(3)}}{3!}.$$

Therefore the number of 3-subsets is $\dfrac{5 \times 4 \times 3}{3 \times 2 \times 1} = 10$. This agrees with the result of listing all the 3-subsets as we did above.

Extending this reasoning, we can develop a general method for finding the number of r-subsets of a set of n elements. We note of course, that $\{a, b, c\} = \{a, c, b\} = \{b, a, c\}$, etc. In selecting a subset of a given set, the order in which the elements are selected is immaterial. We can, therefore, define an r-subset as follows.

DEFINITION.   An r-subset of a set of n elements is a selection of r of the elements *without regard to order* $(r \in W, n \in N)$.

We could regard finding the number of r-arrangements of n objects as first finding the number of r-subsets of the set of n elements, and then finding the number of ways of rearranging the elements of each of the subsets.

To Find the Number of r-Subsets of a Set of n Elements

Let the number of r-subsets be x.   Each of the x subsets can be rearranged in $r!$ different orders.

Therefore the number of r-arrangements is $x(r!)$.

But the number of r-arrangements of n objects is $n_{(r)}$.   Hence

$$x(r!) = n_{(r)}.$$

$$x = \frac{n_{(r)}}{r!}.$$

Therefore the number of r-subsets is $\dfrac{n_{(r)}}{r!}$.

The symbol used for the number of r-subsets of a set of n elements is $\dbinom{n}{r}$

Therefore

$$\binom{n}{r} = \frac{n_{(r)}}{r!}.$$

Other symbols used are $C(n, r)$ and $_nC_r$.   Also, since

$$n_{(r)} = \frac{n!}{(n-r)!},$$

therefore

$$\binom{n}{r} = \frac{n!}{(n-r)!\,r!}.$$

Example 1.   Find the number of 2-subsets of a set of twelve elements.

Solution:

$$\text{Number of 2-subsets} = \binom{12}{2}$$

$$= \frac{12 \times 11}{2 \times 1}$$

$$= 66$$

Example 2.   Prove that $\dbinom{n}{r} = \dbinom{n}{n-r}$.

Solution:

$$\binom{n}{r} = \frac{n!}{(n-r)!\,r!}.$$

$$\binom{n}{n-r} = \frac{n!}{[n-(n+r)]!\,(n-r)!}$$

$$= \frac{n!}{(n-r)!\,r!}.$$

Therefore

$$\binom{n}{r} = \binom{n}{n-r}.$$

These examples indicate that in the more practical type of problem where an evaluation is necessary, as in Example 1, it is usually simpler to use the form $\binom{n}{r} = \frac{n_{(r)}}{r!}$, but in the more theoretical type of examples as in Example 2, the factorial form is usually the more useful.

Example 2 also gives a most useful result.

$$\binom{8}{6} = \frac{8 \times 7 \times 6 \times 5 \times 4 \times 3}{6 \times 5 \times 4 \times 3 \times 2 \times 1}.$$
$$\binom{8}{2} = \frac{8 \times 7}{2 \times 1}.$$

From Example 2, we know that $\binom{8}{6} = \binom{8}{2}$ and thus to evaluate $\binom{8}{6}$, it is obviously simpler to evaluate $\binom{8}{2}$. This is no accident. For every subset of r elements selected from a set of n elements, there must be a corresponding set of the $(n - r)$ elements which were *not* selected. In the example of the 3-subsets of the set $A = \{a, b, c, d, e\}$ used at the beginning of this section, corresponding to the subset $\{a, b, c\}$ of the elements selected, there is the subset $\{d, e\}$ of the elements not selected. If we form the corresponding subsets of elements not selected for each subset selected, we will obtain the ten 2-subsets of the set A.

Example 3. Find the number of 18-subsets of a set of twenty elements.

Solution:

$$\text{Number of subsets} = \binom{20}{18}$$
$$= \binom{20}{2}$$
$$= \frac{20 \times 19}{2 \times 1}$$
$$= 190.$$

Example 4. In a club with twelve members,
  (a) in how many ways can a committee of three be selected?
  (b) in how many ways can a president, secretary, and treasurer be appointed?

Solution:

  (a) Number of ways of selecting committee

$$= \binom{12}{3}$$
$$= \frac{12 \times 11 \times 10}{3 \times 2 \times 1}$$
$$= 220.$$

(b) Number of ways of appointing officers

$$= 12_{(3)}$$
$$= 12 \times 11 \times 10$$
$$= 1320 .$$

We note that in the first part a committee of John, Jane, and Tom is exactly the same committee as Jane, Tom, and John. The order of selection is unimportant. This indicates that 3-subsets are required.

In the second part the appointment of John as president, Jane as secretary, and Tom as treasurer is *not* the same as Jane as president, Tom as secretary, and John as treasurer.   The order is of importance and the number of 3-arrangements is required.

Example 5.   In how many ways can six 3's and four 2's be arranged in a row so that the 2's are always apart?

Solution:

■ 3 ■ 3 ■ 3 ■ 3 ■ 3 ■ 3 ■

We can first arrange the 3's in a row.   The 2's must now be placed in position. The seven possible positions for the 2's are marked ■ in the diagram and the four 2's may be placed in any four of these seven positions.   Thus we require the number of 4-subsets of the seven positions.   Therefore the number of ways of arranging the 3's and 2's is

$$\binom{7}{4} = \frac{7 \times 6 \times 5}{3 \times 2 \times 1}$$
$$= 35 .$$

Example 6.   Ten boys volunteered to assist in the organization of a school dance. It was agreed that three would be responsible for decorating, two for ticket sales, and the remaining five for clean-up after the dance.   In how many ways could the ten boys be chosen for the different groups?

Solution: For the decorating group, 3 are selected from 10 in $\binom{10}{3}$ ways.

For tickets, 2 are selected from the remaining 7 in $\binom{7}{2}$ ways.

For clean-up, 5 are selected from the remaining 5 in $\binom{5}{5}$ ways.

Therefore the number of ways of selecting the groups is

$$\binom{10}{3}\binom{7}{2}\binom{5}{5} = \frac{10 \times 9 \times 8}{3 \times 2 \times 1} \times \frac{7 \times 6}{2 \times 1} \times 1$$
$$= 2520 .$$

EXERCISE 8.4

1. Evaluate each of the following.

(a) $\binom{8}{6}$ (b) $\binom{5}{2}$ (c) $\binom{14}{12}$ (d) $\binom{9}{9}$ (e) $\binom{9}{0}$

(f) $\binom{21}{3}$ (g) $\binom{52}{50}$ (h) $\binom{100}{99}$ (i) $\binom{600}{1}$ (j) $\binom{15}{6}$

2. Find the number of 2-subsets of the set $\{0, 1, 2, 3\}$.

3. Find the number of 5-subsets of the set $\{a, b, c, d, e, f, g\}$.

4. For the set $\{1, 2, 3, 4\}$, find the number of 0-subsets, the number of 1-subsets, the number of 2-subsets, the number of 3-subsets, the number of 4-subsets. What is the total number of subsets of the given set?

5. (a) In how many ways can a committee of 3 be selected from 12 students?

   (b) In how many ways can a president, secretary, and treasurer be chosen from twelve students?

6. If fourteen points, no three of which are collinear, are marked on a sheet of paper, how many line segments can be drawn to join pairs of points?

7. How many diagonals has a polygon of twelve sides?

8. How many diagonals has a polygon of n sides?

9. Ten friends attend a reunion. Each shakes hands with each of the others. How many handshakes occur?

10. In how many ways can a committee of three men and two women be selected from eight men and six women?

11. In how many ways can a committee of five be selected from eight men and six women if at least three of the committee members must be men?

12. In how many ways can a committee of five be selected from ten men and seven women if at least one of the committee members must be a man?

13. The student council of Brandex High School consists of twenty members. In how many ways can a committee of four be selected if the president and secretary must be included?

14. In how many ways can a committee of four be selected from eight men and seven women if Miss Jones refuses to serve on the same committee as Mr. Smith?

15. In how many ways can twelve similar books be arranged on three shelves if each shelf must contain at least one book?

16. In how many ways can twelve similar books be arranged on three shelves if there is no restriction and one shelf may receive all of the books?

17. Twelve different books are to be shared so that Tom receives five, Dick receives four, and Harry receives three. In how many different ways can the books be distributed?

18. Solve for x: $\dbinom{x+1}{3} = \dbinom{x}{2}$.

19. Solve for x: $\dbinom{x}{2} = 28$.

20. Solve for x: $\dbinom{x}{3} = 3(x_{(2)})$.

21. Prove that $\dbinom{n}{r} + \dbinom{n}{r+1} = \dbinom{n+1}{r+1}$.

22. Prove that $r\dbinom{n}{r} = n\dbinom{n-1}{r-1}$.

23. In how many ways can a bridge hand of thirteen cards be dealt from a deck of fifty-two cards?   (Solution may be left in factorial form!)

24. In how many ways can thirteen cards be dealt to each of four players from a deck of fifty-two cards?   (Solution may be left in factorial form!)

25. In how many ways can eight different books be divided into two parcels of five books in one parcel and three in the other?

26. In how many ways can eight different books be divided into parcels of four books in each parcel?

8.5. Number of Subsets of a Given Set

In question (4), Exercise 8.4, we were asked to find the number of 0-subsets, 1-subsets, 2-subsets, 3-subsets, and 4-subsets of the set $\{1, 2, 3, 4\}$. These are all the possible subsets of a set of four elements and the total number of subsets is

$$\binom{4}{0} + \binom{4}{1} + \binom{4}{2} + \binom{4}{3} + \binom{4}{4} = 1 + 4 + 6 + 4 + 1$$
$$= 16.$$

If the number of elements in the given set is large, it is obviously time consuming to calculate the total number of subsets in this way.

We can consider the problem in another way. Each element of the set $\{1, 2, 3, 4\}$ either is a member of a particular subset or is not a member. The first element may be either selected or not selected as a member of a subset. It can, therefore, be treated in two ways, selected or rejected. For each of these two ways, the second element may be treated in two ways, selected or rejected.

Therefore the first two elements may be treated in four ways (2×2).   Similarly, the third element may be either selected or rejected in two ways for each of these four ways.   Hence the first three elements may be treated in 2^3 ways, and the four elements, in 2^4 ways.   The total number of subsets is, therefore, $2^4 = 16$. We note that this includes the possibility that none of the elements is selected (the empty set) or that all of the elements are selected (the given set itself).   In particular problems one or other or both of these possibilities may have to be rejected.

By continuing the argument, we can show in the same way that the number of subsets of a set of n elements is 2^n.

The set consisting of all the subsets of a given set A is known as the *Power Set of A* and is symbolized by $\mathcal{P}(A)$.

Therefore, if

$$n(A) = n ,$$

$$n[\mathcal{P}(A)] = 2^n .$$

If $A = \{1, 2, 3\}$,

$$\mathcal{P}(A) = \{\phi, \{1\}, \{2\}, \{3\}, \{1, 2\}, \{1, 3\}, \{2, 3\}, \{1, 2, 3\}\} .$$

$$n(A) = 3$$

and

$$n[\mathcal{P}(A)] = 2^3 = 8 .$$

Also we see that

$$\binom{n}{0} + \binom{n}{1} + \binom{n}{2} + \cdots + \binom{n}{n} = 2^n .$$

This last result will be proved in a different way in Chapter 10 (the Binomial Theorem).

Example 1.   How many different sums of money can be obtained by selecting from a $10 bill, a $5 bill, a $2 bill, and a $1 bill?

Solution: Since the empty set is not a solution,

not interested with the empty set.

$$\text{the number of sums} = 2^4 - 1$$

$$= 16 - 1$$

$$= 15 .$$

It may happen on certain occasions that we require the number of subsets of a set which contain repetitions of certain elements.   Normally we do not repeat elements in a set, for instance $\{1, 2, 2, 2, 3\} = \{1, 2, 3\}$; but for some purposes we may wish to consider all five elements of this set and not simply the different elements.

Example 2.   Find the number of different divisors of the number 2520, not including 1 or 2520.

Solution: If we first find all the prime factors of 2520, we see that

$$2520 = 2^3 \times 3^2 \times 5 \times 7.$$

The set of prime factors of 2520 is

$$\{2, 2, 2, 3, 3, 5, 7\}.$$

2	2520
2	1260
2	630
3	315
3	105
5	35
7	7
	1

The product of any number of these factors will be a divisor of 2520.   For example, 2, 2×2, $2 \times 2 \times 3 \times 3 \times 5$, are divisors of 2520.

What we require, therefore, is the number of subsets of a set of seven elements of which three are alike of one kind (the three 2's) and two are alike of a second kind (the two 3's).

For any subset we may select no, one, two, or three 2's.   Hence the 2's may be selected in four ways.   Similarly for each of these ways, the two 3's may be selected in three ways.

Therefore the 2's and 3's may be selected in 4×3 ways, and for each of these ways, the remaining unlike numbers (5 and 7) may be selected in 2^2 ways.

Therefore, the number of subsets is $4 \times 3 \times 2^2$.   However, this includes the empty set and also the set $\{2, 2, 2, 3, 3, 5, 7\}$ itself, which are not required.   (The latter set gives 2520 as the product of its elements.)

$$\text{Therefore the number of divisors} = 4 \times 3 \times 2^2 - 2$$
$$= 48 - 2$$
$$= 46.$$

In the same way we may prove that the number of subsets of a set of n elements, of which p are alike of one kind, q are alike of a second kind, and r are alike of a third kind $(n \geq p + q + r)$, is

$$(p + 1)(q + 1)(r + 1)\, 2^{n-p-q-r}.$$

The proof of this is asked in Exercise 8.5.

Example 3.   How many selections, any number at a time, may be made from three red pencils, four blue pencils, one green pencil, and one white pencil if at least one must be chosen?

Solution: $$\text{Number of selections} = (3 + 1)(4 + 1)\, 2^2 - 1$$
$$= 4 \times 5 \times 4 - 1$$
$$= 79.$$

EXERCISE 8.5

1. State the number of subsets of each of the following sets.

$A = \{a, b, c\}$ $B = \{1, 2, 3, 4, 5\}$ $C = \{x \in N \mid x < 10\}$

$D = \{x \in I \mid 3 < x < 8\}$ $E = \{x \in N \mid x < 30 \text{ and } x \text{ is prime}\}$

2. If $A = \{a, b, c, d\}$, list the elements of $\mathcal{P}(A)$.

3. If $n[\mathcal{P}(X)] = 128$, what is the value of $n(X)$?

4. How many different weights can be formed from weights of 1 lb., 2 lb., 4 lb., 8 lb., and 16 lb.?

5. How many different sums of money can be obtained by selecting from 1 penny, 1 nickel, 1 dime, and 1 quarter?

6. If $U = \{1, 2, 3, \cdots, 20\}$, $A = \{x \in U \mid x < 6\}$, $B = \{x \in U \mid 3 < x < 8\}$, $C = \{x \in U \mid x \text{ is prime}\}$, find the number of subsets of each of the following sets.

(a) $A \cap B$ (b) $A \cup B$ (c) $C \cap B'$

(d) $(B \cup C)'$ (e) $(A \cup C)'$ (f) $(A' \cup B') \cap C$

7. Find the number of different divisors of 432, not including 1 or 432.

8. Find the number of different divisors of 27,720, not including 1 or 27,720.

9. Find the number of subsets of $\{1, 1, 2, 2, 2, 3, 3, 4, 5\}$.

10. How many subsets of $\{1, 1, 2, 2, 2, 3, 3, 4, 5\}$ will contain all three 2's?

11. Find the number of subsets of $\{a, a, b, b, b, b, c\}$.

12. Prove that the number of subsets of a set of n elements, of which p are alike of one kind, q alike of a second kind, and r alike of a third kind, is

$$(p + 1)(q + 1)(r + 1) 2^{n-p-q-r} \quad (n \geq p + q + r).$$

8.6. Arrangements of Subsets

In many problems which require finding the number of arrangements (or permutations) of subsets of particular sets, it is necessary first of all to select the subsets before considering the possible arrangements of each group of subsets.

If we are asked to find the number of arrangements, each consisting of two vowels and three consonants, from the letters a, e, i, o, u, p, q, r, s, t, we are considering arrangements of letters selected from two sets, the set of vowels $\{a, e, i, o, u\}$ and the set of consonants $\{p, q, r, s, t\}$.

We must first find the number of 2-subsets of the set of five vowels and then the number of 3-subsets of the set of five consonants. Each of those subsets may then be combined and the number of arrangements calculated.

Example 1. Find the number of 5-arrangements, each consisting of two vowels and three consonants, of the letters a, e, i, o, u, p, q, r, s, t.

Solution: The vowels may be selected in $\binom{5}{2}$ ways.

For each of these selections, the consonants may be selected in $\binom{5}{3}$ ways.

Therefore the number of selections is $\binom{5}{2}\binom{5}{3}$.

The letters in each selection may be arranged in 5! ways.   Therefore

$$\begin{aligned} \text{number of 5-arrangements} &= \binom{5}{2}\binom{5}{3} 5! \\ &= 10 \times 10 \times 120 \\ &= 12,000 . \end{aligned}$$

When elements of the given set are repeated, we know how to find the number of arrangements when *all* of the elements are used in each arrangement.   When only some of the elements are used in each arrangement, we first have to select the possible subsets before we can find the number of arrangements.

Example 2. How many different four-digit numbers can be formed from the digits 1, 1, 1, 2, 2, 3, 3, 4, 5?

Solution:

Digits	Cases	Subsets	Arrangements
1, 1, 1	3 like, 1 different	$\binom{1}{1}\binom{4}{1} = 4$	$4 \times \dfrac{4!}{3!} = 16$
2, 2			
3, 3	2 like, 2 like	$\binom{3}{2} = 3$	$3 \times \dfrac{4!}{2!2!} = 18$
4			
5	2 like, 2 different	$\binom{3}{1}\binom{4}{2} = 18$	$18 \times \dfrac{4!}{2!} = 216$
	4 different	$\binom{5}{4} = 5$	$5 \times 4! = 120$

Therefore the number of four-digit numbers $= 16 + 18 + 216 + 120$
$$= 370 .$$

EXERCISE 8.6

1. How many arrangements, each consisting of three vowels and three consonants, can be made from five different vowels and ten different consonants?

2. From nine boys and six girls, four boys and three girls are to be selected to sit along one side of a table. How many seating arrangements are possible?

3. In question (2), how many seating arrangements are possible if the four boys and three girls are to sit around a circular table, if all the chairs are identical?

4. How many six-digit numbers, each consisting of three odd digits and three even digits, can be formed from the digits 1, 2, 3, 4, 5, 6, 7, 8, 9?

5. How many six-digit numbers, each consisting of three odd digits and three even digits, can be formed from the digits 0, 1, 2, 3, 4, 5, 6, 7, 8, 9?

6. Find the number of 3-subsets of the set $\{a, a, a, b, b, c, d\}$.

7. How many arrangements, each consisting of three letters, can be made from the letters of the word *Toronto*?

8. How many different three-digit numbers can be formed from the digits 3, 3, 3, 4, 4, 5, 6, 7?

9. How many different four-digit numbers can be formed from five 3's, four 4's, two 5's, two 6's, one 7, and one 8?

10. How many different four-digit numbers, each greater than 3,000, can be formed from two 1's, three 2's, and two 3's?

Chapter Summary

Definitions

An *r-arrangement* of n objects is an ordered selection of r of the objects ($r \in W$, $n \in N$).

An *r-subset* of a set of n elements is a selection of r of the elements *without regard to order* ($r \in W$, $n \in N$).

Formulae and Symbols

(1) $$n(A \times B) = n(A) \cdot n(B).$$

(2) The number of *r*-arrangements of n objects is

$$n_{(r)} = n(n-1)(n-2)\cdots(n-r+1) \qquad (n \geq r)$$
$$= \frac{n!}{(n-r)!},$$

where $n! = n(n-1)(n-2)\cdots 3 \cdot 2 \cdot 1$ and $0! = 1$.

(3) The number of *r*-subsets of a set of n elements is

$$\binom{n}{r} = \frac{n_{(r)}}{r!} = \frac{n!}{r!(n-r)!}.$$

(4) The number of n-arrangements of n objects if n_1 are alike of one kind, n_2 alike of a second kind, $\cdots$, n_r alike of an rth kind is

$$\frac{n!}{n_1!n_2!\cdots n_r!} \quad (n \geq n_1 + n_2 + \cdots + n_r).$$

(5)
$$\binom{n}{r} = \binom{n}{n-r}.$$

(6) The number of subsets of a set of n objects is 2^n, or, if $n(A) = n$, then $n[\mathscr{P}(A)] = 2^n$.

REVIEW EXERCISE 8

1. Evaluate each of the following.
   (a) $7_{(3)}$ (b) $7_{(5)}$ (c) $100_{(2)}$ (d) $12_{(3)}$

   (e) $\binom{7}{3}$ (f) $\binom{8}{8}$ (g) $\binom{100}{99}$ (h) $\binom{12}{5}$

   (i) $\dfrac{12!}{10!}$ (j) $\dfrac{7 \times 5!}{3!}$ (k) $\dfrac{8!}{4!} - \dfrac{7!}{3!}$ (l) $\dfrac{8!}{3!} - \dfrac{7!}{4!}$

2. Simplify as far as possible.
   (a) $\dfrac{x!}{(x-1)!}$ (b) $\dfrac{(x+1)!}{(x-1)!}$ (c) $\dfrac{(n-r)!}{(n-r-1)!}$

3. Prove that $\dfrac{(2n+2)!}{(n+1)!} = \dfrac{2(2n+1)!}{n!}$.

4. Prove that $5\binom{8}{5} = 8\binom{7}{4}$.

5. Prove that $\binom{n+1}{r+1} = \dfrac{n+1}{r+1}\binom{n}{r}$.

6. In how many ways can a committee of five be formed from six men and five women if
   (a) there is no restriction?
   (b) the committee must contain exactly three men?
   (c) the committee must contain at least one man?

7. A starting line-up for a hockey team must consist of one goalkeeper, two defencemen, and three forwards.
   (a) In how many ways can a starting line-up be selected from two goalkeepers, five defencemen, and nine forwards?
   (b) In how many ways can the different positions be filled if the same two goalkeepers, five defencemen, and nine forwards are available?

8. How many different arrangements can be made from all the letters of the word *distinct* if
   (a) there is no restriction?
   (b) the first and last letters must be alike?

9. How many different seven-digit numbers can be formed from the digits 1, 1, 1, 2, 2, 3, 3?

10. How many different seven-digit numbers can be formed from the digits 0, 0, 1, 1, 2, 2, 2?

11. How many different licence plates, each consisting of one letter and either four or five digits, can be formed from the letters H, J, K, L, M, and from the digits 0 to 9, if 0 cannot be the first digit and repetitions are allowed?

12. In how many ways can six different books be arranged in a row if two specified books must always be together?

13. In how many ways can twelve copies of the same book be arranged on three shelves if each shelf must contain at least one copy?

14. How many arrangements can be formed from all the letters of the word *combine* if the vowels must always be in the same order?

15. How many arrangements can be formed from all of the letters of the word *combine* if the vowels must occupy the second, fifth, and seventh positions?

16. An examination consists of three compulsory questions and another six questions of which the candidate may select any four.   In how many ways may the candidate select the questions to be answered?

17. Find the number of divisors of 6006, excluding 1 and 6006.

18. Find the number of divisors of 3150, excluding 1 and 3150.

19. In how many ways can a committee of four be selected from twelve members?

20. In how many ways can a committee, consisting of a president, a secretary, and two other members, be chosen from twelve members?

21. In how many ways can twelve people be divided into three groups consisting of four, five, and three individuals?

22. In how many ways can twelve people be divided into three groups, each consisting of four individuals?

23. How many arrangements, each consisting of two vowels and two consonants, can be formed from the letters a, e, i, o, u, b, c, d, f?

24. How many diagonals has an octagon?

25. How many sides has a polygon if it has thirty-five diagonals?

26. Solve the following equations.

    (a) $\dbinom{n}{2} = 45$

    (b) $n_{(3)} = 2\dbinom{n}{2}$

    (c) $n! = 5(n-1)!$

    (d) $10\dbinom{n}{r-1} = 3\dbinom{n}{r};\ 4\dbinom{n}{r+1} = 9\dbinom{n}{r}$

27. How many different three-digit numbers can be formed from three 4's, three 3's, two 2's, and two 1's?

28. How many arrangements of four letters each can be formed from the letters of the word *Tennessee*?

29. How many different four-digit numbers, each greater than 5,000, can be formed from three 2's, two 3's, two 4's, and two 5's?

30. How many different three-digit numbers, each greater than 400, can be formed from three 1's, two 2's, two 4's, and one 5?

Chapter 9

MATHEMATICAL INDUCTION

9.1. Sigma Notation

If we consider the finite series

$$1 + 3 + 5 + 7 + 9 + 11,$$

we see that it can be rewritten as

$$[2(1) - 1] + [2(2) - 1] + [2(3) - 1] + [2(4) - 1] + [2(5) - 1] + [2(6) - 1].$$

Each term of the series is of the form $2k - 1$ and the terms of the series can be formed by letting k take, in turn, the value of each member of the set

$$\{1, 2, 3, 4, 5, 6\}.$$

A very useful shorthand notation to indicate such a series is obtained by using the Greek capital letter $\sum$ (sigma), called the summation sign. In our example we can write

$$1 + 3 + 5 + 7 + 9 + 11 = \sum_{k=1}^{6} (2k - 1).$$

This is read as "the sum of $2k - 1$ from $k = 1$ to $k = 6$."

1 and 6 are called the *lower* and *upper* limits of summation; $\{1, 2, 3, 4, 5, 6\}$ is called the *domain of summation*. The *summand* is $2k - 1$.

In the same way,

$$\sum_{i=1}^{n} a_i = a_1 + a_2 + a_3 + \cdots + a_n$$

In this case the lower and upper limits of summation are 1 and n.

The summation symbol $\sum$ may sometimes be used to indicate the sum of the series as well as the series itself. In order to make this clear we shall use expressions such as "compute", "evaluate", or "find the sum of" when the sum of the series is required.

Example 1.   Express $\sum_{k=1}^{6} (k + 1)$ in expanded form.

Solution:

$$\sum_{k=1}^{6} (k + 1) = (1 + 1) + (2 + 1) + (3 + 1) + (4 + 1) + (5 + 1) + (6 + 1)$$
$$= 2 + 3 + 4 + 5 + 6 + 7 \, .$$

Example 2.   Evaluate $\sum_{n=1}^{5} 2^n$.

Solution:

$$\sum_{n=1}^{5} 2^n = 2^1 + 2^2 + 2^3 + 2^4 + 2^5$$
$$= 2 + 4 + 8 + 16 + 32$$
$$= 62 \, .$$

Example 3.   Prove that $\sum_{k=1}^{n} 3k^2 = 3 \sum_{k=1}^{n} k^2$.

Solution:

$$\sum_{k=1}^{n} 3k^2 = 3(1)^2 + 3(2)^2 + 3(3)^2 + \cdots + 3n^2$$
$$= 3(1^2 + 2^2 + 3^2 + \cdots + n^2)$$
$$= 3 \sum_{k=1}^{n} k^2 \, .$$

EXERCISE 9.1

1.   Express each of the following series in expanded form.

(a) $\sum_{i=1}^{6} i$ (b) $\sum_{j=1}^{6} j$ (c) $\sum_{n=1}^{7} (2 - n)$

(d) $\sum_{n=1}^{8} (2n + 3)$ (e) $\sum_{k=1}^{4} 3k$ (f) $\sum_{n=1}^{7} |\, 2 - n \,|$

(g) $\sum_{i=1}^{6} (-1)^i$ (h) $\sum_{k=1}^{n} k^2$ (i) $\sum_{k=1}^{n} \frac{k(k + 1)}{2}$

2.   By expanding each series, prove the following results.

(a) $\sum_{k=3}^{8} k = \sum_{k=1}^{6} (k + 2)$

(b) $\sum_{i=3}^{7} i^2 = \sum_{i=1}^{5} (i + 2)^2$

(c) $\displaystyle\sum_{j=0}^{5}(j+2) = \sum_{j=1}^{6}(j+1)$

(d) $\displaystyle\sum_{i=1}^{n} a_i = \sum_{i=0}^{n-1} a_{i+1}$

(e) $\displaystyle\sum_{n=1}^{6}(3n^2 + n) = 3\sum_{n=1}^{6} n^2 + \sum_{n=1}^{6} n$

(f) $\displaystyle\sum_{n=1}^{8}(n+1) = 8 + \sum_{n=1}^{8} n$

3. Evaluate each of the following.

(a) $\displaystyle\sum_{k=1}^{8} k$ (b) $\displaystyle\sum_{t=1}^{5} t^2$ (c) $\displaystyle\sum_{n=2}^{6} 2^{n-2}$

(d) $\displaystyle\sum_{n=0}^{7}(2n+1)$ (e) $\displaystyle\sum_{i=1}^{10}(-1)^i$ (f) $\displaystyle\sum_{i=1}^{11}(-1)^i$

4. Write each of the following series using sigma notation.
   (a) $1+2+3+4+5+6$
   (b) $1+4+9+16+25+36+49$
   (c) $2+4+8+16+32+64$
   (d) $2-4+8-16+32-64$
   (e) $a_1^2 + a_2^2 + a_3^2 + \cdots + a_n^2$
   (f) $ab + a^2b^2 + a^3b^3 + a^4b^4$
   (g) $a + a^2b + a^3b^2 + a^4b^3 + a^5b^4$
   (h) $3 + 7 + 11 + 15 + 19 + 23$
   (i) $2 + 6 + 18 + 54 + 162$

9.2. Properties of Summation

In the previous section, some of the examples should have suggested the possibility of certain properties which could be used to simplify operations using sigma notation. In this section we shall deduce these properties and formally prove them.

The expression $\displaystyle\sum_{i=1}^{n} 3$ states that we have to write a series of n terms, each term being 3. Therefore

$$\sum_{i=1}^{n} 3 = 3 + 3 + 3 + \cdots \text{ to } n \text{ terms}$$

$$= 3n\,.$$

This will be obviously true for any constant and we obtain
Summation Property 1.

$$\sum_{i=1}^{n} a = a + a + a + \cdots \text{ to } n \text{ terms}$$

$$= na .$$

One fairly trivial property, but one which is frequently forgotten, is
Summation Property 2.

$$\sum_{i=1}^{n} a_i = \sum_{j=1}^{n} a_j .$$

This is very easily proved.

Proof:

$$\sum_{i=1}^{n} a_i = a_1 + a_2 + a_3 + \cdots + a_n .$$

$$\sum_{j=1}^{n} a_j = a_1 + a_2 + a_3 + \cdots + a_n .$$

Therefore

$$\sum_{i=1}^{n} a_i = \sum_{j=1}^{n} a_j .$$

In Section 9.1 we proved that

$$\sum_{k=1}^{n} 3k^2 = 3 \sum_{k=1}^{n} k^2 .$$

This can now be extended to the more general form of
Summation Property 3.

$$\sum_{i=1}^{n} a(b_i) = a \sum_{i=1}^{n} b_i .$$

Proof:

$$\sum_{i=1}^{n} a(b_i) = ab_1 + ab_2 + ab_3 + \cdots + ab_n$$

$$= a(b_1 + b_2 + b_3 + \cdots + b_n) .$$

Therefore

$$\sum_{i=1}^{n} a(b_i) = a \sum_{i=1}^{n} b_i .$$

Question (2e), Exercise 9.1 asked us to prove that

$$\sum_{n=1}^{6} (3n^2 + n) = 3 \sum_{n=1}^{6} n^2 + \sum_{n=1}^{6} n .$$

This again is a particular case of a combination of Property 3 and

Summation Property 4.

$$\sum_{i=1}^{n} (a_i + b_i) = \sum_{i=1}^{n} a_i + \sum_{i=1}^{n} b_i .$$

Proof:

$$\sum_{i=1}^{n} (a_i + b_i) = (a_1 + b_1) + (a_2 + b_2) + \cdots + (a_n + b_n)$$

$$= (a_1 + a_2 + \cdots + a_n) + (b_1 + b_2 + \cdots + b_n) .$$

Therefore

$$\sum_{i=1}^{n} (a_i + b_i) = \sum_{i=1}^{n} a_i + \sum_{i=1}^{n} b_i .$$

A final and more subtle property which is often very useful permits us to add the same constant (positive or negative) to the lower *and* upper limits of summation.

Summation Property 5.

$$\sum_{i=m}^{n} a_i = \sum_{i=m+p}^{n+p} a_{i-p} .$$

Proof:

$$\sum_{i=m}^{n} a_i = a_m + a_{m+1} + a_{m+2} + \cdots + a_n .$$

$$\sum_{i=m+p}^{n+p} a_{i-p} = a_{m+p-p} + a_{m+p-p+1} + \cdots + a_{n+p-p}$$

$$= a_m + a_{m+1} + \cdots + a_n .$$

Therefore

$$\sum_{i=m}^{n} a_i = \sum_{i=m+p}^{n+p} a_{i-p} .$$

This property is probably most frequently used to change the lower limit of summation to 1.   For example,

$$\sum_{k=6}^{20} k^3 = \sum_{k=1}^{15} (k + 5)^3 .$$

-5 is added to the lower limit to produce 1.   Hence -5 must also be added to the upper limit and $+5$ to the summation variable in the summand.

Another method to produce the same result if we wish to evaluate the series is

$$\sum_{i=m}^{n} a_i = \sum_{i=1}^{n} a_i - \sum_{i=1}^{m-1} a_i .$$

The proof of this is required in Exercise 9.2 but an example should demonstrate its plausibility.

$$\sum_{k=6}^{20} k = \sum_{k=1}^{20} k - \sum_{k=1}^{5} k .$$

This states that the sum of all the positive integers from 6 to 20 is equal to the sum of all the positive integers from 1 to 20 less the sum of the positive integers from 1 to 5.

In the examples we will quote by number the property or properties being used. This is only for the purpose of emphasizing the authority until we become familiar with it, and after some practice, it may be omitted. In the same way certain steps in the development may easily be omitted after some facility has been acquired.

Example 1.   Express $\sum_{k=1}^{n} (3k - 1)^2$ in terms of monomial summations.

Solution:

$$\sum_{k=1}^{n} (3k - 1)^2 = \sum_{k=1}^{n} (9k^2 - 6k + 1)$$

$$= \sum_{k=1}^{n} 9k^2 - \sum_{k=1}^{n} 6k + \sum_{k=1}^{n} 1 \qquad \text{property 4}$$

$$= 9 \sum_{k=1}^{n} k^2 - 6 \sum_{k=1}^{n} k + n . \qquad \text{properties 3 and 1}$$

Example 2.   Prove that $\sum_{k=6}^{12} k^2 = \sum_{k=1}^{7} k^2 + 10 \sum_{k=1}^{7} k + 175 .$

Solution:

$$\sum_{k=6}^{12} k^2 = \sum_{k=1}^{7} (k + 5)^2 \qquad \text{property 5}$$

$$= \sum_{k=1}^{7} (k^2 + 10k + 25)$$

$$= \sum_{k=1}^{7} k^2 + \sum_{k=1}^{7} 10k + \sum_{k=1}^{7} 25 \qquad \text{property 4}$$

$$= \sum_{k=1}^{7} k^2 + 10 \sum_{k=1}^{7} k + 175 . \qquad \text{properties 3 and 1}$$

EXERCISE 9.2

1. Express the following in terms of monomial summations.

(a) $\sum_{i=1}^{n} (3a_i + b_i)$ 　　(b) $\sum_{k=1}^{10} (2k^2 - 6k)$ 　　(c) $\sum_{k=1}^{n} (k^3 + 6k^2 - 5)$

(d) $\sum_{p=1}^{n} (2^p + 3p)$ 　　(e) $\sum_{i=1}^{10} (-1)^i (i^2 + 2i)$ 　　(f) $\sum_{k=1}^{n} (2k^3 - 6k^2 + k - 2)$

2. Simplify each of the following.

(a) $\sum_{i=1}^{n} (3i + 2) + \sum_{k=1}^{n} (3k + 2)$

(b) $\sum_{a=7}^{12} a^2 - \sum_{b=1}^{6} (b^2 + 12b + 36)$

3. Rewrite each of the following with 1 as the lower limit of summation.

(a) $\sum_{k=12}^{20} k$

(b) $\sum_{a=-5}^{5} \frac{a}{a+6}$

(c) $\sum_{n=3}^{8} \frac{n+1}{n-2}$

(d) $\sum_{p=0}^{9} (p + 1)$

(e) $\sum_{k=7}^{10} 2k^2$

(f) $\sum_{i=-2}^{3} (i^2 + i)$

4. Prove that $\sum_{i=m}^{n} a_i = \sum_{i=1}^{n} a_i - \sum_{i=1}^{m-1} a_i$.

9.3. Induction

If we consider the arithmetic series

$$1 + 3 + 5 + \cdots + (2n - 1) + \cdots,$$

we see that

$$
\begin{aligned}
S_1 &= 1 & &= 1 = 1^2, \\
S_2 &= 1 + 3 & &= 4 = 2^2, \\
S_3 &= 1 + 3 + 5 & &= 9 = 3^2, \\
S_4 &= 1 + 3 + 5 + 7 &= 16 &= 4^2.
\end{aligned}
$$

From the results of these four sums, it would appear that

$$S_n = 1 + 3 + 5 + \cdots + (2n - 1) = n^2 \text{ for all } n \in N.$$

In coming to this conclusion from a few cases, we are using the method of induction. We cannot be certain that the result will hold for all $n \in N$. The more cases we consider, the more certain we become that our result is probably correct, but we can never test it for every positive integer. In spite of this lack of absolute certainty, induction is a very valuable mathematical and scientific tool. It can lead us to probable results which may be worth the effort of trying to prove deductively. We must, however, keep in mind that a result obtained inductively can never be finally accepted until it has been proved deductively. The most that we can say for the conclusion given above is that it appears *likely* that

$$\sum_{k=1}^{n} (2k - 1) = n^2.$$

Many problems in mathematics may first be visualized by examining a number of special cases and seeing a general pattern emerge. From this a general result may be conjectured. A deductive proof of this result may or may not be possible.

Goldbach's conjecture states that every even integer greater than 4 may be written as the sum of two odd primes in at least one way. So far no exception has been found, but neither has a deductive proof of the statement.

$$6 = 3 + 3, \qquad\qquad 8 = 5 + 3, \qquad\qquad 10 = 7 + 3 = 5 + 5,$$
$$12 = 7 + 5, \qquad\qquad 26 = 13 + 13 = 19 + 7 = 23 + 3,$$

are all examples which support the conjecture. In this case, the proof of the conjecture has eluded mathematicians, but in many cases the main difficulty arises in formulating the conjecture.

It is impossible to lay down hard and fast rules for reaching an inductive conclusion. A sense of pattern has to be developed and, in the case of sequences and series, it is often valuable to compare the various results for particular cases with the sequence of positive integers.

Example 1. Attempt to derive a general formula to evaluate

$$\sum_{k=1}^{n} \frac{k(k+1)}{2}.$$

Solution:

$$\sum_{k=1}^{n} \frac{k(k+1)}{2} = \frac{1 \times 2}{2} + \frac{2 \times 3}{2} + \frac{3 \times 4}{2} + \frac{4 \times 5}{2} + \frac{5 \times 6}{2} + \cdots$$
$$= 1 + 3 + 6 + 10 + 15 + \cdots .$$

We see that

$$S_1 = 1,$$
$$S_2 = 4,$$
$$S_3 = 10,$$
$$S_4 = 20,$$
$$S_5 = 35.$$

Probably no pattern is immediately obvious but we might notice that $S_4 = 20 = 4 \times 5$. This might lead us to begin by writing $n(n+1)$ for S_n, even though it is obviously not true for other values. However, it is a start. Let us set these under each partial sum.

S_1	S_2	S_3	S_4	S_5
1	4	10	20	35
1×2	2×3	3×4	4×5	5×6

We might now look at S_5 and note that $35 = 5 \times 7$. This can be obtained by multiplying 5×6 by 7 and dividing the result by 6. This is also successful for S_4; so let us try it for each case.

S_1	S_2	S_3	S_4	S_5
1	4	10	20	35
$\dfrac{1 \times 2 \times 3}{6}$	$\dfrac{2 \times 3 \times 4}{6}$	$\dfrac{3 \times 4 \times 5}{6}$	$\dfrac{4 \times 5 \times 6}{6}$	$\dfrac{5 \times 6 \times 7}{6}$

We see that the result holds in each case and that it appears to be true that

$$\sum_{k=1}^{n} \frac{k(k+1)}{2} = \frac{n(n+1)(n+2)}{6}.$$

We now test our conclusion for $n = 6$ and $n = 7$. If it is still true, we may feel more confident that our general formula is correct. However, we must remain conscious of the fact that it is still only a conjecture. Our next problem will be to attempt a proof that it is indeed true for all $n \in N$.

EXERCISE 9.3

By inductive methods, attempt to derive a general formula to evaluate each of the following.

1. $1 + 2 + 3 + \cdots + n$

2. $\displaystyle\sum_{k=1}^{n} \frac{1}{k(k+1)}$

3. $\displaystyle\sum_{k=1}^{n} \frac{1}{(3k-2)(3k+1)}$

4. $\displaystyle\sum_{i=1}^{n} \frac{2}{(2i-1)(2i+1)}$

5. $\displaystyle\sum_{k=1}^{n} \frac{1}{(3k-1)(3k+2)}$

6. $\displaystyle\sum_{p=1}^{n} (3p+1)$

7. $\displaystyle\sum_{k=1}^{n} \frac{1}{(4k-2)(4k+2)}$

Assuming that the following sequences continue in the most obvious manner, formulate an expression for the nth term (t_n).

8. $1, 4, 7, 10, \cdots$

9. $1, 2, 4, 8, \cdots$

10. $\frac{1}{2}, \frac{2}{3}, \frac{3}{4}, \frac{4}{5}, \cdots$

11. $3, 7, 15, 31, \cdots$

12. $\frac{3}{2}, \frac{8}{3}, \frac{15}{4}, \frac{24}{5}, \cdots$

13. $\frac{7}{3}, \frac{19}{9}, \frac{55}{27}, \frac{163}{81}, \cdots$

14. $1, 3, 6, 10, \cdots$

15. $1, 5, 19, 65, \cdots$

16. For a certain sequence, $t_n = n^3 - 6n^2 + 14n - 8$. Evaluate t_1, t_2, t_3 and attempt to derive a simpler formula for t_n which will give the same first three terms but a different fourth term.

9.4. Proof by Mathematical Induction

In the previous section we predicted that

$$\sum_{i=1}^{n} (2i - 1) = 1 + 3 + 5 + \cdots + (2n - 1) = n^2.$$

We came to this conclusion by examining a limited number of special cases, but we could not be certain that the proposition would hold for all $n \in N$. We *do know*, however, that the proposition is true for a set S of some natural numbers where $S \subseteq N$. Certainly it is true for $n = 1$ and the problem that remains is to prove that $S = N$. To do this we make use of the *Axiom of Mathematical Induction*.

A set S of natural numbers is the set N of all natural numbers if

1. $1 \in S$,

2. $k + 1 \in S$ whenever $k \in S$.

We note that, if $k + 1 \in S$ whenever $k \in S$, then, since $1 \in S$, $1 + 1 = 2 \in S$. Since $2 \in S$, $2 + 1 = 3 \in S$, and so on. S is the set of all natural numbers and $S = N$.

To use the axiom to determine whether a set S of natural numbers is, in fact, the set N of all natural numbers, we must prove *two* things about S:

1. that $1 \in S$,

2. that, if we assume that $k \in S$ (the induction hypothesis), then it follows that $k + 1 \in S$.

If *both* of these can be established, then $S = N$.

In the example, to establish that $\sum_{i=1}^{n} (2i - 1) = n^2$ is true for all $n \in N$, we must first establish that the proposition is true for $n = 1$. When this is established, then

$$1 \in S.$$

Secondly, if we assume that the result is true for $k \in S$, (induction hypothesis) where $S \subseteq N$, that is,

$$\sum_{i=1}^{k} (2i - 1) = k^2,$$

then we must prove that $k + 1$ is also an element of S (that is, $k + 1 \in S$). We must establish that

$$\sum_{i=1}^{k+1} (2i - 1) = (k + 1)^2.$$

We can form the sum of $k+1$ terms by adding the $(k+1)$st term to the sum of k terms.   From our assumption that

$$\sum_{i=1}^{k} (2i - 1) = k^2,$$

we can state that

$$\sum_{i=1}^{k} (2i - 1) + t_{k+1} = k^2 + t_{k+1};$$

that is,

$$\sum_{i=1}^{k+1} (2i - 1) = k^2 + t_{k+1}.$$

What we now have to do is prove that the right side is indeed $(k+1)^2$.

Example 1.   Prove that $\sum_{i=1}^{n} (2i - 1) = n^2$.

Solution: Let S be the set of natural numbers for which $\sum_{i=1}^{n} (2i - 1) = n^2$.

1.

$$\sum_{i=1}^{1} (2i - 1) = 2(1) - 1 = 1 = 1^2.$$

Therefore

$$1 \in S.$$

2.   Assume that $k \in S$.

$$\sum_{i=1}^{k} (2i - 1) = k^2.$$

Then

$$\sum_{i=1}^{k} (2i - 1) + t_{k+1} = k^2 + t_{k+1}.$$

Therefore

$$\sum_{i=1}^{k+1} (2i - 1) = k^2 + 2(k + 1) - 1$$
$$= k^2 + 2k + 1$$
$$= (k + 1)^2.$$

Therefore

$$k + 1 \in S \text{ if } k \in S \text{ and } 1 \in S.$$

Therefore

$$S = N,$$

and so

$$\sum_{i=1}^{n} (2i - 1) = n^2 \quad \text{for all } n \in N.$$

Example 2. Prove that the sum of n terms of the geometric series

$$a + ar + ar^2 + \cdots + ar^{n-1}$$

is equal to

$$\frac{a(r^n - 1)}{r - 1}, \quad (r \neq 1).$$

Solution: Let T be the set of natural numbers for which $S_n = \dfrac{a(r^n - 1)}{r - 1}$.

1.
$$S_1 = \frac{a(r - 1)}{r - 1} = a \quad (r \neq 1).$$

Therefore
$$1 \in T.$$

2. Assume that $k \in T$.
$$S_k = \frac{a(r^k - 1)}{r - 1}.$$

Therefore
$$S_k + t_{k+1} = \frac{a(r^k - 1)}{r - 1} + ar^k$$

and
$$S_{k+1} = \frac{a(r^k - 1) + ar^k(r - 1)}{r - 1}$$
$$= \frac{a(r^k - 1 + r^{k+1} - r^k)}{r - 1}$$
$$= \frac{a(r^{k+1} - 1)}{r - 1}.$$

Therefore
$$k + 1 \in T \text{ if } k \in T \text{ and } 1 \in T.$$

Therefore
$$T = N,$$

and so
$$S_n = \frac{a(r^n - 1)}{r - 1} \text{ for all } n \in N.$$

Before considering our next example we should consider some properties of the integers. If a and b are two integers, both divisible by an integer n, then $a + b$, $a - b$, and ab are also divisible by n. These results are easily proved.

Since a and b are divisible by n, let $a = nx$ and $b = ny$. Then

$$a + b = nx + ny = n(x + y), \text{ which is divisible by } n;$$
$$a - b = nx - ny = n(x - y), \text{ which is divisible by } n;$$
$$ab = nx \cdot ny = n^2xy, \text{ which is divisible by } n.$$

Note that $a/b = nx/ny = x/y$ is not necessarily divisible by n.

Example 3.   Prove that $3^{4n} - 1$ is divisible by 80 for all $n \in N$.

Solution: Let T be the set of all natural numbers for which $3^{4n} - 1$ is divisible by 80.

1. $$3^{4(1)} - 1 = 81 - 1 = 80.$$

Therefore
$$1 \in T.$$

2. Assume that $k \in T$.   Therefore
$$3^{4k} - 1 \text{ is divisible by 80.}$$

To show that $3^{4(k+1)} - 1$ is also divisible by 80, we consider the difference between $3^{4(k+1)} - 1$ and $3^{4k} - 1$.

$$\begin{aligned}
(3^{4(k+1)} - 1) - (3^{4k} - 1) &= 3^{4k+4} - 1 - 3^{4k} + 1 \\
&= 3^{4k+4} - 3^{4k} \\
&= 3^{4k}(3^4 - 1) \\
&= 3^{4k}(80).
\end{aligned}$$

Therefore   if $3^{4k} - 1$ is divisible by 80, $3^{4(k+1)} - 1$ is also divisible by 80.   Hence
$$k + 1 \in T \text{ if } k \in T \text{ and } 1 \in T.$$

Therefore
$$T = N,$$

and so
$$3^{4n} - 1 \text{ is divisible by 80 for all } n \in N.$$

We should note that, although this method of proof is given the name mathematical induction, it is a form of *deductive* reasoning and that both parts of the proof are essential.   For example, if we are asked to prove that

$$\sum_{i=1}^{n} (2i - 1) = 3n^2 - 6n + 4,$$

we see that

$$\sum_{i=1}^{1} (2i - 1) = 1,$$

and

$$3(1)^2 - 6(1) + 4 = 1.$$

$$\sum_{i=1}^{2} (2i - 1) = 1 + 3 = 4,$$

and

$$3(2)^2 - 6(2) + 4 = 4.$$

Hence the proposition is true for $n = 1$ and $n = 2$.

It is *not* true, however, for $n = 3$, and this becomes apparent when we attempt part 2 of the proof. We are unable to prove that if

$$\sum_{i=1}^{k} (2i - 1) = 3k^2 - 6k + 4,$$

then

$$\sum_{i=1}^{k+1} (2i - 1) = 3(k + 1)^2 - 6(k + 1) + 4.$$

More formally, let S be the set of all natural numbers for which

$$\sum_{i=1}^{n} (2i - 1) = 3n^2 - 6n + 4.$$

1. $2 - 1 = 3 - 6 + 4.$

Therefore
$$1 \in S.$$

2. Assume $k \in S$.

$$\sum_{i=1}^{k} (2i - 1) = 3k^2 - 6k + 4.$$

Therefore

$$\sum_{i=1}^{k} (2i - 1) + t_{k+1} = 3k^2 - 6k + 4 + 2(k + 1) - 1.$$

$$\sum_{i=1}^{k+1} (2i - 1) = 3k^2 - 4k + 5$$

$$= 3(k^2 + 2k + 1) - 10k + 2$$
$$= 3(k + 1)^2 - 6(k + 1) - 4k + 8$$
$$= 3(k + 1)^2 - 6(k + 1) + 4 \quad \textit{only for } k = 1.$$

Therefore
$$S \neq N,$$
and so

$$\sum_{i=1}^{n} (2i - 1) \neq 3n^2 - 6n + 4 \text{ for all } n \in N.$$

Similarly, if part 1 of the proof fails, there is no point in attempting part 2. To prove only part 2 may lead to erroneous conclusions. For example, if we are asked to prove

$$\sum_{i=1}^{n} (2i - 1) = n^2 + 5.$$

If S is the set of all natural numbers for which $\sum_{i=1}^{n} (2i - 1) = n^2 + 5$, obviously $1 \notin S$. We need go no farther.

Using only part 2, however, assume $k \in S$. Then

$$\sum_{i=1}^{k} (2i - 1) = k^2 + 5,$$

and therefore

$$\sum_{i=1}^{k} (2i - 1) + t_{k+1} = k^2 + 5 + 2(k + 1) - 1.$$

$$\sum_{i=1}^{k+1} (2i - 1) = k^2 + 2k + 6$$

$$= (k + 1)^2 + 5.$$

Therefore

$$k + 1 \in S \text{ if } k \in S.$$

This would lead to a false conclusion since the proposition is false for all $n \in N$.

EXERCISE 9.4

Prove each of the following by mathematical induction.

1. $\displaystyle\sum_{i=1}^{n} i = \frac{n(n + 1)}{2}$.

2. $3 + 5 + 7 + \cdots + (2n + 1) = n(n + 2)$.

3. $a + (a + d) + (a + 2d) + \cdots + [a + (n - 1)d] = \dfrac{n}{2}[2a + (n - 1)d]$.

4. $\displaystyle\sum_{p=1}^{n} (5p - 1) = \frac{n(5n + 3)}{2}$.

5. $\displaystyle\sum_{i=1}^{n} (3i - 2) = \frac{n(3n - 1)}{2}$.

6. $\displaystyle\sum_{i=1}^{n} i^2 = \frac{n(n + 1)(2n + 1)}{6}$.

7. $\displaystyle\sum_{i=1}^{n} i^3 = \frac{n^2(n + 1)^2}{4}$.

8. $\dfrac{1}{(1)(3)} + \dfrac{1}{(3)(5)} + \dfrac{1}{(5)(7)} + \cdots + \dfrac{1}{(2n - 1)(2n + 1)} = \dfrac{n}{2n + 1}$.

9. $\displaystyle\sum_{p=1}^{n} \frac{1}{(3p - 2)(3p + 1)} = \frac{n}{3n + 1}$.

10. $\displaystyle\sum_{k=1}^{n} \frac{1}{k(k + 1)} = \frac{n}{n + 1}$.

11. $1 + 2 + 4 + \cdots + 2^{n-1} = 2^n - 1$.

12. $\sum_{i=1}^{n} 3^i = \frac{3}{2}(3^n - 1)$.

13. Prove that $n(n+1)(n+2)$ is divisible by 6 for all $n \in N$.

14. Prove that $5^{2n} - 1$ is divisible by 3 for all $n \in N$.

Show that each of the statements (15-18) is false.

15. $\sum_{i=1}^{n} 2i = 2(n^2 - n + 1)$.

16. $\sum_{i=1}^{n} 2i = n^2 + n - 1$.

17. $\dfrac{1}{(1)(2)} + \dfrac{1}{(2)(3)} + \dfrac{1}{(3)(4)} + \cdots + \dfrac{1}{n(n+1)} = \dfrac{2n+1}{n+1}$.

18. $\dfrac{1}{(1)(2)} + \dfrac{1}{(2)(3)} + \dfrac{1}{(3)(4)} + \cdots + \dfrac{1}{n(n+1)} = \dfrac{n^3 - 2n^2 - 2}{n+1}$.

19. For the sequence defined by $t_1 = 1,\, t_{n+1} = 1 + \sqrt{1 + t_n}$, prove that
    (a) $t_n < 3$,
    (b) $t_{n+1} > t_n$ for all $n \in N$.

20. For the sequence defined by $t_1 = 4,\, t_{n+1} = \sqrt{t_n + 2}$, prove that
    (a) $t_n > 2$,
    (b) $t_{n+1} < t_n$ for all $n \in N$.

21. For the sequence defined by $t_1 = 2,\, t_{n+1} = \sqrt{2t_n + 5}$, prove that
    (a) $t_n < 4$
    (b) $t_{n+1} > t_n$ for all $n \in N$.

9.5. Sum of a Series

In Exercise 9.4 we were asked to prove certain basic summation formulae by mathematical induction. Among the results proved were the following.

(1) The sum of the arithmetic series

$$a + (a + d) + (a + 2d) + \cdots + [a + (n-1)d] = \frac{n}{2}[2a + (n-1)d].$$

(2) The sum of the geometric series

$$a + ar + ar^2 + \cdots + ar^{n-1} = \frac{a(r^n - 1)}{r - 1} \quad (r \neq 1).$$

(3) The sums of the natural numbers, of the squares of the natural numbers, and of the cubes of the natural numbers

$$\sum_{k=1}^{n} k = \frac{n(n+1)}{2}.$$

$$\sum_{k=1}^{n} k^2 = \frac{n(n+1)(2n+1)}{6}.$$

$$\sum_{k=1}^{n} k^3 = \frac{n^2(n+1)^2}{4}.$$

These formulae can be used to evaluate the sums of other series and may all be proved by methods other than mathematical induction. The first two have been proved in earlier grades but we will repeat the proof of (2).

$$\sum_{k=1}^{n} ar^{k-1} = a + ar + ar^2 + \cdots + ar^{n-2} + ar^{n-1}.$$

$$r \sum_{k=1}^{n} ar^{k-1} = \qquad ar + ar^2 + \cdots + ar^{n-2} + ar^{n-1} + ar^n.$$

$$\sum_{k=1}^{n} ar^{k-1} - r \sum_{k=1}^{n} ar^{k-1} = a - ar^n.$$

Therefore

$$(1 - r) \sum_{k=1}^{n} ar^{k-1} = a(1 - r^n)$$

and

$$\sum_{k=1}^{n} ar^{k-1} = \frac{a(1 - r^n)}{1 - r}, \qquad (r \neq 1).$$

The sum of the natural numbers can be evaluated from the formula for the sum of the arithmetic series since the natural numbers form an arithmetic series with $a = 1$, $d = 1$.

$$\sum_{k=1}^{n} k = 1 + 2 + 3 + \cdots + n$$

$$= \frac{n}{2}[2(1) + (n-1)(1)]$$

$$= \frac{n}{2}(n+1)$$

$$= \frac{n(n+1)}{2}.$$

For the second formulae in (3), we may use the following algebraic identity.

$$n^3 - (n-1)^3 = n^3 - (n^3 - 3n^2 + 3n - 1)$$
$$= 3n^2 - 3n + 1.$$

$$1^3 - 0^3 = 3(1)^2 - 3(1) + 1,$$
$$2^3 - 1^3 = 3(2)^2 - 3(2) + 1,$$
$$3^3 - 2^3 = 3(3)^2 - 3(3) + 1,$$
$$\cdots \cdots \cdots \cdots \cdots \cdots$$
$$(n-1)^3 - (n-2)^3 = 3(n-1)^2 - 3(n-1) + 1,$$
$$n^3 - (n-1)^3 = 3(n^2) - 3(n) + 1.$$

Adding, we obtain

$$n^3 = 3(1^2 + 2^2 + \cdots + n^2) - 3(1 + 2 + \cdots + n) + n$$
$$= 3\sum_{k=1}^{n} k^2 - 3\sum_{k=1}^{n} k + n.$$

Therefore

$$3\sum_{k=1}^{n} k^2 = n^3 + 3\sum_{k=1}^{n} k - n$$
$$= n^3 + \frac{3n(n+1)}{2} - n$$
$$= \frac{2n^3 + 3n(n+1) - 2n}{2}$$
$$= \frac{n(2n^2 + 3n + 3 - 2)}{2}$$
$$= \frac{n(2n^2 + 3n + 1)}{2}.$$
$$3\sum_{k=1}^{n} k^2 = \frac{n(n+1)(2n+1)}{2}.$$

Therefore

$$\sum_{k=1}^{n} k^2 = \frac{n(n+1)(2n+1)}{6}.$$

The method has an obvious advantage over the method of mathematical induction in that it yields the formula directly without the necessity of first having to obtain it by inductive reasoning or "educated guessing". However, the identity $n^3 - (n-1)^3 = 3n^2 - 3n + 1$ does appear apparently "out of the blue", and there is no obvious way of discovering its use other than by an inspired hunch.

Using these formulae and the rules of Summation established in Section 9.2, we can evaluate the sums of many other series.

Example 1.   Evaluate $\sum_{k=1}^{n}(4k^2 - 3k + 2)$.

Solution:

$$\sum_{k=1}^{n}(4k^2 - 3k + 2) = 4\sum_{k=1}^{n}k^2 - 3\sum_{k=1}^{n}k + \sum_{k=1}^{n}2$$

$$= \frac{4n(n+1)(2n+1)}{6} - \frac{3n(n+1)}{2} + 2n$$

$$= \frac{4n(n+1)(2n+1) - 9n(n+1) + 12n}{6}$$

$$= \frac{n(8n^2 + 12n + 4 - 9n - 9 + 12)}{6}$$

$$= \frac{n(8n^2 + 3n + 7)}{6}.$$

Example 2.   Evaluate $\sum_{k=1}^{n}[2(3^k) - 1]$.

Solution:

$$\sum_{k=1}^{n}[2(3^k) - 1] = 2\sum_{k=1}^{n}3^k - \sum_{k=1}^{n}1$$

$$= \frac{2(3^{n+1} - 1)}{3 - 1} - n$$

$$= 3^{n+1} - (n + 1).$$

$$= \frac{3(3^M - 1)}{3 - 1} = \frac{\cancel{2} \times 3 \, (3^n - 1) - M}{\cancel{2}}$$

$$= 3^{M+1} - 3 - M$$

Example 3.   Evaluate $\sum_{k=10}^{20}(2k^2 - k)$.

Solution:

$$\sum_{k=1}^{n}(2k^2 - k) = 2\sum_{k=1}^{n}k^2 - \sum_{k=1}^{n}k$$

$$= \frac{2n(n+1)(2n+1)}{6} - \frac{n(n+1)}{2}$$

$$= \frac{2n(n+1)(2n+1) - 3n(n+1)}{6}$$

$$= \frac{n(n+1)(4n+2-3)}{6}$$

$$= \frac{n(n+1)(4n-1)}{6}.$$

$$\sum_{k=10}^{20}(2k^2 - k) = \sum_{k=1}^{20}(2k^2 - k) - \sum_{k=1}^{9}(2k^2 - k)$$

$$= \frac{20(21)(79)}{6} - \frac{9(10)(35)}{6}$$

$$= 10(7)(79) - 3(5)(35)$$

$$= 7(790 - 75)$$

$$= 5005.$$

EXERCISE 9.5

Derive formulae for the evaluation of each of the following series.

1. $2 + 5 + 8 + \cdots + (3n - 1)$
2. $46 + 42 + 38 + \cdots + (50 - 4n)$

3. $\displaystyle\sum_{k=1}^{n} (3k^2 - k)$
4. $\displaystyle\sum_{k=1}^{n} (k^2 + 2k - 1)$

5. $\displaystyle\sum_{k=1}^{n} (2k^3 - k)$
6. $\displaystyle\sum_{i=1}^{n} (i^2 - 3i + 4)$

7. $(1)(3) + (2)(5) + (3)(7) + \cdots + n(2n + 1)$
8. $(2)(8) + (5)(6) + (8)(4) + \cdots + (3n - 1)(10 - 2n)$
9. $(1)(2)(3) + (2)(3)(4) + (3)(4)(5) + \cdots + n(n + 1)(n + 2)$
10. $(1)(2)(2) + (2)(3)(5) + (3)(4)(8) + \cdots + n(n + 1)(3n - 1)$

Evaluate each of the following.

11. $\displaystyle\sum_{k=1}^{15} k^2$
12. $\displaystyle\sum_{p=1}^{20} (p + 3)$
13. $\displaystyle\sum_{i=1}^{30} (3i^2 - i)$

14. $\displaystyle\sum_{k=1}^{18} (2k^2 - 3k + 2)$
15. $\displaystyle\sum_{k=1}^{8} (k^3 + 3k + 5)$
16. $\displaystyle\sum_{i=1}^{12} (4i^3 - 6i^2 + 2i - 3)$

17. $\displaystyle\sum_{k=20}^{35} (2k + 3)$
18. $\displaystyle\sum_{p=15}^{33} (p^2 - 3p + 2)$
19. $\displaystyle\sum_{k=18}^{25} (4k^3 - 3k^2 + 2)$

20. $\displaystyle\sum_{k=40}^{60} (k^2 - 5k)$
21. $\displaystyle\sum_{k=80}^{85} (k^3 + 3k^2 - 10k)$
22. $\displaystyle\sum_{k=86}^{100} (12k^2 - 10k)$

23. Using the identity $n^4 - (n - 1)^4 = 4n^3 - 6n^2 + 4n - 1$, derive a formula for

$$\sum_{k=1}^{n} k^3.$$

24. Using the methods of this section, derive formulae for

$$\sum_{k=1}^{n} k^4 \quad \text{and} \quad \sum_{k=1}^{n} k^5.$$

9.6. Partial Fractions (Supplementary)

The rational algebraic expressions $\dfrac{2}{1 + x}$ and $\dfrac{-1}{1 - 2x}$ may be added to give $\dfrac{1 - 5x}{1 - x - 2x^2}$. Many series, whose general term is of the form $\dfrac{P(x)}{Q(x)}$, may be summed by using the reverse procedure of separating the fractional polynomial into its *partial fractions*. The first problem is to find the partial fractions.

Example 1. Separate $\dfrac{1-5x}{1-x-2x^2}$ into partial fractions.

Solution:

$$\frac{1-5x}{1-x-2x^2} = \frac{1-5x}{(1+x)(1-2x)}.$$

Let

$$\frac{1-5x}{(1+x)(1-2x)} = \frac{A}{1+x} + \frac{B}{1-2x}.$$

$$= \frac{A(1-2x)+B(1+x)}{(1+x)(1-2x)}.$$

Therefore

$$1-5x \equiv A(1-2x) + B(1+x).$$

(Note that the identity sign $\equiv$ is used to emphasize that this is an identity and hence true for all $x \in Re$.)

Replace x by $\frac{1}{2}$.

$$1-2\tfrac{1}{2} = B(1+\tfrac{1}{2}).$$
$$-1\tfrac{1}{2} = B(1\tfrac{1}{2}).$$

Therefore

$$B = -1.$$

Replace x by -1.

$$1+5 = A(1+2).$$

Therefore

$$A = 2.$$

Therefore

$$\frac{1-5x}{(1+x)(1-2x)} = \frac{2}{1+x} - \frac{1}{1-2x}.$$

When the partial fractions contain only simple linear polynomials as denominators, the process may be quite easily performed mentally. In replacing x by $\frac{1}{2}$, we are making the term $A(1-2x) = 0$. Therefore, replacing x by $\frac{1}{2}$,

$$1-5x = B(1+x),$$

and so

$$B = \frac{1-5x}{1+x}, \quad \text{when } x = \tfrac{1}{2}.$$

Similarly, replacing x by -1,

$$B(1+x) = 0,$$

and so

$$A = \frac{1-5x}{1-2x}, \quad \text{when } x = -1.$$

Hence the numerator for $1-2x$ is the value of $\dfrac{1-5x}{1+x}$ when x is replaced by $\frac{1}{2}$, and the numerator for $1+x$ is the value of $\dfrac{1-5x}{1-2x}$ when x is replaced by -1. It is certainly advisable, however, to perform the complete development as a check, until confidence in performing the mental calculation is acquired.

Example 2. Evaluate $\sum\limits_{k=1}^{n} \dfrac{1}{(3k-2)(3k+1)}$.

Solution: Let

$$\frac{1}{(3k-2)(3k+1)} = \frac{A}{3k-2} + \frac{B}{3k+1}$$

$$= \frac{A(3k+1) + B(3k-2)}{(3k-2)(3k+1)} .$$

Therefore

$$1 \equiv A(3k+1) + B(3k-2) .$$

When k is replaced by $-\frac{1}{3}$,

$$1 = -3B .$$

Therefore

$$B = -\tfrac{1}{3} .$$

When k is replaced by $\frac{2}{3}$,

$$1 = 3A .$$

Therefore

$$A = \tfrac{1}{3} .$$

Therefore

$$\sum_{k=1}^{n} \frac{1}{(3k-2)(3k+1)} = \sum_{k=1}^{n} \left(\frac{1}{3(3k-2)} - \frac{1}{3(3k+1)} \right)$$

$$= \sum_{k=1}^{n} \frac{1}{3(3k-2)} - \sum_{k=1}^{n} \frac{1}{3(3k+1)}$$

$$= \frac{1}{3} \sum_{k=1}^{n} \frac{1}{3k-2} - \frac{1}{3} \sum_{k=1}^{n} \frac{1}{3k+1}$$

$$= \frac{1}{3} \sum_{k=1}^{n} \frac{1}{3k-2} - \frac{1}{3} \sum_{k=2}^{n+1} \frac{1}{3(k-1)+1} \qquad (1)$$

$$= \frac{1}{3} \sum_{k=1}^{n} \frac{1}{3k-2} - \frac{1}{3} \sum_{k=2}^{n+1} \frac{1}{3k-2}$$

$$= \frac{1}{3}\left(\frac{1}{1}\right) - \frac{1}{3}\left(\frac{1}{3(n+1)-2}\right) \qquad (2)$$

$$= \frac{1}{3} - \frac{1}{3(3n+1)}$$

$$= \frac{3n+1-1}{3(3n+1)} .$$

Therefore

$$\sum_{k=1}^{n} \frac{1}{(3k-2)(3k+1)} = \frac{n}{3n+1} .$$

In the step marked (1) we were using Summation Property 5 (Section 9.2). The substitution of k-1 for k is used to have both summands equal and so make step (2) possible.   In step (2) all the terms of each series are equal in value but opposite in sign, with the exception of the term obtained from $k = 1$ in the first series and from $k = n + 1$ in the second.   Compare the result with that obtained by mathematical induction in question (9), Exercise 9.4.   Although the method given here takes longer, we do not have to know the probable result.   The result is produced by the method given here.

EXERCISE 9.6

Resolve the following into partial fractions.

1. $\dfrac{2x + 1}{x^2 + x - 2}$

2. $\dfrac{3}{x^2 + x - 2}$

3. $\dfrac{3x + 1}{x^2 - x - 6}$

4. $\dfrac{x - 4}{2 - 3x + x^2}$

5. $\dfrac{6 + x}{3 + x - 2x^2}$

6. $\dfrac{2k + 5}{4k^2 - 1}$

7. $\dfrac{1}{9k^2 + 3k - 2}$

8. $\dfrac{5}{25k^2 + 5k - 6}$

Derive a formula to evaluate the sum of each of the following series.

9. $\displaystyle\sum_{k=1}^{n} \dfrac{1}{k^2 + k}$

10. $\displaystyle\sum_{i=1}^{n} \dfrac{1}{4i^2 - 1}$

11. $\displaystyle\sum_{p=1}^{n} \dfrac{4}{(4p - 1)(4p + 3)}$

12. $\displaystyle\sum_{p=1}^{n} \dfrac{1}{(4p - 1)(4p + 3)}$

13. $\displaystyle\sum_{i=1}^{n} \dfrac{1}{25i^2 + 5i - 6}$

14. $\displaystyle\sum_{k=1}^{n} \dfrac{3}{9k^2 + 3k - 2}$

15. $\displaystyle\sum_{k=1}^{n} \dfrac{4}{4k^2 - 4k - 3}$

16. $\displaystyle\sum_{k=1}^{n} \dfrac{3}{(3k - 4)(3k + 2)}$

Chapter Summary

$$\sum_{i=1}^{n} a_i = a_1 + a_2 + a_3 + \cdots + a_n .$$

Properties of Summation

(1)
$$\sum_{i=1}^{n} a = na .$$

(2)
$$\sum_{i=1}^{n} a_i = \sum_{j=1}^{n} a_j .$$

(3)
$$\sum_{i=1}^{n} a(b_i) = a \sum_{i=1}^{n} b_i.$$

(4)
$$\sum_{i=1}^{n} (a_i + b_i) = \sum_{i=1}^{n} a_i + \sum_{i=1}^{n} b_i.$$

(5)
$$\sum_{i=m}^{n} a_i = \sum_{i=m+p}^{n+p} a_{i-p}.$$

(6)
$$\sum_{i=m}^{n} a_i = \sum_{i=1}^{n} a_i - \sum_{i=1}^{m-1} a_i.$$

Axiom of Mathematical Induction

A set S of natural numbers is the set N of all natural numbers if

1. $1 \in S$,

2. $k + 1 \in S$ whenever $k \in S$.

Summation Formulae

(1) The sum of the arithmetic series

$$\sum_{k=1}^{n} [a + (k - 1) d] = a + (a + d) + (a + 2d) + \cdots + [a + (n - 1) d]$$

$$= \frac{n}{2} [2a + (n - 1)d].$$

(2) The sum of the geometric series

$$\sum_{k=1}^{n} ar^{k-1} = a + ar + ar^2 + \cdots + ar^{n-1} = \frac{a(r^n - 1)}{r - 1} \qquad (r \neq 1).$$

(3)
$$\sum_{k=1}^{n} k = 1 + 2 + 3 + \cdots + n = \frac{n(n + 1)}{2}.$$

(4)
$$\sum_{k=1}^{n} k^2 = 1^2 + 2^2 + 3^2 + \cdots + n^2 = \frac{n(n + 1)(2n + 1)}{6}.$$

(5)
$$\sum_{k=1}^{n} k^3 = 1^3 + 2^3 + 3^3 + \cdots + n^3 = \frac{n^2(n + 1)^2}{4}.$$

REVIEW EXERCISE 9

1. Express each of the following series in expanded form.

(a) $\sum_{k=1}^{6} (2k - 3)$

(b) $\sum_{n=4}^{10} (-1)^n (2n)$

(c) $\sum_{i=1}^{8} (4 - i)$

(d) $\sum_{i=-3}^{3} (i^2 + 1)$

2. Express each of the following series in sigma notation.
   (a) $1 - 2 + 3 - 4 + 5 - 6 + 7 - 8$
   (b) $3 + 7 + 11 + 15 + 19 + 23 + 27 + 31 + 35$
   (c) $\frac{1}{9} + \frac{1}{3} + 1 + 3 + 9 + 27 + 81$
   (d) $\dfrac{1}{a^2 + 2ab + b^2} + \dfrac{1}{a + b} + 1 + (a + b) + (a^2 + 2ab + b^2)$
   (e) $\dfrac{1}{(3)(4)} + \dfrac{1}{(4)(5)} + \dfrac{1}{(5)(6)} + \dfrac{1}{(6)(7)} + \dfrac{1}{(7)(8)}$
   (f) $\dfrac{1}{(1)(3)} + \dfrac{1}{(2)(5)} + \dfrac{1}{(3)(7)} + \dfrac{1}{(4)(9)} + \cdots + \dfrac{1}{n(2n + 1)}$

3. Express each of the following with 1 as the lower limit of summation.
   (a) $\displaystyle\sum_{i=3}^{8} (2i - 1)$
   (b) $\displaystyle\sum_{k=-2}^{3} k^2$
   (c) $\displaystyle\sum_{k=0}^{n} 2^k$
   (d) $\displaystyle\sum_{p=2}^{n+1} (p^2 - 1)$
   (e) $\displaystyle\sum_{k=4}^{8} |3 - k|$
   (f) $\displaystyle\sum_{i=-1}^{n-2} (-1)^i (3i)$

4. Use the axiom of mathematical induction to prove each of the following.
   (a) $2 + 5 + 8 + \cdots + (3n - 1) = \dfrac{n(3n + 1)}{2}$.
   (b) $\dfrac{1}{2} - \dfrac{1}{4} - \dfrac{1}{8} - \cdots - \dfrac{1}{2^n} = \dfrac{1}{2^n}$.
   (c) $\displaystyle\sum_{p=1}^{n} \dfrac{1}{p^2 + 3p + 2} = \dfrac{n}{2(n + 2)}$.
   (d) $\displaystyle\sum_{k=1}^{n} \dfrac{1}{k(k + 2)} = \dfrac{3n^2 + 5n}{4(n + 1)(n + 2)}$.
   (e) $3^n \geq 2n + 1$ for all $n \in N$.
   (f) $2^n \geq 2n$ for all $n \in N$.
   (g) $3^{2n} - 1$ is divisible by 8 for all $n \in N$.
   (h) $n^2(n + 1)^2$ is divisible by 4 for all $n \in N$.

5. Evaluate each of the following.
   (a) $\displaystyle\sum_{k=1}^{n} (3k - 1)$
   (b) $\displaystyle\sum_{i=1}^{n} (1 + i)$
   (c) $\displaystyle\sum_{p=1}^{n} (3p^2 - 2p + 1)$
   (d) $\displaystyle\sum_{x=1}^{n} (2x - 1)(x + 1)$
   (e) $\displaystyle\sum_{x=1}^{n} (x^3 - 3x + 2)$
   (f) $\displaystyle\sum_{k=1}^{n} (4k^3 - 6k^2 + 2k - 3)$
   (g) $\displaystyle\sum_{k=1}^{12} (5k - 2)$
   (h) $\displaystyle\sum_{k=1}^{15} (2k^2 + k - 4)$
   (i) $\displaystyle\sum_{k=1}^{25} (k^2 + k + 1)$
   (j) $\displaystyle\sum_{k=20}^{30} (4k + 1)$
   (k) $\displaystyle\sum_{x=31}^{40} (3x^2 - x - 2)$
   (l) $\displaystyle\sum_{p=11}^{22} (2p^3 - 3p^2 - p + 2)$

6. Prove that $x^{2n} - y^{2n}$ is divisible by $x + y$ for all $n \in N$.

   Note: $\qquad x^{2k+2} - y^{2k+2} = x^{2k+2} - x^2 y^{2k} + x^2 y^{2k} - y^{2k+2}$.

7. For the sequence defined by $t_1 = 2$, $t_{n+1} = 1 + \sqrt{1 + t_n}$, prove that
   (a) $t_n < 3$,
   (b) $t_{n+1} > t_n$ for all $n \in N$.

8. For the sequence defined by $t_1 = 5$, $t_{n+1} = \sqrt{2t_n + 4}$, prove that
   (a) $t_n > 3$,
   (b) $t_{n+1} < t_n$ for all $n \in N$.

9. (Supplementary)   Resolve into partial fractions.

   (a) $\dfrac{5x + 1}{x^2 + x - 2}$

   (b) $\dfrac{x - 7}{x^2 + x - 6}$

   (c) $\dfrac{4}{1 - x^2}$

   (d) $\dfrac{4}{x^2 + x - 2}$

10. (Supplementary)   Evaluate each of the following.

   (a) $\displaystyle\sum_{k=1}^{n} \dfrac{1}{16k^2 - 4}$

   (b) $\displaystyle\sum_{x=1}^{n} \dfrac{1}{(3x - 1)(3x + 2)}$

   (c) $\displaystyle\sum_{k=1}^{n} \dfrac{5}{25k^2 + 15k - 4}$

   (d) $\displaystyle\sum_{k=2}^{n} \dfrac{2}{k^2 - 1}$

   (e) $\displaystyle\sum_{k=1}^{n} \dfrac{4}{4k^2 - 4k - 3}$

   (f) $\displaystyle\sum_{i=1}^{10} \dfrac{6}{(6i - 1)(6i + 5)}$

Chapter 10

THE BINOMIAL THEOREM

10.1. Powers of a Binomial Base

Let us consider the expansion of $(a + b)^3$, using only the axioms of algebra.

$$
\begin{aligned}
(a + b)^3 &= (a + b)(a + b)(a + b) \\
&= (a + b)[(a + b)(a + b)] && \text{Associative Law} \\
&= (a + b)[(a + b)a + (a + b)b] && \text{Distributive Law} \\
&= (a + b)[aa + ba + ab + bb] && \text{(Dist.)} \\
&= a[aa + ba + ab + bb] + b[aa + ba + ab + bb] && \text{(Dist.)} \\
&= \underset{1}{aaa} + \underset{2}{aba} + \underset{3}{aab} + \underset{4}{abb} + \underset{5}{baa} + \underset{6}{bba} + \underset{7}{bab} + \underset{8}{bbb}. && \text{(Dist.)}
\end{aligned}
$$

The eight terms (Some, of course, are like terms) have been numbered. Each term is the product of three factors, the first being obtained from the first binomial, the second from the second binomial, and the third from the third binomial in $(a + b)(a + b)(a + b)$. All such possible selections are included in the eight terms. The third term, aab, is formed by selecting a from each of the first two binomials and b from the third. Each term will, therefore, be the product of three letters, one selected from each of the binomial factors. In the expansion, a^3 appears only once (aaa), a^2b appears three times (aba, aab, baa), ab^2 appears three times (abb, bba, bab), and b^3 appears once (bbb). Therefore

$$(a + b)^3 = a^3 + 3a^2b + 3ab^2 + b^3.$$

We see that each term of this is formed by selecting one and only one term from each of the three binomial factors, multiplying these terms together, and adding all like products. We note that we can select either none, one, two, or three b's. If we select no b's, then we must select one a from each factor. This can be done in only one way and gives the first term, a^3. If we select one b, we can select it from any one of the three factors. This can be done in $\binom{3}{1} = 3$ ways. For each of these, we must select one a from each of the other two factors and this can be done in only one way.   Hence, we have three terms, each equal to a^2b, giving the second term, $3a^2b$.   We may now select two b's from the three factors in $\binom{3}{2} = 3$ ways, and an a must then be selected in one way from the remaining factor.   This gives the third term, $3ab^2$.   Finally, we may select three b's (one from each factor) in $\binom{3}{3} = 1$ way and we obtain the fourth term, b^3.   Therefore

$$(a + b)^3 = \binom{3}{0}a^3 + \binom{3}{1}a^2b + \binom{3}{2}ab^2 + \binom{3}{3}b^3$$
$$= a^3 + 3a^2b + 3ab^2 + b^3.$$

We note that this may be written as

$$(a + b)^3 = \sum_{k=0}^{3} \binom{3}{k} a^{3-k}b^k.$$

In the expansion of $(a + b)^6$, each term will be of dimension six in a and b since each term will be a product of one letter from each of the six binomial factors; hence it will be of the form $a^{6-r}b^r$, where $r \in \{0, 1, 2, 3, 4, 5, 6\}$.   By using a similar argument to that used in the expansion of $(a + b)^3$, we see that

when $r = 0$, the coefficient of a^6 is $\binom{6}{0}$,

when $r = 1$, the coefficient of a^5b is $\binom{6}{1}$,

when $r = 2$, the coefficient of a^4b^2 is $\binom{6}{2}$,

when $r = 3$, the coefficient of a^3b^3 is $\binom{6}{3}$,

when $r = 4$, the coefficient of a^2b^4 is $\binom{6}{4}$,

when $r = 5$, the coefficient of ab^5 is $\binom{6}{5}$,

when $r = 6$, the coefficient of b^6 is $\binom{6}{6}$.

Therefore

$$(a + b)^6 = \binom{6}{0}a^6 + \binom{6}{1}a^5b + \binom{6}{2}a^4b^2 + \binom{6}{3}a^3b^3 + \binom{6}{4}a^2b^4 + \binom{6}{5}ab^5 + \binom{6}{6}b^6$$
$$= \sum_{r=0}^{6} \binom{6}{r}a^{6-r}b^r$$
$$= a^6 + 6a^5b + 15a^4b^2 + 20a^3b^3 + 15a^2b^4 + 6ab^5 + b^6.$$

EXERCISE 10.1

1. If the numerical coefficients are disregarded, terms of the following form will appear in the expansion of $(a+b)^7$. State the value of the exponent r in each case.

   (a) a^5b^r (b) a^2b^r (c) a^rb^4 (d) a^rb^2

2. In each of the following, write the expansion in sigma-notation form, in r-sub-set notation form $\binom{n}{r}$, and in fully expanded form.

   (a) $(a+b)^4$ (b) $(a+b)^5$ (c) $(x+y)^8$ (d) $(p+q)^7$

3. How many different terms are there in the expansion of each of the binomials in question (2)?

4. Without expanding, state the number of different terms in the expansions of
   (a) $(a+b)^{11}$,   (b) $(x+y)^{15}$,   (c) $(p+q)^{18}$,   (d) $(1+x)^{20}$.

10.2. Expansion of $(a+b)^n$, $n \in N$

$$(a+b)^n = (a+b)(a+b)(a+b) \cdots n \text{ factors.}$$

Each term in the expansion is obtained by forming the product of one term from each binomial factor. Each term of the expansion will, therefore, be of the form

$$a^{n-r}b^r, \quad \text{where } r \in \{0, 1, 2, \ldots, n\}.$$

This general term $a^{n-r}b^r$ is formed by selecting one b from each of r of the n factors. This can be done in $\binom{n}{r}$ ways. For each of these ways, the $(n-r)$ a's can be selected, one from each of the remaining $(n-r)$ binomial factors, in only one way. Hence, the coefficient of $a^{n-r}b^r$ is $\binom{n}{r}$. Therefore

$$(a+b)^n = \sum_{r=0}^{n} \binom{n}{r} a^{n-r}b^r$$

$$= \binom{n}{0}a^n + \binom{n}{1}a^{n-1}b + \binom{n}{2}a^{n-2}b^2 + \cdots + \binom{n}{r}a^{n-r}b^r + \cdots + \binom{n}{n}b^n.$$

We note the following points in this expansion:
   (i)   The number of different terms is $n+1$.

   (ii) The general term $\binom{n}{r}a^{n-r}b^r$ is the $(r+1)$st term.

   (iii) The coefficients of terms equidistant from the ends of this expansion are equal.

The following expansions were obtained from the previous section or are known from earlier work.

$(a + b)^0 = 1$.

$(a + b)^1 = a + b$.

$(a + b)^2 = a^2 + 2ab + b^2$.

$(a + b)^3 = a^3 + 3a^2b + 3ab^2 + b^3$.

$(a + b)^4 = a^4 + 4a^3b + 6a^2b^2 + 4ab^3 + b^4$.

$(a + b)^5 = a^5 + 5a^4b + 10a^3b^2 + 10a^2b^3 + 5ab^4 + b^5$.

$(a + b)^6 = a^6 + 6a^5b + 15a^4b^2 + 20a^3b^3 + 15a^2b^4 + 6ab^5 + b^6$.

It can be seen that the coefficients follow a definite pattern which can be most easily demonstrated by means of Pascal's Triangle.

```
            1
          1   1
        1   2   1
      1   3   3   1
    1   4   6   4   1
  1   5  10  10   5   1
1   6  15  20  15   6   1
```

Can you see how the pattern develops? What will be the next two lines in the triangle? In forming the lines in the triangle, we are making use of the identity which you were asked to prove in question (21), Exercise 8.4.

$$\binom{n}{r} + \binom{n}{r + 1} = \binom{n + 1}{r + 1}.$$

This identity will be used again in the next section.

Example 1.   Express (a) $(a + 2b)^4$,   (b) $(2a - 3b)^7$ using sigma notation.

Solution:

(a)
$$(a + 2b)^4 = \sum_{r=0}^{4} \binom{4}{r} a^{4-r}(2b)^r$$

$$= \sum_{r=0}^{4} \binom{4}{r} 2^r a^{4-r} b^r.$$

(b)
$$(2a - 3b)^7 = \sum_{r=0}^{7} \binom{7}{r} (2a)^{7-r}(-3b)^r$$

$$= \sum_{r=0}^{7} \binom{7}{r} (-1)^r (2^{7-r})(3^r) a^{7-r} b^r.$$

Example 2.   Expand (a) $(a + 2b)^4$,   (b) $(2a - 3b)^7$.

Solution:

(a) $(a + 2b)^4 = \binom{4}{0}a^4 + \binom{4}{1}a^3(2b) + \binom{4}{2}a^2(2b)^2 + \binom{4}{3}a(2b)^3 + \binom{4}{4}(2b)^4$

   $= a^4 + 8a^3b + 24a^2b^2 + 32ab^3 + 16b^4$.

(b) $(2a - 3b)^7 = \binom{7}{0}(2a)^7 + \binom{7}{1}(2a)^6(-3b) + \binom{7}{2}(2a)^5(-3b)^2$

   $+ \binom{7}{3}(2a)^4(-3b)^3 + \binom{7}{4}(2a)^3(-3b)^4 + \binom{7}{5}(2a)^2(-3b)^5$

   $+ \binom{7}{6}(2a)(-3b)^6 + \binom{7}{7}(-3b)^7$

   $= 128a^7 - 1344a^6b + 6048a^5b^2 - 15120a^4b^3 + 22680a^3b^4$
   $- 20412a^2b^5 + 10206ab^6 - 2187b^7$.

Example 3.   Find the first three terms and the seventeenth term in the expansion of $(x - 2y)^{19}$.

Solution:

   $(x - 2y)^{19} = \binom{19}{0}x^{19} + \binom{19}{1}x^{18}(-2y) + \binom{19}{2}x^{17}(-2y)^2 + \cdots$

   $= x^{19} - 38x^{18}y + 684x^{17}y^2 + \cdots$.

   $t_{17} = \binom{19}{16}x^3(-2y)^{16}$

   $= 2^{16} \cdot 969x^3y^{16}$.

Example 4. . Write the term containing a^8 in the expansion of $\left(a^2 - \dfrac{b}{2}\right)^6$.

Solution: Since the required term must contain a^8 or $(a^2)^{6-2}$, the coefficient must be $\binom{6}{2}$. Hence

   $t_3 = \binom{6}{2}(a^2)^4\left(-\dfrac{b}{2}\right)^2$

   $= \dfrac{15a^8b^2}{4}$.

EXERCISE 10.2

1. Write the following expansions in sigma notation.
   (a) $(x + y)^{12}$ (b) $(x - y)^9$ (c) $(2x + y)^7$
   (d) $\left(2x + \dfrac{y}{2}\right)^8$ (e) $(x^2 + 1)^{10}$ (f) $(1 - 2x^2)^{15}$

2. Expand each of the following.

(a) $(a-b)^5$

(b) $(2a+b)^4$

(c) $\left(2x - \dfrac{y}{2}\right)^6$

(d) $\left(x^2 + \dfrac{1}{x}\right)^4$

(e) $\left(4x^2 - \dfrac{x}{2}\right)^4$

(f) $\left(3a - \dfrac{2}{b}\right)^5$

3. Write the first three terms of each of the following expansions.

(a) $(a+b)^{10}$

(b) $(a-b)^8$

(c) $(a+3b)^7$

(d) $(1-3x)^{15}$

(e) $(3a-2)^5$

(f) $(1+2b)^{12}$

(g) $\left(2x - \dfrac{y}{4}\right)^8$

(h) $\left(x^2 - \dfrac{2}{x}\right)^6$

(i) $\left(3x^2 - \dfrac{x}{y}\right)^6$

4. Find the indicated term in each of the following expansions.

(a) $(a+b)^{10}$, t_7

(b) $(a-2b)^7$, t_4

(c) $\left(x^2 + \dfrac{x}{2}\right)^6$, t_3

(d) $\left(x^2 - \dfrac{2}{x}\right)^{10}$, t_4

(e) $\left(2x - \dfrac{y}{3}\right)^7$, t_5

(f) $(3x+2y)^6$,   middle term

(g) $\left(\dfrac{2}{a} + \dfrac{a}{2}\right)^8$, t_5

(h) $\left(\dfrac{2}{a} + \dfrac{a}{2}\right)^{2n}$, t_{n+1}

5. Write the term in the expansion of $(x+2y)^7$ in which the exponent of x is 5.

6. Write the term in the expansion of $(2x^2 - y)^8$ in which the exponent of x is 6.

7. Write the term in the expansion of $\left(3x^2 - \dfrac{2}{y^2}\right)^6$ in which the exponent of y is -8.

8. In the expansion of $(ax+by)^7$, the coefficients of the first two terms are 128 and -224, respectively.   Find the values of a and b.

9. In the expansion of $(ax+by)^n$, the coefficients of the first three terms are 1, $-\frac{16}{3}$, and $\frac{112}{9}$, respectively.   If $a > 0$, find the values of a, b, and n.

10.3. Proof by Mathematical Induction

The binomial theorem may be proved by mathematical induction, but we must, obviously, obtain a possible solution by "intelligent guessing" before we can attempt a proof by this method.   For this reason the proof given in the previous section has the advantage of constructing the expansion as the proof is developed.   We note that it is required to prove that

$$(a+b)^n = \sum_{r=0}^{n} \binom{n}{r} a^{n-r} b^r \qquad (r \in W, n \in N).$$

In the proof we require the identity which we were asked to establish in question (21), Exercise 8.4.

$$\binom{n}{r} + \binom{n}{r+1} = \binom{n+1}{r+1} \tag{1.}$$

We will also use the identities

$$\binom{k}{0} = \binom{k+1}{0} = 1 \text{ and } \binom{k}{k} = \binom{k+1}{k+1} = 1 \tag{2.}$$

Proof: Let S be the set of natural numbers for which

$$(a+b)^n = \sum_{r=0}^{n} \binom{n}{r} a^{n-r} b^r.$$

1.
$$\sum_{r=0}^{1} \binom{1}{r} a^{1-r} b^r = \binom{1}{0} a^1 b^0 + \binom{1}{1} a^0 b^1$$
$$= a + b.$$

Therefore
$$1 \in S.$$

2. Assume that $k \in S$.

Hence

$$(a+b)^k = \sum_{r=0}^{k} \binom{k}{r} a^{k-r} b^r$$

$$= \binom{k}{0} a^k + \binom{k}{1} a^{k-1} b + \binom{k}{2} a^{k-2} b^2 + \cdots + \binom{k}{r-1} a^{k-r+1} b^{r-1}$$

$$+ \binom{k}{r} a^{k-r} b^r + \cdots + \binom{k}{k} b^k.$$

Then

$$(a+b)^{k+1} = (a+b)(a+b)^k$$
$$= a(a+b)^k + b(a+b)^k$$
$$= \binom{k}{0} a^{k+1} + \binom{k}{1} a^k b + \binom{k}{2} a^{k-1} b^2 + \cdots$$
$$+ \binom{k}{r-1} a^{k-r+2} b^{r-1} + \binom{k}{r} a^{k-r+1} b^r + \cdots + \binom{k}{k} ab^k$$
$$+ \binom{k}{0} a^k b + \binom{k}{1} a^{k-1} b^2 + \binom{k}{2} a^{k-2} b^3 + \cdots$$
$$+ \binom{k}{r-1} a^{k-r+1} b^r + \binom{k}{r} a^{k-r} b^{r+1} + \cdots + \binom{k}{k} b^{k+1}$$

$$= \binom{k}{0}a^{k+1} + \left[\binom{k}{0} + \binom{k}{1}\right]a^k b + \left[\binom{k}{1} + \binom{k}{2}\right]a^{k-1}b^2 + \cdots$$

$$+ \left[\binom{k}{r-1} + \binom{k}{r}\right]a^{k-r+1}b^r + \cdots + \binom{k}{k}b^{k+1}$$

$$= \binom{k+1}{0}a^{k+1} + \binom{k+1}{1}a^k b + \binom{k+1}{2}a^{k-1}b^2$$

$$+ \cdots + \binom{k+1}{r}a^{k-r+1}b^r + \binom{k+1}{k+1}b^{k+1}$$

(Here we have used the identities (2) in the first and last terms and identity (1) in the other terms.)

$$= \sum_{r=0}^{k+1} \binom{k+1}{r}a^{k+1-r}b^r .$$

Therefore

$$k+1 \in S \quad \text{if} \quad k \in S .$$

Hence

$$S = N ,$$

and

$$(a+b)^n = \sum_{r=0}^{n} \binom{n}{r}a^{n-r}b^r \quad \text{for all } n \in N .$$

10.4. The General Term

In the expansion of $(a+b)^n$, the general term is $t_{r+1} = \binom{n}{r}a^{n-r}b^r$. Once the general term of any particular expansion has been found, it becomes a relatively simple matter to find any particular term in the expansion.

Example 1. Find, in simplified form, the general term in the expansion of

$$\left(x^2 + \frac{1}{x}\right)^{10}.$$

Solution: In the expansion of $(x^2 + x^{-1})^{10}$,

$$t_{r+1} = \binom{10}{r}(x^2)^{10-r}(x^{-1})^r$$

$$= \binom{10}{r}x^{20-2r}x^{-r}$$

$$= \binom{10}{r}x^{20-3r} .$$

Example 2. Find the coefficients of x^{10}, x^0, and x^{-8} in the expansion of

$$\left(x^3 + \frac{1}{x}\right)^{12}.$$

Solution: In the expansion of $(x^3 + x^{-1})^{12}$,

$$t_{r+1} = \binom{12}{r}(x^3)^{12-r}(x^{-1})^r$$

$$= \binom{12}{r}x^{36-3r}x^{-r}$$

$$= \binom{12}{r}x^{36-4r}.$$

(i) If $36 - 4r = 10$, $r = 6\frac{1}{2}$.
Since $r \in W$, there is no term containing x^{10}.

(ii) If $36 - 4r = 0$, $r = 9$.
Hence the coefficient of x^0 is $\binom{12}{9} = 220$.

(iii) If $36 - 4r = -8$, $r = 11$.
Thus the coefficient of x^{-8} is $\binom{12}{11} = 12$.

Note that when $r = 9$, $t_{10} = 220x^0 = 220$, and when $r = 11$, $t_{12} = 12x^{-8}$.

Example 3. In the expansion of $\left(a - \frac{2}{a}\right)^8$, find the terms containing a^4, a^0, $\frac{1}{a^2}$.

Solution: In the expansion of $(a - 2a^{-1})^8$

$$t_{r+1} = \binom{8}{r}a^{8-r}(-2a^{-1})^r$$

$$= \binom{8}{r}(-2)^r a^{8-r}a^{-r}$$

$$= \binom{8}{r}(-2)^r a^{8-2r}.$$

(i) When $8 - 2r = 4$, $r = 2$. Therefore

$$t_3 = \binom{8}{2}(-2)^2 a^4$$

$$= (28)(4)a^4$$

$$= 112a^4.$$

(ii)   When $8 - 2r = 0$, $r = 4$.   Therefore

$$t_5 = \binom{8}{4}(-2)^4 a^0$$

$$= (70)(16)$$

$$= 1120 .$$

(iii)   When $8 - 2r = -2$, $r = 5$.   Therefore

$$t_6 = \binom{8}{5}(-2)^5 a^{-2}$$

$$= (56)(-32)a^{-2}$$

$$= -\frac{1792}{a^2} .$$

EXERCISE 10.3

1. Find the general term in each of the following expansions.

(a) $(1 + x)^{12}$

(b) $(2 - a)^8$

(c) $(x^2 + x)^7$

(d) $\left(a + \dfrac{1}{a}\right)^7$

(e) $\left(p - \dfrac{1}{p}\right)^8$

(f) $\left(x^2 - \dfrac{1}{x}\right)^{10}$

(g) $\left(2a + \dfrac{1}{a^2}\right)^{10}$

(h) $\left(2a - \dfrac{1}{a^3}\right)^{15}$

(i) $\left(a^3 + \dfrac{2}{a^2}\right)^n$

2. In the expansion of $\left(x + \dfrac{1}{x^2}\right)^{12}$, find the coefficients of x^9, x^3, x^{-9}.

3. Find the term independent of a in the expansion of $\left(a + \dfrac{1}{a^4}\right)^{15}$.

4. In the expansion of $\left(2x + \dfrac{1}{x}\right)^{10}$, find the terms containing x^8, x^0, x^{-4}.

5. In the expansion of $\left(\dfrac{3x}{2} - \dfrac{2}{x^2}\right)^6$, find the term independent of x and the term containing x^{-6}.

6. In the expansion of $\left(a^2 - \dfrac{1}{a^3}\right)^9$, find the coefficients of a^3, a^{-7}, a^{-10}.

7. Find the term independent of x in the expansion of $\left(2x + \dfrac{1}{2\sqrt{x}}\right)^9$.

8. In the expansion of $(x + x^{-1})^n$, the fifth term is independent of x.   Find the value of n.

9. In the expansion of $\left(\dfrac{3x}{2} + \dfrac{1}{x}\right)^n$, the fourth term contains x^3.   Find the value of n.

10. In the expansion of $(1 - x)(1 + x)^n$, the third term is $35x^2$.   Find the value of n.

10.5. Binomial Theorem-Rational Exponents

In the previous sections we have proved, and used, the binomial theorem when the exponent was a positive integer. Is it possible to apply the binomial expansion to $(a + b)^n$ when n is any rational number? The answer to this is a qualified "yes". Certain restrictions apply.

We know that

$$(a + b)^5 = \binom{5}{0} a^5 + \binom{5}{1} a^4 b + \binom{5}{2} a^3 b^2 + \binom{5}{3} a^2 b^3 + \binom{5}{4} ab^4 + \binom{5}{5} b^5.$$

If we now consider $(a + b)^{-\frac{3}{2}}$ we see that the expressions $\binom{-\frac{3}{2}}{0}$ or $\binom{-\frac{3}{2}}{1}$ can have no meaning in the context of our earlier definition of $\binom{n}{r}$.

However,

$$(1 + x)^5 = \binom{5}{0} + \binom{5}{1} x + \binom{5}{2} x^2 + \binom{5}{3} x^3 + \binom{5}{4} x^4 + \binom{5}{5} x^5$$

$$= 1 + \frac{5}{1!} x + \frac{5 \times 4}{2!} x^2 + \frac{5 \times 4 \times 3}{3!} x^3 + \frac{5 \times 4 \times 3 \times 2}{4!} x^4 + \frac{5 \times 4 \times 3 \times 2 \times 1}{5!} x^5.$$

In general, if n is a positive integer, the general term in the expansion of

$$(1 + x)^n \text{ is } t_{r+1} = \frac{n(n - 1)(n - 2) \ldots (n - r + 1)}{r!} x^r.$$

If we now apply this to the expansion of $(1 + x)^{-\frac{3}{2}}$ we have

$$(1 + x)^{-\frac{3}{2}} = 1 + \frac{-\frac{3}{2}}{1!} x + \frac{(-\frac{3}{2})(-\frac{5}{2})}{2!} x^2 + \frac{(-\frac{3}{2})(-\frac{5}{2})(-\frac{7}{2})}{3!} x^3 + \ldots$$

$$+ \frac{(-\frac{3}{2})(-\frac{5}{2})(-\frac{7}{2}) \ldots (-\frac{3}{2} - r + 1)}{r!} x^r + \ldots$$

We immediately note that the right side is an infinite series. In the expansion of $(1 + x)^n$ where n is a positive integer we eventually reach the stage where $n - r + 1 = 1$ and the series terminates at that term. If n is not a positive integer $n - r + 1$ will never equal zero and the series continues indefinitely. As an infinite series there may or may not be a limit to the sum. Hence, the series will only represent the expansion of $(1 + x)^n$ under certain restrictions. Let us consider the expansion of $(1 - x)^{-1}$ as a particular case.

$$(1 - x)^{-1} = 1 + \frac{(-1)}{1!} (-x) + \frac{(-1)(-2)}{2!} (-x)^2 + \frac{(-1)(-2)(-3)}{3!} (-x)^3$$

$$+ \ldots + \frac{(-1)(-2) \ldots (-1 - r + 1)}{r!} x^r + \ldots$$

$$= 1 + x + x^2 + x^3 + \ldots + x^r + \ldots$$

The right side is a geometric series with common ratio x. We know that $S_\infty = \underset{n \to \infty}{\text{Lim}} S_n$ exists only if $|x| < 1$.

If
$$x = \tfrac{1}{2},$$
$$(1 - x)^{-1} = (1 - \tfrac{1}{2})^{-1}$$
$$= (\tfrac{1}{2})^{-1} = 2.$$

and
$$1 + \tfrac{1}{2} + (\tfrac{1}{2})^2 + (\tfrac{1}{2})^3 + \ldots = \frac{1}{1 - \tfrac{1}{2}} = 2.$$

Hence, the expansion does represent $(1 - x)^{-1}$ for $x = \tfrac{1}{2}$.

If
$$x = 2,$$
$$(1 - x)^{-1} = (-1)^{-1} = -1,$$

and
$$1 + 2 + 2^2 + 2^3 + \ldots \neq -1.$$

Hence, the expansion does *not* represent $(1 - x)^{-1}$ for $x = 2$.

It should be pointed out that only a very few expansions form a geometric series but, if n is a rational number, then

$$(1 + x)^n = 1 + \frac{n}{1!}x + \frac{n(n-1)}{2!}x^2 + \frac{n(n-1)(n-2)}{3!}x^3 + \ldots$$

$$+ \frac{n(n-1)(n-2)\ldots(n-r+1)}{r!}x^r + \ldots$$

if and only if $|x| < 1$.

We will not attempt to prove this theorem here. Note that if n is a positive integer the series terminates and the restriction does not apply.

Example 1. Write the first four terms and the general term of the expansion of $(1 + x)^{-3}$, stating restrictions on x.

Solution:
$$(1 + x)^{-3} = 1 + \frac{(-3)}{1!}x + \frac{(-3)(-4)}{2!}x^2 + \frac{(-3)(-4)(-5)}{3!}x^3 + \ldots$$

$$= 1 - 3x + 6x^2 - 10x^3 + \ldots$$

$$t_{r+1} = \frac{(-3)(-4)(-5)\ldots(-3-r+1)}{r!}x^r$$

$$= (-1)^r \frac{3 \cdot 4 \cdot 5 \cdots (r+2)}{r!}x^r \times \frac{n(n-1)}{2 \cdot 1} (n+2)!$$

$$= (-1)^r \frac{(r+1)(r+2)}{2}x^r \qquad (|x| < 1)$$

Example 2. State the general term, the sixth term, and the coefficient of x^8 in the expansion of $(1 + 2x)^{\frac{1}{2}}$ noting restrictions on x.

Solution: In the expansion of $(1 + 2x)^{\frac{1}{2}}$ $\qquad\qquad |2x| < 1$

$$t_{r+1} = \frac{(\tfrac{1}{2})(-\tfrac{1}{2})(-\tfrac{3}{2})(-\tfrac{5}{2})\ldots(\tfrac{1}{2}-r+1)}{r!}(2x)^r \quad |x| < \tfrac{1}{2}.$$

$$= (-1)^{r-1}\frac{(\tfrac{1}{2})(\tfrac{1}{2})(\tfrac{3}{2})(\tfrac{5}{2})\cdots \frac{2r-3}{2}}{r!}2^r x^r$$

$$= (-1)^{r-1} \frac{1 \cdot 1 \cdot 3 \cdot 5 \cdot \ldots (2r-3)}{r!} x^r$$

$$t_6 = (-1)^4 \frac{3 \cdot 5 \cdot 7}{5!} x^5 = \frac{7x^5}{8}.$$ (Note $r = 5$)

Coefficient of x^8 is $(-1)^7 \dfrac{3 \cdot 5 \cdot 7 \cdot 9 \cdot 11 \cdot 13}{8!}$

$$= -\frac{3 \cdot 5 \cdot 7 \cdot 9 \cdot 11 \cdot 13}{8 \cdot 7 \cdot 6 \cdot 5 \cdot 4 \cdot 3 \cdot 2 \cdot 1}$$

$$= -\frac{429}{128}$$

Note that the expansion is of $(1 + x)^n$. If the first term in the binomial is not 1 a rearrangement must be made as in Example 3.

Example 3. Calculate the first four terms and the general term in the expansion of $(8 + 2x)^{-\frac{2}{3}}$.

Solution:

$$(8 + 2x)^{-\frac{2}{3}}$$

$$= 8^{-\frac{2}{3}} \left(1 + \frac{x}{4}\right)^{-\frac{2}{3}}$$

$$= \tfrac{1}{4} \left(1 + \frac{x}{4}\right)^{-\frac{2}{3}}$$

$$= \tfrac{1}{4}\left[1 + \left(-\tfrac{2}{3}\right)\left(\tfrac{x}{4}\right) + \frac{\left(-\tfrac{2}{3}\right)\left(-\tfrac{5}{3}\right)}{2!}\left(\tfrac{x}{4}\right)^2 + \frac{\left(-\tfrac{2}{3}\right)\left(-\tfrac{5}{3}\right)\left(-\tfrac{8}{3}\right)}{3!}\left(\tfrac{x}{4}\right)^3 + \ldots\right]$$

$$= \tfrac{1}{4}\left[1 - \frac{x}{6} + \frac{5x^2}{144} - \frac{5x^3}{648} + \ldots\right]$$

$$= \tfrac{1}{4} - \frac{x}{24} + \frac{5x^2}{576} - \frac{5x^3}{2592} + \ldots$$

$$t_{r+1} = \tfrac{1}{4}\left[\frac{\left(-\tfrac{2}{3}\right)\left(-\tfrac{5}{3}\right)\left(-\tfrac{8}{3}\right) \ldots \left(-\tfrac{2}{3} - r + 1\right)}{r!}\left(\tfrac{x}{4}\right)^r\right]$$

$$= \tfrac{1}{4}\left[(-1)^r \frac{2 \cdot 5 \cdot 8 \cdot \ldots (3r-1)}{3^r r!} \frac{x^r}{4^r}\right]$$

$$= (-1)^r \frac{2 \cdot 5 \cdot 8 \cdot \ldots (3r-1)}{3^r \, 4^{r+1} r!} x^r \qquad \left|\frac{x}{4}\right| < 1$$

$$|x| < 4.$$

Example 4. Calculate $\sqrt[3]{68}$ correct to 3 decimal places.

$$\sqrt[3]{68} = \sqrt[3]{64 + 4}$$

$$= (64 + 4)^{\frac{1}{3}}$$

$$= 64^{\frac{1}{3}} \left(1 + \tfrac{1}{16}\right)^{\frac{1}{3}}$$

$$= 4\left[1 + \left(\tfrac{1}{3}\right)\left(\tfrac{1}{16}\right) + \frac{\left(\tfrac{1}{3}\right)\left(-\tfrac{2}{3}\right)}{2!}\left(\tfrac{1}{16}\right)^2 + \frac{\left(\tfrac{1}{3}\right)\left(-\tfrac{2}{3}\right)\left(-\tfrac{5}{3}\right)}{3!}\left(\tfrac{1}{16}\right)^3 + \ldots\right]$$

$$= 4\left[1 + \tfrac{1}{48} - \frac{2}{3\cdot3\cdot2\cdot16^2} + \frac{2\cdot5}{3\cdot3\cdot3\cdot3\cdot2\cdot16^3} + \cdots\right]$$
$$= 4[1 + \tfrac{1}{48} - \tfrac{1}{2304} + \ldots]$$
$$= 4 + \tfrac{1}{12} - \tfrac{1}{576} + \cdots$$
$$\simeq 4 + .08\dot{3} - .00174 + \cdots$$
$$\simeq 4.082.$$

Note that the expansion of $\left(1 + \tfrac{1}{16}\right)^{\frac{1}{3}}$ is valid since $\left|\tfrac{1}{16}\right| < 1$.

EXERCISE 10.4

In each example state any restriction on the variable.

1. State the first 4 terms in the expansion of
   (a) $(1 + x)^{-1}$ (b) $(1 - x)^{-2}$ (c) $(1 + x)^{-2}$
   (d) $(1 - 2x)^{\frac{1}{2}}$ (e) $(1 - x^2)^{-2}$ (f) $(1 + 2x^2)^{\frac{3}{2}}$
   (g) $(4 - 3x)^{\frac{5}{2}}$ (h) $(9 - 2x)^{-\frac{1}{2}}$ (i) $(8 - 3x)^{\frac{1}{3}}$
   (j) $\sqrt[3]{1 + x}$ (k) $\sqrt{(4 + 2x)^3}$ (l) $(x - x^2)^{-5}$

2. State in simplified form, the general term of the expansions:
   (a) $(1 + x)^{-1}$ (b) $(1 - x)^{-2}$ (c) $(1 + x)^{-3}$
   (d) $(1 - x)^{-3}$ (e) $(1 + x)^{\frac{1}{2}}$ (f) $(2 + x)^{-\frac{1}{2}}$
   (g) $(4 - 2x)^{\frac{5}{2}}$ (h) $(9 - 2x)^{-\frac{3}{2}}$ (i) $(8 + 2x)^{\frac{1}{3}}$
   (j) $(27 - 18x)^{-\frac{1}{3}}$ (k) $\dfrac{3}{\sqrt[3]{27 - 9x}}$ (l) $\dfrac{2}{\sqrt{16 - 4x}}$

3. Calculate the coefficient of x^{10} in the expansion of $(1 + x)^{-3}$.

4. Calculate the coefficient of x^{10} in the expansion of $(1 - x^2)^{-2}$.

5. Calculate the coefficient of x^0 in the expansion of $(x - x^2)^{-6}$.

6. By means of a binomial expansion calculate the value of each of the following correct to 3 decimal places:
   (a) $\sqrt{26}$ (b) $\sqrt{98}$ (c) $\sqrt[3]{30}$ (d) $\dfrac{1}{\sqrt{68}}$

   (e) $(.995)^4$ (f) $\dfrac{1}{1.005}$ (g) $\dfrac{1}{\sqrt[3]{995}}$.

Chapter Summary

If $n \in N$,

$$(a + b)^n = \sum_{r=0}^{n} \binom{n}{r} a^{n-r} b^r$$

$$= \binom{n}{0}a^n + \binom{n}{1}a^{n-1}b + \binom{n}{2}a^{n-2}b^2 + \ldots + \binom{n}{r}a^{n-r}b^r + \ldots + \binom{n}{n}b^n.$$

The general term is

$$t_{r+1} = \binom{n}{r}a^{n-r}b^r.$$

REVIEW EXERCISE 10

1. Write the following expansions using sigma notation.
   (a) $(a + b)^7$ (b) $(x + 2y)^n$ (c) $(2a - b)^{10}$
   (d) $\left(x^2 - \dfrac{1}{x}\right)^8$ (e) $\left(2x^2 + \dfrac{1}{2x}\right)^{15}$ (f) $(2 - x^2)^n$

2. Expand each of the following.
   (a) $(a + b)^6$ (b) $(a - b)^6$ (c) $(2a - 3b)^5$

3. Write the first three terms of each of the following expansions.

   (a) $(a + 2b)^{12}$ (b) $(2x - y)^8$ (c) $\left(2x^2 + \dfrac{x}{2}\right)^{10}$

   (d) $\left(3x - \dfrac{1}{x}\right)^6$ (e) $\left(\dfrac{x}{2} + \dfrac{2}{x}\right)^{10}$ (f) $(ax^2 + b)^{20}$

   (g) $(1 + 2x)^{-1}$ (h) $(4 - x)^{\frac{1}{2}}$ (i) $(4 + 2x)^{-\frac{3}{2}}$

4. State, in simplified form, the general term of the expansions:
   (a) $(1 + 3x)^{-1}$ (b) $(9 + 3x^2)^{-2}$ (c) $\dfrac{1}{\sqrt[3]{8 - 4x}}$

5. Find the eleventh term in the expansion of $\left(3x + \dfrac{1}{x}\right)^{12}$.

6. Find the seventh term in the expansion of $\left(x^2 - \dfrac{1}{x}\right)^{10}$.

7. In the expansion of $(2x - 1)^{10}$, find the term containing x^2.

8. Find the first three terms in the expansion of $(a + 1)^8(2a - 1)^5$.

9. Find the first three terms in the expansion of $(1 - x)^7(2 + x)^4$.

10. In the expansion of $\left(3x + \dfrac{x^2}{3}\right)^{10}$, find the coefficients of x^{12} and x^{15}.

11. Find the term independent of x in the expansion of $\left(2x - \dfrac{1}{x^2}\right)^6$.

12. Find the middle term in the expansion of $\left(\dfrac{2}{x} + \dfrac{x}{2}\right)^{10}$.

13. Calculate the coefficient of a^4 in the expansion of $(a^2 + a^3)^{-2}$.

14. Calculate the coefficient of x^{-8} in the expansion of $(x^6 - x^4)^{-\frac{1}{3}}$.

15. By means of a binomial expansion, calculate the value of each of the following correct to 3 decimal places.

   (a) $\sqrt{102}$ (b) $(3.95)^4$ (c) $\dfrac{1}{\sqrt[3]{120}}$

16. In the expansion of $(1 + px)^n$, the first three terms are $1 - 36x + 594x^2$. Find the values of n and p.

17. In the expansion of $(1 + px)^n$, the first three terms are $1 + 5x + \dfrac{45x^2}{4}$. Find the values of n and p.

18. In the expansion of $\left(a^2 - \dfrac{1}{a^3}\right)^n$, the fifth term is $70a^{-4}$. Find the value of n.

19. In the expansion of $(ax + by)^7$, the coefficients of the first two terms are 128 and -112, respectively. Find the values of a and b.

20. In the expansion of $(ax + by)^n$, the coefficients of the first three terms are 729, 486, and 135, respectively. If $a > 0$, find the values of a, b, and n.

21. If $f(x) = x^n$, find the value of $\dfrac{f(x + h) - f(x)}{h}$ and the value of

$$\lim_{h \to 0} \frac{f(x + h) - f(x)}{h} \, .$$

22. Write the first five terms in the expansion of $\left(1 + \dfrac{1}{n}\right)^n$ and find (correct to 1 decimal place) the value of $\lim_{n \to \infty} \left(1 + \dfrac{1}{n}\right)^n$.

Chapter 11

PROBABILITY

11.1. Introduction and Definitions

Most of us already have some intuitive idea as to what is meant by probability. If we toss a coin, we feel certain that it is just as likely to fall "heads" as to fall "tails"; if we roll a die, we feel that one face is just as likely to end up on top as another. In the case of the coin, we consider that "heads" and "tails" have *equal chances* or are *equally likely outcomes*. With the die, we feel that one dot, two dots, three dots, four dots, five dots, or six dots on top are equally likely outcomes.

If a coin is tossed and we consider heads to be a favourable outcome, then we feel that we have one chance in two of having our wish satisfied. If we consider a three to be a favourable outcome in the toss of a die, then we feel that we have one chance in six of being successful.

In more technical language, we would say that, in the case of the coin, the probability of heads is $\frac{1}{2}$, and, in the case of the die, the probability of three on top is $\frac{1}{6}$. This is usually expressed symbolically as

$$P(\text{head}) = \tfrac{1}{2},$$
$$P(3 \text{ on top}) = \tfrac{1}{6}.$$

We note, of course, that we are considering only a "fair" coin or die. If the die were more heavily loaded on one side, then the opposite side would be more likely to appear on top. The six faces would no longer be equally likely.

If we consider the probability of drawing an honour card (ace, king, queen, jack, or ten) from a well-shuffled deck of playing cards, we know that we have fifty-two possible outcomes, and of these, twenty are favourable (an honour card). The probability of drawing an honour card is $\frac{20}{52}$. That is,

$$P(\text{honour card}) = \tfrac{20}{52} = \tfrac{5}{13}.$$

That all outcomes are equally likely is not always true but, for the moment, we will only consider cases where this is true. In the example of drawing an honour card, there are fifty-two equally likely outcomes. Twenty of these outcomes correspond to the event "honour card drawn" and may be considered as

293

favourable outcomes. In the same way, if n is the number of equally likely outcomes of a specific experiment and exactly m of these outcomes ($m \leq n$) correspond to an event A, then the probability of A is m/n. In symbols,

$$P(A) = \frac{m}{n}.$$

This, of course, does not constitute a rigorous definition of an event or of the probability of an event. It is a useful, intuitive approach and more rigorous definitions will be given in the next section.

Example 1.   If one card is drawn at random from a well-shuffled deck of fifty-two playing cards, what is the probability of each of the following events?

(a) Drawing a spade

(b) Drawing a king

(c) Drawing a red card

(d) Drawing the queen of spades

Solution:

$$P(\text{a spade}) = \tfrac{13}{52} = \tfrac{1}{4}.$$
$$P(\text{a king}) = \tfrac{4}{52} = \tfrac{1}{13}.$$
$$P(\text{red card}) = \tfrac{26}{52} = \tfrac{1}{2}.$$
$$P(\text{queen of spades}) = \tfrac{1}{52}.$$

Example 2.   A letter is chosen at random from the word *probability*.   What is the probability that the letter chosen is

(a) a vowel?   (b) a consonant?   (c) the letter b?   (d) the letter s?

Solution:

$$P(\text{vowel}) = \tfrac{4}{11}.$$
$$P(\text{consonant}) = \tfrac{7}{11}.$$
$$P(b) = \tfrac{2}{11}.$$
$$P(s) = \tfrac{0}{11} = 0.$$

Example 3.   A group of five men and four women agree that three should be chosen by lot to form a special committee.   What is the probability that the committee consists of one man and two women?

Solution: Number of possible committee selections is

$$\binom{9}{3} = \frac{9 \times 8 \times 7}{3 \times 2}$$
$$= 84.$$

Number of possible committee selections consisting of one man and two women is

$$\binom{5}{1}\binom{4}{2} = 5 \times 6$$
$$= 30.$$

Therefore
$$P(1 \text{ man and 2 women}) = \tfrac{30}{84} = \tfrac{5}{14}.$$

Example 4. Twenty tickets are placed in a box and shaken. One ticket is taken from the box and the person whose name is on that ticket receives a prize. What is the probability that Tom wins the prize if his name is on

(a) 4 of the tickets?　　　(b) none of the tickets?　(c) all 20 tickets?

Solution:

(a)　　　　　　　　　$P(\text{Tom wins}) = \tfrac{4}{20} = \tfrac{1}{5}.$

(b)　　　　　　　　　$P(\text{Tom wins}) = \tfrac{0}{20} = 0.$

(c)　　　　　　　　　$P(\text{Tom wins}) = \tfrac{20}{20} = 1.$

This last example illustrates that the probability of any event A is a real number between 0 and 1, that is,

$$0 \le P(A) \le 1.$$

If the event cannot happen, as in Example 4(b), then the probability is zero. If Tom's name does not appear on any of the tickets, he cannot win the prize.

If $P(A) = 1$, then A is certain. If Tom's name appears on all twenty tickets, then he must win. His success is certain and $P(\text{Tom wins}) = 1$.

EXERCISE 11.1

1. If a die is thrown, what is the probability that the upper face shows
   (a) 4 dots?　　　　　　　　　(b) more than 4 dots?
   (c) fewer than 4 dots?　　　　(d) an odd number of dots?
   (e) an even number of dots?　　(f) more than 3 dots?

2. A bag contains five red balls and three black balls. If one ball is drawn from the bag, what is the probability that it is
   (a) a red ball?　　　　　　　　(b) a black ball?

3. A letter is chosen at random from the word *Toronto*. What is the probability that the letter chosen is
   (a) the letter *t*?　　　(b) the letter *o*?　　　(c) a consonant?

4. From a group of twenty men and sixteen women, one person is chosen by lot. What is the probability that a man is chosen?

5. From a group of twenty men and sixteen women, two persons are chosen by lot. What is the probability that
   (a) both are men?　　　　　　　(b) both are women?
   (c) one man and one woman are chosen?
   What is the sum of the three probabilities?

6. Six slips of paper, numbered 1 to 6, are placed in a bag and two are drawn out. Find the probability of each of the following events.
   (a) The numbers 2 and 5 are drawn.
   (b) The numbers 2 and 5 are drawn in that order.
   (c) Two even numbers are drawn.

7. A three-digit number is formed by drawing three slips from a box containing nine slips of paper numbered 1 to 9. The first digit drawn is to be the hundreds digit, the second is to be the tens digit, and the third is to be the units digit. The slips are not replaced after being drawn. What is the probability that the number formed

   (a) is even?   (b) is odd?   (c) has units digit 4?

8. Three books are selected at random from eight different books on a shelf. What is the probability that a specific book is included in the selection?

9. From a group of twelve boys, a selection of three will be made by lot to attend the Stanley Cup final. Tom and Jim are very anxious to win. What is the probability that

   (a) both will be selected?   (b) only one of them will be selected?

10. If two dice are tossed, what is the probability that
    (a) both upper faces show 6?   (b) the upper faces total 4?

11. Assuming that boys and girls have an equal chance of being born, what is the probability that, in a family of three children, all three are girls?

12. If two cards are drawn at random from a well-shuffled deck of fifty-two playing cards, what is the probability of each of the following events?
    (a) Both are clubs.   (b) Both are aces.
    (c) Both are red cards.   (d) Both are black aces.

11.2. Sample Space

If a nickel and a quarter are tossed together, what is the set of all possible outcomes of the experiment? The answer to this question will depend upon what particular aspect of the experiment interests us. If we are interested simply in whether the coins fall alike (both heads or both tails) or differently (one head and one tail), then we have only two possible outcomes, L (like) and D (different). The set of all possible outcomes is

$$S_1 = \{L, D\}.$$

However, we may be interested in the number of heads or the number of tails that show. If we agree to denote x heads and y tails by the ordered pair (x, y), then the set of all possible outcomes is

$$S_2 = \{(2, 0), (1, 1), (0, 2)\}.$$

Any possible outcome of the experiment corresponds to exactly one element of the set S_2.

Again, we may be interested in whether each individual coin falls heads (H) or tails (T). In this case we may list the outcome by the ordered pairs (x, y), where x represents the outcome for the nickel and y, the outcome for the quarter. The set of all possible outcomes is

$$S_3 = \{(H, H), (H, T), (T, H), (T, T)\}.$$

(T, H) means that the nickel fell tails and the quarter fell heads. All possible outcomes are elements of the set S_3.

Each of the sets S_1, S_2, S_3 is a set of all possible outcomes of the experiment. Each set is called a sample space of the experiment. Note that there may be many possible sample spaces of an experiment so that we talk about *a* sample space rather than *the* sample space.

We should also note that S_3 is a more fundamental sample space than either S_1 or S_2. If we know that (T, H) is the actual outcome in S_3, we also know that D is the outcome in S_1, and (1, 1) is the outcome in S_2. However, if we know that L is the outcome in S_1, we do not know the outcome in S_3. It may be (H, H) or (T, T). If we know that the actual outcome in S_2 is (2, 0), then we know that the outcome in S_3 is (H, H); but if the outcome in S_2 is (1, 1), we do not know whether the outcome in S_3 is (H, T) or (T, H).

DEFINITION. A *sample space* of an experiment is a set of elements such that every outcome of the experiment corresponds to exactly one element of the set.

An element in a sample space is often called a sample point. Since the sample space is the set of all possible outcomes, there is a tendency in some texts to use the terms *outcome set* and *outcome* in place of sample space and sample point. There is much to be said in favour of this terminology since by definition a sample space is a set of all possible outcomes. Outcome set would seem to be a more descriptive title. However, although there are good reasons for changing to outcome set, we will continue to use the more traditional title of sample space.

This definition of a sample space now enables us to define an event.

DEFINITION. An *event* is a result of an experiment that may be represented by a subset of a sample space of the experiment.

In a sample space $S_3 = \{(H, H), (H, T), (T, H), (T, T)\}$, the event "both coins fall alike" corresponds to the subset $\{(H, H), (T, T)\}$. The subset in this case contains two elements of the sample space. Other events in this sample space may contain 1, 2, 3, or 4 elements of the sample space.

Example 1.   A bag contains twenty red balls and twenty black balls.   If three balls are drawn from the bag one after the other without replacement, list two sample spaces for the experiment.   How many elements of the most fundamental sample space correspond to the following events?

  (a) drawing two red balls and one black ball
  (b) drawing three red balls
  (c) drawing at least one red ball

Solution:

$$S_1 = \{0, 1, 2, 3\},$$

where each element is the number of red balls drawn.

$$S_2 = \{RRR, RRB, RBR, RBB, BRR, BRB, BBR, BBB\}.$$

A useful method of setting up S_2 is by means of a tree diagram.

Table 11.1

1st draw	2nd draw	3rd draw	Sample space
		R	RRR
	R		
		B	RRB
R			
		R	RBR
	B		
		B	RBB
		R	BRR
	R		
B		B	BRB
		R	BBR
	B		
		B	BBB

  (a) Three elements of S_2 correspond to drawing two red balls and one black ball.
  (b) One element of S_2 corresponds to drawing three red balls.
  (c) Seven elements of S_2 correspond to drawing at least one red ball.

Example 2.   Two dice, one black and one white, are rolled and the number shown on each die is noted.   List a sample space for this experiment.

  We note that we are told that the *number* on each die is noted.   If only the *total* were required, a suitable sample space would be $\{2, 3, 4, \cdots, 12\}$.

Solution: A tabular arrangement is probably the most suitable way to illustrate the elements of this sample space.

Table 11.2

White die (W)

B \ W	1	2	3	4	5	6
1	(1, 1)	(1, 2)	(1, 3)	(1, 4)	(1, 5)	(1, 6)
2	(2, 1)	(2, 2)	(2, 3)	(2, 4)	(2, 5)	(2, 6)
Black 3	(3, 1)	(3, 2)	(3, 3)	(3, 4)	(3, 5)	(3, 6)
die 4	(4, 1)	(4, 2)	(4, 3)	(4, 4)	(4, 5)	(4, 6)
(B) 5	(5, 1)	(5, 2)	(5, 3)	(5, 4)	(5, 5)	(5, 6)
6	(6, 1)	(6, 2)	(6, 3)	(6, 4)	(6, 5)	(6, 6)

Note that each row corresponds to a fixed value of the outcome for the black die, and each column, to a fixed value of the outcome for the white die. There are thirty-six elements in the sample space.

Example 3. Using the sample space in Example 2, how many elements of the sample space correspond to the following events?

(a) Both dice show the same number.

(b) The number on the white die is two more than the number on the black die.

(c) The total for the two dice is seven.

(d) The total for the two dice is eleven.

Solution:

(a) Six elements show the same number on both dice.

(b) Four elements correspond to having the number on the white die two more than the number on the black die.

(c) Six elements correspond to a total of seven for the two dice.

(d) Two elements correspond to a total of eleven for the two dice.

EXERCISE 11.2

1. List two sample spaces for an experiment of tossing three coins.

2. Using the sample spaces in question (1), how many elements of each sample space correspond to two heads and one tail?

3. Use a tree diagram to set up a sample space to study the distribution of boys

and girls in families having three children. How many elements of the sample space correspond to

(a) families having three boys?

(b) families having one boy and two girls?

4. Use a tree diagram to set up a sample space to study the distribution of boys and girls in families having four children. How many elements of the sample space correspond to

(a) families having three girls and one boy?

(b) families having two girls and two boys?

(c) families in which the first two children are girls?

5. A box contains five differently coloured balls: red (R), blue (B), green (G), white (W), and yellow (Y). If three have to be chosen, list a sample space of the $\binom{5}{3}$ possible selections. How many elements of the sample space correspond to

(a) a selection including Y?

(b) a selection excluding Y?

(c) a selection including both B and G?

(d) a selection including either B or G?

6. A bag contains twenty blue marbles, twenty green marbles, and twenty red marbles, identical except for colour. Two marbles are drawn one after the other with the first being replaced before the second is drawn. List a sample space for the experiment. How many elements of the sample space correspond to

(a) drawing two marbles of the same colour?

(b) drawing a blue and a green marble?

(c) drawing a blue or a green marble?

7. Four cards, numbered 1, 2, 3, and 4, are to be placed in four boxes numbered 1, 2, 3, 4, one card in each box. List a sample space of ordered quadruples that indicate the card in each slot. (For example, 1243 indicates card 1 in box 1, card 2 in box 2, card 4 in box 3, and card 3 in box 4.) How many elements of the sample space correspond to the following events?

(a) Exactly two card numbers and two box numbers coincide.

(b) At least two card numbers and two box numbers coincide.

(c) No card number coincides with its box number.

11.3. Probabilities in a Finite Sample Space

In Section 11.2, we listed three sample spaces for the example of tossing two coins.

$S_1 = \{L, D\}$, where L indicated that both coins fell heads or both fell tails, and D indicated that one fell heads and the other, tails.

$S_2 = \{(2, 0), (1, 1), (0, 2)\}$, where the ordered pairs (x, y) indicated x heads and y tails.

$S_3 = \{(H, H)\ (H, T), (T, H), (T, T)\}$, where the ordered pairs (x, y) indicated the outcome for the nickel (x) and for the quarter (y).

In Section 11.1, we stated that the probability of an event A is $\dfrac{m}{n}$, where n is the number of equally likely outcomes and exactly m of these outcomes correspond to event A.

In the experiment of tossing two coins, what is the probability that one falls heads and the other, tails? Using S_1, the outcome corresponding to a favourable event is D, that is, one outcome of the two possible outcomes. From this it would appear that

$$P(1 \text{ head and 1 tail}) = \tfrac{1}{2}.$$

However, if we consider the three outcomes in S_2 to be equally likely, only the pair $(1, 1)$ corresponds to the favourable event, 1 head and 1 tail. From this it would appear that

$$P(1 \text{ head and 1 tail}) = \tfrac{1}{3}.$$

From S_3, it would appear that

$$P(1 \text{ head and 1 tail}) = \tfrac{2}{4} = \tfrac{1}{2}.$$

The difficulty arises because the outcomes in S_2 are not equally likely. If we assume that the outcome of one coin is independent of the outcome of the other, then the four outcomes in S_3 are equally likely and each can be assigned a probability of $\tfrac{1}{4}$. In this case the outcomes in S_2 are not equally likely and

$$P(2, 0) = \tfrac{1}{4}, \quad P(1, 1) = \tfrac{1}{2}, \quad P(0, 2) = \tfrac{1}{4}.$$

It is essential when using a sample space either to ensure that each of the outcomes is equally likely or to know the probability of each possible outcome.

In Table 11.2 of the last section, we set up thirty-six elements of the sample space for the experiment of rolling two dice, one white and one black, when the number on each die is noted. Naturally we would expect thirty-six elements in this sample space even if they were not listed. If B is the set of all possible outcomes for the black die and W is the set of all possible outcomes for the white die, then

$$B = \{1, 2, 3, 4, 5, 6\} \quad \text{and} \quad n(B) = 6,$$
$$W = \{1, 2, 3, 4, 5, 6\} \quad \text{and} \quad n(W) = 6.$$

The set of all possible outcomes of the experiment of rolling both dice is

$$B \times W = \{(b, w) \mid b \in B \text{ and } w \in W\}$$

and

$$
\begin{aligned}
n(B \times W) &= n(B) \times n(W) \\
&= 6 \times 6 \\
&= 36 .
\end{aligned}
$$

Since there are thirty-six equally likely outcomes of the experiment of rolling both dice, we assign a probability of $\frac{1}{36}$ to each possible outcome. If the sample space contains n *equally likely* outcomes, we assign probability $1/n$ to each element of the sample space.

An event corresponds to a subset of the sample space. For example, if A is the event that both dice show the same number, then A corresponds to the subset $\{(1,1), (2,2), (3,3), (4,4), (5,5), (6,6)\}$ of S, where S is the sample space in Table 11.2. Therefore

$$P(A) = \frac{6}{36} = \frac{1}{6} .$$

Of course, it may happen that the elements of the sample space are not equally likely outcomes and we prefer to have a definition of the probability of an event that will cover all cases.

In the two-coin experiment, if $S_3 = \{(H, H), (H, T), (T, H), (T, T)\}$ is the sample space, and if A is the event "at least one coin falls heads", then

$$A = \{(H, H), (H, T), (T, H)\} \quad \text{and} \quad P(A) = \frac{3}{4} .$$

If we use $S_2 = \{(2, 0), (1, 1), (0, 2)\}$, then

$$A = \{(2, 0), (1, 1)\} .$$

Then

$$P(2, 0) = \frac{1}{4}, \quad P(1, 1) = \frac{1}{2} ,$$

and

$$P(A) = \frac{1}{4} + \frac{1}{2} = \frac{3}{4} .$$

To each element of a sample space, we assign a real number called a *probability*. These probabilities must satisfy two conditions.

(1) A probability is a real number x such that $0 \leq x \leq 1$.

(2) The sum of the probabilities assigned to all the elements of any sample space is 1.

Using this, we may define the probability of an event.

DEFINITION.   If A is an event which corresponds to a subset of a sample space, then the probability of A, $P(A)$, is the sum of the probabilities of the elements of the subset corresponding to A.

Example 1.   List the sample space to study the distribution of boys and girls in a family of three children.   What is the probability that

   (a) all three children are boys?

   (b) the first two children are girls?

   (c) there are two girls and one boy in a family?

Solution:

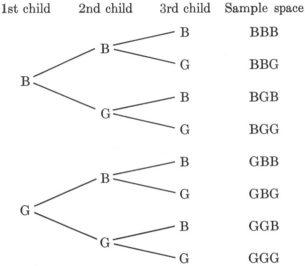

| 1st child | 2nd child | 3rd child | Sample space |

There are 8 elements in the sample space.

$$P(3 \text{ boys}) = \tfrac{1}{8}.$$
$$P(\text{First 2 are girls}) = \tfrac{2}{8} = \tfrac{1}{4}.$$
$$P(2 \text{ girls, 1 boy}) = \tfrac{3}{8}.$$

Note that we are assuming that, when a child is born, it is just as likely to be a boy as a girl.   In actual practice, there are slightly more boys born than girls, but for most purposes our assumption is adequate.

Example 2. Using the sample space in Table 11.2 for the two-dice experiment, what is the probability that

   (a) the number on the white die is two more than the number on the black die? $(w = b + 2)$

   (b) the total for the two dice is seven? $(b + w = 7)$

   (c) the total for the two dice is eleven? $(b + w = 11)$

Solution:

$$P(w = b + 2) = \tfrac{4}{36} = \tfrac{1}{9}.$$
$$P(b + w = 7) = \tfrac{6}{36} = \tfrac{1}{6}.$$
$$P(b + w = 11) = \tfrac{2}{36} = \tfrac{1}{18}.$$

Example 3. Using the sample space in Table 11.2 for the two-dice experiment, state the following probabilities.

  (a) $P(A)$, where $A = \{(b, w) \mid b \geq 3\}$
  (b) $P(B)$, where $B = \{(b, w) \mid w \leq 3\}$
  (c) $P(A \text{ and } B)$, where A and B are as described above
  (d) $P(A \text{ or } B)$ (Note that *or* is inclusive.)

Solution:

  (a) $$P(A) = \tfrac{24}{36} = \tfrac{2}{3}.$$
  (b) $$P(B) = \tfrac{18}{36} = \tfrac{1}{2}.$$
  (c) $$P(A \text{ and } B) = \tfrac{12}{36} = \tfrac{1}{3}.$$
  (d) $$P(A \text{ or } B) = \tfrac{30}{36} = \tfrac{5}{6}.$$

Note that

$$P(A) + P(B) - P(A \text{ and } B) = \tfrac{2}{3} + \tfrac{1}{2} - \tfrac{1}{3}$$
$$= \tfrac{5}{6}$$
$$= P(A \text{ or } B).$$

Compare this with the known formula

$$n(A \cup B) = n(A) + n(B) - n(A \cap B).$$

Example 4. A box contains five differently coloured balls: red (R), green (G), blue (B), white (W), and yellow (Y). If a selection of three of the balls is made, state the following probabilities.

  (a) The selection includes Y.
  (b) The selection excludes Y.
  (c) The selection includes both B and G.
  (d) The selection includes either B or G.

Solution:

  $S = \{$RGB, RGW, RGY, RBW, RBY, RWY, GBW, GBY, GWY, BWY$\}.$

  (a) $$P(\text{Y included}) = \tfrac{6}{10} = \tfrac{3}{5}.$$
  (b) $$P(\text{Y excluded}) = \tfrac{4}{10} = \tfrac{2}{5}.$$
  (c) $$P(\text{B and G included}) = \tfrac{3}{10}.$$
  (d) $$P(\text{B or G included}) = \tfrac{9}{10}.$$

Alternative Solution:

Number of selections without restriction is

$$\binom{5}{3} = 10.$$

Number of selections with Y included is

$$\binom{4}{2} = 6 .$$

Number of selections with Y excluded is

$$\binom{4}{3} = 4 .$$

Number of selections with both B and G included is

$$\binom{3}{1} = 3 .$$

Number of selections with B and G excluded is

$$\binom{3}{3} = 1 .$$

Therefore the number of selections with B or G included is 9. Hence

$$P(Y \text{ included}) = \tfrac{6}{10} = \tfrac{3}{5} ,$$
$$P(Y \text{ excluded}) = \tfrac{4}{10} = \tfrac{2}{5} ,$$
$$P(B \text{ and } G \text{ included}) = \tfrac{3}{10} ,$$
$$P(B \text{ or } G \text{ included}) = \tfrac{9}{10} .$$

EXERCISE 11.3

1. Using the sample space given in Table 11.2 for the two-dice experiment, calculate the following probabilities.
   (a) The numbers on the two dice differ by two.
   (b) The total is ten or greater.
   (c) The total is less than seven.
   (d) The black die shows less than the white die.
   (e) The total is six.
   (f) The black die shows less than two.
   (g) The white die shows greater than four.
   (h) The black die shows less than two and the white die shows greater than four.
   (i) The black die shows less than two or the white die shows greater than four.
   (j) The total on the two dice is a prime number.

(k) If it is known that the total on the two dice is odd, what is the probability that it is seven?

(l) If it is known that the total on the two dice is even, what is the probability that it is seven?

2. In an experiment to investigate the cavity-reducing properties of four different toothpastes, 300 students are divided at random into four equal groups. John and Mary both take part in the test. What is the probability that

(a) they are both assigned to the same group?

(b) they are assigned to different groups?

(c) they are both assigned to group 1?

(d) John is assigned to either group 1 or 2 and Mary is assigned to either 3 or 4?

3. A coin is tossed three times.

(a) What is the probability of three heads?

(b) What is the probability of exactly two heads?

(c) What is the probability of at least two heads?

(d) What is the probability of not more than two heads?

4. Six students, John, Jim, Dick, Mary, Helen, and Betty, have the qualifications for an all-expenses paid trip to New York but, unfortunately, only two can be selected. They agree to make the selection by placing the six names on slips of paper and having the school principal draw two slips at random. What is the probability that

(a) John is selected?

(b) both Mary and Betty are selected?

(c) either Mary or Betty (not both) is selected?

(d) two girls are selected?

5. List a sample space to study the distribution of boys and girls in families having four children. (See question (4), Exercise 11.2.) What is the probability that

(a) a family has three boys and one girl?

(b) a family has two girls and two boys?

(c) the two eldest children are girls?

6. Four cards numbered 1, 2, 3, and 4 are shuffled and placed in four boxes numbered 1, 2, 3, 4, one card to a box. What is the probability that

(a) exactly two card numbers and two box numbers coincide?

(b) at least two card numbers and two box numbers coincide?

(c) no card number coincides with its box number?

(d) all card numbers and box numbers coincide?

7. John, Jim, Dick, Mary, and Helen are candidates for three positions on the students' council. Assuming the selection of any three is equally likely, what is the probability that
   (a) Jim is selected?
   (b) Mary and Helen are both selected?
   (c) Dick is not selected?
   (d) either Mary or Helen (or both) is selected?

11.4. Odds

If we consider the sample space in Table 11.2 for the experiment of throwing two dice, we know that it contains thirty-six elements. Any event A will correspond to a subset of the sample space. For any discussion of probabilities in this sample space, the universe of the discussion is the sample space S. If A is the event "throwing a double", the event A is a subset of S.

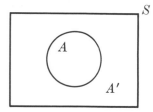

$$n(S) = 36 \quad \text{and} \quad n(A) = 6 ,$$

so that
$$P(A) = \tfrac{6}{36} = \tfrac{1}{6} .$$

The set A' will correspond to the event not-A or "not throwing a double".

$$n(A') = 30 \quad \text{and} \quad P(A') = \tfrac{30}{36} = \tfrac{5}{6} .$$

In general, if
$$P(A) = \frac{m}{n} ,$$

$$P(A') = \frac{n - m}{n}$$

$$= 1 - \frac{m}{n}$$

$$= 1 - P(A) .$$

The relative probabilities of event A and event not-A are frequently expressed in terms of the *odds in favour* of A.

Odds in favour of A are $P(A)$ to $P(A')$,

that is,
$$\frac{m}{n} \text{ to } \frac{n - m}{n} ,$$

or
$$m \text{ to } n - m .$$

Also,

$$\text{odds against } A \text{ are P}(A') \text{ to } \text{P}(A),$$

that is,

$$n - m \text{ to } m.$$

The odds in favour of throwing a double in the two-dice experiment will be given by

$$\text{P(throwing a double) to P(not throwing a double)},$$

that is,

$$\frac{1}{6} \text{ to } \frac{5}{6}$$

or

$$1 \text{ to } 5 \, .$$

If the odds in favour of an event A are a to b, then

$$\frac{\text{P}(A)}{\text{P}(A')} = \frac{a}{b} \, .$$

Thus

$$\frac{\text{P}(A)}{1 - \text{P}(A)} = \frac{a}{b}$$

$$b \cdot \text{P}(A) = a - a \cdot \text{P}(A) \, .$$

$$(a + b)\text{P}(A) = a \, .$$

Therefore

$$\text{P}(A) = \frac{a}{a + b} \, .$$

Example 1.   If two dice are rolled, what are the odds in favour of throwing

(a) 7?   (b) 11?

Solution:

$$\text{P}(7) = \frac{6}{36} = \frac{1}{6} \, .$$

Therefore the odds in favour of 7 are 1 to $(6 - 1)$ or 1 to 5.

$$\text{P}(11) = \frac{2}{36} = \frac{1}{18} \, .$$

Therefore the odds in favour of 11 are 1 to 17.

Example 2. If the odds against a certain event are given as 5 to 2, what is the probability of the event?

Solution: Denote the event by A.

$$P(A') = \frac{5}{5+2} = \frac{5}{7}.$$
$$P(A) = 1 - P(A')$$
$$= 1 - \frac{5}{7}$$
$$= \frac{2}{7}.$$

EXERCISE 11.4

1. A bag contains seven red balls and four black balls. If one ball is drawn from the bag, what are the odds in favour of its being
   (a) a red ball?   (b) a black ball?

2. If a die is thrown, what are the odds in favour of the upper face showing
   (a) 4?   (b) more than 4?
   What are the odds against the upper face showing six?

3. If one letter is chosen at random from the word *Toronto*, what are the odds in favour of its being the letter *o*? What are the odds against its being the letter *t*?

4. A committee of three is to be chosen by lot from seven candidates. What are the odds that a particular candidate not be selected?

5. From a group of eight men and five women, two are chosen by lot. What are the odds in favour of both chosen individuals being men?

6. If two coins are tossed, what are the odds in favour of both showing heads?

7. In a family of three children, what are the odds against all three being girls?

8. Two cards are drawn at random from a deck of fifty-two playing cards. What are the odds
   (a) that both cards are red?
   (b) against drawing a king?
   (c) in favour of drawing two aces?

9. If two dice are rolled, what are the odds
   (a) in favour of a total of nine?
   (b) against a total of six?
   (c) in favour of a total of more than seven?
   (d) against a total of less than five?

10. Eight men enter a doubles tennis tournament in which partners are selected by lot. What are the odds against having two specified men, A and B, selected as partners?

11. A committee of five is selected by lot from a group of six men and four women. What are the odds in favour of having a specified man and a specified woman on the committee?

12. A plant breeder crosses two plants each possessing the gene pair Aa. Each parent contributes either A or a to the offspring, where the two are combined. What are the odds in favour of the offspring's being of the same genetic type as the parents, that is, Aa?

11.5. Addition of Probabilities

In Example 3 of Section 11.3 we discussed the following problem.

Using the sample space given in Table 11.2 for the two-dice experiment, state the following probabilities.

(a) $P(A)$, where $A = \{(b, w) \mid b \geq 3\}$

(b) $P(B)$, where $B = \{(b, w) \mid w \leq 3\}$

(c) $P(A \text{ and } B)$, where A and B are described above

(d) $P(A \text{ or } B)$

We note that A and B are subsets of the sample space, and that the set A *and* B may be written in set notation as $A \cap B$, while the set A *or* B may be written as $A \cup B$.

In this particular example, n$(S) = 36$, where S is the sample space, n$(A) = 24$, n$(B) = 18$, and n$(A \cap B) = 12$ as shown in the Venn diagram. We note from the Venn diagram that, when we total the number of elements in the sets A and B, the elements in $A \cap B$ have been counted twice. These twelve elements in this example must then be subtracted in order to obtain the correct number of elements in $A \cup B$. Therefore

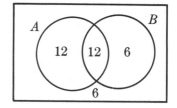

$$P(A) = \tfrac{24}{36} = \tfrac{2}{3}.$$

$$P(B) = \tfrac{18}{36} = \tfrac{1}{2}.$$

$$P(A \cap B) = \tfrac{12}{36} = \tfrac{1}{3}.$$

$$P(A \cup B) = \tfrac{30}{36} = \tfrac{5}{6}.$$

And in this case

$$P(A \cup B) = P(A) + P(B) - P(A \cap B).$$

This result is true in general and, provided that the sample space consists of *equally likely outcomes*, we may prove it by using a result from Chapter 7.

$$n(A \cup B) = n(A) + n(B) - n(A \cap B).$$

$$P(A \cup B) = \frac{n(A \cup B)}{n(S)}$$

$$= \frac{n(A) + n(B) - n(A \cap B)}{n(S)}$$

$$= \frac{n(A)}{n(S)} + \frac{n(B)}{n(S)} - \frac{n(A \cap B)}{n(S)}$$

$$= P(A) + P(B) - P(A \cap B).$$

Therefore

$$P(A \cup B) = P(A) + P(B) - P(A \cap B).$$

We should note that this proof is valid only if the sample space consists of equally likely outcomes, since $P(A \cup B) = \frac{n(A \cup B)}{n(S)}$ only in that case. An alternative proof which does not depend on this restriction is now given.

In the Venn diagram, the subset shaded in red is the set $A' \cap B$. The set $A \cup B$ can be expressed as the union of the disjoint subsets A and $A' \cap B$ while the set B can be expressed as the union of the disjoint subsets $A \cap B$ and $A' \cap B$. Then, by definition,

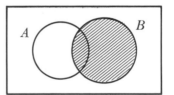

$$P(A \cup B) = P(A) + P(A' \cap B).$$

But

$$P(B) = P(A \cap B) + P(A' \cap B).$$

Thus

$$P(A' \cap B) = P(B) - P(A \cap B).$$

Therefore

$$P(A \cup B) = P(A) + P(B) - P(A \cap B).$$

Example 1.   A box contains five differently coloured balls: red (R), green (G), blue (B), white (W), and yellow (Y).   If a selection of three of the balls is made, state the probabilities of each of the following.

   (a)   The selection includes either Y or G.

   (b)   The selection includes Y or both B and G.

Solution: Total number of selections without restriction is

$$\binom{5}{3} = 10.$$

Number of selections which include Y is

$$\binom{4}{2} = 6 \,.$$

Number of selections which include G is

$$\binom{4}{2} = 6 \,.$$

Number of selections which include both Y and G is

$$\binom{3}{1} = 3 \,.$$

Number of selections which include both B and G is

$$\binom{3}{1} = 3 \,.$$

Number of selections which include B, G, and Y is 1.

(a) $$P(Y \cup G) = P(Y) + P(G) - P(Y \cap G)$$
$$= \tfrac{6}{10} + \tfrac{6}{10} - \tfrac{3}{10}$$
$$= \tfrac{9}{10} \,.$$

(b) $$P[Y \cup (B \cap G)] = P(Y) + P(B \cap G) - P(Y \cap B \cap G)$$
$$= \tfrac{6}{10} + \tfrac{3}{10} - \tfrac{1}{10}$$
$$= \tfrac{4}{5} \,.$$

It is suggested that this example should also be solved by forming a sample space as in Example 4 of Section 11.3.

Example 2.   One number, x, is selected at random from the set $\{1, 2, 3, \cdots, 10\}$. What is the probability that
 (a) $x < 4$?
 (b) x is odd?
 (c) $x < 4$ or x is odd.

Solution:

(a) $$P(x < 4) = \tfrac{3}{10} \,.$$
(b) $$P(x \text{ is odd}) = \tfrac{5}{10} = \tfrac{1}{2} \,.$$
(c) $$P(x < 4 \text{ and } x \text{ is odd}) = \tfrac{2}{10} = \tfrac{1}{5} \,.$$
$$P(x < 4 \text{ or } x \text{ is odd}) = \tfrac{3}{10} + \tfrac{5}{10} - \tfrac{2}{10}$$
$$= \tfrac{3}{5} \,.$$

EXERCISE 11.5

1. Using the sample space in Table 11.2 for the two-dice experiment, calculate the following probabilities, where b is the number on the black die and w is the number on the white die.
   (a) $b < 3$ and $w > 4$.
   (b) $b < 3$ or $w > 4$.
   (c) $b < 4$ or $w < 4$.
   (d) $b + w = 7$ or $b + w = 11$.

2. One number is selected at random from the set $\{1, 2, 3, \cdots, 20\}$. If x is the number selected, calculate the following probabilities.
   (a) $P(x > 15)$
   (b) $P(A)$, where $A = \{x \mid x \text{ is even}\}$
   (c) $P(B)$, where $B = \{x \mid x < 12\}$
   (d) $P(A \cup B)$

3. If a bag contains four white balls, five red balls, six green balls, and four yellow balls, and one ball is drawn from the bag at random, what is the probability that
   (a) a red ball is selected?
   (b) the ball selected is either red or green?

4. A committee of three is selected by lot from four men and six women. What is the probability that either Mrs. Smith or Mr. Jones is selected? (Note that we always assume the inclusive *or* unless otherwise stated.)

5. John has been given permission to select any three books from a collection of six books $\{A, B, C, D, E, F\}$. Calculate the following probabilities.
   (a) The selection includes A.
   (b) The selection includes either A or B.
   (c) The selection includes C or both A and B.
   (d) The selection includes both A and C or both E and F.
   (e) The selection includes both A and C or both C and D.

6. The four aces and four kings are removed from a pack of cards. If two cards are drawn at random from these eight cards, what is the probability that they are both aces or both red?

7. If two cards are drawn at random from a pack of fifty-two cards, what is the probability that they are both aces or both red?

8. There are three tickets available for an N.H.L. game and ten boys agree to draw lots to decide which three will receive the tickets. Calculate each of the following probabilities.
   (a) Either Tom or Jim will be included.

(b) Either Tom and Jim or Jim and Ken will be included.

(c) Either Tom and Jim or Ted and Ken will be included.

9. In a certain school, 15% of the students failed Mathematics, 12% failed English, and 5% failed both Mathematics and English. What is the probability that a particular student, selected at random, failed either English or Mathematics? If there were 550 students who wrote both examinations, how many failed at least one of these subjects?

10. The odds against John's winning a race are 3 to 1 and the odds against Bill's winning are 4 to 1. What is the probability that either Bill or John will win? (Note that a tie is excluded.)

11.6. Mutually Exclusive Events

In question (1d) of Exercise 11.5, we were asked to find the probability that $b + w = 7$ or $b + w = 11$, using Table 11.2 for the two-dice experiment. If $A = \{(b,w) \mid b + w = 7\}$ and $B = \{(b,w) \mid b + w = 11\}$, then $n(A) = 6$ and $n(B) = 2$. It is obvious that $A \cap B = \phi$ and $n(A \cap B) = 0$. Hence

$$P(A \cup B) = P(A) + P(B) - P(A \cap B)$$
$$= \tfrac{6}{36} + \tfrac{2}{36} - \tfrac{0}{36}$$
$$= \tfrac{2}{9}.$$

In this instance, $P(A \cup B) = P(A) + P(B)$.

When two events in a given sample space have no elements in common, and their intersection is the empty set, they are said to be mutually exclusive events.

DEFINITION. If two events in a given sample space have no elements in common, they are *mutually exclusive events* or disjoint events.

This definition can be extended to cover any number of events in a given sample space. n events are mutually exclusive if no two of them have any elements in common. In the Venn diagram, the events A, B, C, and D are mutually exclusive.

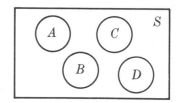

Theorem. If two events A and B are mutually exclusive, then

$$P(A \cap B) = 0$$

and

$$P(A \cup B) = P(A) + P(B).$$

Proof: If A and B are mutually exclusive, then

$$A \cap B = \phi.$$

Therefore

$$n(A \cap B) = 0$$

and

$$P(A \cap B) = 0.$$

Therefore

$$P(A \cup B) = P(A) + P(B) - P(A \cap B)$$
$$= P(A) + P(B).$$

Corollary.   If $A, B,$ and C are mutually exclusive events, then

$$P(A \cup B \cup C) = P(A) + P(B) + P(C).$$

It must be noted that this only applies if the events are known to be mutually exclusive. If the events do have elements in common and all outcomes are equally likely, we should be able to prove, using the formula for $n(A \cup B \cup C)$ developed in Chapter 7, that

$$P(A \cup B \cup C) =$$
$$P(A) + P(B) + P(C) - P(A \cap B) - P(B \cap C) - P(A \cap C) + P(A \cap B \cap C).$$

EXERCISE 11.6

1. In an experiment of throwing two dice, one white and one black, state which of the following events are mutually exclusive.
    (a) The total is seven.   Black die shows four.
    (b) The total is five.   White die shows six.
    (c) White die shows five.   Black die shows two.
    (d) White die shows greater than four.   Black die shows less than four.
    (e) White die shows greater than four.   Total is less than five.

2. If two coins are tossed, which of the following events are mutually exclusive?
    (a) One coin shows heads.   Both coins show heads.
    (b) One coin shows heads.   Both coins show tails.
    (c) One coin shows tails.   The coins fall differently.
    (d) One coin shows heads.   The coins fall alike.

3. In a family of three children, which of the following events are mutually exclusive?
    (a) The two eldest are girls.   All three are of the same sex.
    (b) The eldest is a boy.   The family has two girls.

(c) Two children are boys. The youngest is a boy.

(d) Two children are boys. The eldest and youngest are girls.

(e) All three are girls. The youngest is a boy.

4. In rolling a single die, A is the event "die shows 3", and B is the event "die shows an odd number". Are A and B mutually exclusive? What is $P(A \cup B)$?

5. In rolling a single die, A is the event "die shows 3", and B is the event "die shows an even number". Are A and B mutually exclusive? What is $P(A \cup B)$?

6. In an experiment of rolling two dice, b represents the number on the black die and w, the number on the white die. Find $P(A \cup B)$ for each of the following events A and B.

(a) $A = \{ (b, w) \mid b + w = 7 \}$, $B = \{ (b, w) \mid b = 4 \}$.

(b) $A = \{ (b, w) \mid b + w = 5 \}$, $B = \{ (b, w) \mid w = 6 \}$.

(c) $A = \{ (b, w) \mid b + w < 5 \}$, $B = \{ (b, w) \mid w > 4 \}$.

(d) $A = \{ (b, w) \mid w = 5 \}$, $B = \{ (b, w) \mid b = 2 \}$.

(e) $A = \{ (b, w) \mid w > 4 \}$, $B = \{ (b, w) \mid b < 4 \}$.

(f) $A = \{ (b, w) \mid b \text{ is odd} \}$, $B = \{ (b, w) \mid w = b + 1 \}$.

7. If two coins are tossed, find the probability of each of the following.

(a) One coin shows heads or both coins show heads.

(b) One coin shows heads or both coins show tails.

(c) One coin shows tails or the coins fall differently.

(d) One coin shows heads or both coins fall alike.

8. Find the probability of the following distributions in families of three children.

(a) The two eldest are girls or all are of the same sex.

(b) The eldest is a boy or the family has exactly two girls.

(c) Exactly two children are boys or the youngest is a boy.

(d) Exactly two children are boys or the eldest and youngest are girls.

(e) All three are girls or the youngest is a boy.

9. Two cards are drawn from a pack of fifty-two playing cards. Find the probability of each of the following events.

(a) Both cards are clubs.

(b) Both cards are black.

(c) Both cards are kings.

(d) Both cards are black kings.

(e) Both cards are kings or both cards are black.

10. Two cards are drawn from a pack of fifty-two playing cards. What is the probability that the cards drawn are the ace and king of spades or that they are both diamonds?

11.7. Independent Events

If, in considering the distribution of children in families, we understand that BGB means that the eldest child is a boy, the second is a girl, and the youngest is a boy, then a sample space, S, of all possible distributions is

$$S = \{BBB, BBG, BGB, BGG, GBB, GBG, GGB, GGG\}.$$

If X is the event "eldest child is a boy", and Y is the event "second child is a girl", then

$$P(X) = \tfrac{4}{8} = \tfrac{1}{2},$$
$$P(Y) = \tfrac{4}{8} = \tfrac{1}{2},$$
$$P(X \cap Y) = \tfrac{2}{8} = \tfrac{1}{4}.$$

Here we notice that

$$P(X \cap Y) = P(X) \cdot P(Y).$$

If Z is the event "all three are boys", then

$$P(Z) = \tfrac{1}{8}$$

and

$$P(X \cap Z) = \tfrac{1}{8}.$$

In this case

$$P(X \cap Z) \neq P(X) \cdot P(Z).$$

We note also that

$$P(Y \cap Z) = 0$$

and

$$P(Y \cap Z) \neq P(Y) \cdot P(Z).$$

Intuitively, we feel that events X and Y are independent of each other. The sex of the eldest child has no effect on the sex of the second. These events are independent. The events X and Z cannot be regarded as independent. If all three children are boys, such an event does depend on the eldest's being a boy. The two events are dependent. Events Y and Z are, by definition, mutually exclusive. It is impossible for all three children to be boys and the second child to be a girl.

Event X is one that we expect to occur in about one half of all births of eldest children. About one half of all three-child families will have a boy as the eldest child. Restricting ourselves to this one half, we would expect that one half of this group would have a girl as the second child. The fraction of three-child families having a boy as the eldest and a girl as second, would therefore be expected to be about $\tfrac{1}{2} \times \tfrac{1}{2}$ or $\tfrac{1}{4}$.

Our intuition agrees with the mathematical result in these cases. Independent events are events which have no effect on each other. However, the rather vague statement "having no effect on each other", is not suitable as a mathematical definition.

The results of our example lead us to a definition which satisfies the requirements of mathematical rigour.

DEFINITION. Two events, A and B, are *independent* if and only if

$$P(A \cap B) = P(A) \cdot P(B).$$

Note that this allows us to state that, if two events are such that

$$P(A \cap B) = P(A) \cdot P(B),$$

then we can say that the events are independent. Conversely, if we know that two events are independent, we can state that

$$P(A \cap B) = P(A) \cdot P(B).$$

Note: Confusion sometimes arises between mutually exclusive events and independent events. This should not happen if we remember that, in general, *mutually exclusive events can never be independent*. This can only occur for two events A and B if $P(A) = 0$ or $P(B) = 0$. For two events A and B to be mutually exclusive, $P(A \cap B) = 0$. But, for two events to be independent $P(A \cap B) = P(A) \cdot P(B)$ can only be zero if either $P(A) = 0$ or $P(B) = 0$. If A and B are independent events with *nonzero* probabilities, then $P(A \cap B) \neq 0$, but if the events are mutually exclusive, $P(A \cap B) = 0$.

DEFINITION. Two events, A and B, are dependent if and only if

$$P(A \cap B) \neq P(A) \cdot P(B) \quad \text{and} \quad P(A \cap B) \neq 0.$$

In the example of the three-child family,

$$P(X \cap Y) = P(X) \cdot P(Y)$$

and events X and Y are independent.

$$P(X \cap Z) \neq P(X) \cdot P(Z) \quad \text{and} \quad P(X \cap Z) \neq 0,$$

and events X and Z are dependent.

$$P(Y \cap Z) = 0 \neq P(Y) \cdot P(Z)$$

and events Y and Z are mutually exclusive.

When three or more events are independent, the probability that all occur is the product of their probabilities.

For example, if A, B, and C are independent events, then

$$P(A \cap B \cap C) = P(A) \cdot P(B) \cdot P(C).$$

Example 1. In the two-dice experiment (See Table 11.2.), where b represents the number showing on the black die and w, the number showing on the white die, state which of the following pairs of events are independent, dependent, or mutually exclusive.

(a) $b = 3$, $\qquad w = 4$.
(b) $b + w = 7$, $\qquad b = 3$.
(c) $b + w = 7$, $\qquad b < 3$.
(d) $b + w = 7$, $\qquad b \neq 3$.
(e) $b + w = 11$, $\quad b \neq 5$.
(f) $b + w = 11$, $\quad b + w = 7$.

Solution:

(a) Let A be the event $b = 3$ and B, the event $w = 4$.

$$P(A) = \tfrac{6}{36} = \tfrac{1}{6}.$$
$$P(B) = \tfrac{6}{36} = \tfrac{1}{6}.$$
$$P(A \cap B) = \tfrac{1}{36}.$$

Therefore $P(A \cap B) = P(A) \cdot P(B)$ and events A and B are independent.

(b) Let C be the event $b + w = 7$ and D, the event $b = 3$.

$$P(C) = \tfrac{6}{36} = \tfrac{1}{6} \quad \text{and} \quad P(D) = \tfrac{6}{36} = \tfrac{1}{6}.$$
$$P(C \cap D) = \tfrac{1}{36}.$$

Therefore $P(C \cap D) = P(C) \cdot P(D)$ and events C and D are independent.

(c) Let C be the event $b + w = 7$ and E, the event $b < 3$.

$$P(C) = \tfrac{1}{6} \quad \text{and} \quad P(E) = \tfrac{12}{36} = \tfrac{1}{3}.$$
$$P(C \cap E) = \tfrac{2}{36} = \tfrac{1}{18}.$$

Therefore $P(C \cap E) = P(C) \cdot P(E)$ and events C and E are independent.

(d) Let C be the event $b + w = 7$ and F, the event $b \neq 3$.

$$P(C) = \tfrac{1}{6} \quad \text{and} \quad P(F) = \tfrac{30}{36} = \tfrac{5}{6}.$$
$$P(C \cap F) = \tfrac{5}{36}.$$

Therefore $P(C \cap F) = P(C) \cdot P(F)$ and events C and F are independent.

(e) Let G be the event $b + w = 11$ and H, the event $b \neq 5$.

$$P(G) = \tfrac{2}{36} = \tfrac{1}{18} \quad \text{and} \quad P(H) = \tfrac{30}{36} = \tfrac{5}{6}.$$
$$P(G \cap H) = \tfrac{1}{36}.$$

Therefore $P(G \cap H) \neq P(G) \cdot P(H)$ and events G and H are dependent.

(f) Let G be the event $b + w = 11$ and C, the event $b + w = 7$.

$$P(G) = \tfrac{1}{18} \quad \text{and} \quad P(C) = \tfrac{1}{6}.$$
$$P(G \cap C) = 0.$$

Events G and C are mutually exclusive.

Example 2. A bag contains twenty red balls and ten black balls. If one ball is drawn from the bag and returned, and then a second ball is drawn from the bag, what is the probability that the first ball drawn is red and the second, black? (Since the first ball is returned, the events are independent.)

Solution:

$$P(\text{red ball}) = \tfrac{20}{30} = \tfrac{2}{3}.$$
$$P(\text{black ball}) = \tfrac{10}{30} = \tfrac{1}{3}.$$
$$P(\text{red ball followed by black ball}) = \tfrac{2}{3} \times \tfrac{1}{3}$$
$$= \tfrac{2}{9}.$$

EXERCISE 11.7

1. In the two-dice experiment (see Table 11.2), state whether the following pairs of events are independent, dependent, or mutually exclusive. b represents the number showing on the black die and w, the number showing on the white die.
    (a) $b = 6,$ $w = 6.$
    (b) $w < 3,$ $b + w = 8.$
    (c) $w < 2,$ $b + w = 8.$
    (d) $w \neq 5,$ $b + w = 8.$
    (e) $b = 3$ or $w = 3,$ $b = 5.$
    (f) $b = 3$ or $w = 3,$ $b \neq 5.$

2. A die is thrown three times. Assuming that the throws are independent events, what is the probability that the first throw shows a six, the second shows an even number, and the third shows a five?

3. A coin is tossed six times. Each throw is independent of the other throws. What is the probability of six heads?

4. A bag contains twenty red balls and ten black balls.   One ball is drawn from the bag and returned.   A second ball is then drawn from the bag.   Assuming that the outcomes are independent events, calculate the following probabilities.
   (a) Both balls are red.
   (b) Both balls are black.
   (c) One ball is red and the other is black.   (Order is not considered.)

5. Three coins are tossed.   Are the following events independent, dependent, or mutually exclusive?
   (a) Heads on first two coins, tails on third coin
   (b) Heads on first two coins, tails on second two coins
   (c) Heads on first two coins, heads on all three coins

6. A bag contains six black balls, four red balls, and five white balls.   Three balls are drawn in succession, each one being replaced before the next is drawn. Calculate the following probabilities.
   (a) First is black, second is red, third is white.
   (b) All three are black.
   (c) All three are white.
   (d) First two are black and the third is red.

7. In a family of three children, calculate the following probabilities.
   (a) First is a boy and next two are girls.
   (b) First two are boys and the third is a girl.
   (c) First two are boys or the third is a girl.

8. In a certain school, 15% of the students failed Mathematics, 12% failed English, and 5% failed both English and Mathematics.   Are the events "student failed English" and "student failed Mathematics", independent?

9. If two cards are drawn at random from a pack of fifty-two cards, are the events "both cards aces" and "both cards red", independent?

10. If two cards are drawn at random from a pack of fifty-two cards, are the events "first card an ace" and "second card a king", independent?   Assume that the first card is returned to the pack before the second is drawn.

11.8. Binomial Distribution

If a bag contains twenty red balls and ten black balls, and six balls are drawn at random with the ball drawn being replaced and the bag well shaken before the next ball is drawn, what is the probability that exactly two red balls are drawn?

Here we have a case of six independent events in which P (red ball) = $\frac{2}{3}$ and P (black ball) = $\frac{1}{3}$ for each event.   If, in drawing six balls, we obtain two red balls and four black balls, we have a successful event. Any other combination is not successful.

One successful event is RRBBBB, where R represents a red ball and B, a black ball. The probability of this event is

$$\left(\tfrac{2}{3}\right)\left(\tfrac{2}{3}\right)\left(\tfrac{1}{3}\right)\left(\tfrac{1}{3}\right)\left(\tfrac{1}{3}\right)\left(\tfrac{1}{3}\right) = \left(\tfrac{1}{3}\right)^4\left(\tfrac{2}{3}\right)^2 .$$

However, if a red ball occupies any two of the six positions, we have a successful event. Each of these successful events will have the same probability and all such events are mutually exclusive. The number of such events is $\binom{6}{2}$ and so the probability of exactly two red balls is

$$\binom{6}{2}\left(\tfrac{1}{3}\right)^4\left(\tfrac{2}{3}\right)^2 = 15 \times \tfrac{1}{81} \times \tfrac{4}{9}$$
$$= \tfrac{20}{243} .$$

In the same way, if there are n independent events for which the probability of success in any one event is p and the probability of failure is $q = 1 - p$, that is, there are only two possible outcomes for each event, then the probability for exactly r successes in the n events is

$$\binom{n}{r}q^{n-r}p^r .$$

This is the $(r + 1)$st term of the binomial expansion of $(q + p)^n$.

In the example of twenty red balls and ten black balls, where we were seeking the probability of drawing exactly two red balls in six trials;

$$p = \tfrac{2}{3}, \quad q = \tfrac{1}{3}, \quad n = 6 .$$

Therefore

$$(q + p)^n = \left[\left(\tfrac{1}{3}\right) + \left(\tfrac{2}{3}\right)\right]^6$$
$$= \binom{6}{0}\left(\tfrac{1}{3}\right)^6\left(\tfrac{2}{3}\right)^0 + \binom{6}{1}\left(\tfrac{1}{3}\right)^5\left(\tfrac{2}{3}\right) + \binom{6}{2}\left(\tfrac{1}{3}\right)^4\left(\tfrac{2}{3}\right)^2 + \binom{6}{3}\left(\tfrac{1}{3}\right)^3\left(\tfrac{2}{3}\right)^3 +$$
$$\binom{6}{4}\left(\tfrac{1}{3}\right)^2\left(\tfrac{2}{3}\right)^4 + \binom{6}{5}\left(\tfrac{1}{3}\right)\left(\tfrac{2}{3}\right)^5 + \binom{6}{6}\left(\tfrac{1}{3}\right)^0\left(\tfrac{2}{3}\right)^6$$
$$= \tfrac{1}{729} + \tfrac{4}{243} + \tfrac{20}{243} + \tfrac{160}{729} + \tfrac{80}{243} + \tfrac{64}{243} + \tfrac{64}{729} .$$

The successive terms give the probabilities of drawing 0, 1, 2, 3, 4, 5, or 6 red balls, respectively, in any drawing of six balls with replacement between each drawing. It must be emphasized that the events *have to be independent*.

If $P(x)$ represents the drawing of x red balls in any drawing of six balls, then

$$P(0) = \tfrac{1}{729}, \quad P(1) = \tfrac{4}{243}, \quad P(2) = \tfrac{20}{243},$$
$$P(3) = \tfrac{160}{729}, \quad P(4) = \tfrac{80}{243}, \quad P(5) = \tfrac{64}{243}, \quad P(6) = \tfrac{64}{729} .$$

We note that the outcomes, "no red balls", "one red ball", "two red balls", etc., are not equally likely outcomes. Also

$$P(0) + P(1) + P(2) + P(3) + P(4) + P(5) + P(6) = 1 .$$

This should have been expected since these results give all possible results. Also $q + p = 1$ and hence $(q + p)^n = 1$.

Example 1. If a bag contains twenty red balls and ten black balls and six balls are drawn at random with the ball drawn being replaced before the next ball is drawn, what is the probability that at least three red balls are drawn?

Solution 1:

$$P(3) = \binom{6}{3}\left(\tfrac{1}{3}\right)^3\left(\tfrac{2}{3}\right)^3 = \tfrac{160}{729} .$$
$$P(4) = \binom{6}{4}\left(\tfrac{1}{3}\right)^2\left(\tfrac{2}{3}\right)^4 = \tfrac{240}{729} .$$
$$P(5) = \binom{6}{5}\left(\tfrac{1}{3}\right)\left(\tfrac{2}{3}\right)^5 = \tfrac{192}{729} .$$
$$P(6) = \binom{6}{6}\left(\tfrac{2}{3}\right)^6 \quad = \tfrac{64}{729} .$$

Therefore

$$P(\text{at least 3 red balls}) = \tfrac{160}{729} + \tfrac{240}{729} + \tfrac{192}{729} + \tfrac{64}{729}$$
$$= \tfrac{656}{729} .$$

Solution 2:

$$P(0) = \binom{6}{0}\left(\tfrac{1}{3}\right)^6 \quad = \tfrac{1}{729} .$$
$$P(1) = \binom{6}{1}\left(\tfrac{1}{3}\right)^5\left(\tfrac{2}{3}\right) = \tfrac{12}{729} .$$
$$P(2) = \binom{6}{2}\left(\tfrac{1}{3}\right)^4\left(\tfrac{2}{3}\right)^2 = \tfrac{60}{729} .$$
$$P(0) + P(1) + P(2) = \tfrac{73}{729} .$$

Therefore

$$P(\text{at least 3 red balls}) = 1 - \tfrac{73}{729}$$
$$= \tfrac{656}{729} .$$

Depending on the particular problem, Solution 1 or Solution 2 may be the quicker method. In this particular example, there is little to choose between the two methods. If we were asked for the probability of at least five red balls, Solution 1 would be the more useful, but, if we were asked for the probability of at least two red balls, Solution 2 would be the more useful.

Example 2. In families of four children, calculate the following probabilities.
    (a) Exactly three are boys.
    (b) At least three are boys.
    (c) At least one is a boy.

Solution:
    (a) $p = \tfrac{1}{2}$, $q = \tfrac{1}{2}$, where p is the probability of a boy.

$$P(3 \text{ boys}) = \binom{4}{3}\left(\tfrac{1}{2}\right)\left(\tfrac{1}{2}\right)^3$$
$$= 4 \times \tfrac{1}{16}$$
$$= \tfrac{1}{4} .$$

(b)
$$P(4 \text{ boys}) = \binom{4}{4} \left(\tfrac{1}{2}\right)^0 \left(\tfrac{1}{2}\right)^4$$
$$= \tfrac{1}{16}.$$

Therefore
$$P(\text{at least 3 boys}) = \tfrac{1}{4} + \tfrac{1}{16}$$
$$= \tfrac{5}{16}.$$

(c)
$$P(\text{no boys}) = \binom{4}{0} \left(\tfrac{1}{2}\right)^4 \left(\tfrac{1}{2}\right)^0$$
$$= \tfrac{1}{16}.$$

Therefore
$$P(\text{at least 1 boy}) = 1 - \tfrac{1}{16}$$
$$= \tfrac{15}{16}.$$

Example 3. A student writes a test which contains ten questions. For each question, four possible answers are given and the student has to underline the only correct answer. If the student has done no studying and has to guess at all the solutions, calculate the following probabilities.

(a) He will obtain at least 50% (5 correct answers).

(b) He will obtain 100% (all answers correct).

Solution:

(a) $p = \tfrac{1}{4}, \qquad q = \tfrac{3}{4}, \qquad n = 10.$

$$P(5) = \binom{10}{5} \left(\frac{3}{4}\right)^5 \left(\frac{1}{4}\right)^5$$
$$= 252 \left(\frac{243}{1024}\right) \left(\frac{1}{1024}\right)$$
$$= \frac{61{,}236}{1{,}048{,}576}.$$

$$P(6) = \binom{10}{6} \left(\frac{3}{4}\right)^4 \left(\frac{1}{4}\right)^6$$
$$= 210 \left(\frac{81}{4^{10}}\right)$$
$$= \frac{17{,}010}{1{,}048{,}576}.$$

$$P(7) = \binom{10}{7} \left(\frac{3}{4}\right)^3 \left(\frac{1}{4}\right)^7$$
$$= \frac{3{,}240}{1{,}048{,}576}.$$

$$P(8) = \binom{10}{8}\left(\frac{3}{4}\right)^2\left(\frac{1}{4}\right)^8$$

$$= \frac{405}{1{,}048{,}576}.$$

$$P(9) = \binom{10}{9}\left(\frac{3}{4}\right)\left(\frac{1}{4}\right)^9$$

$$= \frac{30}{1{,}048{,}576}.$$

$$P(10) = \binom{10}{10}\left(\frac{1}{4}\right)^{10}$$

$$= \frac{1}{1{,}048{,}576}.$$

Therefore

$$P(\text{at least 5 correct}) = \frac{61{,}236 + 17{,}010 + 3{,}240 + 405 + 30 + 1}{1{,}048{,}576}$$

$$= \frac{81{,}922}{1{,}048{,}576}$$

$$\simeq .078.$$

(b) $P(\text{perfect paper}) = \binom{10}{10}\left(\frac{1}{4}\right)^{10}$

$$= \frac{1}{1{,}048{,}576}$$

$$\simeq .0000001.$$

EXERCISE 11.8

1. Four dice are thrown.   Calculate each of the following probabilities.
    (a) Two sixes show.
    (b) Three fives show.
    (c) At least one six shows.

2. Five coins are tossed.   Calculate each of the following probabilities.
    (a) Three show heads.
    (b) At least three show heads.
    (c) All five show tails.

3. In a family of five children, calculate the following probabilities.
    (a) Three are boys.
    (b) At least three are girls.

(c) All five are girls.

(d) At least one is a boy.

4. A baseball player is batting .250. Assuming that this is the probability that he will hit safely on any one time at bat, what are the following probabilities?

(a) He will hit safely on his next twice at bat.·

(b) He will hit safely twice during his next five times at bat.

5. Records show that a certain treatment will successfully cure a particular disease in one third of the cases treated. If six patients are treated, what is the probability that at least three will be cured?

6. A pair of dice is rolled three times. Calculate each of the following probabilities.

(a) A total of seven is rolled each time.

(b) A total of seven is obtained once only.

(c) A total of seven is obtained at least once.

(d) A total of eleven is obtained at least once.

7. If the probability that a child will inherit a certain disease is 0.25, calculate the following probabilities for a family of four children.

(a) One child will inherit the disease.

(b) Three children will inherit the disease.

(c) At least two of the children will be free of the disease.

(d) All the children will inherit the disease.

8. On a test of ten questions, a student had to select the correct answer from four given possible answers. If the student knew the correct answer to three of the questions and decided to guess at the others, what is the probability that he will pass the test if five correct answers constitute a pass?

9. In a family of five children, it is known that the three eldest are boys. What is the probability that the other two are also boys?

10. If a bag contains six red balls and four black balls, and three balls are drawn without replacement, calculate the probability that all the balls drawn are red.

11. Using the data in question (10), calculate the probability that all the balls drawn are red if the balls are drawn one at a time and replaced before the next is drawn.

12. On a bridge hand of thirteen cards, the probability of obtaining no aces in any one hand is approximately 0.3. What is the probability that a player will obtain no aces in any two of three consecutive hands?

13. Calculate the probability that a bridge player will receive no honour cards (ace, king, queen, jack, or ten) on any two of three consecutive hands.

11.9. Conditional Probability

Consider the two-dice experiment (Table 11.2). We know that if A is the event that the number on the white die exceeds the number on the black die by 2, and B is the event that the number on the black die is greater than 3, then

$$P(A) = \tfrac{4}{36} = \tfrac{1}{9} \text{ and } P(B) = \tfrac{18}{36} = \tfrac{1}{2}.$$

Also

$$P(A \cap B) = \tfrac{1}{36}.$$

If a friend rolls the black die and informs us that it shows a number greater than 3, what is the probability that when we throw the white die the number on the white die will exceed the number on the black die by 2?   In this case, the sample space has been reduced to 18 elements since we know that the number on the black die is greater than 3.   We also know that only one of these elements (black 4 and white 6) constitutes a favourable outcome.   Hence, the probability of A given B is $\dfrac{1}{18}$.   Here we are calculating the probability of an event A given that an event B has already occurred.   Such a probability is called a *conditional probability* and is denoted by

$P(A \mid B)$ which is read "the probability of A given B".

In the example, $P(A) = \dfrac{1}{9}$ and $P(A \mid B) = \dfrac{1}{18}$.

We also note that $\dfrac{P(A \cap B)}{P(B)} = \dfrac{\frac{1}{36}}{\frac{1}{2}} = \tfrac{1}{18} = P(A|B).$

In the diagram, S is a sample space of equally likely outcomes, A is an event consisting of $a + x$ elements, and B is an event consisting of $b + x$ elements with $x = n(A \cap B)$.

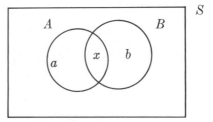

If B is given, then
$$
\begin{aligned}
P(A|B) &= \frac{x}{b + x} \\[6pt]
&= \frac{n(A \cap B)}{n(B)} \\[6pt]
&= \frac{\dfrac{n(A \cap B)}{n(S)}}{\dfrac{n(B)}{n(S)}}
\end{aligned}
$$

Hence,

$$P(A|B) = \frac{P(A \cap B)}{P(B)}.$$

It should be noted that this demonstration assumes equally likely outcomes and appeals to a Venn diagram. Hence it cannot be regarded as a rigorous proof. It is common to regard the statement

$$P(A|B) = \frac{P(A \cap B)}{P(B)}$$

as a definition of conditional probability. Obviously, it is only valid if $P(B) \neq 0$.

From this definition we also obtain

$$P(A \cap B) = P(B) \cdot P(A|B).$$

Similarly, $P(B \cap A) = P(A) \cdot P(B|A),$

but $P(A \cap B) = P(B \cap A).$

Hence, $P(A) \cdot P(B|A) = P(B) \cdot P(A|B).$

We also know that if A and B are independent events, then

$$P(A \cap B) = P(A) \cdot P(B),$$

but

$$P(A \cap B) = P(B) \cdot P(A|B).$$

Hence, if A and B are independent events

$$P(A|B) = P(A)$$

and, indeed, this is frequently used as the definition of independent events.

Example 1. Calculate the probability that a family of 3 children consists of 2 boys and 1 girl given that it contains at least 1 boy.

Solution: Let $A = \{2 \text{ boys and 1 girl}\}$
$$B = \{\text{at least 1 boy}\}.$$

$$P(\text{no boys}) = \binom{3}{0}(\tfrac{1}{2})^3 = \tfrac{1}{8}.$$

$$P(B) = 1 - \tfrac{1}{8} = \tfrac{7}{8}.$$

Since,

$$A \subset B, P(A \cap B) = P(A)$$
$$= \binom{3}{1}(\tfrac{1}{2})^2(\tfrac{1}{2})$$
$$= \tfrac{3}{8}$$

$$P(A|B) = \frac{P(A \cap B)}{P(B)} = \frac{\tfrac{3}{8}}{\tfrac{7}{8}}$$
$$= \tfrac{3}{7}.$$

Example 2. In a factory, in one day, the operator of machine A manufactures 200 parts, of which 6 are faulty. The operator of machine B manufactures 250 parts of which 9 are faulty. If a particular part is faulty, calculate the probability that it came from a particular machine.

Solution:

Let $A = $ {Parts from A}; $P(A) = \frac{200}{450} = \frac{4}{9}$.
Let $B = $ {Parts from B}; $P(B) = \frac{250}{450} = \frac{5}{9}$.
Let $F = $ {Faulty parts}; $P(F) = \frac{15}{450} = \frac{1}{30}$.

$$P(F|A) = \frac{6}{200} = \frac{3}{100}$$
$$P(F|B) = \frac{9}{250}$$
$$P(B) \cdot P(F|B) = P(F) \cdot P(B|F)$$
$$\frac{5}{9} \cdot \frac{9}{250} = \frac{1}{30} \cdot P(B|F)$$
$$P(B|F) = \frac{5}{9} \cdot \frac{9}{250} \cdot \frac{30}{1} = \frac{3}{5}$$
$$P(F) \cdot P(A|F) = P(A) \cdot P(F|A)$$
$$\frac{1}{30} P(A|F) = \frac{4}{9} \cdot \frac{3}{100}$$
$$P(A|F) = \frac{4}{9} \cdot \frac{3}{100} \cdot \frac{30}{1} = \frac{2}{5}.$$

Hence, if an item is faulty, the probability that it came from machine A is $\frac{2}{5}$ and from machine B is $\frac{3}{5}$.

Note that, since the item must have come from machine A or machine B, $P(A|F) + P(B|F) = 1$. This could have saved the last part of the calculation. However, it is useful to calculate $P(A|F)$ independently and use the sum as a check.

Example 3. If A, B, and C throw a die in that order and the first to throw a 6 wins, calculate the probability that A wins on his first or second throw.

Solution:

Let $A = $ {A wins on 1st throw}
$B = $ {B wins on 1st throw}
$C = $ {C wins on 1st throw}
$D = $ {A wins on 2nd throw}.
$$P(A) = \tfrac{1}{6}, \ P(A') = \tfrac{5}{6}.$$

For B to win, A must have lost.
$$P(B|A') = \tfrac{1}{6}.$$
$$P(B \cap A') = P(A') \cdot P(B|A')$$
$$= \tfrac{5}{6} \cdot \tfrac{1}{6} = \tfrac{5}{36}$$

For C to win, A and B must have lost.
Let $E = $ {A' and B'}
$$P(B'|A') = \tfrac{5}{6}$$
$$P(E) = P(A' \cap B') = P(A') \cdot P(B'|A')$$
$$= \tfrac{5}{6} \cdot \tfrac{5}{6} = \tfrac{25}{36}$$
$$P(C \cap E) = P(E) \cdot P(C|E)$$
$$= \tfrac{25}{36} \cdot \tfrac{1}{6} = \tfrac{25}{216}$$

For A to win on second throw, all must have lost on first throw.

$$\text{Let } F = \{A, B, C \text{ lost on first throw}\}$$
$$P(F) = P(C' \cap E)$$
$$= P(C'|E) \cdot P(E)$$
$$= \tfrac{5}{6} \cdot \tfrac{25}{36} = \tfrac{125}{216}$$
$$P(D \cap F) = P(F) \cdot P(D|F)$$
$$= \tfrac{125}{216} \cdot \tfrac{1}{6} = \tfrac{125}{1296}$$
$$P(A \cap D) = P(A) + P(D) \qquad \text{(Mutually exclusive}$$
$$= \tfrac{1}{6} + \tfrac{125}{1296} \qquad\qquad \text{events)}$$
$$= \tfrac{341}{1296}$$
$$\simeq .26.$$

Probability that A wins on first or second throw is .26 (approx.).

Note: The probability that A wins on first or second throw is
$$\tfrac{1}{6} + \tfrac{1}{6}(\tfrac{5}{6})^3$$
This can be extended to the probability that A eventually wins is
$$\tfrac{1}{6} + \tfrac{1}{6}(\tfrac{5}{6})^3 + \tfrac{1}{6}(\tfrac{5}{6})^6 + \cdots$$
This is an infinite geometric series with
$$a = \tfrac{1}{6}, r = (\tfrac{5}{6})^3$$
$$P(A \text{ wins}) = \frac{a}{1 - r}$$
$$= \frac{\tfrac{1}{6}}{1 - \tfrac{125}{216}}$$
$$= \tfrac{1}{6} \times \tfrac{216}{91}$$
$$= \tfrac{36}{91}$$
$$\simeq .4$$

It is suggested that you calculate the probabilities that B and C eventually win.

EXERCISE 11.9

1. If $P(A) = .3$, $P(B) = .4$, $P(A \cup B) = .6$, calculate $P(A|B)$ and $P(B|A)$.

2. (a) If $P(A) = \tfrac{1}{5}$, $P(B) = \tfrac{1}{2}$, $P(A \cup B) = \tfrac{3}{5}$, calculate $P(A|B)$ and $P(B|A)$.
   (b) What do the results in (a) show about the events A and B?

3. If $A \subseteq B$, prove that $P(A|B) = \dfrac{P(A)}{P(B)}$ $(P(B) \neq 0)$

4. In a game of dice, a player will win if he throws a 7 but lose if he throws a 2 or 11. If he throws any other number, he neither wins nor loses, but continues to throw until he obtains 7, 2, or 11. Calculate the probability of winning.

5. In a factory, machine A produces 40% of the output of a certain item and machine B produces 60%. 0.4% of the output from machine A is faulty as is 0.5% of the output from machine B. Calculate the probability that a faulty item came from machine A.

6. In a bottling plant, machine A fills and caps 1,000 bottles per hour, machine B, 1,200 bottles per hour and machine C, 1,500 bottles per hour. Of this output, 5 bottles from A, 5 from B, and 10 from C are improperly capped. If a bottle is improperly capped, calculate the probability that it came from machine B.

7. In a family of 4 children, it is known that at least one is a girl. Calculate the probability the family consists of two girls and two boys.

8. Three men each toss a coin and A notes that his coin shows heads. Calculate the probability that all 3 show heads.

9. A, B, and C toss a coin in that order. The first to throw a head wins.
   (a) Calculate the probability that C wins on the first throw.
   (b) Calculate the probability that A wins on the first or second throw.
   (c) Calculate the probability that A eventually wins.
   (d) Calculate the probability that B eventually wins.
   (e) Calculate the probability that C eventually wins.

Chapter Summary

Definitions

(1) A sample space of an experiment is a set of elements such that every outcome of the experiment corresponds to exactly one element of the set.

(2) An event is a result of an experiment that may be represented by a subset of a sample space of the experiment.

(3) If A is an event corresponding to a subset of a sample space, then P(A), the probability of A, is the sum of the probabilities of the elements of the subset corresponding to A.

(4) Mutually-exclusive events or disjoint events are two or more events in a given sample space which have no elements in common.
$$P(A \cap B) = 0.$$

(5) Two events, A and B, are independent if and only if
$$P(A \cap B) = P(A) \cdot P(B).$$

(6) Two events, A and B, are dependent if and only if
$$P(A \cap B) \neq P(A) \cdot P(B) \quad \text{and} \quad P(A \cap B) \neq 0.$$

Formulae

(1) For any event A,
$$0 \leq P(A) \leq 1.$$

If $P(A) = m/n$, then
$$P(A') = (n - m)/n$$
$$= 1 - P(A).$$

(2) Odds in favour of A are
$$P(A) \text{ to } P(A').$$

If $P(A) = m/n$, then
$$P(A) \text{ to } P(A') \text{ is } m \text{ to } n - m.$$

(3) $$P(A \cup B) = P(A) + P(B) - P(A \cap B).$$

(4) If events A and B are mutually exclusive,
$$P(A \cup B) = P(A) + P(B).$$

(5) For n independent events in which the probability of success in any one event is p and the probability of failure is $q = 1 - p$, the probability for exactly r successes in the n events is
$$P(r) = \binom{n}{r} q^{n-r} p^r.$$

REVIEW EXERCISE 11

1. Construct sample spaces of *equally-likely outcomes* for each of the following.
    (a) Four books are to be chosen at random from six different books, A, B, C, D, E, F.
    (b) The five honour cards in spades (ace, king, queen, jack, and ten) are placed in one bundle and the five honour cards in hearts in a second bundle.   One card is drawn from each bundle.

2. John, Jim, Bert, Bill, and Andy form the starting line-up for the school basketball team.   The coach has obtained three tickets for a display by the Harlem Globetrotters.   It is decided that the five boys will draw lots for the three tickets.   Calculate the following probabilities.
    (a) John will be selected.
    (b) John and Bill will be selected.
    (c) John or Bill will be selected.
    (d) John, and Bill or Jim will be selected.
    (e) Jim and Bert, or Bill and Andy will be selected.
    (f) Andy, Jim, and Bill will be selected.

3. If two dice are thrown, state the following probabilities.   (b is the number on the black die and w is the number on the white die.)
    (a) Exactly one shows a three.
    (b) Both show three.

(c) The total is six.

(d) The total is ten.

(e) $b < 3$ and $w > 3$.

(f) $b < 3$ or $w > 3$.

(g) $b < 3$ and $w > 3$, or $b > 3$ and $w < 3$.

4. If one card is drawn from a pack of fifty-two playing cards, calculate the following probabilities.

(a) The card is an ace. (b) The card is a black ace.

(c) The card is a diamond. (d) The card is an ace or a king.

(e) The card is an honour card.

5. From a group of fifteen men and ten women, a committee of three is chosen by lot.   Calculate the following probabilities.

(a) The committee contains two specified men.

(b) The committee consists of two men and one woman.

(c) The committee consists of three women.

6. A drawer contains eight black socks and six brown socks well-mixed.   If a man opens the drawer in the dark and removes two socks, what is the probability that he has a matched par?   If he removes three socks, what is the probability that he has a matched pair?

7. A bag contains seven red balls and four black balls.   If three balls are drawn at random without replacement, calculate the following probabilities.

(a) All three are red. (b) All three are black.

(c) Two are red and one is black. (d) Two are black and one is red.

8. If four cards are drawn from a pack of fifty-two playing cards, what are the odds that none of the cards is an ace?

9. Two balls are drawn without replacement from a bag containing eight red balls and five black balls.   What are the odds that both balls are red?

10. Four coins are tossed.   Are the following events independent, dependent, or mutually exclusive?

(a) First three show heads; fourth shows tails.

(b) First shows heads; first three show heads.

(c) First three show tails; last three show heads.

(d) Second shows heads; fourth shows heads.

11. 5% of the population belong to blood group B and 15% of the population have the Rh^- factor in their blood.   What is the probability that an individual is of blood group B and Rh^-?

12. If 40% of the population belong to blood group O, what is the probability that, of five people chosen at random, at least two belong to group O?

13. A bag contains ten red balls and five black balls. If six balls are drawn from the bag, each ball being replaced before the next is drawn, calculate the following probabilities.
    (a) Four red and two black balls are drawn.
    (b) Two red and four black balls are drawn.
    (c) At least two red balls are drawn.
    (d) At least four black balls are drawn.

14. In a batch of twenty light bulbs it is known that four are defective. In a selection of five of the bulbs, what is the probability that at least two are defective?

15. In a family of six children, calculate the following probabilities.
    (a) Two are boys and four are girls.
    (b) At least two are boys.
    (c) At least five are boys.
    (d) All are girls.

16. In a test consisting of forty-five questions, five answers are given to each question. Only one of the answers is correct and the correct answer is to be underlined. When the test is marked, it is found that 20% of those writing obtained less than eleven correct solutions. It is, therefore, decided that a score of eleven or more correct will constitute a pass. What is the probability that a student who knew nothing about the subject matter but guessed at every answer would obtain a pass? (It is suggested that logarithms be used to obtain approximations for the various probabilities involved.)

17. If A and B are mutually exclusive events, state $P(A|B)$.

18. If 2 dice are rolled and one shows a number greater than 4, calculate the probability that the sum is 7.

19. A box contains 4 red balls and 3 white balls. If two balls are drawn in succession without replacement, calculate
    (a) the probability that the first is red and the second white,
    (b) the probability that both are white.

20. If $P(B|A) = \frac{5}{8}$, $P(A|B) = \frac{3}{4}$, $P(B) = \frac{1}{5}$, calculate $P(A)$.

21. If three workers A, B, and C produce 45%, 30%, and 25%, respectively, of the output of a certain toy, but 2%, $1\frac{1}{2}$%, and 1% of the respective outputs are faulty, calculate the probability that a faulty item was produced by C.

Chapter 12

LOGICAL REASONING

12.1. Sentences and Statements

It has been stated that the laws of logic are simply the laws of English grammar (or the laws of French grammar if one happens to be using the French language). While there is considerable truth in this assertion, it is an over-simplification. However, weakness in the use of language does lead to errors in reasoning and hence to errors in mathematics.

The type of sentence used in logic is the *declarative sentence*. This is a sentence that declares or states something. Some examples follow.

    (a) John is weak in mathematics.

    (b) All boys dislike homework.

    (c) $4 + 5 > 3$.

    (d) The world will end on January 16, 2176.

Interrogative sentences such as, "Did you manage to solve question (8)?" are not used in logic. Imperative sentences such as, "Report to the Principal's office", are not used in logic. Exclamatory sentences such as, "Hurrah, it is now time for the mathematics lesson!", are not used in logic.

DEFINITION. *A statement* is a meaningful declarative sentence that is either true or false, but not both.

If a sentence is meaningless, it cannot be classified as a statement. However, what is meaningless to one person may be meaningful to someone else. The sentence "The base angles of an isosceles triangle are equal" would be meaningless to someone who had never studied geometry. The sentence *"La plume de ma tante est sur le bureau de mon oncle"* would be meaningless to someone who knew no French.

In addition, the truth or falsity of a sentence will depend on the person making the judgment or on the time and circumstances in which the statement was made.

The sentence "The world will end on January 16, 2176" is certainly either true or false, but we will never know which. The sentence "John is weak in mathematics" may be judged true by his teacher since John made only 60% on the last test. However, John's friend, Bob, may judge it to be false since Bob made only 30%!

Examples.

(1) "Fish live in water" is a true declarative sentence (a statement).

(2) "$4 + 3 = 12$" is a false declarative sentence (a statement).

(3) "All hignals are progals" is a meaningless sentence (not a statement). (Note that it would cease to be meaningless if hignals and progals had been previously defined.)

(4) "He enjoys mathematics" is a sentence that is neither true nor false (not a statement).

(5) "$x + 7 = 10$" is a sentence that is neither true nor false (not a statement).

Examples 4 and 5 are known as *open sentences*. The pronoun "he" in Example 4 prevents us from being able to state whether the sentence is true or false. The pronoun is a *variable* that may be replaced by the names of suitable elements from a *replacement set*. Such a set is the *domain* of the variable. In Example 4, the domain of the variable might be the set of all boys in your mathematics class. We should then presume that the open sentence would become a true statement whenever "he" is replaced by the name of any member of the replacement set!

In Example 5, the variable is x and the domain of the variable might be the set of natural numbers. Only when x is replaced by 3 does the open sentence become a true statement. For all other elements of the domain, it is a false statement.

EXERCISE 12.1

Answer the following questions about each of the sentences below.

(a) Is it a declarative sentence?

(b) Is it a statement? (If so, is it true or false?)

(c) Is it an open sentence? (If so, state a possible domain.)

1. All rational numbers are integers.

2. How old are you?

3. He is Prime Minister of New Zealand.

4. $7 + 5 = 12$.

5. $6 > 2$.

6. For all $x \in Re$, $x^2 - 1 = (x - 1)(x + 1)$.

7. For all $x \in Re$, $x^2 - 1 = 15$.

8. Some boys dislike football.

9. All boys dislike football.

10. No boys dislike football.

11. Do questions (1) to (15) for homework.

12. Alternate angles are equal.

13. Some alternate angles are equal.

14. Parallel lines are coplanar.

15. She enjoys dancing.

16. Why did you not do your homework?

17. Is $2 + 3 = 5$?

18. A circle is the set of points in a plane that are a constant distance from a given point in the plane.

19. $2x + 3 = 12$.

20. For some $x \in Re$, $\frac{x}{0} = 1$.

21. For all $x \in Re$, $\frac{x}{0} = 1$.

22. For some $x \in Re$, $\frac{0}{0} = x$.

23. For all $x \in Re$, $\frac{0}{0} = x$.

24. The Yukon is in Europe.

25. $2n + 1$ is an odd number.

12.2. Definitions

A definition is not a statement since it is neither true nor false. In a definition, we give a name to a particular subset of a known set. When we examine the set of all quadrilaterals, we notice that special properties apply to quadrilaterals in which the opposite sides are parallel. Since we find that this particular subset of the set of all quadrilaterals occurs frequently in our investigations, it becomes cumbersome to be constantly saying, "A quadrilateral with opposite sides parallel".

Consequently we decide to invent a special name for such quadrilaterals and so the word "parallelogram" can be used in place of the description. Note that we are following this procedure for convenience only and that to say "A parallelogram is a quadrilateral with opposite sides parallel" merely informs others of the title we are giving to this particular subset of the set of all quadrilaterals. The sentence is neither true nor false but is only an agreement to use a particular name. Hence a definition is not a statement. However, a definition must conform to certain characteristics.

(a) The term being defined must be named in the sentence.

(b) All terms in the sentence, except the term being defined, should be known terms.

(c) The term being defined is placed in a known set.

(d) The characteristics that distinguish the term from other members of its set must be stated.

(e) The sentence should not contain any unnecessary or irrelevant information.

(f) The sentence should be reversible.

Let us consider the definition of an isosceles triangle: an isosceles triangle is a triangle with two equal sides. Does it satisfy the necessary prerequisites of a good definition?

(a) The term being defined, an isosceles triangle, is named in the definition.
(b) The terms "triangle", "equal", and "sides" have been previously defined.
(c) The term "isosceles triangle" is placed in the known set of all triangles.
(d) The characteristic that distinguishes an isosceles triangle from other members of the set of all triangles is stated.
(e) The sentence contains no unnecessary information. For instance, it does not state that an isosceles triangle has two equal angles. While this fact is true, it is unnecessary information, since it is a consequence of the definition and can be proved from the information given. However, it should be pointed out that this property of not giving unnecessary information may not always be possible and, while desirable, it is not so vital as the other points.
(f) The reversed sentence "A triangle with two equal sides is an isosceles triangle" is an equivalent sentence.

Example. Criticize the following definitions.
(a) A square is a rectangle with all four sides equal.
(b) A splot is an ink-blot which covers an area of more than 10 square inches.
(c) A turkey is an animal with two legs.

Solution:

(a) The definition gives unnecessary information. Since a rectangle has opposite sides equal and the square belongs to the set of rectangles, it is only necessary to state that two adjacent sides are equal.

(b) Assuming that we know the meaning of ink-blot, area, and 10 square inches, this sentence fulfils all the requirements of a definition.

(c) This "definition" places a turkey in the set of all animals but, since many other members of the set of all animals possess the quality of having two legs, it fails to distinguish between the turkey and these other members. In addition the sentence is not reversible. This defect is a natural consequence of the first criticism.

EXERCISE 12.2

1. Criticize the following definitions.
    (a) A circle is a plane figure enclosed by one line.
    (b) An even integer is an integer that is twice an odd integer.
    (c) A chord of a circle is a line segment joining any two points on the circle.
    (d) A cowraffe is a cow with a neck five feet long.
    (e) A quadratic polynomial is $2x^2 - 3x + 7$.
    (f) A set is a collection of objects.
    (g) A point is a position which has no dimensions.
    (h) A hignal is a progal with two left feet.
    (i) A Canadian is a person who is a citizen of Canada.
    (j) A rational number is a number that is not irrational.

2. Try to give suitable definitions for each of the following.
    (a) An even integer (b) A rational number
    (c) A quadratic polynomial (d) Happiness
    (e) School (f) The United Nations

3. In the following definitions, state which terms must have been previously defined or accepted as undefined.
    (a) A line segment is the set of points consisting of two points on a line and all those points on the line lying between these two points.
    (b) A chord of a circle is a line segment joining any two points on the circle.
    (c) A Canadian is a person who is a citizen of Canada.
    (d) A complex number is a number of the form $a + bi$ where a, $b \in Re$ and $i^2 = -1$.
    (e) A triangle is a polygon of three sides.

12.3. Logical Connectives (And, Or)

Statements may be combined by means of connectives of which the two principal ones are *and* and *or*. We shall represent simple statements by means of lower case letters p, q, etc. Note that the equality sign is being used here in the sense of "represents".

If $p = $ *All triangles are isosceles*, and $q = $ *The sum of two odd integers is an even integer*, then *p and q* represents the compound statement *All triangles are isosceles and the sum of two odd integers is an even integer*; *p or q* represents the statement *All triangles are isosceles or the sum of two odd integers is an even integer*. The first compound statement is the *conjunction* of the two original statements and the second is the *disjunction* of the two original statements. We shall examine each of these in turn.

Conjunction.

The word *and* placed between two statements p, q produces a new statement *p and q* called the *conjunction* of p and q.

If $p = $ *All triangles are isosceles*, and $q = $ *The sum of two odd integers is an even integer*, then p is false and q is true. The conjunction *p and q* or *All triangles are isosceles and the sum of two odd integers is an even integer* is also false. For a conjunction to be true, both component statements must be true. If one or both component statements are false, the conjunction is false.

Example. Determine the truth or falsity of the compound statement *p and q* in (1) to (3). If it is false, give a reason.

(1) $p = 3 + 1 > 2$.
$q = $ All similar triangles are congruent.

(2) $p = 3 + 1 > 2$.
$q = $ All congruent triangles are similar.

(3) $p = (x + y = xy)$ for all $x, y \in N$.
$q = $ Alexander the Great was a Roman citizen.

Solution:

(1) *p and q* is false since q is false.

(2) *p and q* is true since both p and q are true.

(3) *p and q* is false since both p and q are false.

Disjunction.

The word *or* placed between two statements p, q produces a new statement *p or q* called the disjunction of p and q.

We note that *or* is used mathematically in the inclusive sense; *p or q* means *either p or q or both*. If we wish to use the exclusive *or*, then we must state *p or q but not both*.

In ordinary English usage, the statement "I should make over 75% in mathematics or physics" does not exclude the possibility of over 75% in both. Hence, *or* is used in the inclusive sense. However, the statement "Tomorrow I will travel to Winnipeg by car or by train" means that we will use only one of the means of travel but not both. In this case, *or* is used in the exclusive sense. In mathematics, the inclusive *or* is always understood unless otherwise specified.

If $p = $ *All triangles are isosceles*, and $q = $ *The sum of two odd integers is an even integer*, the disjunction p or q is the statement *All triangles are isosceles or the sum of two odd integers is an even integer*. The disjunction is true since q is true. A disjunction is true whenever one or both of the component statements is true. A disjunction is false only if both component statements are false.

Example. Using the statements p, q given in the example for conjunction, determine the truth or falsity of the statement p or q, giving reasons.

Solution:

(1) p *or* q is true since p is true.

(2) p *or* q is true since both p and q are true.

(3) p *or* q is false since both p and q are false.

EXERCISE 12.3

For each of the following statements, determine whether the conjunction is true or false and whether the disjunction is true or false. Give a reason in each case.

1. $p = $ 5 and 6 are consecutive integers.
   $q = $ All right angles are equal.

2. $p = $ London is the capital city of the United Kingdom.
   $q = $ Dogs have four legs.

3. $p = $ The equation $y = x^2 + 6$ determines a function.
   $q = $ London is the capital city of Belgium.

4. $p = $ The equation $x^2 + y^2 = 16$ is the equation of a line.
   $q = $ The sum of two consecutive integers is an even integer.

5. $p = $ -3 is a positive integer.
   $q = $ π is a rational number.

6. $p = $ Equal chords of a circle are equidistant from the centre.
   $q = $ The line $y = 3x + 2$ has slope 3.

7. $p = $ If $y = \sin x$, $x \in Re$, then $0 \le y \le 1$.
   $q = $ All professors are absent-minded.

8. $p = $ The eighth term of the arithmetic sequence 1, 4, 7, $\cdots$ is 22.
   $q = $ $\sqrt{2}$ is not a rational number.

9. p = An acute angled triangle is a triangle in which one of the angles is an acute angle.

   q = The seventh term of the geometric sequence 1, 2, 4, $\cdots$ is 64.

10. $p = \left(\dfrac{x^2 - 4}{x - 2} = x + 2\right)$ for all $x \in Re$.

    $q = 4 + 5 > 3$.

11. p = The system of equations $2x - y = 7$ and $6x - 3y = 8$ has a solution set consisting of one ordered pair of real numbers.

    q = The solution set of the system of equations $x - 3y = 1$ and $2x + 3y = 11$ is $\{(1, 4)\}$.

12. p = The moon is approximately 250,000 miles from the earth.

    q = The graph of $y = 2x^2 - 3x + 6$ is a parabola.

12.4. Negation

If p is the statement *All triangles are isosceles*, then *not p* is the statement *Not all triangles are isosceles*. The new statement is the negation of p. The negation may be worded in several ways in addition to that given. Other forms would be *It is false that all triangles are isosceles*, or *It is not true that all triangles are isosceles*.

We should be careful that the word 'not' be correctly placed. The statement "All triangles are not isosceles" is not the negation of p. In this statement, the adjective "isosceles" has been negated instead of the whole statement. The statement "Not all triangles are isosceles" implies that some triangles may be isosceles, while the statement "All triangles are not isosceles" implies that no isosceles triangles exist. Some care is necessary here since in colloquial English usage the sentence might be taken to mean, "Not all triangles are isosceles". This case is one in which carelessness in English usage can lead to a false conclusion. Later, we shall see other ways of negating a statement containing the word "all".

If a statement p is true, then the statement *not p* is false. If a statement p is false, then the negation of p is true. The statement *All triangles are isosceles* is false, but the negation *Not all triangles are isosceles* is a true statement.

When p is a simple statement, the negation of p is fairly obvious. However, the negation of compound statements containing the connectives "and" or "or" requires some careful thought.

The statement *Mary is blonde and John is tall* asserts that *Mary is blonde* and *John is tall* are both true statements. For the conjunction to be true, both simple statements must be true. The negation denies that *both* are true and, therefore, asserts that *at least one* is false. The negation is *Mary is not blonde or John is not tall*.

This situation may be summarized by stating that the negation of p *and* q is (*not p*) *or* (*not q*).

The statement *Mary is blonde or John is tall* asserts that *at least one* of the statements *Mary is blonde* and *John is tall* is a true statement.   For the disjunction to be true, either one or both of the simple statements must be true.   To negate the disjunction, we must assert that *both* statements are false.   The negation is *Mary is not blonde and John is not tall.*

The negation of *p or q* is (*not p*) *and* (*not q*).

The negation of the statement (5) *is not an even integer* is the statement (5) *is an even integer.*

In general, the negation of (*not p*) is *p.*   The negation of *Mary is blonde* may be written in various forms.

(1) *Mary is not blonde.*

(2) *It is false that Mary is blonde.*

(3) *It is not true that Mary is blonde.*

EXERCISE 12.4

Write the negation of each of the following statements.   If possible, state whether the statement or its negation is true.

1. $4 + 5 = 20$.

2. All right angles are equal.

3. The world will end on January 16, 2176.

4. The sum of two consecutive integers is an even integer.

5. -3 is a positive integer.

6. π is a rational number.

7. $3 + 1 > 2$.

8. $x^2 + y^2 = 16$ is the equation of a line.

9. $\sqrt{2}$ is not a rational number.

10. Toronto is the capital city of Canada.

11. $2 + 3 = 5$ and dogs have four legs.

12. All right angles are equal and the graph of $y = 3x^2$ is a circle.

13. $2 + 3 = 5$ or dogs have four legs.

14. All right angles are equal or the graph of $y = 3x^2$ is a circle.

15. All similar triangles are congruent or -3 is a natural number.

16. 100 is 20% of 800 and the angle in a semicircle is a right angle.

17. π is a rational number or $\sqrt{2}$ is a rational number.

18. Alexander the Great was a Roman citizen and $2x + 1 = 3$.

12.5. Conditional Statements

The statement *The base angles of an isosceles triangle are equal* is a *conditional* or *implicative* statement. To clarify this, we may rewrite the statement as follows:
If a triangle is isosceles, then its base angles are equal.

The statement is a compound statement formed by using the connective *if . . . , then . . .* to connect two simple statements. If p represents the statement *A triangle is isosceles*, and q represents the statement *The base angles are equal*, then the conditional may be written as "If p, *then* q", or as "p *implies* q". This is frequently written symbolically as $p \Rightarrow q$. Statement p is called the *antecedent* and statement q is called the *consequent* of the conditional statement.

Conditional statements may be written in various equivalent forms and it is essential that we recognize the different phrasings in reading mathematics.

We shall consider the statement *Congruent triangles are similar*. This may be written as follows: *If two triangles are congruent, then the triangles are similar.*

Another possible phrasing is *A sufficient condition for two triangles to be similar is that the triangles be congruent.*

We not that our statement also implies that if the triangles are not similar, then they cannot be congruent since congruency implies similarity.

Hence, other possible phrasings are

(1) A *necessary* condition for two triangles to be congruent is that the triangles be similar;

(2) Two triangles are congruent *only if* they are similar.

>If $p = Two\ triangles\ are\ congruent,$
> $q = The\ triangles\ are\ similar,$

then the possible phrasings for the conditional statement $p \Rightarrow q$ are as follows:

(a) If p, then q.   (b) q, if p.

(c) p implies q.   (d) p is sufficient for q.

(e) p, only if q.   (f) q is necessary for p.

When is a conditional statement true and when is it false? To examine this question, we shall use two simple statements.

$p = It\ rains\ tomorrow.$
$q = The\ game\ will\ be\ cancelled.$

If John makes the statement *If it rains tomorrow, then the game will be cancelled*, under what conditions is he speaking the truth? He is stating that $p \Rightarrow q$.

If p is true and q is true, then obviously John is speaking the truth. It does rain and the game is cancelled.

Suppose p is true and q is false. It does rain but the game is not cancelled. John's statement is false.

Suppose p is false and q is true. It does not rain and the game is cancelled.

John only stated that if it did rain, the game would be cancelled.   He did not make any statement about what would happen if it did not rain.   His statement is true.

Suppose p is false and q is false.   It does not rain and the game is not cancelled.   John's statement is true.

We note that a conditional statement is always considered to be true when the antecedent is false.   Only when the antecedent is true and the consequent false can we consider the statement to be false.

Since the disjunction of *not p* and q, that is, *(not p) or q*, is also a false statement only when p is true and q is false, the conditional statement, $p \Rightarrow q$ is equivalent to the statement *(not p) or q*.

The statement *If it rains tomorrow, then the game will be cancelled* is equivalent to the statement, *It will not rain tomorrow or the game will be cancelled.*

The statement *If two triangles are congruent, then they are similar* is equivalent to the statement, *Two triangles are not congruent or they are similar.*

Since the negation of a disjunction is the conjunction of the negations of the simple statements, the negation of *(not p) or q*, and hence also of $p \Rightarrow q$, is the statement *p and (not q)*.   This also follows from the fact that an implication is false only when the antecedent is true and the consequent false.   Hence, the negation is true only when the antecedent is true and the consequent false.

The negation of the statement *If it rains tomorrow, then the game will be cancelled* is the statement *It will rain tomorrow and the game will not be cancelled.*

The negation of the statement *If two triangles are congruent, then they are similar* is the statement *Two triangles are congruent but they are not similar.*   Note that the word *but* is equivalent to *and* in this statement.

It must be emphasized that the negation of a conditional statement is *not* a conditional statement but is a conjunction of two statements.

EXERCISE 12.5

1. For each of the following statements p and q, write the conditional statements $p \Rightarrow q$ and $q \Rightarrow p$.   State which conditional statements are true and which false.

(a) $p = $ (In $\triangle ABC$, $\angle ABC = 90°$.)
     $q = $ ($AC^2 = AB^2 + BC^2$.)

(b) $p = $ ($1 + 3 = 5$.)
     $q = $ ($2 + 3 = 6$.)

(c) $p = $ ($2 + 3 = 6$.)
     $q = $ Ottawa is the capital of Canada.

(d) $p = $ ($\triangle ABC \equiv \triangle DEF$.)
     $q = $ ($\triangle ABC = \triangle DEF$.)

(e) $p = $ Air contains 90% hydrogen.
     $q = $ Sicily is a country in South America.

(f) $p = $ Quadrilateral ABCD has its opposite sides equal.
     $q = $ Quadrilateral ABCD is a parallelogram.

(g) $p = $ Quadrilateral ABCD has its opposite sides equal.
     $q = $ Quadrilateral ABCD is a rectangle.

(h) $p = 7 + 1 > 5$.
     $q = 2 + 1 > 5$.

2. Rewrite each of the sentences in parts (a) to (h) in each of the following ways.

    (i)   Using the words, "If . . ., then"

    (ii)   Using the words, "sufficient condition"

    (iii)   Using the words, "necessary condition"

    (iv)   Using the words, "only if"

(a) Two lines are parallel if the alternate angles formed by a transversal are equal.

(b) Congruent triangles are equal in area.

(c) The solution of the equation $2x + 1 = 5$ is $x = 2$.

(d) A parallelogram is a quadrilateral in which the opposite sides are parallel.

(e) Since $x = 0$, $xy = 0$.

(f) $x = 0$ if $xy = 0$.

(g) The sum of two consecutive integers is an odd integer.

(h) A normal dog is an animal with four legs.

3. Write the negation of each of the statements in question (2) and state whether the original statement or the negation is true.

4. John was told by his father, "You may remain in school if you do your homework." John did not do his homework but his father allowed him to remain in school. Is John's father truthful?

5. The students' council of Brandex High School stated, "A deposit of $1 is sufficient to reserve your copy of the yearbook." John only had 50¢. In view of the council's statement, could the treasurer accept John's 50¢ and reserve a copy of the yearbook for him?

6. Albert Jones is employed by the Grimm company. A sentence in his contract states, "An employee shall work overtime only if he is over 25 years of age." Albert is 32. Must he work overtime?

12.6. Converse, Inverse, and Contrapositive

If

$$p = \triangle ABC \equiv \triangle DEF,$$

and

$$q = \triangle ABC \,|||\, \triangle DEF,$$

then $p \Rightarrow q$ is the statement "If $\triangle ABC \equiv \triangle DEF$ then $\triangle ABC \,|||\, \triangle DEF$." p is the antecedent and q is the consequent of the conditional statement. By interchanging the antecedent and consequent of the statement, we form a new conditional statement, which is the *converse* of the given statement.

The converse of $p \Rightarrow q$ is $q \Rightarrow p$.

In this case, the converse statement is

$$\text{If } \triangle ABC \mid \mid \mid \triangle DEF, \text{ then } \triangle ABC \equiv \triangle DEF.$$

While the original conditional statement is true, the converse is false. The truth or falsity of a given conditional statement tells us nothing about the truth or falsity of the converse statement. The converse statement may also be written in the following equivalent forms.

(1) $\triangle ABC \equiv \triangle DEF$ if $\triangle ABC \mid \mid \mid \triangle DEF$.

(2) $\triangle ABC \mid \mid \mid \triangle DEF$ implies that $\triangle ABC \equiv \triangle DEF$.

(3) $\triangle ABC \mid \mid \mid \triangle DEF$ is sufficient for $\triangle ABC \equiv \triangle DEF$.

(4) $\triangle ABC \mid \mid \mid \triangle DEF$ only if $\triangle ABC \equiv \triangle DEF$.

(5) $\triangle ABC \equiv \triangle DEF$ is a necessary condition for $\triangle ABC \mid \mid \mid \triangle DEF$.

If both the original statement and the converse are true statements; that is, if $p \Rightarrow q$ and $q \Rightarrow p$ are both true, then p and q are *equivalent* statements. The statement *The base angles of an isosceles triangle are equal* may be written as *If a triangle is isosceles, then the base angles are equal.* This is a true statement, and the converse statement, *If a triangle has equal base angles, then the triangle is isosceles,* is also a true statement. We shall let p be the statement $\triangle ABC$ *is isosceles with* $AB = AC$, and q be the statement $\angle ABC = \angle ACB$. The *biconditional* statement $p \Rightarrow q$ and $q \Rightarrow p$ can be written as $p \Leftrightarrow q$. Again, this statement may be written in various forms.

(1) If p, then q, and if q, then p.

(2) If p, then q, and conversely.

(3) If q, then p, and conversely.

(4) p, if and only if q.

(5) q, if and only if p.

(6) p is a necessary and sufficient condition for q.

(7) q is a necessary and sufficient condition for p.

Sometimes, instead of $\Leftrightarrow$, the symbol $\equiv$ is used with exactly the same meaning. However, the use of the latter symbol, especially in geometrical arguments, might lead to confusion, for the same symbol is used to denote congruence of triangles.

"If and only if" is often abbreviated to "iff" in mathematical writing. Thus, (4) and (5) may be written in the forms p iff q and q iff p, respectively. (Similar abbreviations are used in mathematics written in other languages. The French *si et seulement si* becomes *ssi*.)

Since $p \Rightarrow q$ is true except when p is true and q is false, and $q \Rightarrow p$ is true except when q is true and p is false, $p \Leftrightarrow q$ will be true except when one of p and

q is true and the other false. That is, $p \Leftrightarrow q$ is a true statement if both p and q are true or if both p and q are false.

In the discussion of definitions we stated that a definition must be reversible. The definition *An isosceles triangle is a triangle with two equal sides* could be written in each of the following ways.

(1) A triangle is isosceles if and only if it is a triangle with two equal sides.

(2) A necessary and sufficient condition for a triangle to be isosceles is that the triangle have two equal sides.

From the conditional statement *If $\triangle ABC$ is congruent to $\triangle DEF$, then $\triangle ABC$ is similar to $\triangle DEF$*, we may form a new statement by negating both the antecedent and consequent of the original statement. Such a statement is the inverse of the original statement. The inverse of the given statement is *If $\triangle ABC$ is not congruent to $\triangle DEF$, then $\triangle ABC$ is not similar to $\triangle DEF$*.

The *inverse* of $p \Rightarrow q$ is $(not\ p) \Rightarrow (not\ q)$.

In the example given, the original conditional statement is true but the inverse is false. The truth or falsity of a statement does not guarantee the truth or falsity of the inverse.

By taking the same original statement and negating both the antecedent and consequent of the converse statement, we produce a new statement called the *contrapositive* of the original conditional statement. The contrapositive of the statement *If $\triangle ABC$ is congruent to $\triangle DEF$, then $\triangle ABC$ is similar to $\triangle DEF$* is the statement *If $\triangle ABC$ is not similar to $\triangle DEF$, then $\triangle ABC$ is not congruent to $\triangle DEF$*.

In this case, both the original conditional statement and its contrapositive are true.

The *contrapositive* of $p \Rightarrow q$ is $(not\ q) \Rightarrow (not\ p)$.

A conditional statement and its contrapositive are *equivalent* statements. If the statement is true, then so is the contrapositive and if a statement is false, then so is the contrapositive.

The statement $p \Rightarrow q$ is false only if p is true and q is false. The statement $(not\ q) \Rightarrow (not\ p)$ is false only if $not\ q$ is true and $not\ p$ is false, that is, when q is false and p is true. These criteria are identical and so the conditional statement is equivalent to its contrapositive.

EXERCISE 12.6

1. For each of the following sentences, write
   (i) the converse,   (ii) the inverse,   (iii) the contrapositive
   (a) If roses are red, then violets are blue.
   (b) If $2 + 3 = 5$, then $2 + 2 < 5$.
   (c) A quadrilateral is a parallelogram if its opposite sides are parallel.
   (d) If we have no homework tonight, then I am a Martian.

(e)   An integer is odd if it is the sum of two consecutive integers.

(f)   Congruent triangles are equal in area.

(g)   If $3x + 1 = 10$, then $x = 3$.

(h)   If $3x + 1 = 10$, then $x = 4$.

(i)   If Mr. Jones lives in Marseilles, then he lives in France.

(j)   Opposite angles of a cyclic quadrilateral are supplementary.

2.   Rewrite each of the following sentences using the "if and only if" and "necessary and sufficient" wording.

(a)   Collinear points are points which lie on the same line.

(b)   A Mexican is a person who is a citizen of Mexico.

(c)   A rational number is a number of the form $\dfrac{a}{b}$ where a and b are integers and $b \neq 0$.

(d)   A radius of a circle is a line segment joining the centre to any point on the circle.

(e)   An obtuse angle is an angle greater than 90° but less than 180°.

(f)   A parallelogram is a quadrilateral with its opposite sides parallel.

(g)   If a transversal intersects two parallel lines, then the alternate angles are equal, and conversely.

12.7. Quantifiers

The open sentence $x + 2 > 0$ cannot be said to be true or false unless we know the domain of the variable x.   However, open sentences can be converted into statements by the use of *quantifiers*.   The sentence

$$\textit{For all positive integers } x, \ x + 2 > 0$$

is a true sentence and hence, a statement.
     The sentence

$$\textit{For all integers } x, \ x + 2 > 0$$

is a false sentence and hence, a statement.
     Equivalent ways of wording the first sentence are

(1)   *For any positive integer* x, $x + 2 > 0$,

(2)   *For each positive integer* x, $x + 2 > 0$,

(3)   *For every positive integer* x, $x + 2 > 0$.

The statement *For all integers* x, $x + 2 > 0$ is false since -5 is a member of the domain and $-5 + 2 \not> 0$. However, the statement *For some integers* x, $x + 2 > 0$ is a true statement.   This may be reworded in the following equivalent ways.

(1) *There exists an integer* x *such that* $x + 2 > 0$.

(2) *For at least one integer* x, $x + 2 > 0$.

The words *all, any, some, there exists* give us an idea of quantity and so are known as *quantifiers*.

For all (and its equivalents) is known as the *universal quantifier*.

There exists (and its equivalents) is known as the *existential quantifier*.

The word *no* is also used as a quantifier but it is possible to replace it by *all*.

The statement *No boys are silly* is equivalent to the statement *All boys are not silly*.   We should be careful here since a common error in English usage is to state that this is equivalent to the statement *Not all boys are silly*.   A close examination of the two statements should show the difference.

(1) All boys are not silly.

(2) Not all boys are silly.

Sentence (1) states that *each* and *every* boy is not silly.

Sentence (2) states that *some* boys or *at least one* boy is not silly.

If we wish to negate a statement containing a quantifier, we must consider both the quantifier and the part of the statement following the quantifier.

The statement *For all* $x \in N$, $x + 1 = 4$ affirms that for all natural numbers x, $x + 1 = 4$.   To deny this assertion is to say that for at least one natural number x, $x + 1 \neq 4$.   If there is at least one natural number x such that $x + 1 \neq 4$, our original assertion is false and the negation is true.

In general, the quantifier *all* (and its equivalents) is negated by replacing it by the quantifier *some* or its equivalents, and then negating the second part of the statement.

The statement *Some men are bad drivers* asserts that at least one man is a bad driver.   For this statement to be false, it would be necessary to assert that the statement *All men are good drivers* is true.   The quantifier *some* is negated by replacing it by the quantifier *all*, and then negating the remainder of the sentence.

Examples.

1. Statement: *All angles are right angles.*
    Negation: *Some angles are not right angles.*

2. Statement: *For some positive integer* x, $x + 1 = 5$.
    Negation: *For all positive integers* x, $x + 1 \neq 5$.

3. Statement: *No boys are silly.*
   Equivalent: *All boys are not silly.*
   Negation: *Some boys are silly.*

4. Statement: *Not all boys are silly.*
   Equivalent: *Some boys are not silly.*
   Negation: *All boys are silly.*

Alternative ways of wording the negation of example (1) are:
There exist angles which are not right angles.
There is at least one angle which is not a right angle.
Not all angles are right angles.

Alternative wordings for the negation of example (2) are:
For every positive integer x, $x + 1 \neq 5$.
For each positive integer x, $x + 1 \neq 5$.
For no positive integer x *is* $x + 1 = 5$.

In most mathematical work, quantifiers are understood rather than stated. However, when precision is necessary or when doubt is possible, the quantifier must be used.

When we state *The base angles of an isosceles triangle are equal*, we understand the quantifier *all* and the statement would read *For all isosceles triangles T, the base angles* of T *are equal*.

When we state $a(a + b) = a^2 + ab$, we are stating *For all numbers a and b*, $a(a + b) = a^2 + ab$.

When we write $2x - 1 = 5$, we mean *There exists a number x such that* $2x - 1 = 5$ or *For some numbers x*, $2x - 1 = 5$.

EXERCISE 12.7

1. Use the quantifiers *all* or *some* or their equivalents to make each of the following a true statement.
   (a) $(x - 1)^2 = x^2 - 2x + 1$.
   (b) $3x + 2 = 17$.
   (c) $|x| = x$.
   (d) $\sqrt{x^2 + 9} \neq x + 3$.
   (e) The opposite sides of a parallelogram are equal.
   (f) No triangles are parallelograms.
   (g) Not all triangles are isosceles.
   (h) $x + 2x = 3x$.
   (i) The opposite angles of a cyclic quadrilateral are supplementary.
   (j) Not all rectangles are squares.

2. Negate each of the following statements.
   (a) For all $x \in Re$, $|x| = x$.
   (b) For some $x \in N$, $x^2 = 2$.
   (c) Every rational number is a real number.
   (d) For all $n \in N$, $n^2 - n + 41$ is a prime integer.
   (e) All triangles are not isosceles.
   (f) Not all triangles are isosceles.
   (g) Not all students are clever.
   (h) All students are not clever.
   (i) No students are stupid.
   (j) There exist numbers x and y such that $(x^2 - y^2) = (x - y)^2$.
   (k) For at least one $x \in Re$, $x^2 = -4$.
   (l) For any positive integer x, $x + 4 < 10$.

12.8. Principles of Proof

In proving any mathematical theorem, we show that the truth of the theorem follows by *logical inference* from statements which we have previously proved or accepted as true.

Statements accepted as true are the axioms or postulates that are the basis of the mathematical system. For example, in geometry we state as one of the axioms that, corresponding to any two points, there is one and only one line.

In proving theorems, we make use of six logical principles. These are based on the work of the preceding sections of this chapter.

(1) *Principle of Detachment*

If $p \Rightarrow q$ is true (either previously proved or accepted as an axiom), and p is true, then q is true. The statement $p \Rightarrow q$ is the *major premise*, p is the *minor premise*, and q is the *conclusion*. An example follows.

Major premise: *If x is even, then x is divisible by 2.* $p \Rightarrow q$.
Minor premise: *x is even.* p.
Conclusion: *x is divisible by 2.* $\therefore q$.

One of the commonest errors in logical reasoning is to assume that if $p \Rightarrow q$ is true and q is true, then p is true. Here we are assuming the converse and from Section 12.6 we know that the converse of a true statement is not necessarily a true statement.

Major Premise: *If John lives in Calcutta, then he lives in Bengal.* $p \Rightarrow q$.
Minor Premise: *John lives in Bengal.* q.
Conclusion: *John lives in Calcutta.* $\therefore p$.

The conclusion may be true or false. The reasoning is faulty and our conclusion cannot be deduced from the premises. A *valid* argument is one in which the premises imply the conclusion. If an argument is not valid, we call it *invalid*. The argument above is invalid. We should also note that an argument is valid or invalid, but a statement is true or false. We may not speak of a true argument or a valid statement.

(2) *Principle of Equivalence*

If two statements are equivalent and one of them is true, then the other is true. If $p \Leftrightarrow q$ is true and p is true, then q is true. If $p \Leftrightarrow q$ is true and q is true, then p is true.

Major Premise:	$2x - 1 = 5$ *iff* $x = 3$.	$p \Leftrightarrow q$.
Minor Premise:	$2x - 1 = 5$.	p.
Conclusion:	$x = 3$.	$\therefore q$.

Major Premise:	$2x - 1 = 5$ *iff* $x = 3$.	$p \Leftrightarrow q$.
Minor Premise:	$x = 3$.	q.
Conclusion:	$2x - 1 = 5$.	$\therefore p$.

(3) *Principle of Disjunction*

If p or q is true and p is false, then q is true. Note that if p is true then q may be either true or false. The principle of disjunction does not guarantee which case holds.

Premises:	(i) $AB \parallel CD$ or $AB \nparallel CD$.	p *or* q.
	(ii) $AB \nparallel CD$ is false.	*not* q.
Conclusion:	$AB \parallel CD$.	$\therefore p$.

This is the logical principle which we have frequently used in the past when proving a theorem by indirect proof. We consider the various possible results and show that all but one are false. The one remaining possibility has to be true.

(4) *Principle of the Contrapositive*

If $p \Rightarrow q$ is true and q is false, then p is false. In this example we shall use the word *hypotheses* (whose singular form is *hypothesis*), instead of premises. The words are synonymous and "hypothesis" is more frequently used in mathematics.

Hypotheses:	(i) *If* $x = 3$, *then* $x + 2 \ngtr 4$.	$p \Rightarrow q$.
	(ii) $x + 2 \ngtr 4$.	*not* q.
Conclusion:	$x \neq 3$.	*not* p.

This argument uses the contrapositive, *not* $q \Rightarrow$ *not* p, of the original $p \Rightarrow q$.

A common error in reasoning is to use the inverse instead of the contrapositive. The inverse does not provide a valid argument.   In the example below, the inverse gives the argument.

Hypotheses: (i) *If $x = 3$, then $x + 2 > 4$.* $p \Rightarrow q$.

(ii) $x \neq 3$.   *not p.*

Conclusion: $x + 2 \not> 4$.   *not q.*

The conclusion may be true or false.   The argument is invalid since the inverse of a true statement is not necessarily a true statement.

(5) *Principle of the Syllogism*

If $p \Rightarrow q$ is true and $q \Rightarrow r$ is true, then $p \Rightarrow r$ is true.

Hypotheses: (i) *If $4x+7 = x + 1$, then $3x = -6$.* $p \Rightarrow q$.

(ii) *If $3x = -6$, then $x = -2$.* $q \Rightarrow r$.

Conclusion: *If $4x + 7 = x + 1$, then $x = -2$.* $p \Rightarrow r$.

(6) *Principle of Substitution*

(i) *Substitution for a variable*

If an open sentence is made into a statement by using a quantifier so that the statement is true for all elements of the domain of the variable, then substitution of a specific element of the domain for the variable will produce a true statement.

Hypothesis: (i) All rational numbers are real numbers.

(ii) $-\frac{4}{5}$ is a rational number.

Conclusion: $-\frac{4}{5}$ is a real number.

(ii) *Substitution for statements*

If $p \Leftrightarrow q$ is a true statement, then q may be substituted for p in any statement involving p.

Hypotheses: (i) A parallelogram is a rectangle if and only if it has one angle a right angle.

(ii) A parallelogram with one angle a right angle has equal diagonals.

Conclusion: A rectangle has equal diagonals.

In all proofs, each step must follow from one of these principles of logic.   While we will not normally state which principle we are using in reaching a conclusion, we should at all times be prepared to justify the steps in a proof.   The only justification is that we have used correctly one of these logical principles.

As an example of the use of the principles of logic we will consider the following set of axioms.   These are statements assumed to be true as the basis of a given discussion.   Any conclusion reached is arrived at by valid reasoning using the principles of logic, and if our axioms are accepted as being true then our conclusion must also be a true statement.

Axiom 1. *All students work hard.*

Axiom 2. *People who work hard are successful.*

Axiom 3. *Successful people are not foolish.*

Axiom 4. *Unhappy people are foolish.*

Example 1. Prove the following statement: *If Bill works hard, then he will be happy.*

Solution:	Bill works hard.	Hypothesis
∴	Bill is successful.	Substitution and Detachment in Axiom 2
∴	Bill is not foolish.	Substitution and Detachment in Axiom 3
∴	Bill is happy.	Substitution and Contrapositive in Axiom 4
∴	If Bill works hard, he is happy.	

Example 2. Prove the following statement: *If Bill is unhappy, then he is not a student.*

Solution 1:	Bill is unhappy.	Hypothesis
∴	Bill is foolish.	Substitution and Detachment in Axiom 4
∴	Bill is not successful.	Substitution and Contrapositive in Axiom 3
∴	Bill does not work hard.	Substitution and Contrapositive in Axiom 2
∴	Bill is not a student.	Substitution and Contrapositive in Axiom 1
∴	If Bill is unhappy, he is not a student.	

Solution 2:	Bill is unhappy.	Hypothesis
∴	Bill does not work hard.	Substitution and Contrapositive in Theorem 1
∴	Bill is not a student.	Substitution and Contrapositive in Axiom 1
∴	If Bill is unhappy, he is not a student.	

Solution 3:	Either Bill is a student or Bill is not a student.	
	Assume that Bill is a student.	
∴	Bill works hard.	Substitution and Detachment in Axiom 1
∴	Bill is happy.	Substitution and Detachment in Theorem 1
	But Bill is unhappy.	Hypothesis
∴	Bill is a student is false.	
∴	Bill is not a student.	Principle of Disjunction
∴	If Bill is unhappy, he is not a student.	

We note that once a theorem has been proved, then it may be used in the same manner as our axioms and regarded as a true statement in further discussion. This procedure avoids the necessity of returning to our axioms in every case and enables us to provide shorter proofs in later theorems.

EXERCISE 12.8

In each of the following, state whether the reasoning is valid or invalid. If valid, state the logical principle used, and, if invalid, state the reason.

1. Hypotheses: All right angles are equal.
   $\angle A$ and $\angle B$ are right angles.
   Conclusion: $\angle A = \angle B$.

2. Hypotheses: If snow is falling, then it is winter.
   Snow is falling.
   Conclusion: It is winter.

3. Hypotheses: If two triangles are congruent, then they are equal in area.
   Two triangles are equal in area.
   Conclusion: The triangles are congruent.

4. Hypotheses: $a = 6$ or $a = 10$.
   $a \neq 6$.
   Conclusion: $a = 10$.

5. Hypotheses: $AB = CD$ or $AB \parallel CD$.
   $AB \parallel CD$.
   Conclusion: $AB \neq CD$.

6. Hypotheses: If $x = 2$, then $2x + 1 = 5$.
   $2x + 1 \neq 5$.
   Conclusion: $x \neq 2$.

7. Hypotheses: If $5x + 2 = 3x + 6$, then $2x = 4$.
   If $2x = 4$, then $x = 2$.
   Conclusion: If $5x + 2 = 3x + 6$, then $x = 2$.

8. Hypotheses: If John studies, then he is successful.
   If John is successful, then he is happy.
   Conclusion: If John is happy, then John studies.

9. Hypotheses: John is successful if he studies.
   John does not study.
   Conclusion: John is not successful.

10. Hypotheses: John is successful only if he studies.
    John does not study.
    Conclusion: John is not successful.

On the basis of the following set of axioms prove each of the theorems in questions (11) and (12).

Axiom 1. *Every line is a set of points.*

Axiom 2. *For each line l, there is a point not on l.*

Axiom 3. *There exist at least two points.*

Axiom 4. *For every pair of distinct points, there is one and only one line containing these points.*

11. There are at least two lines containing any point.

12. There are at least three lines.

12.9. Disproof

When a statement involves a quantifier, either stated or implied, it may sometimes be difficult to prove that the statement is true.   If we doubt the truth of the statement, then we may attempt to disprove it.   This may sometimes be just as difficult as trying to prove the truth of the statement but often it is a simpler task.

The statement *For all $n \in I^+$, $n^2 + n + 41$ is a prime integer* asserts that the statement is true for all positive integers n.   To prove the statement false, we have to prove that the negation *For at least one positive integer, $n^2 + n + 41$ is not a prime integer* is a true statement.   All we have to do is to find one positive integer n such that $n^2 + n + 41$ is not prime.   This is known as disproof by counter-example.

In this example, when $n = 41$.

$$n^2 + n + 41 = 41^2 + 41 + 41$$
$$= 41(41 + 1 + 1)$$
$$= 41(43) \quad \text{which is not a prime integer.}$$

There are actually many positive integral values of n for which $n^2 + n + 41$ is not prime.   The smallest such value is $n = 40$.

The statement *For some positive integer x, $x + 5 < 2$* asserts that we can find at least one such positive integer.   To prove the statement true, we only have to demonstrate the existence of one such integer.   To disprove the statement, we must prove that the negation *For all positive integers x, $x + 5 \not< 2$* is a true statement. Although this is simple to prove in this example, it will obviously be more difficult to prove than the first type in many instances.

If

$$x + 5 < 2,$$

then

$$x < -3.$$

Therefore,

$$x \notin I^+.$$

A conditional statement, such as *If two triangles are similar, then they are congruent,* is false only if the antecedent is true and the consequent is false. To prove the statement false, we must demonstrate that it is possible to have two similar triangles which are not congruent. Any example will suffice and so this is really equivalent to our disproof of statements beginning "For all . . .". In fact, the statement *For all* $n \in I^+$, $n^2 + n + 41$ *is a prime integer* is basically a conditional statement and could be rewritten as *If* $n \in I^+$, *then* $n^2 + n + 41$ *is a prime integer.*

To disprove the assertion *If two triangles are similar, then they are congruent,* we may proceed as follows.

Let

$$\triangle ABC \text{ have } AB = 1 \text{ in., } BC = 2 \text{ in., } AC = 2 \text{ in.}$$

and

$$\triangle DEF \text{ have } DE = 3 \text{ in., } EF = 6 \text{ in., } DF = 6 \text{ in.}$$

$$\therefore \quad \frac{AB}{DE} = \frac{BC}{EF} = \frac{AC}{DF}.$$

$$\therefore \quad \triangle ABC \,|||\, \triangle DEF.$$

But

$$AB \neq DE.$$

$$\therefore \quad \triangle ABC \not\equiv \triangle DEF.$$

Therefore the statement is false.

In general, to disprove any statement, we must prove that the negation of that statement is a true statement.

EXERCISE 12.9

Prove that the following statements are false.

1. If a triangle is right-angled, then it is isosceles.

2. For all $n \in I^+$, $n^2 + n + 11$ is a prime integer.

3. For some $n \in I^+$, $n(n + 1)$ is an odd integer.

4. If a quadrilateral is cyclic, then its opposite angles are equal.

5. All triangles have the property of not being isosceles.

6. If $x > 5$, then $x + 2 > 10$.

7. For all $x \in I^+$, $x < 5$ or $x > 5$.

8. For some real number x, $x^2 + 1 = 0$.

9. $\sqrt{2}$ is a rational number.

10. For all real numbers a and b, $|a| + |b| = |a + b|$.

11. For some $n \in I^+$, $n^2 + 5n + 4$ is a prime integer.

12. If a quadrilateral is not a square, then it is not a rectangle.

12.10. Symbolic Logic (Supplementary)

As in all mathematical studies, a judicious use of symbols becomes valuable in the examination of logic beyond the elementary level. By the use of symbols, an algebra of logic may be developed. However, in the elementary study of logic, it is more important to understand the ideas of logic than to become adept at manipulating symbols. It is quite simple to develop rules for "symbol pushing" while forgetting completely what the symbols actually mean. However, once we understand the elementary ideas of logical reasoning and wish to examine more complex statements, an algebra of logic does become useful.

If we understand the algebra of set theory, then we can also perform the algebra of elementary logic. The two systems are isomorphic although usually slightly different symbols are used. Logical reasoning may be interpreted in terms of set operations. Two statements p and q may be handled in the same way as two sets A and B. The commonly-used terminology in both systems is listed below with equivalent notations in the same row.

	Logic		Set Theory	
$p \wedge q$	(*p and q*)	$A \cap B$	(*A* intersection *B*)	
$p \vee q$	(*p or q or both*)	$A \cup B$	(*A* union *B*)	
$\sim p$	(*not p*)	A'	(*A* complement)	
$p \Rightarrow q$	(*if p, then q*)	$A \subseteq B$	(*A* is a subset of *B*)	

If

$$p = 3 \text{ is a natural number,}$$
$$q = \pi \text{ is a rational number,}$$

then

$$p \wedge q = 3 \text{ is a natural number and } \pi \text{ is a rational number,}$$
$$q \vee p = 3 \text{ is a natural number or } \pi \text{ is a rational number,}$$
$$\sim p = 3 \text{ is not a natural number.}$$

We know that the negation of (*p and q*) is (*not p*) or (*not q*). In symbols,

$$\sim(p \wedge q) \Leftrightarrow \sim p \vee \sim q .$$

Compare this with the algebra of sets where

$$(A \cap B)' = A' \cup B' .$$

Similarly, $\sim(p \vee q) \Leftrightarrow \sim p \wedge \sim q$, which may be compared with

$$(A \cup B)' = A' \cap B' .$$

If
$$p = \triangle ABC \equiv \triangle DEF, \quad q = \triangle ABC \;|||\; \triangle DEF,$$
then
$$p \Rightarrow q = If \; \triangle ABC \equiv \triangle DEF, \; then \; \triangle ABC \;|||\; \triangle DEF.$$

This sentence states that the set of all congruent triangles is a subset of the set of all similar triangles. If A is the set of all congruent triangles and B is the set of all similar triangles, then
$$A \subseteq B.$$

In this case, A is a proper subset of $B(A \subset B)$. However, if
$$p = In \; \triangle CDE, \; \angle CDE = 90°, \quad q = (CE^2 = CD^2 + DE^2),$$
then

$A =$ *The set of all right-angled triangles,*

$B =$ *The set of all triangles in which the measure of the area of the square on one side is equal to the sum of the measures of the areas of the squares on the other two sides,*
then
$$p \Rightarrow q \quad and \quad q \Rightarrow p.$$
Hence,
$$p \Leftrightarrow q.$$
Also,
$$A \subseteq B \quad and \quad B \subseteq A.$$
Hence,
$$A = B.$$

We have seen that the conditional statement $p \Rightarrow q$ is equivalent to the statement (*not p*) *or q* and that the negation of $p \Rightarrow q$ is *p and* (*not q*). Symbolically,

(1)
$$(p \Rightarrow q) \Leftrightarrow \sim p \lor q,$$

(2)
$$\sim(p \Rightarrow q) \Leftrightarrow p \land \sim q.$$

Statement (2) can be proved by using Statement (1) and the statement

$$\sim(p \lor q) \Leftrightarrow \sim p \land \sim q.$$

Example 1. Prove that
$$(p \Rightarrow q) \Leftrightarrow (\sim p \lor q).$$

Solution:
$$\sim(p \Rightarrow q) \Leftrightarrow \sim(\sim p \lor q)$$
$$\Leftrightarrow \sim(\sim p) \land \sim q$$
$$\Leftrightarrow p \land \sim q.$$

Example 2.   Prove that

$$\sim (p \Leftrightarrow q) \Leftrightarrow (p \wedge \sim q) \vee (q \wedge \sim p) .$$

Solution:

$$\sim (p \Leftrightarrow q) \Leftrightarrow \sim [(p \Rightarrow q) \wedge (q \Rightarrow p)]$$
$$\Leftrightarrow \sim (p \Rightarrow q) \vee \sim (q \Rightarrow p)$$
$$\Leftrightarrow \sim (\sim p \vee q) \vee \sim (\sim q \vee p)$$
$$\Leftrightarrow (p \wedge \sim q) \vee (q \wedge \sim p) .$$

To avoid the temptation to reduce the whole operation to mechanical manipulation of symbols, it is instructive to translate the various statements into English.

$$\sim (p \Leftrightarrow q) \Leftrightarrow (p \wedge \sim q) \vee (q \wedge \sim p)$$

states that it is false that p is equivalent to q if and only if p is true and q is false, or q is true and p is false.   We see that the symbolism does help to shorten a lengthy compound statement, and, in such a situation, is of value.   Mechanical manipulation is certainly useful once we clearly understand the meanings of the symbols.

Symbols used for quantifiers are

$\forall_x$ (for all x) the universal quantifier ,
$\exists_x$ (for some x) the existential quantifier .

In using quantifiers, we are converting an open sentence into a statement provided we state the domain of the variable.   The statement "For all $x \in N$, $x + 2 > 1$" may be written

$\forall_x, x \in N \ (x + 2 > 1)$, and this is a true statement.

Similarly,

$\forall_x, x \in I \ (x + 2 > 1)$ is a false statement

and

$\exists_x, x \in I \ (x + 2 > 1)$ is a true statement.

If S_x is an open sentence and x is an element of a specified domain, then

$\forall_x(S_x)$ and $\exists_x(S_x)$ are statements.

The negation of $\forall_x(S_x)$ is the statement $\sim \forall_x(S_x)$ or the statement $\exists_x(\sim S_x)$. Hence,

$$\sim \forall_x(S_x) \Leftrightarrow \exists_x(\sim S_x).$$

Similarly,

$$\sim \exists_x(S_x) \Leftrightarrow \forall_x(\sim S_x).$$

EXERCISE 12.10

1. If $p = 5$ and 6 are consecutive integers,
   $q = $ all right angles are equal,
   $r = 4 + 5 = 3$,

   write each of the following statements symbolically.
   (a) If 5 and 6 are consecutive integers, then all right angles are equal.
   (b) All right angles are equal if $4 + 5 = 3$.
   (c) All right angles are equal and $4 + 5 = 3$.
   (d) 5 and 6 are consecutive integers or $4 + 5 = 3$.
   (e) If $4 + 5 = 3$ and all right angles are equal, then 5 and 6 are consecutive integers.
   (f) $4 + 5 \neq 3$ and all right angles are equal.
   (g) 5 and 6 are not consecutive integers if $4 + 5 \neq 3$.
   (h) If $4 + 5 = 3$, then all right angles are unequal or 5 and 6 are not consecutive integers.
   (i) All right angles are equal if and only if $4 + 5 \neq 3$ and 5 and 6 are consecutive integers.

2. Prove each of the following for statements p, q, r.
   (a) $[(p \Rightarrow q) \Rightarrow r] \Leftrightarrow (p \wedge \sim q) \vee r$.
   (b) $[\sim (p \vee q) \Rightarrow r] \Leftrightarrow p \vee q \vee r$.
   (c) $\sim [(p \wedge q) \wedge \sim (q \wedge r)] \Leftrightarrow (\sim p \vee \sim q) \vee (q \wedge r)$

3. Write the negation for each of the following.
   (a) $p \wedge \sim q$
   (b) $\sim p \vee (q \wedge r)$
   (c) $\forall_x, x \in N$ ($2x$ is even) in two forms
   (d) $p \Rightarrow q$ in two forms
   (e) $\exists_x, x \in Re$ ($2x^2 + 7 = 3$) in two forms
   (f) $\forall_x (P_x \Rightarrow Q_x)$ in three forms
   (g) $\exists_x (S_x \Rightarrow P_x)$ in three forms

4. If P_x is x is a prime integer,
   Q_x is x is an even integer,
   R_x is x is divisible by 2,

   translate each of the following into English.
   (a) $\forall_x (Q_x \Rightarrow R_x)$ (b) $\exists_x (P_x \wedge Q_x)$
   (c) $\sim \exists_x (P_x \wedge Q_x)$ (d) $\forall_x (\sim P_x \vee R_x)$
   (e) $\forall_x (P_x \Rightarrow \sim R_x)$ (f) $\exists_x (P_x \Leftrightarrow Q_x)$

Chapter Summary

A statement is a meaningful declarative sentence which is either true or false, but not both.

Logical Connectives

p and q	Conjunction
p or q	Disjunction
not p	Negation
if p then q	Conditional
p if and only if q	Biconditional

Statement	Negation
p	*not p*
p or q	*(not p) and (not q)*
p and q	*(not p) or (not q)*
not p	*p*
$p \Rightarrow q$	*p and (not q)*

Converse of $p \Rightarrow q$ is $q \Rightarrow p$.

Inverse of $p \Rightarrow q$ is $(not\ p) \Rightarrow (not\ q)$.

Contrapositive of $p \Rightarrow q$ is $(not\ q) \Rightarrow (not\ p)$.

Quantifiers
    For all . . .
    For some . . .

Principles of Proof
    Detachment
    Equivalence
    Disjunction
    Contrapositive
    Syllogism
    Substitution

Symbolic Logic (supplementary)

REVIEW EXERCISE 12

1. Write the negation of each of the following statements.   Determine whether the statement or the negation is true.
    (a) 7 and 11 are consecutive integers.
    (b) The inverse of a true statement is always a true statement.
    (c) The converse of a true statement is always a true statement.

   (d) The contrapositive of a true statement is always a true statement.

   (e) Opposite angles of a cyclic quadrilateral are supplementary or $2 + 1 = 5$.

   (f) Opposite angles of a cyclic quadrilateral are supplementary and $2 + 1 = 5$.

   (g) If a triangle is right-angled, then the triangle is isosceles.

   (h) If Lisbon is the capital city of Corsica, then Montreal is in Texas.

   (i) If Lisbon is the capital city of Corsica, then Ottawa is the capital of Canada.

   (j) For all $x \in Re$, $x^2 - 1 = (x - 1)(x + 1)$

   (k) For some $x \in Re$, $2(x + 1) = 2x + 1$.

   (l) For all $x \in Re$, $3x + 2 = 15$.

2. Write the inverse, converse, and contrapositive of each of the following statements.

   (a) If a triangle is right-angled, then the triangle is isosceles.

   (b) If $2x + 3 = 9$, then $x = 3$.

   (c) Two triangles are equal in area if they are congruent.

   (d) If two integers are odd, then their sum is even.

   (e) If Winnipeg is the capital city of Ontario, then Montreal is in Texas.

   (f) Winnipeg is the capital city of Ontario only if Ottawa is the capital of Canada.

   (g) A sufficient condition for two triangles to be similar is that they be congruent.

   (h) A necessary condition for two triangles to be similar is that they be congruent.

   (i) A sufficient condition for two lines to be parallel is the equality of the alternate angles formed by a transversal.

   (j) A necessary condition for a quadrilateral to be a parallelogram is the equality of the opposite angles.

   (k) If the opposite angles of a quadrilateral are supplementary the vertices are concyclic.

   (l) If a line is a tangent to a circle, then it is perpendicular to a radius.

3. Rewrite each of the following statements using the words "sufficient condition", "necessary condition", "only if".

   (a) If two triangles are congruent, then they are equal in area.

   (b) If two lines are parallel, then the corresponding angles formed by a transversal are equal.

   (c) If it is raining, then the streets are wet.

   (d) If John studies logic, then he will never be confused.

   (e) A rectangle is a square if it has one pair of adjacent sides equal.

   (f) A rhombus is a square if it has one angle equal to a right angle.

(g) $2x^2 + 1 < 9$ if $-2 < x < 2$.

(h) If $x \in I^+$, then $2x + 1$ is an odd integer.

(i) A real number is an irrational number if it can be represented by a non-recurring decimal.

(j) The product of two integers m and n is even if each of m and n is even.

(k) The roots of a quadratic equation $ax^2 + bx + c = 0$ are real if $b^2 \geq 4ac$.

(l) If a, b, and c are the lengths of the hypotenuse and the two other sides, respectively, of a triangle, then $a^2 = b^2 + c^2$.

4. In each of the following, state whether the reasoning is valid or invalid. If valid, state the logical principle used and, if invalid, state why.

(a) Hypotheses: Parallel lines are coplanar lines which do not intersect.
Coplanar lines which do not intersect have the same slope.
Conclusion: Parallel lines have the same slope.

(b) Hypotheses: John is either at home or at school.
John is not at school.
Conclusion: John is at home.

(c) Hypotheses: $AB \parallel CD$ or $AB = CD$.
$AB \parallel CD$.
Conclusion: $AB \neq CD$.

(d) Hypotheses: If two lines are parallel, then they are coplanar.
If two lines are coplanar, then they are not skew.
Conclusion: If two lines are parallel, then they are not skew.

(e) Hypotheses: If a number is even, then it is divisible by 2.
27 is not divisible by 2.
Conclusion: 27 is not even.

(f) Hypotheses: If it is raining, then the streets are wet.
It is not raining.
Conclusion: The streets are not wet.

(g) Hypotheses: All men are mortal.
Mr. Smith is a man.
Conclusion: Mr. Smith is mortal.

(h) Hypotheses: All men are mortal.
A dog is mortal.
Conclusion: A dog is a man.

(i) Hypotheses: $\angle A$ is an obtuse angle if any only if $90° < \angle A < 180°$.
$90° < \angle A < 180°$.
Conclusion: $\angle A$ is an obtuse angle.

(j) Hypotheses: If two triangles are congruent, then they are similar.
If two triangles are congruent, then they are equal in area.
Conclusion: If two triangles are similar, then they are equal in area.

5. Using the axioms given, prove each of the theorems which follow.

Axiom 1.   *All mathematicians are logical.*
Axiom 2.   *Careful people are not foolish.*
Axiom 3.   *Discontented people are foolish.*
Axiom 4.   *Logical people are careful.*
Theorem 1.   Mathematicians are contented.
Theorem 2.   Foolish people are not logical.
Theorem 3.   Careless people are not mathematicians.

6. Prove that the following statements are false.

(a) For all $n \in I^+$, $n^2 - n + 87$ is a prime integer.

(b) For all $n \in I^+$, $2n^2$ is an odd integer.

(c) For some $n \in I^+$, $n^2 + 2n$ is a prime integer.

Supplementary

7. Determine the truth or falsity of the following statements.   The domain of both x and y is I.

(a) $\forall_x (\exists_y (x = y + 1))$

(b) $\exists_y (\forall_x (x = y + 1))$

(c) $\exists_y (\forall_x (x + y = x))$

8. Prove the following statements for p, q, r.

(a) $[p \vee (q \wedge r)] \Leftrightarrow [(p \vee q) \wedge (p \vee r)]$

(b) $[p \wedge (q \vee r)] \Leftrightarrow [(p \wedge q) \vee (p \wedge r)]$

9. Write the following statement symbolically.

For all positive ϵ, there exists a positive δ such that the absolute value of the difference of $f(x)$ and $f(y)$ is less than ϵ whenever the absolute value of the difference of x and y is less than δ.

AN INTRODUCTION TO ALGEBRAIC SYSTEMS

13.1. Introduction

In this chapter we introduce the student to a more general view of mathematical systems.

We begin our study by considering sets of elements other than numbers, primarily sets consisting of mappings or transformations. We then consider combinations of such set elements by the introduction of binary operations with examples from different topics in algebra and geometry. This leads us to a study of the properties of such binary operations. Finally, by examining examples of such sets with operations, we see certain patterns emerging which lead to generalizations producing algebraic systems known as groupoids, semigroups, groups, rings, and fields. Indeed, we have already examined the pattern of the properties of the sets Ra, Re, and C under the operations of addition and multiplication, and we have noted that these systems have a common core of properties which we labelled as "field properties". These number field systems are special cases of the more general situation.

EXERCISE 13.1

1. List the field properties associated with the sets Ra, Re, and C.

13.2. Sets of Permutations

Suppose that a set of three books A, B, and C is sitting in this order on a shelf and that a student passes by and interchanges books B and C. Originally the books stood ABC; now they stand ACB. The change in order or rearrangement effected by the student is an example of a mapping of the set {A, B, C} of books onto itself; such a mapping is called a permutation. In this mapping, book B is replaced by (changed to, transformed into, mapped onto) book C, book C is replaced by book B, and book A is unchanged (or mapped onto itself). We indicate this mapping or permutation by the symbol

$$\begin{pmatrix} A & B & C \\ A & C & B \end{pmatrix}$$

in which the first line gives the original arrangement of the books and the second line gives the rearrangement after the mapping or transformation or permutation has been applied. Such a mapping is a function; the top line gives the domain and the bottom line, the range. (They are the same set for a permutation.)

We know from our earlier work that 3! or six such permutations are possible:

$$\begin{pmatrix} A & B & C \\ A & B & C \end{pmatrix}, \begin{pmatrix} A & B & C \\ A & C & B \end{pmatrix}, \begin{pmatrix} A & B & C \\ C & B & A \end{pmatrix}, \begin{pmatrix} A & B & C \\ B & A & C \end{pmatrix}, \begin{pmatrix} A & B & C \\ B & C & A \end{pmatrix}, \begin{pmatrix} A & B & C \\ C & A & B \end{pmatrix}.$$

The first of these permutations is the mapping of the set of books in which each book is left in its original position; this is the identity or neutral permutation.

Note that we would obtain exactly the same set of permutations if we were rearranging a set of pictures of three N.H.L. hockey players or the names of three Canadian cities. The elements of the set being rearranged are quite immaterial but, of course, the number of elements in the set being rearranged will be important in determining the permutations and the number of such permutations. A set {A, B, C, D} of four books would give rise to a set of 4! or 24 possible permutations.

Example 1. Write permutations of the set {A, B, C, D} in which A and D are
(a) interchanged,   (b) unchanged.

Solution: (a) The required permutations have the form

$$\begin{pmatrix} A & B & C & D \\ D & * & * & A \end{pmatrix}$$

There are only two such permutations,

$$\begin{pmatrix} A & B & C & D \\ D & B & C & A \end{pmatrix} \quad \text{and} \quad \begin{pmatrix} A & B & C & D \\ D & C & B & A \end{pmatrix}.$$

(b) The required permutations are

$$\begin{pmatrix} A & B & C & D \\ A & B & C & D \end{pmatrix} \quad \text{and} \quad \begin{pmatrix} A & B & C & D \\ A & C & B & D \end{pmatrix}.$$

Example 2.   Write the permutations of the set {A, B, C, D, E} in which A, C, and D are unchanged.

Solution: The required permutations are of the form

$$\begin{pmatrix} A & B & C & D & E \\ A & * & C & D & * \end{pmatrix}.$$

There are only two such permutations,

$$\begin{pmatrix} A & B & C & D & E \\ A & B & C & D & E \end{pmatrix} \quad \text{and} \quad \begin{pmatrix} A & B & C & D & E \\ A & E & C & D & B \end{pmatrix}.$$

EXERCISE 13.2

1. How many permutations are there on a set of two books?   Write symbols for these permutations.

2. Write the set of permutations on three objects, using the symbols 1, 2, and 3 for the objects.

3. Write the set of permutations of the set {A, B, C, D}.

4. Write the permutations of the set {1, 2, 3, 4} in which 2 and 4 are interchanged.

5. Give the permutations of the set {A, B, C, D, E} in which
   (a) A and E are unchanged,
   (b) A and E are interchanged,
   (c) B, C, and D are unchanged,
   (d) B is changed into C, C into D, and D into B.

6. Give the permutations of the set {1, 2, 3, 4, 5} in which
   (a) 1, 2, and 4 are unchanged,
   (b) 3 and 5 are unchanged,
   (c) 4 and 5 are interchanged,
   (d) 1 and 3 are interchanged and 2 and 5 are interchanged,
   (e) 1 is changed into 3, 3 into 5, and 5 into 1.

7. Write the permutations of the set {1, 2, 3, 4, 5, 6} in which
   (a) 4, 5, and 6 are unchanged,
   (b) 1, 2, and 3 are unchanged,
   (c) 1 and 4, 2 and 5, 3 and 6 are interchanged,
   (d) 1 and 6, 2 and 5 are interchanged.

8. How many permutations on *n* distinct symbols are there which leave two given symbols unchanged?

13.3. Sets of Motions

Consider the square shown in Figure 13.1(a). The Lines H, V, D_1, and D_2 are drawn in (b) for convenience in our discussion. It may prove useful to construct a square out of cardboard. If the square were rotated through 90° counterclockwise about O while we were not looking, we would be unable to tell anything had been changed. (Try it!) In carrying out that rotation, we have mapped the square onto itself. Alternatively, we can consider the situation in which the square of cardboard is fitted into a corresponding square hole. If the square is picked up and rotated through 90°, it can be fitted back into the hole.

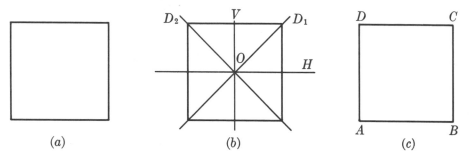

Figure 13.1

We can consider the set of rigid motions which move the square in such a way that it can be put back into the square hole. In these cases we can tell that the square has been moved only if it is marked in some way. We list these motions.

(1) R_{90}, a counterclockwise rotation of 90° about O

(2) R_{180}, a counterclockwise rotation of 180° about O

(3) R_{270}, a counterclockwise rotation of 270° about O

(4) H, a rotation of 180° about the line H

(5) V, a rotation of 180° about the line V

(6) D_1, a rotation of 180° about the line D_1

(7) D_2, a rotation of 180° about the line D_2

Finally, we include the identity or neutral motion.

(8) R_0, a counterclockwise rotation of 0° about O

(Note that a rotation of 360° replaces the square in its original position; thus, R_{360} is identical with R_0.) This set

$$\{R_0, R_{90}, R_{180}, R_{270}, H, V, D_1, D_2\}$$

is called the set of motions of the square.

Note that a rotation of 180° about line H involves rotating the square in 3-space. Try it with a cardboard model; observe that such a motion is impossible if the cardboard must remain on a table top (that is, in a plane). If we wished to consider the square as remaining in a plane, we would obtain the same result as motion H by considering a reflection of the square in the line H.

All of the above motions can be described as permutations of the vertices A, B, C, and D of the square (Figure 13.1(c)). For example, R_{270} will correspond to permutation

$$\begin{pmatrix} A & B & C & D \\ D & A & B & C \end{pmatrix}.$$

We use the equals sign here to mean "corresponds to" and write

$$R_{270} = \begin{pmatrix} A & B & C & D \\ D & A & B & C \end{pmatrix}.$$

Similarly,

$$V = \begin{pmatrix} A & B & C & D \\ B & A & D & C \end{pmatrix}.$$

Of course we will obtain only eight such permutations in this way, so that not every permutation on $\{A, B, C, D\}$ will correspond to a rigid motion of the square.

We will see in the exercises that the number of elements in the set of rigid motions of a geometrical figure depends on the symmetry possessed by the figure.

EXERCISE 13.3

What rigid motions carry the following figures into themselves? State the corresponding permutations in each case. (A diagram is essential.)

1. A triangle of three unequal sides

2. An isosceles triangle

3. A quadrilateral with four unequal sides

4. An equilateral triangle

5. A nonsquare rectangle

6. A nonsquare rhombus

7. A square

8. A regular pentagon

9. A regular hexagon

10. A regular octagon

11. How many permutations are there corresponding to the motions of a regular polygon of n sides?

12. Which permutations on $\{A, B, C, D\}$ do not correspond to motions of the square?

13.4. Some Additional Sets

In addition to the sets of permutations and motions that we have just studied, and the sets of numbers that we have studied earlier, there are sets of other types of elements that will prove useful to us as examples.

(1) *The Set of Translations in the Plane*

The transformation performed by the mapping

$$(x, y) \rightarrow (u, v) ,$$

with $u = x + h$ and $v = y + k$, is a translation of the plane. We may use the symbol $T_{h,k}$ to refer to such a transformation and write

$$T_{h,k} \colon (x, y) \rightarrow (x + h, y + k) ,$$

or, since this merely indicates that the image of x is $x + h$ and that of y is $y + k$, we often write

$$T_{h,k} \begin{bmatrix} x \\ y \end{bmatrix} = \begin{bmatrix} x + h \\ y + k \end{bmatrix}$$

to indicate the same thing. The latter is a useful notation when we study matrices. Thus, for example, $T_{2,5}$ is the transformation under which

$$(x, y) \rightarrow (x + 2, y + 5) ,$$

that is,

$$T_{2,5} \begin{bmatrix} x \\ y \end{bmatrix} = \begin{bmatrix} x + 2 \\ y + 5 \end{bmatrix} .$$

The set consisting of all such translations $T_{h,k}$ will contain an infinite number of elements. It will contain the identity or neutral translation $T_{0,0}$ under which

$$(x, y) \rightarrow (x, y) .$$

(2) *The Set of Rotations in the Plane*

The transformation performed by the mapping

$$(x, y) \rightarrow (u, v) ,$$

with $u = x \cos \theta - y \sin \theta$ and $v = x \sin \theta + y \cos \theta$, is a rotation of the plane through angle θ measured counterclockwise about the origin. We may use the symbol $R_{(\theta)}$ to refer to such a rotation. Thus, $R_{(\pi/4)}$ is the transformation under which

$$(x, y) \rightarrow \left(\frac{x - y}{\sqrt{2}}, \; \frac{x + y}{\sqrt{2}} \right).$$

We write

$$R_{(\pi/4)} : (x, y) \rightarrow \left(\frac{x - y}{\sqrt{2}}, \frac{x + y}{\sqrt{2}}\right)$$

or

$$R_{(\pi/4)}\begin{bmatrix} x \\ y \end{bmatrix} = \begin{bmatrix} \dfrac{x - y}{\sqrt{2}} \\ \dfrac{x + y}{\sqrt{2}} \end{bmatrix}.$$

Again, the set of all such rotations $R_{(\theta)}$ will contain an infinite number of elements. It will contain the identity or neutral rotation $R_{(0)}$ under which

$$(x, y) \rightarrow (x, y) .$$

(3)   A Set of Reflections

The finite set $\{I, R_x, R_y, R_{xy}\}$ consisting of the following four reflections in the plane will be used as an example in this chapter.

$I: (x, y) \rightarrow (x, y)$; the identity or neutral mapping

$R_x: (x, y) \rightarrow (x, -y)$; reflection in the x-axis

$R_y: (x, y) \rightarrow (-x, y)$; reflection in the y-axis

$R_{xy}: (x, y) \rightarrow (-x, -y)$; reflection in both the x- and y-axes,
that is, reflection in the origin

We will also write

$$R_x\begin{bmatrix} x \\ y \end{bmatrix} = \begin{bmatrix} x \\ -y \end{bmatrix}$$

etc.   There should be no confusion between these symbols for reflections and the symbol $R_{(\theta)}$ for rotations. The reader is encouraged to draw some diagrams illustrating the effect of these reflections on various geometrical figures.

(4)   Sets of Linear Transformations

The elements in (2) and (3) above are special cases of the more general type of mapping in the plane defined by

$$(x, y) \rightarrow (ax + by, cx + dy) .$$

These mappings are known as linear transformations. Thus, for example, the rotation $R_{(\pi/4)}$ given in (2) above is a linear transformation with

$$a = -b = c = d = \frac{1}{\sqrt{2}} .$$

(5) *Sets of Functions*

Sets of functions defined on a certain domain will be used as examples in this chapter. We have already pointed out that permutations are functions, as, indeed, are the transformations we have described.

(6) *Sets of 2 × 2 Real Matrices*

A 2×2 real matrix is a rectangular array consisting of two rows and two columns of real numbers.

$$\begin{bmatrix} a_{11} & a_{12} \\ a_{21} & a_{22} \end{bmatrix}$$

We use a_{ij} to denote the entry or component in row i and column j. Sets of 2×2 real matrices will be used as examples in this chapter.

EXERCISE 13.4

1. Write the mappings corresponding to the following symbols.
   (a) $T_{3,4}$ (b) $T_{-2,1}$ (c) $T_{0,0}$ (d) $T_{0,-3}$ (e) $T_{-3,-3}$
   (f) $R_{(\pi/3)}$ (g) $R_{(\pi/2)}$ (h) $R_{(\pi)}$ (i) $R_{(-\pi/4)}$ (j) $R_{(3\pi/2)}$

2. State the transformations which translate the points with co-ordinates
   (a) $(3, 2)$ (b) $(-5, 2)$ (c) $(-4, 0)$ (d) $(2, -3)$ (e)$(-3, -3)$
   to the origin.

3. State the transformations which translate the points with integral co-ordinates on the following ellipse to the origin.
   $$\frac{x^2}{9} + \frac{y^2}{4} = 1.$$

4. State the transformations which rotate the plane so that the points with the following co-ordinates lie on the x-axis.
   (a) $(1, \sqrt{3})$ (b) $(-1, \sqrt{3})$ (c) $(-1, -\sqrt{3})$ (d) $(1, -\sqrt{3})$

5. State the transformations which rotate the plane so that the points with the following co-ordinates lie on the y-axis.
   (a) $\left(\frac{\sqrt{3}}{2}, \frac{1}{2}\right)$ (b) $\left(-\frac{\sqrt{3}}{2}, \frac{1}{2}\right)$ (c) $\left(-\frac{\sqrt{3}}{2}, -\frac{1}{2}\right)$ (d) $\left(\frac{\sqrt{3}}{2}, -\frac{1}{2}\right)$

6. State the transformations representing the linear functions
   $$f_{a, b}: x \rightarrow ax + b,$$
   if $a, b \in I$ and $a^2 + b^2 = 4$.

7. Write the set of all 2×2 real matrices with $a_{12} = a_{21} = 0$ and $a_{11}, a_{22} \in I$, where $a_{11}^2 + a_{22}^2 \leq 9$.

13.5. Binary Operations

A binary operation Θ on the elements of a set $\{a, b, c, \cdots\}$ is an operation that associates with each pair of elements of the set a unique element to which we give the symbol $a \Theta b$.   (Symbols such as $a \circ b$, $a \times b$, etc., may also be used.) In considering pairs of elements of the set, we will consider a and a, b and b, c and c, etc., as suitable pairs so that we will have elements $a \Theta a$, $b \Theta b$, $c \Theta c$, etc., formed by the binary operation.

It sometimes proves useful to think of a binary operation as a meat-grinding machine with two openings at the top into which elements can be stuffed and a single opening at the bottom from which the result emerges.   This emphasizes that a binary operation acts on *pairs* of elements to produce in each case a single element. Note also that the machine has a left opening and a right opening so that both $a \Theta b$ and $b \Theta a$ are produced, and there is no reason to assume that these are the same element.

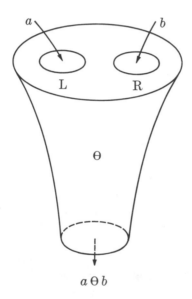

Figure 13.2

Binary Operation Machine

We are already familiar with the binary operations of addition and multiplication of real numbers.   Indeed we are so familiar with these operations that their application is automatic.   This sometimes clouds the fact that these operations are binary.   Given 5, 6, and 7 to add, for example, we may lose sight of the fact that the addition is performed mentally on two integers at a time: $(5 + 6) + 7$, $5 + (6 + 7)$, etc.

In this section, and the next two, we wish to consider binary operations on the elements of the sets we have just studied, sets of permutations, motions, etc. In so doing, we normally will refer to the operation Θ as the "product operation" and to $a \Theta b$ as the "product" of a and b, even though Θ may bear absolutely no relation to the multiplication of real numbers.

The following example indicates the possibility of binary operations on real numbers apart from ordinary addition and multiplication.

Example 1. Find the following products if $a \Theta b$ is defined to be the greatest common factor of a and b.

(a) $6 \Theta 9$ (b) $4 \Theta 7$ (c) $-5 \Theta 5$

Solution:

(a) $\qquad\qquad\qquad 6 \Theta 9 = 3 .$

(b) $\qquad\qquad\qquad 4 \Theta 7 = 1 .$

(c) $\qquad\qquad\qquad -5 \Theta 5 = 5 .$

Example 2. Find the following products if $a \Theta b = a + ab$.

(a) $5 \Theta 3$ (b) $3 \Theta 5$ (c) $3 \Theta 3$

Solution:

(a) $\qquad\qquad\qquad 5 \Theta 3 = 5 + 5(3) = 20 .$

(b) $\qquad\qquad\qquad 3 \Theta 5 = 3 + 3(5) = 18 .$

(c) $\qquad\qquad\qquad 3 \Theta 3 = 3 + 3(3) = 12 .$

Note that $5 \Theta 3 \neq 3 \Theta 5$ for this binary operation Θ.

Binary operations called addition and multiplication can be defined for 2×2 real matrices. Addition is defined in terms of the addition of corresponding components.

$$\begin{bmatrix} a_{11} & a_{12} \\ a_{21} & a_{22} \end{bmatrix} + \begin{bmatrix} b_{11} & b_{12} \\ b_{21} & b_{22} \end{bmatrix} = \begin{bmatrix} a_{11} + b_{11} & a_{12} + b_{12} \\ a_{21} + b_{21} & a_{22} + b_{22} \end{bmatrix}$$

The definition for multiplication is more complicated.

$$\begin{bmatrix} a_{11} & a_{12} \\ a_{21} & a_{22} \end{bmatrix} \begin{bmatrix} b_{11} & b_{12} \\ b_{21} & b_{22} \end{bmatrix} = \begin{bmatrix} a_{11} b_{11} + a_{12} b_{21} & a_{11} b_{12} + a_{12} b_{22} \\ a_{21} b_{11} + a_{22} b_{21} & a_{21} b_{12} + a_{22} b_{22} \end{bmatrix}$$

$$= \begin{bmatrix} c_{11} & c_{12} \\ c_{21} & c_{22} \end{bmatrix} .$$

As an aid to remembering this definition, note that c_{ij}, the component in row i and column j of the product matrix, is the sum of the products of corresponding elements of row i of the left matrix and column j of the right matrix.

$$c_{11} = a_{11} \, b_{11} + a_{12} \, b_{21} = \underset{row \ 1}{(a_{11} \quad a_{12})} \binom{b_{11}}{b_{21}} \quad column \ 1$$

$$c_{12} = a_{11} \, b_{12} + a_{12} \, b_{22} = \underset{row \ 1}{(a_{11} \quad a_{12})} \binom{b_{12}}{b_{22}} \quad column \ 2$$

etc.

Example 3. Find the sum and product of the matrices

$$A = \begin{bmatrix} 4 & -1 \\ -2 & 3 \end{bmatrix} \quad \text{and} \quad B = \begin{bmatrix} -3 & 1 \\ 5 & 2 \end{bmatrix}.$$

Solution:

$$A + B = \begin{bmatrix} 4 & -1 \\ -2 & 3 \end{bmatrix} + \begin{bmatrix} -3 & 1 \\ 5 & 2 \end{bmatrix} = \begin{bmatrix} 4 - 3 & -1 + 1 \\ -2 + 5 & 3 + 2 \end{bmatrix}$$

$$= \begin{bmatrix} 1 & 0 \\ 3 & 5 \end{bmatrix}.$$

$$AB = \begin{bmatrix} 4 & -1 \\ -2 & 3 \end{bmatrix} \begin{bmatrix} -3 & 1 \\ 5 & 2 \end{bmatrix} = \begin{bmatrix} (4)(-3) + (-1)(5) & (4)(1) + (-1)(2) \\ (-2)(-3) + (3)(5) & (-2)(1) + (3)(2) \end{bmatrix}$$

$$= \begin{bmatrix} -17 & 2 \\ 21 & 4 \end{bmatrix}.$$

EXERCISE 13.5

1. Find   (i) $5 \ominus 2$ (ii) $2 \ominus 5$ (iii) $3 \ominus 6$

             (iv) $5 \ominus 5$ (v) $(2 \ominus 5) \ominus 3$ (vi) $6 \ominus (2 \ominus 3)$

for the binary operations defined as follows.

(a) $a \ominus b = a - b$.

(b) $a \ominus b = a^2 + b^2$.

(c) $a \ominus b = (a + b)^2$.

(d) $a \ominus b = 2a + 3b$.

(e) $a \ominus b = \dfrac{a}{b}$.

(f) $a \ominus b = $ maximum of a and b.

(g) $a \ominus b = $ l.c.m. of a and b.

(h) $a \ominus b = a$.

(i) $a \ominus b = b$.

(j) $a \ominus b = \dfrac{a + b}{2}$.

(k) $a \ominus b = a^b$.

(l) $a \ominus b = a - ab$.

(m) $a \ominus b = $ remainder when a is divided by b.

(n) $a \ominus b = $ remainder when b is divided by a.

2. Find $A + B$, $B + A$, AB, and BA in the following.

(a) $A = \begin{bmatrix} 2 & -1 \\ 4 & 7 \end{bmatrix}$, $\qquad\qquad$ $B = \begin{bmatrix} 2 & 1 \\ 0 & -4 \end{bmatrix}$.

(b) $A = \begin{bmatrix} 1 & -5 \\ 4 & 2 \end{bmatrix}$, $\qquad\qquad$ $B = \begin{bmatrix} 4 & 1 \\ 5 & 3 \end{bmatrix}$.

(c) $A = \begin{bmatrix} 4 & 1 \\ 3 & 1 \end{bmatrix}$, $\qquad\qquad$ $B = \begin{bmatrix} 1 & -1 \\ 5 & 0 \end{bmatrix}$.

(d) $A = \begin{bmatrix} 2 & 1 \\ 3 & 1 \end{bmatrix}$, $\qquad\qquad$ $B = \begin{bmatrix} -3 & 1 \\ 5 & 2 \end{bmatrix}$.

(e) $A = \begin{bmatrix} 4 & 2 \\ 5 & 1 \end{bmatrix}$, $\qquad\qquad$ $B = \begin{bmatrix} 3 & 2 \\ 4 & 0 \end{bmatrix}$.

(f) $A = \begin{bmatrix} 1 & 0 \\ 0 & -1 \end{bmatrix}$, $\qquad\qquad$ $B = \begin{bmatrix} 0 & 1 \\ -1 & 0 \end{bmatrix}$.

(g) $A = \begin{bmatrix} \frac{1}{2} & 0 \\ 0 & \frac{1}{4} \end{bmatrix}$, $\qquad\qquad$ $B = \begin{bmatrix} 2 & 0 \\ 0 & 4 \end{bmatrix}$.

13.6. Products of Permutations • Products of Motions

Consider the two permutations

$$P = \begin{pmatrix} 1 & 2 & 3 & 4 \\ 4 & 1 & 2 & 3 \end{pmatrix} \quad \text{and} \quad Q = \begin{pmatrix} 1 & 2 & 3 & 4 \\ 2 & 1 & 4 & 3 \end{pmatrix}.$$

Both of these permutations produce rearrangements of the four symbols 1, 2, 3, 4. Now consider the result of first performing permutation P and then permutation Q. We trace the result on the symbols of such a combination of permutations.

$$\begin{array}{ccc} \text{under } P & \text{under } Q \\ 1 \longrightarrow 4 \longrightarrow 3 \\ 2 \longrightarrow 1 \longrightarrow 2 \\ 3 \longrightarrow 2 \longrightarrow 1 \\ 4 \longrightarrow 3 \longrightarrow 4 \end{array}$$

The overall result of this combination of permutations is thus equal to the permutation

$$\begin{pmatrix} 1 & 2 & 3 & 4 \\ 3 & 2 & 1 & 4 \end{pmatrix}.$$

We define this permutation to be the product $P \ominus Q$ of the permutations P and Q (in that order).

DEFINITION.   The product $P \ominus Q$ of two permutations P and Q on the same symbols is the single permutation equal to the successive performance of permutations P and Q (P first, Q second).

Example 1.   Find the product $Q \ominus P$ for the permutations above.

Solution: We write

$$Q \ominus P = \begin{pmatrix} 1 & 2 & 3 & 4 \\ 2 & 1 & 4 & 3 \end{pmatrix} \ominus \begin{pmatrix} 1 & 2 & 3 & 4 \\ 4 & 1 & 2 & 3 \end{pmatrix}$$

and trace the "fate" of each symbol as a result of the successive application of Q and P.   This is normally done mentally.

$$
\begin{aligned}
1 &\longrightarrow 2 \longrightarrow 1 \\
2 &\longrightarrow 1 \longrightarrow 4 \\
3 &\longrightarrow 4 \longrightarrow 3 \\
4 &\longrightarrow 3 \longrightarrow 2
\end{aligned}
$$

Therefore

$$Q \ominus P = \begin{pmatrix} 1 & 2 & 3 & 4 \\ 1 & 4 & 3 & 2 \end{pmatrix}.$$

We note that $Q \ominus P \neq P \ominus Q$ so that this binary operation, multiplication or combination of permutations, is not always commutative.

Example 2.   Find $P^2 = P \ominus P$ and $P^2 \ominus P$ if

$$P = \begin{pmatrix} 1 & 2 & 3 & 4 & 5 \\ 2 & 4 & 1 & 5 & 3 \end{pmatrix}.$$

Solution:

$$P \ominus P = \begin{pmatrix} 1 & 2 & 3 & 4 & 5 \\ 2 & 4 & 1 & 5 & 3 \end{pmatrix} \ominus \begin{pmatrix} 1 & 2 & 3 & 4 & 5 \\ 2 & 4 & 1 & 5 & 3 \end{pmatrix} = \begin{pmatrix} 1 & 2 & 3 & 4 & 5 \\ 4 & 5 & 2 & 3 & 1 \end{pmatrix}.$$

Therefore

$$P^2 = \begin{pmatrix} 1 & 2 & 3 & 4 & 5 \\ 4 & 5 & 2 & 3 & 1 \end{pmatrix}.$$

$$P^2 \ominus P = \begin{pmatrix} 1 & 2 & 3 & 4 & 5 \\ 4 & 5 & 2 & 3 & 1 \end{pmatrix} \ominus \begin{pmatrix} 1 & 2 & 3 & 4 & 5 \\ 2 & 4 & 1 & 5 & 3 \end{pmatrix} = \begin{pmatrix} 1 & 2 & 3 & 4 & 5 \\ 5 & 3 & 4 & 1 & 2 \end{pmatrix}.$$

We have already seen that motions of rectilinear figures (squares, triangles, etc.) may be studied by studying the permutations of the vertices of these figures. Thus it is natural, in the light of our definition of the product of two permutations, to define the product $M_1 \ominus M_2$ of two motions M_1 and M_2 to be the single motion equal to the application of motion M_1 followed by the application of motion M_2.

Example 3. Find $H \ominus R_{90}$ and $R_{90} \ominus H$ for the motions H and R_{90} of the square. (See Section 13.3.)

Solution: By definition, $H \ominus R_{90}$ is the result of carrying out motion H, and then motion R_{90}.

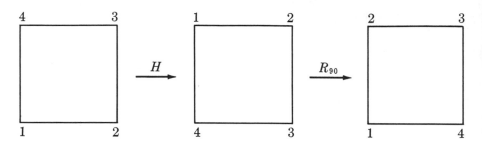

Thus $H \ominus R_{90}$ is the motion

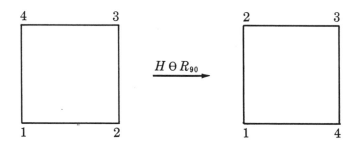

so that $H \ominus R_{90} = D_1$.

Similarly,

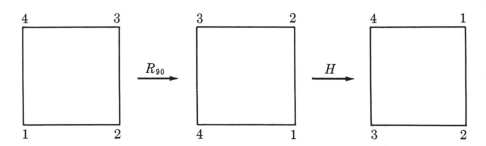

so that $R_{90} \ominus H = D_2$.

Again we see that $H \ominus R_{90} \neq R_{90} \ominus H$, so that multiplication of motions is not necessarily commutative.

Example 4.   Set up a multiplication table for the motions R_0, R_{180}, D_1, D_2 of the rhombus which are as indicated in the diagram.

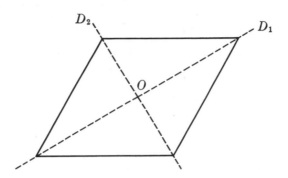

Solution: R_0 and R_{180} are counterclockwise rotations of 0° and 180° about O and D_1 and D_2 are reflections in the diagonals D_1 and D_2.

The following multiplication table may be checked.

$\ominus$	R_0	R_{180}	D_1	D_2
R_0	R_0	R_{180}	D_1	D_2
R_{180}	R_{180}	R_0	D_2	D_1
D_1	D_1	D_2	R_0	R_{180}
D_2	D_2	D_1	R_{180}	R_0

Note that the entries in the table follow the pattern shown below in which the first motion is in the left column and the second is in the top row.

$\ominus$	P
.	.
.	.
.	.
Q	$\cdots Q \ominus P \cdots$
.	.
.	.
.	.

EXERCISE 13.6

1. Find $P \ominus Q$, $Q \ominus P$, P^2, and Q^2 for the following permutations.

   (a) $P = \begin{pmatrix} 1 & 2 & 3 \\ 3 & 1 & 2 \end{pmatrix}$, $\quad Q = \begin{pmatrix} 1 & 2 & 3 \\ 2 & 1 & 3 \end{pmatrix}$.

   (b) $P = \begin{pmatrix} 1 & 2 & 3 & 4 \\ 4 & 1 & 2 & 3 \end{pmatrix}$, $\quad Q = \begin{pmatrix} 1 & 2 & 3 & 4 \\ 2 & 1 & 3 & 4 \end{pmatrix}$.

   (c) $P = \begin{pmatrix} 1 & 2 & 3 & 4 & 5 \\ 5 & 1 & 4 & 3 & 2 \end{pmatrix}$, $\quad Q = \begin{pmatrix} 1 & 2 & 3 & 4 & 5 \\ 2 & 1 & 4 & 3 & 5 \end{pmatrix}$.

   (d) $P = \begin{pmatrix} a & b & c & d & e \\ c & e & d & a & b \end{pmatrix}$, $\quad Q = \begin{pmatrix} a & b & c & d & e \\ b & c & d & e & a \end{pmatrix}$.

   (e) $P = \begin{pmatrix} 1 & 2 & 3 & 4 & 5 & 6 & 7 & 8 & 9 \\ 4 & 1 & 2 & 3 & 8 & 7 & 9 & 6 & 5 \end{pmatrix}$, $Q = \begin{pmatrix} 1 & 2 & 3 & 4 & 5 & 6 & 7 & 8 & 9 \\ 5 & 2 & 7 & 3 & 1 & 4 & 8 & 6 & 9 \end{pmatrix}$.

2. Find $(P \ominus Q) \ominus R$ and $P \ominus (Q \ominus R)$ in the following.

   (a) P and Q from question (1a), $R = \begin{pmatrix} 1 & 2 & 3 \\ 3 & 2 & 1 \end{pmatrix}$.

   (b) P and Q from question (1b), $R = \begin{pmatrix} 1 & 2 & 3 & 4 \\ 2 & 3 & 4 & 1 \end{pmatrix}$.

   (c) P and Q from question (1c), $R = \begin{pmatrix} 1 & 2 & 3 & 4 & 5 \\ 2 & 3 & 4 & 1 & 5 \end{pmatrix}$.

   (d) P and Q from question (1d), $R = \begin{pmatrix} a & b & c & d & e \\ b & c & a & e & d \end{pmatrix}$.

3. From the results of question (2), draw a conclusion regarding the multiplication of permutations.

4. If E_1, E_2, and E_3 refer to the reflections of the equilateral triangle ABC as shown, and R_0, R_{120}, R_{240}, to the usual rotations about the centre, find

   (a) $E_1 \ominus R_{120}$,   (b) $E_2 \ominus E_3$,   (c) $R_{240} \ominus E_2$.

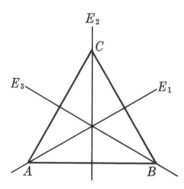

5. The symbols in (a) to (l) refer to motions of the square (Section 8.3). Find the following products.

(a) $R_{90} \ominus R_{180}$ (b) $R_{180} \ominus R_{90}$ (c) $R_{90} \ominus R_{90}$

(d) $R_{180} \ominus R_{180}$ (e) $H \ominus V$ (f) $V \ominus H$

(g) $R_{90} \ominus D_1$ (h) $D_1 \ominus R_{90}$ (i) $D_1 \ominus D_2$

(j) $D_2 \ominus D_1$ (k) $D_1 \ominus V$ (l) $H \ominus R_{270}$

6. Let $\{I, R_x, R_y, R_{xy}\}$ be the set consisting of the identity mapping I and the reflections about x-axis, the y-axis, and the origin, respectively. (See Section 13.4.) Complete the following multiplication table in which $R_x \ominus R_y$ means a reflection in the x-axis followed by a reflection in the y-axis, etc.

$\ominus$	I	R_x	R_y	R_{xy}
I	I	R_x	*	*
R_x	*	*	*	*
R_y	R_y	*	*	*
R_{xy}	*	*	*	I

13.7. Products of Transformations • Products of Functions

In this section we will introduce a binary operation on the elements of a set of transformations.

It often happens that a mapping or transformation T can be followed by a second transformation S and the overall result is equal to the performance of a single mapping which, by definition, we call the product of the two transformations.

DEFINITION. The product ST of two transformations S and T is the single transformation which is equal to performing first T and then S.

Note that there is no misprint here; ST indicates T first, S second. The reason for using this order in the symbol will be seen in our examples. Symbols such as $S \ominus T$ or $S \circ T$ could also be used to indicate this product, but ST seems to be more convenient.

We have used the phrase "transformation which is equal to" in our definition. We should point out that, by definition, two transformations are equal if they are mappings of the same set and if each element of the set has the same image under the two transformations. Thus, if $T(a)$ represents the image of element a under transformation T, then by definition, $T = S$ if T and S are both mappings of a set A and $T(a) = S(a)$ for all $a \in A$.

Example 1. Find $T_{2,3}\ T_{4,6}$ if

$$T_{2,3}\begin{bmatrix} x \\ y \end{bmatrix} = \begin{bmatrix} x+2 \\ y+3 \end{bmatrix} \quad \text{and} \quad T_{4,6}\begin{bmatrix} x \\ y \end{bmatrix} = \begin{bmatrix} x+4 \\ y+6 \end{bmatrix}, \quad x,\ y \in Re.$$

Solution: By definition,

$$(T_{2,3}\ T_{4,6})\begin{bmatrix} x \\ y \end{bmatrix} = T_{2,3}\left(T_{4,6}\begin{bmatrix} x \\ y \end{bmatrix}\right) \qquad \text{(Perform } T_{4,6} \text{ first.)}$$

$$= T_{2,3}\begin{bmatrix} x+4 \\ y+6 \end{bmatrix} \qquad \text{(Then perform } T_{2,3}.)$$

$$= \begin{bmatrix} (x+4)+2 \\ (y+6)+3 \end{bmatrix}$$

$$= \begin{bmatrix} x+(4+2) \\ y+(6+3) \end{bmatrix}$$

$$= \begin{bmatrix} x+6 \\ y+9 \end{bmatrix} = T_{6,9}\begin{bmatrix} x \\ y \end{bmatrix}.$$

Therefore

$$T_{2,3}\ T_{4,6} = T_{6,9}.$$

The result of performing the translation $T_{4,6}$ first, followed by the translation $T_{2,3}$, is equal to the single translation $T_{6,9}$.

Example 2. Find ST and TS if

$$S\begin{bmatrix} x \\ y \end{bmatrix} = \begin{bmatrix} 2x+y \\ x+3y \end{bmatrix} \quad \text{and} \quad T\begin{bmatrix} x \\ y \end{bmatrix} = \begin{bmatrix} 4x-y \\ -x+2y \end{bmatrix}.$$

Solution: By definition,

$$(ST)\begin{bmatrix} x \\ y \end{bmatrix} = S\left(T\begin{bmatrix} x \\ y \end{bmatrix}\right) \qquad \text{(Perform } T \text{ first.)}$$

$$= S\begin{bmatrix} 4x-y \\ -x+2y \end{bmatrix} \qquad \text{(Then perform } S.)$$

$$= \begin{bmatrix} 2(4x-y)+(-x+2y) \\ (4x-y)+3(-x+2y) \end{bmatrix}$$

$$= \begin{bmatrix} 7x \\ x+5y \end{bmatrix}.$$

Therefore $ST = R$, where

$$R\begin{bmatrix} x \\ y \end{bmatrix} = \begin{bmatrix} 7x \\ x+5y \end{bmatrix}.$$

Also

$$(TS)\begin{bmatrix} x \\ y \end{bmatrix} = T\left(S\begin{bmatrix} x \\ y \end{bmatrix}\right)$$

$$= T\begin{bmatrix} 2x + y \\ x + 3y \end{bmatrix}$$

$$= \begin{bmatrix} 4(2x + y) - (x + 3y) \\ -(2x + y) + 2(x + 3y) \end{bmatrix}$$

$$= \begin{bmatrix} 7x + y \\ 5y \end{bmatrix}.$$

Therefore $TS = U$, where

$$U\begin{bmatrix} x \\ y \end{bmatrix} = \begin{bmatrix} 7x + y \\ 5y \end{bmatrix}.$$

Note that $TS \neq ST$ for these transformations S and T.

Example 3. Show that $R_{(\pi/4)} R_{(\pi/4)} = R_{(\pi/2)}$, where

$$R_{(\alpha)}\begin{bmatrix} x \\ y \end{bmatrix} = \begin{bmatrix} x \cos \alpha - y \sin \alpha \\ x \sin \alpha + y \cos \alpha \end{bmatrix}.$$

Solution:

$$x \cos \frac{\pi}{4} - y \sin \frac{\pi}{4} = \frac{1}{\sqrt{2}} (x - y)$$

$$x \sin \frac{\pi}{4} + y \cos \frac{\pi}{4} = \frac{1}{\sqrt{2}} (x + y)$$

Therefore

$$(R_{(\pi/4)} R_{(\pi/4)})\begin{bmatrix} x \\ y \end{bmatrix} = R_{(\pi/4)}\left(R_{(\pi/4)}\begin{bmatrix} x \\ y \end{bmatrix}\right)$$

$$= R_{(\pi/4)} \begin{bmatrix} \dfrac{1}{\sqrt{2}} (x - y) \\ \dfrac{1}{\sqrt{2}} (x + y) \end{bmatrix}$$

$$= \begin{bmatrix} \dfrac{1}{\sqrt{2}}\left\{\dfrac{1}{\sqrt{2}} (x - y) - \dfrac{1}{\sqrt{2}} (x + y)\right\} \\ \dfrac{1}{\sqrt{2}}\left\{\dfrac{1}{\sqrt{2}} (x - y) + \dfrac{1}{\sqrt{2}} (x + y)\right\} \end{bmatrix}$$

$$= \begin{bmatrix} -y \\ x \end{bmatrix}.$$

Also

$$x \cos \frac{\pi}{2} - y \sin \frac{\pi}{2} = -y ,$$

$$x \sin \frac{\pi}{2} + y \cos \frac{\pi}{2} = x .$$

Therefore

$$R_{(\pi/2)}\begin{bmatrix} x \\ y \end{bmatrix} = \begin{bmatrix} -y \\ x \end{bmatrix},$$

and so

$$R_{(\pi/4)}\, R_{(\pi/4)} = R_{(\pi/2)}.$$

We may define the product $f \ominus g$ of two functions f and g to be the function $f(g)$. (We assume that the domain and range of f and g are such that $f(g)$ is indeed a function.) Again, $f \circ g$ is sometimes used to indicate this product.

Example 4. Find $f \ominus g$ and $g \ominus f$ if f and g are the functions

$$f : x \rightarrow 4x - 3, \qquad x \in Re,$$
$$g : x \rightarrow -2x + 5, \qquad x \in Re.$$

Solution:

$$f(g) \text{ is the function: } x \xrightarrow{g} -2x + 5$$
$$\xrightarrow{f} 4(-2x + 5) - 3,$$

that is, the function

$$f \ominus g : x \rightarrow -8x + 17, \qquad x \in Re.$$

$$g(f) \text{ is the function: } x \xrightarrow{f} 4x - 3$$
$$\xrightarrow{g} -2(4x - 3) + 5,$$

that is, the function

$$g \ominus f : x \rightarrow -8x + 11, \qquad x \in Re.$$

Note that $f \ominus g \neq g \ominus f$ for this binary operation $\ominus$.

EXERCISE 13.7

1. Find the products, in both orders, of the following pairs of translations.
   (a) $T_{3,4}$ and $T_{1,1}$
   (b) $T_{5,2}$ and $T_{3,-2}$
   (c) $T_{2,4}$ and $T_{-2,-4}$
   (d) $T_{-1,-3}$ and $T_{-2,4}$

2. Show algebraically the truth of the following statements regarding rotations.
   (a) $R_{(\pi/2)}\, R_{(\pi/2)} = R_{(\pi)}$.
   (b) $R_{(\pi)}\, R_{(\pi)} = R_0$.
   (c) $R_{(\pi/6)}\, R_{(\pi/3)} = R_{(\pi/2)}$.
   (d) $R_{(\pi/3)}\, R_{(\pi/6)} = R_{(\pi/2)}$.

3. Find $f \ominus g$ and $g \ominus f$ (that is, $f(g)$ and $g(f)$) for the following functions defined on Re.
   (a) $f : x \rightarrow 2x + 7, \quad g : x \rightarrow 3x - 4$
   (b) $f : x \rightarrow -3x + 4, \quad g : x \rightarrow -6x + 1$
   (c) $f : x \rightarrow x^2 + 3, \quad g : x \rightarrow 3x - 2$
   (d) $f : x \rightarrow x^2 - x + 1, \quad g : x \rightarrow x^2 + x + 1$

13.8. Groupoids

We have been discussing binary operations $\ominus$ on the elements of a given set. We have seen that $\ominus$ acts on a pair of set elements a and b (in that order) to produce the element which we call $a \ominus b$.   Now $a \ominus b$ may or may not be an element of the given set.   If $a \ominus b$ is an element of the given set for every pair of elements a and b of the set, then we say that the set is closed under the binary operation $\ominus$.

We define the following algebraic system.

DEFINITION.   A groupoid is an algebraic system consisting of a set S and an operation $\ominus$, which is such that S is closed under $\ominus$.

A groupoid requires the following three things:
  (i) a set S,
  (ii) a binary operation $\ominus$ defined on the elements of S,
  (iii) closure of S under $\ominus$, that is,

$$a \ominus b \in S \quad \text{whenever } a, b \in S.$$

Example 1.   Is the set of positive integers a groupoid under the binary operation $\ominus$ which is such that $a \ominus b = a - b$?

Solution: $3 \ominus 5 = 3 - 5 = -2$, which is not a positive integer.   This algebraic system is not a groupoid.

Example 2.   Is the system in Example (1) a groupoid if $\ominus$ is such that $a \ominus b = 3a + 4b$?

Solution: $3a + 4b$ is a positive integer for every pair (a, b) of positive integers; this system is a groupoid.

Example 3.   Is the set of permutations on the symbols $\{A, B, C\}$ a groupoid under the binary operation $\ominus$ of multiplication of permutations defined in Section 13.6?

Solution: The product of two permutations on $\{A, B, C\}$ is always a permutation on the same set.   Let P be the permutation

$$P = \begin{pmatrix} A & B & C \\ A^* & B^* & C^* \end{pmatrix};$$

then (A^*, B^*, C^*) is simply a rearrangement of (A, B, C) so that we may write Q as

$$\begin{pmatrix} A^* & B^* & C^* \\ A^{**} & B^{**} & C^{**} \end{pmatrix},$$

and then

$$P \ominus Q = \begin{pmatrix} A & B & C \\ A* & B* & C* \end{pmatrix} \ominus \begin{pmatrix} A* & B* & C* \\ A** & B** & C** \end{pmatrix} = \begin{pmatrix} A & B & C \\ A** & B** & C** \end{pmatrix},$$

which is a permutation on $\{A, B, C\}$.   For example, if

$$P = \begin{pmatrix} 1 & 2 & 3 \\ 3 & 1 & 2 \end{pmatrix} \quad \text{and} \quad Q = \begin{pmatrix} 1 & 2 & 3 \\ 1 & 3 & 2 \end{pmatrix},$$

we may rewrite Q as

$$\begin{pmatrix} 3 & 1 & 2 \\ 2 & 1 & 3 \end{pmatrix},$$

and then

$$P \ominus Q = \begin{pmatrix} 1 & 2 & 3 \\ 3 & 1 & 2 \end{pmatrix} \ominus \begin{pmatrix} 3 & 1 & 2 \\ 2 & 1 & 3 \end{pmatrix} = \begin{pmatrix} 1 & 2 & 3 \\ 2 & 1 & 3 \end{pmatrix}.$$

EXERCISE 13.8

Examine the following algebraic systems.   (The set is given and the operation $\ominus$ is described or defined.)   Which of the systems are groupoids?

1. (a) I; $\ominus$ is ordinary addition, $a \ominus b = a + b$.
   (b) Ra; $\ominus$ is ordinary multiplication, $a \ominus b = ab$.
   (c) Re; $\ominus$ is ordinary subtraction, $a \ominus b = a - b$.

2. (a) The set E of even integers under ordinary addition
   (b) The set E of even integers under ordinary multiplication
   (c) The set of positive even integers with $a \ominus b = a - b$
   (d) The set O of odd integers under ordinary addition
   (e) The set O of odd integers under ordinary multiplication
   (f) The set of positive odd integers under ordinary multiplication

3. (a) The set $\{0, 1\}$ under ordinary multiplication
   (b) The set $\{0, 1\}$ under ordinary addition
   (c) The set $\{-1, 0, 1\}$ under ordinary multiplication

4. (a) The set of all integral multiples of 5 under ordinary addition
   (b) The set of all integral multiples of 5 under ordinary multiplication
   (c) The set of all integral multiples of 5 with $a \ominus b = a - b$
   (d) The set of all integral multiples of 5 with $a \ominus b = a/b$
   (e) The set of all integral powers of 5 under ordinary multiplication
   (f) The set of all integral powers of 5 with $a \ominus b = a/b$

5. (a) The set of all real numbers of the form $a + b\sqrt{2}$, a, $b \in I$, under ordinary addition

   (b) The set of (a) under ordinary multiplication

   (c) The set of all real numbers of the form $a - b\sqrt{7}$, a, $b \in I$, under ordinary addition

   (d) The set of (c) under ordinary multiplication

6. (a) The set $\{1, -1, i, -i\}$ under multiplication of complex numbers (Construct a multiplication table.)

   (b) C; $\ominus$ is addition of complex numbers.

   (c) C; $\ominus$ is multiplication of complex numbers.

   (d) The set $\{1, (-1 + i\sqrt{3})/2, (-1 - i\sqrt{3})/2\}$ under multiplication of complex numbers (Construct a multiplication table.)

   (e) The set of all complex numbers $a + bi$ with $a^2 + b^2 = 1$ under multiplication of complex numbers

   (f) C; $a \ominus b = a/b$.

7. (a) N; $a \ominus b = 2a - b$. (b) N; $a \ominus b = a^2 + b^2$.

   (c) N; $a \ominus b = (a + b)^2$. (d) N; $a \ominus b = 2a + 3b$.

   (e) N; $a \ominus b = a/b$. (f) N; $a \ominus b =$ maximum of a and b.

   (g) N; $a \ominus b =$ l.c.m. of a and b. (h) N; $a \ominus b =$ g.c.d. of a and b.

   (i) N; $a \ominus b = a$. (j) N; $a \ominus b = b$.

   (k) N; $a \ominus b = (a + b)/2$. (l) N; $a \ominus b = a^b$.

   (m) N; $a \ominus b = a - ab$. (n) N; $a \ominus b = a + b + ab$.

   (o) N; $a \ominus b = \frac{1}{2}$ [(l.c.m. of a and b) + (g.c.d. of a and b)].

   (p) N; $a \ominus b =$ remainder when a is divided by b.

   (q) N; $a \ominus b =$ remainder when b is divided by a.

8. (a) The set $\{R_0, R_{180}, D_1, D_2\}$ of motions of the rhombus (Example (4), Section 13.6) under multiplication of mappings

   (b) $\{I, R_x, R_y, R_{xy}\}$ under multiplication of mappings (See question (6) Exercise 13.6.)

   (c) The set $\{R_0, R_{90}, R_{180}, R_{270}, H, V, D_1, D_2\}$ of motions of the square under multiplication of mappings. Set up a multiplication table. (The results of question (5), Exercise 13.6 will be useful.)

   (d) The subset $\{R_0, R_{180}, H, V\}$ of the set in (c) under multiplication of mappings.

   (e) The set $\{R_0, R_{120}, R_{240}, E_1, E_2, E_3\}$ of motions of the equilateral triangle (see question (4), Exercise 13.6 for diagram) under multiplication of mappings. Construct a multiplication table.

9. (a) The set of 2×2 real matrices under addition of matrices

   (b) The set of 2×2 real matrices under multiplication of matrices

10. (a) The set of all real linear functions
$$f : x \rightarrow ax + b$$
with $f \ominus g = f(g)$

(b) The set of all real quadratic functions
$$f : x \rightarrow ax^2 + bx + c, \quad a \neq 0,$$
with $f \ominus g = f(g)$

(c) The set in (a) with $f \ominus g$ defined as $f + g$

(d) The set in (b) with $f \ominus g$ defined as $f + g$

(e) The set of real functions

$$f_1 : t \rightarrow t \qquad f_2 : t \rightarrow \frac{1}{t} \qquad f_3 : t \rightarrow 1 - t$$

$$f_4 : t \rightarrow \frac{1}{1 - t} \qquad f_5 : t \rightarrow \frac{t - 1}{t} \qquad f_6 : t \rightarrow \frac{t}{t - 1}$$

with $f \ominus g = f(g)$.   Construct a multiplication table.

11. (a) The set of translations of the plane under the multiplication of mappings

(b) The set of rotations of the plane under the multiplication of mappings

(c) The set $\{R_0, R_{60}, R_{120}, R_{180}, R_{240}, R_{300}\}$ of rotations of the plane under multiplication of mappings, noting that
$$R_{180} \ominus R_{240} = R_{420} = R_{60},$$
$$R_{180} \ominus R_{300} = R_{480} = R_{120},$$
etc.

12. (a) The set of all permutations on $\{A, B, C\}$ under the multiplication of permutations

(b) The set of all permutations on $\{1, 2, 3, 4\}$ under the multiplication of permutations

(c) The set of all permutations on $\{x_1, x_2, \cdots x_n\}$ under the multiplication of permutations

13. (a) The set $\{A, B, C\}$ with multiplication defined by the following table

$\ominus$	A	B	C
A	A	B	C
B	B	C	A
C	C	A	B

(b) The set $\{A, B, C\}$ with multiplication defined by the table

Θ	A	B	C
A	A	B	C
B	B	A	A
C	C	B	A

(c) The set $\{A, B, C\}$ with multiplication defined by the table

Θ	A	B	C
A	A	B	C
B	A	B	C
C	A	B	C

(d) The set $\{A, B, C, D\}$ with multiplication defined by the table

Θ	A	B	C	D
A	A	B	C	D
B	B	A	D	C
C	C	D	A	B
D	D	C	B	A

14. The set of transformations T such that
$$T\begin{bmatrix} x \\ y \end{bmatrix} = \begin{bmatrix} ax + by \\ cx + dy \end{bmatrix}, \quad a, b, c, d \in Re,$$
under the multiplication of transformations.

15. The set of transformations T such that
$$T\begin{bmatrix} x \\ y \end{bmatrix} = \begin{bmatrix} ax \\ by \end{bmatrix}, \quad a, b \in Re,$$
under the multiplication of transformations.

13.9. Semigroups

We have seen that a groupoid is an algebraic system consisting of a set S that is closed under a binary operation Θ. If, in addition, the operation Θ is associative, so that

$$(a \Theta b) \Theta c = a \Theta (b \Theta c),$$

for all a, b, and c in S, the algebraic system is called a semigroup.

DEFINITION. A semigroup is a groupoid in which the binary operation Θ is associative.

Thus a semigroup requires the following four things:

(i) a set S,

(ii) a binary operation Θ defined on the elements of S,

(iii) closure, $a \Theta b \in S$ whenever $a, b \in S$,

(iv) associativity, $(a \Theta b) \Theta c = a \Theta (b \Theta c)$ for all $a, b, c \in S$.

We will re-examine the examples of Section 13.8 to see if they involve semigroups.

Example 1.   Is the set of positive integers a semigroup under the binary operation Θ such that $a \Theta b = a - b$?

Solution: This system is not a groupoid and hence not a semigroup.

Example 2.   Is the system in Example 1 a semigroup if $a \Theta b = 3a + 4b$?

Solution: The system is a groupoid.   Also,

$$(a \Theta b) \Theta c = (3a + 4b) \Theta c = 3(3a + 4b) + 4c$$
$$= 9a + 12b + 4c,$$

and

$$a \Theta (b \Theta c) = a \Theta (3b + 4c) = 3a + 4(3b + 4c)$$
$$= 3a + 12b + 16c.$$

Therefore $(a \Theta b) \Theta c \neq a \Theta (b \Theta c)$ and the system is not a semigroup.

Example 3.   Is the set of permutations on the symbols $\{A, B, C\}$ a semigroup under the multiplication of permutations?

Solution: We showed in Example 3, Section 13.8 that this set is a groupoid under the multiplication of permutations.   Let P, Q, and R be permutations on these symbols and let

$$P = \begin{pmatrix} A & B & C \\ A^* & B^* & C^* \end{pmatrix}.$$

Then we may write

$$Q = \begin{pmatrix} A^* & B^* & C^* \\ A^{**} & B^{**} & C^{**} \end{pmatrix} \quad \text{and} \quad R = \begin{pmatrix} A^{**} & B^{**} & C^{**} \\ A^{***} & B^{***} & C^{***} \end{pmatrix},$$

where (A^*, B^*, C^*) and (A^{**}, B^{**}, C^{**}) are rearrangements of (A, B, C).
Then

$$(P \ominus Q) \ominus R = \left\{ \begin{pmatrix} A & B & C \\ A^* & B^* & C^* \end{pmatrix} \ominus \begin{pmatrix} A^* & B^* & C^* \\ A^{**} & B^{**} & C^{**} \end{pmatrix} \right\} \ominus R$$

$$= \begin{pmatrix} A & B & C \\ A^{**} & B^{**} & C^{**} \end{pmatrix} \ominus \begin{pmatrix} A^{**} & B^{**} & C^{**} \\ A^{***} & B^{***} & C^{***} \end{pmatrix}$$

$$= \begin{pmatrix} A & B & C \\ A^{***} & B^{***} & C^{***} \end{pmatrix}.$$

The reader is requested to show that it is also true that

$$P \ominus (Q \ominus R) = \begin{pmatrix} A & B & C \\ A^{***} & B^{***} & C^{***} \end{pmatrix}.$$

Therefore

$$(P \ominus Q) \ominus R = P \ominus (Q \ominus R)$$

for any three such permutations and so the system is a semigroup.

Example 4. Does the set of motions $\{R_0, R_{180}, D_1, D_2\}$ of the rhombus, described in Example 4, Section 13.6, form a semigroup under the multiplication of mappings?

Solution: That the system is a groupoid is shown by examining the multiplication table (why?). To check that it is a semigroup, we would have to check that

$$(P \ominus Q) \ominus R = P \ominus (Q \ominus R)$$

for any three motions P, Q, and R. This would mean checking $4 \times 4 \times 4$ such cases and this is tedious. Instead we use the following general statement.

General Statement. If a set of *mappings* is closed under multiplication of mappings, then the multiplication is associative.

The reasoning here is that $(P \ominus Q) \ominus R$ and $P \ominus (Q \ominus R)$ both imply the mapping equivalent to performing mappings P, Q, and R in that order, assuming that the products involved can be formed (this is possible if we have closure).
Thus the system in Example 4 is a semigroup since we have already shown closure by means of a multiplication table.

EXERCISE 13.9

Check to see which of the groupoids in Exercise 13.8 are semigroups.

13.10. Identity or Neutral Elements

We know that the sets Ra, Re, and C contain certain special elements called identity or neutral elements; 0 is the identity element under the operation of addition and 1 is the identity element under multiplication.

In general, an identity or neutral element of an algebraic system consisting of a set S with a binary operation Θ is an element e such that

$$e \Theta a = a \Theta e = a$$

for all $a \in S$.

We will see in the examples and exercises that it may be possible to have

$$e \Theta a = a$$

for all $a \in S$, but

$$a \Theta e \neq a.$$

In this case, e is called a left identity of the system. On the other hand, if

$$a \Theta e = a$$

for all $a \in S$, we call e a right identity of the system. If e is both a left and a right identity, we call it simply an identity.

Example 1. Does the set of integers under the operation Θ such that $a \Theta b = a - b$ possess an identity element?

Solution:
$$a \Theta 0 = a$$
for all $a \in I$, but
$$0 \Theta b = -b.$$

Thus the system possesses a right identity 0 but no left identity.

Example 2. Does the set of integers under the operation Θ such that $a \Theta b = 3a + 4b$ possess an identity element?

Solution: Suppose that $4 \Theta b = 4$ for some element b (the element b is then a right identity *for the element* 4); then
$$4 \Theta b = 12 + 4b = 4,$$
and so
$$b = -2.$$
But
$$3 \Theta (-2) = 3(3) + 4(-2) = 1 \neq 3$$

and so -2 is not a right identity for 3. Thus there is no right identity in this system and similarly it can be shown that there is no left identity.

We have already seen that the set of permutations on $\{A, B, C\}$ contains an identity or neutral permutation

$$I = \begin{pmatrix} A & B & C \\ A & B & C \end{pmatrix},$$

and that the sets of motions of various plane figures that we have studied all possess an identity or neutral motion R_0, a counterclockwise rotation of $0°$ about the centre of the figure.

We have seen that some algebraic systems possess identity or neutral elements, some possess right identities but not left identities (Example 1), or left identities but not right, and some possess no identities at all (Example 2). The following theorem tells us that an algebraic system can have at most one identity element.

Theorem. If e and f are identity elements in an algebraic system, then

$$e = f.$$

Proof: If e is an identity, then

$$e \ominus a = a \ominus e = a$$

for all a.

If f is an identity, then

$$f \ominus a = a \ominus f = a$$

for all a. Therefore

$$e \ominus f = f,$$

since e is an identity, and

$$e \ominus f = e,$$

since f is an identity. Therefore

$$e = f, \quad \text{as required.}$$

EXERCISE 13.10

1. Check to see which of the algebraic systems in Exercise 13.8
    (a) have no identities,
    (b) have right but no left identities,
    (c) have left but no right identities,
    (d) have both left and right identities.

2. Prove that if e is a *left* identity in an algebraic system and f is a *right* identity, then $e = f$.

13.11. Inverses

We know that, to every element of the sets Ra, Re, and C, there corresponds in the same set an element called its additive inverse. Thus $-3/2$ is the additive inverse of $3/2$ in Ra, $-\sqrt{2}$ is the additive inverse of $\sqrt{2}$ in Re, and $-3 - 2i$ is the additive inverse of $3 + 2i$ in C.

Similarly, to every *nonzero* element of the sets Ra, Re, and C, there corresponds in the same set an element called its multiplicative inverse. Thus $2/3$ is the multiplicative inverse of $3/2$ in Ra, $1/\sqrt{2}$ is the multiplicative inverse of $\sqrt{2}$ in Re, and $1/(3 + 2i)$ or $3/13 - 2i/13$ is the multiplicative inverse of $3 + 2i$ in C.

In general, if an algebraic system consisting of a set S and a binary operation Θ possesses an identity element e (and hence a unique identity), then an element $a \in S$ is said to possess a multiplicative inverse b if $b \in S$ and

$$a \Theta b = b \Theta a = e.$$

Of course it may be possible in some systems that $a \Theta b = e$ but $b \Theta a \neq e$; in this case b is called a right inverse of a. (Similarly left inverses may exist.) Also some elements of a system may have an inverse even if others do not.

Example 1. Does every element of the algebraic system consisting of the set of positive rationals under ordinary multiplication possess an inverse?

Solution: The system contains a multiplicative identity 1 and, for every positive rational a/b, we know that b/a is a positive rational such that

$$\frac{a}{b} \times \frac{b}{a} = \frac{b}{a} \times \frac{a}{b} = 1.$$

Every element of this system possesses a multiplicative inverse.

Example 2. Does every element of the system with set Ra and ordinary multiplication possess an inverse?

Solution: The rational number 0 does not possess an inverse in this system; the other elements do.

Example 3. Does every element of the system with set Ra and ordinary addition possess an inverse?

Solution: This system contains an identity 0 and the inverse of the rational number a/b is the rational number $-a/b$. Every element of this system possesses an inverse.

Example 4. What is the inverse of the permutation

$$P = \begin{pmatrix} 1 & 2 & 3 \\ 3 & 1 & 2 \end{pmatrix} ?$$

Solution: The inverse of P is the permutation

$$Q = \begin{pmatrix} 3 & 1 & 2 \\ 1 & 2 & 3 \end{pmatrix}$$

found by inverting the symbol for P.   We may write

$$Q = \begin{pmatrix} 3 & 1 & 2 \\ 1 & 2 & 3 \end{pmatrix} = \begin{pmatrix} 1 & 2 & 3 \\ 2 & 3 & 1 \end{pmatrix}.$$

We easily check that

$$P \ominus Q = \begin{pmatrix} 1 & 2 & 3 \\ 3 & 1 & 2 \end{pmatrix} \ominus \begin{pmatrix} 3 & 1 & 2 \\ 1 & 2 & 3 \end{pmatrix} = \begin{pmatrix} 1 & 2 & 3 \\ 1 & 2 & 3 \end{pmatrix} = I$$

and

$$Q \ominus P = \begin{pmatrix} 1 & 2 & 3 \\ 2 & 3 & 1 \end{pmatrix} \ominus \begin{pmatrix} 1 & 2 & 3 \\ 3 & 1 & 2 \end{pmatrix} = \begin{pmatrix} 1 & 2 & 3 \\ 1 & 2 & 3 \end{pmatrix} = I.$$

Example 5.   Examine for inverses the system of permutations on $\{A, B, C, D\}$ under the multiplication of permutations.

Solution: The system possesses an identity permutation

$$I = \begin{pmatrix} A & B & C & D \\ A & B & C & D \end{pmatrix}.$$

Also, corresponding to every permutation

$$P = \begin{pmatrix} A & B & C & D \\ A* & B* & C* & D* \end{pmatrix},$$

there is a permutation

$$Q = \begin{pmatrix} A* & B* & C* & D* \\ A & B & C & D \end{pmatrix}$$

such that

$$P \ominus Q = Q \ominus P = I.$$

Example 6.   Examine for inverses the system consisting of the set $\{1, 2, 3, 4\}$ with multiplication $\ominus$ defined by the table

$\ominus$	1	2	3	4
1	1	2	3	4
2	2	4	1	3
3	3	1	4	2
4	4	3	2	1

Solution: The system possesses an identity element 1. Also, from the table

$$1 \ominus 1 = 1,$$
$$2 \ominus 3 = 3 \ominus 2 = 1,$$
$$4 \ominus 4 = 1,$$

so that every element of the system possesses an inverse. The elements 1 and 4 are their own inverses; 2 and 3 are the inverses of each other.

Example 7. State the inverse of the elements R_0, R_{180}, D_1, D_2 of the system in Example 4, Section 13.6.

Solution: From the multiplication table we see that the identity is R_0 and that

$$R_0 \ominus R_0 = R_0; \quad R_{180} \ominus R_{180} = R_0; \quad D_1 \ominus D_1 = R_0; \quad D_2 \ominus D_2 = R_0.$$

Thus each element is its own inverse.

The following theorem shows that, if an element a in a semigroup possesses an inverse, that inverse is unique.

Theorem. If a is an element of a semigroup with an identity e and

$$a \ominus b = b \ominus a = e$$

and also

$$a \ominus c = c \ominus a = e,$$

then

$$b = c.$$

Proof:

$$
\begin{aligned}
b &= b \ominus e && \text{(e is the identity.)} \\
&= b \ominus (a \ominus c) && \text{(given)} \\
&= (b \ominus a) \ominus c && \text{(associativity in semigroups)} \\
&= e \ominus c && \text{(given)} \\
&= c && \text{(identity).}
\end{aligned}
$$

Therefore

$$b = c,$$

as required.

If an element a of an algebraic system with identity e possesses a unique inverse, we use the symbol a^{-1} to represent that element; thus

$$a \ominus a^{-1} = a^{-1} \ominus a = e.$$

Then, for example, we refer to the inverse of the permutation P as P^{-1}; if

$$P = \begin{pmatrix} 1 & 2 & 3 \\ 3 & 1 & 2 \end{pmatrix},$$

then (see Example 4)

$$P^{-1} = \begin{pmatrix} 1 & 2 & 3 \\ 2 & 3 & 1 \end{pmatrix}.$$

Example 8. Find the inverse of the function

$$f : x \rightarrow 2x - 3, \quad x \in Re$$

in the algebraic system of real linear functions if $f \ominus g = f(g)$.

Solution: The function

$$f_1 : x \rightarrow x, \quad x \in Re,$$

is the identity function in this algebraic system. Then the function

$$g : x \rightarrow ax + b, \quad x \in Re$$

is an inverse for f if

$$f(g) = g(f) = f_1.$$

Now

$$f(g) : x \rightarrow 2(ax + b) - 3$$
$$= 2ax + (2b - 3)$$

and

$$2ax + (2b - 3) = x$$

if and only if

$$2a = 1 \quad \text{and} \quad 2b - 3 = 0.$$

Then g is the function,

$$g : x \rightarrow \frac{1}{2}x + \frac{3}{2}, \quad x \in Re.$$

Check:

$$g(f) : x \rightarrow \frac{1}{2}(2x - 3) + \frac{3}{2}$$
$$= x.$$

We use the symbol f^{-1} for this inverse function.

$$f^{-1} : x \rightarrow \frac{1}{2}x + \frac{3}{2}, \quad x \in Re.$$

EXERCISE 13.11

1. Check those algebraic systems of Exercise 13.8 that contain an identity (omit 9(b)) to see which systems contain inverses for all elements. List the inverses for all elements in systems containing a finite number of elements.

2. Write the inverses of the following permutations.

(a) $\begin{pmatrix} 1 & 2 & 3 \\ 2 & 1 & 3 \end{pmatrix}$ (b) $\begin{pmatrix} A & B & C & D \\ D & C & A & B \end{pmatrix}$ (c) $\begin{pmatrix} 1 & 2 & 3 & 4 & 5 \\ 2 & 5 & 1 & 3 & 4 \end{pmatrix}$

(d) $\begin{pmatrix} A & B & C & D & E \\ C & A & D & E & B \end{pmatrix}$ (e) $\begin{pmatrix} 1 & 2 & 3 & 4 & 5 & 6 \\ 5 & 1 & 6 & 2 & 4 & 3 \end{pmatrix}$

3. Find the inverses of the following functions.

   (a) $f : x \rightarrow 4x - 1, \quad x \in Re$ (b) $f : x \rightarrow \frac{1}{2}x + 3, \quad x \in Re$

   (c) $f : x \rightarrow -2x + 3, \quad x \in Re$ (d) $f : x \rightarrow -4x - 7, \quad x \in Re$

4. Prove that if a is an element of a semigroup with identity e and if $a \ominus b = e$ and $c \ominus a = e$, then $b = c$.

5. Prove that if every element of a semigroup with identity e has a left inverse, then every element also has a right inverse.

13.12. Groups

If a semigroup possesses an identity element and every element possesses an inverse, we call the algebraic system a group.

DEFINITION.   A group is a semigroup with an identity element, in which each element possesses an inverse.

We may restate this definition as follows.

DEFINITION.   A group is a set of elements G together with a binary operation $\ominus$ such that

(1) G is closed under $\ominus$;

(2) $(a \ominus b) \ominus c = a \ominus (b \ominus c)$ for all $a, b, c \in G$;

(3) $e \in G$ such that $e \ominus a = a \ominus e = a$ for $a \in G$;

(4)   for every $a \in G$ there exists $a^{-1} \in G$ such that $a^{-1} \ominus a = a \ominus a^{-1} = e$.

We refer to the binary operation $\ominus$ as group multiplication. If, in addition, the elements of a group G satisfy the postulate

(5) $a \ominus b = b \ominus a$ for all $a, b \in G$,

then we call G a commutative or abelian group (named after the brilliant Norwegian mathematician Niels Henrik Abel (1802-1829)). Otherwise G is a noncommutative or nonabelian group.

Example 1.   Show that the set Ra^+ is a group under ordinary multiplication.

Solution:

(1) Ra^+ is closed under multiplication.

(2) $(ab)c = a(bc)$ for $a, b, c \in Ra^+$.

(3) $1 \times a = a \times 1 = a$ for all $a \in Ra^+$.

(4) Every positive rational a/b has an inverse b/a which is a positive rational.

Thus this system is a group.   In addition, $ab = ba$ for any two positive rationals a and b; hence this system is a commutative group.

Example 2.   Show that the set Ra is not a group under ordinary multiplication.

Solution: The rational number 0 does not possess a multiplicative inverse.

Example 3.   Show that the set of nonzero integers is not a group under ordinary multiplication.

Solution: The integer 7 does not possess an inverse in this set.   (1/7 is not a member of this set.)

Example 4.   Is the set Re a group under ordinary addition?

Solution:

(1) Re is closed under addition.

(2) $(a + b) + c = a + (b + c)$ for $a, b, c \in Re$.

(3) $0 + a = a + 0 = a$ for all $a \in Re$.

(4) $(-a) + a = a + (-a) = 0$ for all $a \in Re$.

This system is a group.   In addition, this system is an abelian group (why?).

Example 5.   Show that the set of permutations on $\{A, B, C\}$ is a group under the multiplication of permutations.

Solution: We have already shown closure, associativity, and the existence of an identity and inverses; this system is a group.   We have also seen that

$$\begin{pmatrix} A & B & C \\ C & A & B \end{pmatrix} \theta \begin{pmatrix} A & B & C \\ A & C & B \end{pmatrix} = \begin{pmatrix} A & B & C \\ B & A & C \end{pmatrix}$$

and

$$\begin{pmatrix} A & B & C \\ A & C & B \end{pmatrix} \theta \begin{pmatrix} A & B & C \\ C & A & B \end{pmatrix} = \begin{pmatrix} A & B & C \\ C & B & A \end{pmatrix}$$

so that this group is a noncommutative group.

Example 6. Is the system consisting of the set $\{1, 2, 3, 4\}$ with multiplication θ defined by the following table a group?

θ	1	2	3	4
1	1	2	3	4
2	2	4	1	3
3	3	1	4	2
4	4	3	2	1

Solution: We see from the table that the set is closed under multiplication and that the set contains the identity 1. We have seen earlier that each element possesses an inverse.

$$1\,\theta\,1 = 1; \quad 2\,\theta\,3 = 3\,\theta\,2 = 1; \quad 4\,\theta\,4 = 1.$$

Finally we may check that associativity holds. Similarly, we may check that commutativity holds so that the system is a commutative group.

Example 7. Show that the set $\{R_0, R_{180}, D_1, D_2\}$ of motions of the rhombus (Example 4, Section 13.6) is a group under multiplication of mappings.

Solution: By examining the multiplication table

θ	R_0	R_{180}	D_1	D_2
R_0	R_0	R_{180}	D_1	D_2
R_{180}	R_{180}	R_0	D_2	D_1
D_1	D_1	D_2	R_0	R_{180}
D_2	D_2	D_1	R_{180}	R_0

we may check that all of the postulates for an abelian group hold.

Example 8.   Show that the set of real linear functions

$$f : x \rightarrow ax + b, \quad a \neq 0, \quad x \in Re$$

is a group under the binary operation $\ominus$ with $f \ominus g = f(g)$.

Solution:

(1) If f and g are the functions
$$f : x \rightarrow ax + b, \quad a \neq 0, \quad x \in Re,$$
$$g : x \rightarrow cx + d, \quad c \neq 0, \quad x \in Re,$$

then
$$f(g) : x \rightarrow a(cx + d) + b$$
$$= (ac)x + (ad + b).$$

Thus the set of such functions is closed under $\ominus$.

(2) $\ominus$ is associative.   (See question (5), Exercise 13.12.)

(3) $f_1 : x \rightarrow x$, $x \in Re$, is the identity.

(4) $f^{-1} : x \rightarrow \dfrac{1}{a}x - \dfrac{b}{a}$, $x \in Re$, is the inverse of f.   (See question (6), Exercise 13.12.)

The system is a group but it is not a commutative group.   (See question (7), Exercise 13.12.)

Will the result of this example be true for the set of all linear functions

$$f : x \rightarrow ax + b, \quad a \neq 0,$$

if a and b are integers? rational numbers?

Some groups contain a finite number of elements and we call such groups finite groups; if a group contains n elements, it is called a group of order n.   Thus the group of Example 5 has order 6, while those of Examples 6 and 7 both have order 4.   If a group is not a finite group, then it is an infinite group; the groups of Examples 1, 4, and 8 are infinite groups.

We will see in the following exercises that the sets of motions associated with certain geometrical figures form groups.   This is true in general for such geometrical figures.   As we have seen, the number of such motions depends on the amount of symmetry of the geometrical figure.   Thus the order of the group associated in this way with a geometrical figure will be related to the symmetry of the figure: the greater the order of the group, the greater the symmetry of the corresponding figure.

EXERCISE 13.12

1. Re-examine the algebraic systems of Exercise 13.8 (omit 9(b)) to determine which of them are groups, making use of the results of Exercises 13.8 to 13.11.

2. Which of the above groups are commutative groups?

3. Under which of the following definitions of multiplication will the set $\{1, 2, 3, 4\}$ form a group?   Give a complete discussion in each case.

(a)

θ	1	2	3	4
1	1	2	3	4
2	2	3	4	1
3	3	4	2	1
4	4	3	1	2

(b)

θ	1	2	3	4
1	2	1	4	3
2	1	2	3	4
3	4	3	2	1
4	3	4	1	2

(c)

θ	1	2	3	4
1	1	1	1	1
2	2	2	2	2
3	3	3	3	3
4	4	4	4	4

(d)

θ	1	2	3	4
1	1	2	3	4
2	2	1	4	3
3	3	4	1	2
4	4	3	2	1

4. Which quadrilateral other than a square has the most symmetry?   Justify your answer in terms of the order of the corresponding group of motions.

5. Prove that the binary operation θ of Example 8 is associative.

6. Verify that the function labelled f^{-1} in Example 8 is indeed the inverse of f.

7. Prove that the group in Example 8 is not a commutative group.

8. Prove that if a and b are elements of a group G, then the linear equation $a \, θ \, x = b$ has a unique solution in G.

9. Repeat question (8) for the linear equation $y \, θ \, a = b$.

10. Why is it necessary to consider the two types of linear equations in questions (8) and (9)?

13.13. Groups of Matrices Under Multiplication

Consider the set of all real 2×2 matrices

$$\begin{bmatrix} a & b \\ c & d \end{bmatrix}.$$

We have defined the product of two such matrices to be

$$\begin{bmatrix} a_1 & b_1 \\ c_1 & d_1 \end{bmatrix}\begin{bmatrix} a_2 & b_2 \\ c_2 & d_2 \end{bmatrix} = \begin{bmatrix} a_1a_2 + b_1c_2 & a_1b_2 + b_1d_2 \\ c_1a_2 + d_1c_2 & c_1b_2 + d_1d_2 \end{bmatrix}.$$

Example 1. Find the product of the matrices

$$A = \begin{bmatrix} 3 & 5 \\ -1 & 2 \end{bmatrix} \qquad \text{and} \qquad B = \begin{bmatrix} 4 & -3 \\ 2 & 7 \end{bmatrix}.$$

Solution:

$$A B = \begin{bmatrix} 3 & 5 \\ -1 & 2 \end{bmatrix}\begin{bmatrix} 4 & -3 \\ 2 & 7 \end{bmatrix} = \begin{bmatrix} (3)(4) + (5)(2) & (3)(-3) + (5)(7) \\ (-1)(4) + (2)(2) & (-1)(-3) + (2)(7) \end{bmatrix}$$

$$= \begin{bmatrix} 22 & 26 \\ 0 & 17 \end{bmatrix}.$$

It is immediate from the definition that the set of all 2×2 real matrices is closed under multiplication. It is also true that multiplication is associative; this is verified (but not proved!) in the following example.

Example 2. Find $(AB)C$ and $A(BC)$ if A and B are as in Example 1 and

$$C = \begin{bmatrix} 2 & 1 \\ -5 & 3 \end{bmatrix}.$$

Solution: From Example 1,

$$(A B) C = \begin{bmatrix} 22 & 26 \\ 0 & 17 \end{bmatrix}\begin{bmatrix} 2 & 1 \\ -5 & 3 \end{bmatrix} = \begin{bmatrix} -86 & 100 \\ -85 & 51 \end{bmatrix}.$$

Also

$$B C = \begin{bmatrix} 4 & -3 \\ 2 & 7 \end{bmatrix}\begin{bmatrix} 2 & 1 \\ -5 & 3 \end{bmatrix} = \begin{bmatrix} 23 & -5 \\ -31 & 23 \end{bmatrix}$$

so that

$$A (B C) = \begin{bmatrix} 3 & 5 \\ -1 & 2 \end{bmatrix}\begin{bmatrix} 23 & -5 \\ -31 & 23 \end{bmatrix} = \begin{bmatrix} -86 & 100 \\ -85 & 51 \end{bmatrix}.$$

Therefore $(A B) C = A (B C)$ for these matrices.

Now the matrix

$$I = \begin{bmatrix} 1 & 0 \\ 0 & 1 \end{bmatrix}$$

is an identity in this system. (See question (4), Exercise 13.13.)

Finally, the matrix

$$\begin{bmatrix} \dfrac{d}{ad-bc} & \dfrac{-b}{ad-bc} \\ \dfrac{-c}{ad-bc} & \dfrac{a}{ad-bc} \end{bmatrix}$$

is an inverse for the matrix

$$\begin{bmatrix} a & b \\ c & d \end{bmatrix},$$

provided $ad - bc \neq 0$. (See question (5), Exercise 13.13.)

Combining these results we conclude that the set of all real 2×2 matrices of the form

$$\begin{bmatrix} a & b \\ c & d \end{bmatrix}$$

with $ad - bc \neq 0$ is a group under the multiplication of matrices.

The following example shows that this group is not a commutative group.

Example 3. Evaluate BA for A and B as in Example 1.

Solution:

$$BA = \begin{bmatrix} 4 & -3 \\ 2 & 7 \end{bmatrix}\begin{bmatrix} 3 & 5 \\ -1 & 2 \end{bmatrix} = \begin{bmatrix} 15 & 14 \\ -1 & 24 \end{bmatrix}.$$

Therefore $AB \neq BA$ since 2×2 real matrices are equal if and only if corresponding entries are equal.

EXERCISE 13.13

1. Find AB and BA for the following matrices.

(a) $A = \begin{bmatrix} 1 & 2 \\ 2 & 4 \end{bmatrix}$, $B = \begin{bmatrix} 3 & 0 \\ 2 & 1 \end{bmatrix}$. (b) $A = \begin{bmatrix} -1 & 5 \\ 0 & 2 \end{bmatrix}$, $B = \begin{bmatrix} 4 & 2 \\ -1 & 1 \end{bmatrix}$.

(c) $A = \begin{bmatrix} 4 & -1 \\ 1 & 3 \end{bmatrix}$, $B = \begin{bmatrix} 3 & 1 \\ 2 & 6 \end{bmatrix}$. (d) $A = \begin{bmatrix} 0 & 3 \\ -1 & 2 \end{bmatrix}$, $B = \begin{bmatrix} 1 & 5 \\ 5 & -2 \end{bmatrix}$.

2. Find $(AB)C$ and $A(BC)$ for the matrices A and B of question (1) and the matrix

$$C = \begin{bmatrix} 1 & 3 \\ -2 & 4 \end{bmatrix}.$$

3. Find the inverses A^{-1} and B^{-1} of the matrices A and B of question (1). Check your answers by multiplication.

4. Prove that $IA = AI = A$ for every real 2×2 matrix if

$$I = \begin{bmatrix} 1 & 0 \\ 0 & 1 \end{bmatrix}.$$

5. Show that the inverse of the matrix

$$A = \begin{bmatrix} a & b \\ c & d \end{bmatrix} \quad \text{with } ad - bc \neq 0$$

is

$$\begin{bmatrix} \dfrac{d}{ad - bc} & \dfrac{-b}{ad - bc} \\ \dfrac{-c}{ad - bc} & \dfrac{a}{ad - bc} \end{bmatrix}$$

6. Prove that the set of all real 2×2 matrices of the form

$$\begin{bmatrix} a & 0 \\ 0 & b \end{bmatrix}$$

with $ab \neq 0$ is a commutative group.

7. Is the set of all 2×2 matrices of the form

$$\begin{bmatrix} a & b \\ c & d \end{bmatrix}$$

with a, b, c, d integers and $ad - bc \neq 0$, a group under multiplication? If not, which of the group postulates are violated?

8. The rotation of the plane $(x, y) \rightarrow (u, v)$ with

$$u = x \cos \alpha - y \sin \alpha$$
$$v = x \sin \alpha + y \cos \alpha$$

may be represented by the matrix

$$R_\alpha = \begin{bmatrix} \cos \alpha & -\sin \alpha \\ \sin \alpha & \cos \alpha \end{bmatrix}.$$

Show that $R_\alpha R_\beta = R_{\alpha + \beta} = R_\beta R_\alpha$. Explain the geometric significance of this.

9. Show that $R_\alpha{}^{-1} = R_{(-\alpha)}$ in question (8).

10. Prove that the set of matrices R_α is a group.

11. The reflections in the plane given by the following systems of equations

$$I \begin{cases} u = x + 0y \\ v = 0x + y \end{cases} \qquad R_x \begin{cases} u = x + 0y \\ v = 0x - y \end{cases}$$

$$R_y \begin{cases} u = -x + 0y \\ v = 0x + y \end{cases} \qquad R_{xy} \begin{cases} u = -x + 0y \\ v = 0x - y \end{cases}$$

can be represented by the following matrices. (We use the same symbols for the matrices.)

$$I = \begin{bmatrix} 1 & 0 \\ 0 & 1 \end{bmatrix}, \quad R_x = \begin{bmatrix} 1 & 0 \\ 0 & -1 \end{bmatrix}, \quad R_y = \begin{bmatrix} -1 & 0 \\ 0 & 1 \end{bmatrix}, \quad R_{xy} = \begin{bmatrix} -1 & 0 \\ 0 & -1 \end{bmatrix}.$$

Show that the set $\{I, R_x, R_y, R_{xy}\}$ of four matrices is a group under multiplication. Construct a multiplication table for this group.

13.14. Rings

We have now gone as far as we can go in this course in discussing algebraic systems with a single binary operation. In this section and the next we introduce two mathematical systems that contain *two* binary operations. The first of these is the algebraic system known as a ring.

A ring is an algebraic system consisting of a set of elements and two binary operations with the system obeying certain postulates. We call the two operations "addition" and "multiplication", and we use the symbols $a \oplus b$ and $a \otimes b$ or ab for their result on two elements a and b, even though these operations may bear absolutely no similarity to ordinary addition and multiplication.

DEFINITION. A ring is an algebraic system consisting of a set R of elements and two binary operations $\oplus$ and $\otimes$ such that

(1) R is a commutative group under $\oplus$;

(2) R is closed under $\otimes$;

(3) multiplication is associative:
$$(ab)c = a(bc) \text{ or } (a \otimes b) \otimes c = a \otimes (b \otimes c);$$

(4) multiplication is distributive over addition:
$$a(b \oplus c) = ab \oplus ac \text{ and } (a \oplus b)c = ac \oplus bc.$$

Example 1. Show that the set I of integers is a ring under ordinary addition and multiplication.

Solution:

(1) We have already checked that I is a commutative group under addition (Exercise 13.12.)

(2) I is closed under multiplication.

(3) Multiplication of integers is associative.

(4) Multiplication is distributive over addition.

Thus I is a ring under $+$ and $\times$. In addition, this algebraic system contains a multiplicative identity; we say that this system is a ring with unit or a ring with multiplicative identity. Further, the multiplication is commutative; the system is thus a commutative ring with unit.

Example 2. Is the set I^+ of positive integers a ring under ordinary addition and multiplication?

Solution: I^+ is not a group under addition since I^+ does not contain 0 or additive inverses. Thus I^+ cannot be a ring under $+$ and $\times$.

Example 3.   Show that the set of all integral multiples of 3 is a ring under ordinary addition and multiplication.

Solution:

(1) (a) The sum of two multiples of 3 is a multiple of 3.
  (b) Addition of integers is associative.
  (c) 0 is a multiple of 3.
  (d) $3m$ and $-3m$ are both multiples of 3 if m is an integer.
  (e) Addition of integers is commutative.

Therefore this set is a commutative group under $+$.

(2) The product of two multiples of 3 is a multiple of 3.

(3) Multiplication of integers is associative.

(4) Multiplication of integers is distributive over addition.

Thus the set of all integral multiples of 3 is a ring under $+$ and $\times$.   The system does not contain a multiplicative identity since 1 is not an integral multiple of 3. However, multiplication of integers is commutative so that this system is a commutative ring.

Example 4.   Show that the set $\{0, 1\}$ is a ring under addition and multiplication as defined by the tables

$\oplus$	0	1
0	0	1
1	1	0

$\otimes$	0	1
0	0	0
1	0	1

Solution:

(1) By examining the table for addition, we see that $\{0, 1\}$ is a commutative group under addition.   (Check the postulates.)

(2) The table for $\otimes$ shows closure under this operation.

(3) Associativity may be checked from the table.

(4) To check distributivity, we need only observe that

$$1 \otimes (0 \oplus 0) = 1 \otimes 0 = 0 = 1 \otimes 0 \oplus 1 \otimes 0,$$
$$1 \otimes (1 \oplus 0) = 1 \otimes 1 = 1 = 1 \otimes 1 \oplus 1 \otimes 0,$$
$$1 \otimes (1 \oplus 1) = 1 \otimes 0 = 0 = 1 \otimes 1 \oplus 1 \otimes 1,$$

since multiplication by 0 is obviously distributive.   Therefore this system is a ring.   Check that it is a commutative ring with unit.

EXERCISE 13.14

1. Check to see which of the following algebraic systems are rings under the operations of ordinary addition and multiplication.

   (a) The set of even integers   (b) The set of integral multiples of 5

   (c) The set of rational numbers   (d) The set of positive rationals

   (e) The set of rationals of the form $a/2$, where a is an integer

   (f) The set of rationals of the form $a/7$, where a is an integer

   (g) The set of real numbers   (h) The set of positive real numbers

   (i) The set of real numbers of the form $a + b\sqrt{2}$, a and b integers

   (j) The set $\{1, -1, i, -i\}$ of complex numbers

   (k) The set of all complex numbers

   (l) The set of all complex numbers $a + bi$ with a and b even integers.

   (m) The set of all complex numbers $a + bi$ with a and b rational

2. Is the set of all polynomials with integral coefficients a ring under the addition and multiplication of polynomials?

3. Is the set of all real 2×2 matrices a ring under the addition and multiplication of matrices?

4. (a) Is the set of all matrices

$$\begin{pmatrix} a & b \\ c & d \end{pmatrix}, \quad a, b, c, d \in I,$$

   a ring under the addition and multiplication of matrices?

   (b) Is it a ring if $b = c = 0$?

   (c) Is it a ring if $b = c = 0$ and $d = a$?

   (d) Is it a ring if $b = c = 0$ and $d = 2a$?

   (e) Is it a ring if $b = c = 0$ and $d = a^2$?

5. Is the set $\{0, 1, 2\}$ with addition and multiplication defined by the following tables, a ring?

$\oplus$	0	1	2
0	0	1	2
1	1	2	0
2	2	0	1

$\otimes$	0	1	2
0	0	0	0
1	0	1	2
2	0	2	1

6. Which of the rings in questions (1) to (5) are
    (a) commutative rings?
    (b) rings with unit?
    (c) commutative rings with unit?

7. In which of the systems in questions (1) to (5) is it possible to have $ab = 0$ and yet $a \neq 0$ and $b \neq 0$?

8. Why is it necessary to stipulate both distributive laws
$$a(b \oplus c) = ab \oplus ac \text{ and } (a \oplus b)c = ac \oplus bc$$
in the postulates for a ring?

9. A ring with a finite number of elements is called a finite ring; otherwise it is an infinite ring. Which of the examples of this section are finite rings? Which of the rings in questions (1) to (5) are finite rings?

13.15. Fields

Finally we consider the postulates of the algebraic system called a field. We have already considered these postulates at other stages in our study of the rational, real, and complex number systems, but we present them here formally in order to round out the present discussion.

DEFINITION.   A field is an algebraic system consisting of a set F and two binary operations called addition and multiplication and such that

(1) F is a commutative group under addition,

(2) $F - 0$ (the set of nonzero elements of F) is a commutative group under multiplication,

(3) multiplication is distributive over addition.

We list the eleven field postulates implied in questions (1) to (3) in full. A field is an algebraic system consisting of a set F and two binary operations called addition and multiplication and such that

(i) F is closed under addition,

(ii) addition is associative,

(iii) F contains an identity 0 under addition,

(iv) F contains an additive inverse $(-a)$ for each element a,

(v) addition is commutative,

(vi) F is closed under multiplication,

(vii) multiplication is associative,

(viii) F contains an identity 1 under multiplication,

(ix) F contains a multiplicative inverse a^{-1} for each nonzero element a,

(x) multiplication is commutative,

(xi) multiplication is distributive over addition.

We have stated that the sets of rational numbers, real numbers, and complex numbers are fields under addition and multiplication. Indeed it was through a study of the properties of these systems that the definition of a field was formulated.

Example 1.   Is the set I of integers a field under ordinary $+$ and $\times$?

Solution: All of the postulates for a field are satisfied by I under $+$ and $\times$, except the existence of multiplicative inverses for nonzero elements; there is no integer which is the multiplicative inverse of 7 for example.   Therefore this system is not a field.

Example 2.   Is the set of all integral multiples of 3 a field under $+$ and $\times$?

Solution: We have seen (Example 3, Section 13.14) that this system is a commutative ring.   However it does not contain multiplicative inverses and so is not a field.

Example 3.   Show that the set $\{0,1\}$ of integers is a field under addition and multiplication as defined by the tables

$\oplus$	0	1
0	0	1
1	1	0

$\otimes$	0	1
0	0	0
1	0	1

Solution: We have seen (Example 4, Section 13.14) that this system is a commutative ring with unit.   The only field postulate we need to check is the existence of inverses for nonzero elements.   But the only non-zero element is 1 and it is its own multiplicative inverse.   Hence this system is a field; it is an example of a finite field.

EXERCISE 13.15

1. Check to see which of the algebraic systems of Exercise 13.14 are fields.
2. Is the set $\{0, 1, 2, 3\}$ a field under the following operations?

$\oplus$	0	1	2	3
0	0	1	2	3
1	1	2	3	0
2	2	3	0	1
3	3	0	1	2

$\otimes$	0	1	2	3
0	0	0	0	0
1	0	1	2	3
2	0	2	0	2
3	0	3	2	1

3. Show that if a and b belong to a field, then ab can equal zero if and only if at least one of a or b is zero.

4. Is the set of all real 2×2 matrices
$$\begin{pmatrix} a & b \\ c & d \end{pmatrix}$$
with $ad - bc \neq 0$ a field under addition and multiplication of matrices?

13.16. Rigid Motions of the Cube and Regular Tetrahedron (Supplementary)

In this section we will consider the sets of rigid rotations that map the cube into itself and those that map the regular tetrahedron into itself.

It will prove very helpful if the student constructs a cardboard model of the cube and the regular tetrahedron. (The latter can be constructed by taping together four equilateral triangles.) By a rigid motion of the cube, we will mean a motion that can actually be performed in space; we will not consider any other mappings at this time. (Recall that in studying the motions of a square we considered reflections along a diagonal but pointed out that the same result could be obtained by a rotation of 180° (in space) about that diagonal.)

Rigid Motions of the Cube

The three types of rigid motions of the cube are exhibited in Figure 13.3. The three types are the following.

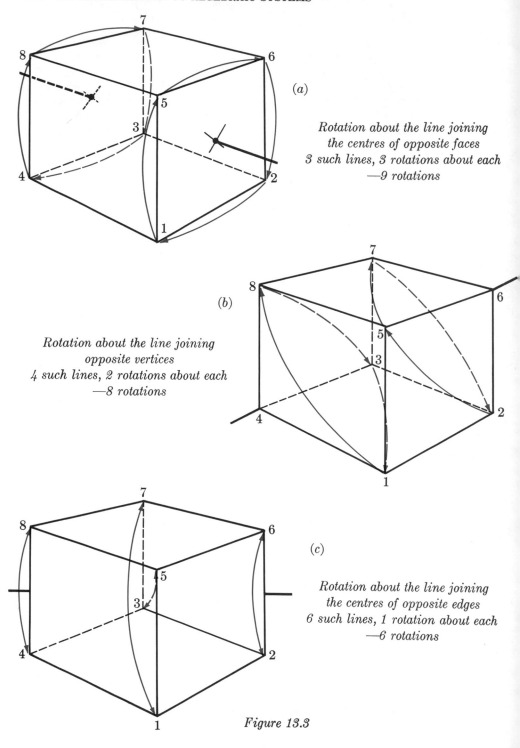

(a)

*Rotation about the line joining
the centres of opposite faces
3 such lines, 3 rotations about each
—9 rotations*

(b)

*Rotation about the line joining
opposite vertices
4 such lines, 2 rotations about each
—8 rotations*

(c)

*Rotation about the line joining
the centres of opposite edges
6 such lines, 1 rotation about each
—6 rotations*

Figure 13.3

Type 1:   rotation about a line joining the centres of opposite faces,

Type 2:   rotation about a line joining opposite vertices,

Type 3:   rotation about a line joining the centres of opposite edges.

Type 1 : Figure 13.3(*a*) indicates a rotation of 90° about the line joining the centres of faces 1 2 6 5 and 4 3 7 8.   Rotations of 90°, 180°, and 270° about this line are possible (rotation of 360° or 0° is the identity rotation).   The rotation of 90° about this line produces the permutation

$$\begin{pmatrix} 1 & 2 & 3 & 4 & 5 & 6 & 7 & 8 \\ 5 & 1 & 4 & 8 & 6 & 2 & 3 & 7 \end{pmatrix}$$

on the vertices of the cube.   (Write the permutations corresponding to rotations of 180° and 270°.)

Since there are three such lines possible, there are 3×3 or 9 rigid motions of Type 1 of the cube (apart from the identity).

Type 2 : Figure 13.3(*b*) indicates a rotation of 120° about the line joining opposite vertices 4 and 6.   Rotations of 120° and 240° about this line are possible. Rotation of 360° or 0° is the identity.   The rotation of 120° shown produces the permutation

$$\begin{pmatrix} 1 & 2 & 3 & 4 & 5 & 6 & 7 & 8 \\ 8 & 5 & 1 & 4 & 7 & 6 & 2 & 3 \end{pmatrix}$$

on the vertices of the cube.   Note that 4 and 6 are unchanged.   (Write the permutation corresponding to a rotation of 240°.)

Since there are four such lines possible, there are 4×2 or 8 rigid motions of Type 2 of the cube (apart from the identity).

Type 3 : Figure 13.3(*c*) indicates a rotation of 180° about the line joining the midpoints of edges 2 6 and 4 8; this rotation produces the permutation

$$\begin{pmatrix} 1 & 2 & 3 & 4 & 5 & 6 & 7 & 8 \\ 7 & 6 & 5 & 8 & 3 & 2 & 1 & 4 \end{pmatrix}$$

There are six such lines and so there are six rigid motions of Type 3 for the cube (apart from the identity).

Thus, altogether there are $1 + 9 + 8 + 6$ or 24 rigid motions that map the cube into itself.   It can be shown that these 24 motions form a group.

Rigid Motions of the Regular Tetrahedron

The two types of rigid motions of the regular tetrahedron (a regular tetrahedron has four faces that are equilateral triangles) are exhibited in Figure 13.4. The two types are the following

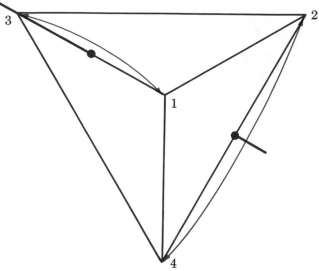

(a)   *Rotation about the line joining the centres of opposite edges*
3 such lines, 1 rotation about each—3 rotations

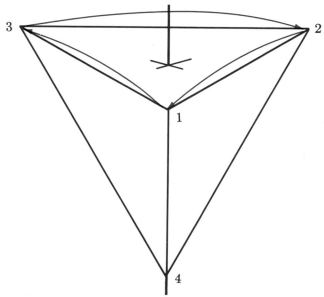

(b)   *Rotation about the line joining the vertex to the centre of the opposite face*
4 such lines, 2 rotations about each—8 rotations

Figure 13.4

Type 1:   rotation about a line joining the midpoints of opposite edges,

Type 2:   rotation about a line joining a vertex to the centre of the opposite face.

Type 1: Figure 13.4(*a*) indicates a rotation of 180° about the line joining the midpoints of opposite edges 1 3 and 2 4.   This rotation produces the permutation

$$\begin{pmatrix} 1 & 2 & 3 & 4 \\ 3 & 4 & 1 & 2 \end{pmatrix}$$

on the vertices of the tetrahedron.

There are three such lines and so there are three rigid motions of Type 1 of the regular tetrahedron (apart from the identity).

Type 2: Figure 13.4(*b*) indicates a rotation of 120° about the line joining vertex 4 to the centre of face 123.   Rotations of 120° and 240° are possible.   Rotation of 360° or 0° is the identity.   The rotation of 120° produces the permutation

$$\begin{pmatrix} 1 & 2 & 3 & 4 \\ 3 & 1 & 2 & 4 \end{pmatrix}$$

on the vertices of the tetrahedron.   (State the permutation produced by a rotation of 240°.)

There are four such lines and so there are 4 × 2 or eight rigid motions of Type 2 of the regular tetrahedron (apart from the identity).

Thus, altogether there are 1 + 3 + 8 or 12 rigid motions that map the regular tetrahedron into itself.   Again it can be shown that these 12 motions form a group.

Such groups as the above, and other similar geometric groups, have importance in crystallography and nuclear fundamental particle theory.

EXERCISE 13.16

1. Write the permutations corresponding to rotations of the cube about the line joining
    (a) centres of faces 1584 and 2673,
    (b) centres of faces 1234 and 5678,
    (c) opposite vertices 1 and 7,
    (d) opposite vertices 2 and 8,
    (e) opposite vertices 3 and 5,
    (f) midpoints of edges 15 and 37,
    (g) midpoints of edges 12 and 87,
    (h) midpoints of edges 56 and 43,
    (i) midpoints of edges 14 and 67,
    (j) midpoints of edges 58 and 23.

2. Write the permutations corresponding to rotations of the regular tetrahedron about the line joining
   (a) midpoints of edges 12 and 34,
   (b) midpoints of edges 23 and 14,
   (c) vertex 1 to the centre of face 234,
   (d) vertex 2 to the centre of face 134,
   (e) vertex 3 to the centre of face 124.

3. Find the rotations which are the inverses of those in questions (1)(a), (c), (2)(a), (c).

4. Show that the rotations of the regular tetrahedron form a group.

5. Show that the following sets are groups.
   (a) The Type 1 rigid motions of the cube
   (b) The Type 2 rigid motions of the cube
   (c) The Type 3 rigid motions of the cube
   (d) The Type 1 rigid motions of the regular tetrahedron
   (e) The Type 2 rigid motions of the regular tetrahedron

Chapter Summary

Permutations · Motions of a plane figure · Translations, rotations, reflections · Functions · 2 × 2 real matrices · Binary operations · Multiplication of the elements of a set · Products of permutations, motions, transformations, etc. · Multiplication tables · Groupoids · Semigroups · Identity or neutral elements · Inverses · Groups · Rings · Fields · Rigid motions of the cube and the tetrahedron

REVIEW EXERCISE 13

1. Determine which of the group postulates are satisfied by the following algebraic systems.
   (a) Ra with $a \ominus b = |ab|$ (b) I with $a \ominus b = aba$
   (c) $\left\{ \begin{pmatrix} 1 & 2 & 3 \\ 1 & 2 & 3 \end{pmatrix}, \quad \begin{pmatrix} 1 & 2 & 3 \\ 2 & 3 & 1 \end{pmatrix}, \quad \begin{pmatrix} 1 & 2 & 3 \\ 3 & 1 & 2 \end{pmatrix} \right\}$
        under the multiplication of permutations
   (d) $\left\{ \begin{pmatrix} 1 & 2 & 3 & 4 \\ 1 & 2 & 3 & 4 \end{pmatrix}, \quad \begin{pmatrix} 1 & 2 & 3 & 4 \\ 2 & 3 & 4 & 1 \end{pmatrix}, \quad \begin{pmatrix} 1 & 2 & 3 & 4 \\ 3 & 4 & 1 & 2 \end{pmatrix}, \quad \begin{pmatrix} 1 & 2 & 3 & 4 \\ 4 & 1 & 2 & 3 \end{pmatrix} \right\}$
        under the multiplication of permutations
   (e) The set of all integral multiples of 4 under ordinary multiplication
   (f) The set $\{0, 1, 2, 3\}$ with $\ominus$ as defined by the following table

⊖	0	1	2	3
0	0	1	2	3
1	1	2	3	0
2	2	3	0	1
3	3	0	1	2

(g) The set $\{0, 1, 2, 3\}$ with ⊖ as defined by the following table

⊖	0	1	2	3
0	0	0	0	0
1	0	1	2	3
2	0	2	1	0
3	0	3	0	1

2. Determine which of the ring postulates are satisfied by the following algebraic systems.
   (a) All integral multiples of 4 under ordinary addition and multiplication
   (b) All rationals of the form $a/5$ under ordinary addition and multiplication
   (c) All complex numbers $a + bi$ with $a^2 + b^2 = 1$ under ordinary addition and multiplication
   (d) All complex numbers $a + ai$ under ordinary addition and multiplication
   (e) I with ordinary addition but $a \otimes b = 0$ for all a, b
   (f) The set $\{0, 1, 2, 3\}$ with addition defined as in question (1)(f) and multiplication defined as in question (1)(g).

3. Which of the systems in question (2) have
   (a) commutative multiplication?
   (b) unit elements?

4. Which of the systems in question (2) are fields?   If a system is not a field, state which field postulates do not hold.

TRIGONOMETRIC FUNCTIONS

ANGLE		SINE	COSINE	TANGENT	COTANGENT	SECANT	COSECANT
Degrees	Radians						
0°	.0000	.0000	1.0000	.0000	undefined	1.000	undefined
1°	.0175	.0175	.9998	.0175	57.2900	1.000	57.30
2°	.0349	.0349	.9994	.0349	28.6363	1.001	28.65
3°	.0524	.0523	.9986	.0524	19.0811	1.001	19.11
4°	.0698	.0698	.9976	.0699	14.3007	1.002	14.34
5°	.0873	.0872	.9962	.0875	11.4301	1.004	11.47
6°	.1047	.1045	.9945	.1051	9.5144	1.006	9.567
7°	.1222	.1219	.9925	.1228	8.1443	1.008	8.206
8°	.1396	.1392	.9903	.1405	7.1154	1.010	7.185
9°	.1571	.1564	.9877	.1584	6.3138	1.012	6.392
10°	.1745	.1736	.9848	.1763	5.6713	1.015	5.759
11°	.1920	.1908	.9816	.1944	5 1446	1.019	5.241
12°	.2094	.2079	.9781	.2126	4.7046	1.022	4.810
13°	.2269	.2250	.9744	.2309	4.3315	1.026	4.445
14°	.2443	.2419	.9703	.2493	4.0108	1.031	4.134
15°	.2618	.2588	.9659	.2679	3.7321	1.035	3.864
16°	.2793	.2756	.9613	.2867	3.4874	1.040	3.628
17°	.2967	.2924	.9563	.3057	3.2709	1.046	3.420
18°	.3142	.3090	.9511	.3249	3.0777	1.051	3.236
19°	.3316	.3256	.9455	.3443	2.9042	1.058	3.072
20°	.3491	.3420	.9397	.3640	2.7475	1.064	2.924
21°	.3665	.3584	.9336	.3839	2.6051	1.071	2.790
22°	.3840	.3746	.9272	.4040	2.4751	1.079	2.669
23°	.4014	.3907	.9205	.4245	2.3559	1.086	2.559
24°	.4189	.4067	.9135	.4452	2.2460	1.095	2.459
25°	.4363	.4226	.9063	.4663	2.1445	1.103	2.366
26°	.4538	.4384	.8988	.4877	2.0503	1.113	2.281
27°	.4712	.4540	.8910	.5095	1.9626	1.122	2.203
28°	.4887	.4695	.8829	.5317	1.8807	1.133	2.130
29°	.5061	.4848	.8746	.5543	1.8040	1.143	2.063
30°	.5236	.5000	.8660	.5774	1.7321	1.155	2.000
31°	.5411	.5150	.8572	.6009	1.6643	1.167	1.942
32°	.5585	.5299	.8480	.6249	1.6003	1.179	1.887
33°	.5760	.5446	.8387	.6494	1.5399	1.192	1.836
34°	.5934	.5592	.8290	.6745	1.4826	1.206	1.788
35°	.6109	.5736	.8192	.7002	1.4281	1.221	1.743
36°	.6283	.5878	.8090	.7265	1.3764	1.236	1.701
37°	.6458	.6018	.7986	.7536	1.3270	1.252	1.662
38°	.6632	.6157	.7880	.7813	1.2799	1.269	1.624
39°	.6807	.6293	.7771	.8098	1.2349	1.287	1.589
40°	.6981	.6428	.7660	.8391	1.1918	1.305	1.556
41°	.7156	.6561	.7547	.8693	1.1504	1.325	1.524
42°	.7330	.6691	.7431	.9004	1.1106	1.346	1.494
43°	.7505	.6820	.7314	.9325	1.0724	1.367	1.466
44°	.7679	.6947	.7193	.9657	1.0355	1.390	1.440
45°	.7854	.7071	.7071	1.0000	1.0000	1.414	1.414

TRIGONOMETRIC FUNCTIONS

Angle		Sine	Cosine	Tangent	Cotangent	Secant	Cosecant
Degrees	Radians						
45°	.7854	.7071	.7071	1.0000	1.0000	1.414	1.414
46°	.8029	.7193	.6947	1.0355	.9657	1.440	1.390
47°	.8203	.7314	.6820	1.0724	.9325	1.466	1.367
48°	.8378	.7431	.6691	1.1106	.9004	1.494	1.346
49°	.8552	.7547	.6561	1.1504	.8693	1.524	1.325
50°	.8727	.7660	.6428	1.1918	.8391	1.556	1.305
51°	.8901	.7771	.6293	1.2349	.8098	1.589	1.287
52°	.9076	.7880	.6157	1.2799	.7813	1.624	1.269
53°	.9250	.7986	.6018	1.3270	.7536	1.662	1.252
54°	.9425	.8090	.5878	1.3764	.7265	1.701	1.236
55°	.9599	.8192	.5736	1.4281	.7002	1.743	1.221
56°	.9774	.8290	.5592	1.4826	.6745	1.788	1.206
57°	.9948	.8387	.5446	1.5399	.6494	1.836	1.192
58°	1.0123	.8480	.5299	1.6003	.6249	1.887	1.179
59°	1.0297	.8572	.5150	1.6643	.6009	1.942	1.167
60°	1.0472	.8660	.5000	1.7321	.5774	2.000	1.155
61°	1.0647	.8746	.4848	1.8040	.5543	2.063	1.143
62°	1.0821	.8829	.4695	1.8807	.5317	2.130	1.133
63°	1.0996	.8910	.4540	1.9626	.5095	2.203	1.122
64°	1.1170	.8988	.4384	2.0503	.4877	2.281	1.113
65°	1.1345	.9063	.4226	2.1445	.4663	2.366	1.103
66°	1.1519	.9135	.4067	2.2460	.4452	2.459	1.095
67°	1.1694	.9205	.3907	2.3559	.4245	2.559	1.086
68°	1.1868	.9272	.3746	2.4751	.4040	2.669	1.079
69°	1.2043	.9336	.3584	2.6051	.3839	2.790	1.071
70°	1.2217	.9397	.3420	2.7475	.3640	2.924	1.064
71°	1.2392	.9455	.3256	2.9042	.3443	3.072	1.058
72°	1.2566	.9511	.3090	3.0777	.3249	3.236	1.051
73°	1.2741	.9563	.2924	3.2709	.3057	3.420	1.046
74°	1.2915	.9613	.2756	3.4874	.2867	3.628	1.040
75°	1.3090	.9659	.2588	3.7321	.2679	3.864	1.035
76°	1.3265	.9703	.2419	4.0108	.2493	4.134	1.031
77°	1.3439	.9744	.2250	4.3315	.2309	4.445	1.026
78°	1.3614	.9781	.2079	4.7046	.2126	4.810	1.022
79°	1.3788	.9816	.1908	5.1446	.1944	5.241	1.019
80°	1.3963	.9848	.1736	5.6713	.1763	5.759	1.015
81°	1.4137	.9877	.1564	6.3138	.1584	6.392	1.012
82°	1.4312	.9903	.1392	7.1154	.1405	7.185	1.010
83°	1.4486	.9925	.1219	8.1443	.1228	8.206	1.008
84°	1.4661	.9945	.1045	9.5144	.1051	9.567	1.006
85°	1.4835	.9962	.0872	11.4301	.0875	11.47	1.004
86°	1.5010	.9976	.0698	14.3007	.0699	14.34	1.002
87°	1.5184	.9986	.0523	19.0811	.0524	19.11	1.001
88°	1.5359	.9994	.0349	28.6363	.0349	28.65	1.001
89°	1.5533	.9998	.0175	57.2900	.0175	57.30	1.000
90°	1.5708	1.0000	.0000	undefined	.0000	undefined	1.000

THE LOGARITHMIC FUNCTION TO BASE 10

	0	1	2	3	4	5	6	7	8	9
10	0000	0043	0086	0128	0170	0212	0253	0294	0334	0374
11	0414	0453	0492	0531	0569	0607	0645	0682	0719	0755
12	0792	0828	0864	0899	0934	0969	1004	1038	1072	1106
13	1139	1173	1206	1239	1271	1303	1335	1367	1399	1430
14	1461	1492	1523	1553	1584	1614	1644	1673	1703	1732
15	1761	1790	1818	1847	1875	1903	1931	1959	1987	2014
16	2041	2068	2095	2122	2148	2175	2201	2227	2253	2279
17	2304	2330	2355	2380	2405	2430	2455	2480	2504	2529
18	2553	2577	2601	2625	2648	2672	2695	2718	2742	2765
19	2788	2810	2833	2856	2878	2900	2923	2945	2967	2989
20	3010	3032	3054	3075	3096	3118	3139	3160	3181	3201
21	3222	3243	3263	3284	3304	3324	3345	3365	3385	3404
22	3424	3444	3464	3483	3502	3522	3541	3560	3579	3598
23	3617	3636	3655	3674	3692	3711	3729	3747	3766	3784
24	3802	3820	3838	3856	3874	3892	3909	3927	3945	3962
25	3979	3997	4014	4031	4048	4065	4082	4099	4116	4133
26	4150	4166	4183	4200	4216	4232	4249	4265	4281	4298
27	4314	4330	4346	4362	4378	4393	4409	4425	4440	4456
28	4472	4487	4502	4518	4533	4548	4564	4579	4594	4609
29	4624	4639	4654	4669	4683	4698	4713	4728	4742	4757
30	4771	4786	4800	4814	4829	4843	4857	4871	4886	4900
31	4914	4928	4942	4955	4969	4983	4997	5011	5024	5038
32	5051	5065	5079	5092	5105	5119	5132	5145	5159	5172
33	5185	5198	5211	5224	5237	5250	5263	5276	5289	5302
34	5315	5328	5340	5353	5366	5378	5391	5403	5416	5428
35	5441	5453	5465	5478	5490	5502	5514	5527	5539	5551
36	5563	5575	5587	5599	5611	5623	5635	5647	5658	5670
37	5682	5694	5705	5717	5729	5740	5752	5763	5775	5786
38	5798	5809	5821	5832	5843	5855	5866	5877	5888	5899
39	5911	5922	5933	5944	5955	5966	5977	5988	5999	6010
40	6021	6031	6042	6053	6064	6075	6085	6096	6107	6117
41	6128	6138	6149	6160	6170	6180	6191	6201	6212	6222
42	6232	6243	6253	6263	6274	6284	6294	6304	6314	6325
43	6335	6345	6355	6365	6375	6385	6395	6405	6415	6425
44	6435	6444	6454	6464	6474	6484	6493	6503	6513	6522
45	6532	6542	6551	6561	6571	6580	6590	6599	6609	6618
46	6628	6637	6646	6656	6665	6675	6684	6693	6702	6712
47	6721	6730	6739	6749	6758	6767	6776	6785	6794	6803
48	6812	6821	6830	6839	6848	6857	6866	6875	6884	6893
49	6902	6911	6920	6928	6937	6946	6955	6964	6972	6981
50	6990	6998	7007	7016	7024	7033	7042	7050	7059	7067
51	7076	7084	7093	7101	7110	7118	7126	7135	7143	7152
52	7160	7168	7177	7185	7193	7202	7210	7218	7226	7235
53	7243	7251	7259	7267	7275	7284	7292	7300	7308	7316
54	7324	7332	7340	7348	7356	7364	7372	7380	7388	7396

THE LOGARITHMIC FUNCTION TO BASE 10

	0	1	2	3	4	5	6	7	8	9
55	7404	7412	7419	7427	7435	7443	7451	7459	7466	7474
56	7482	7490	7497	7505	7513	7520	7528	7536	7543	7551
57	7559	7566	7574	7582	7589	7597	7604	7612	7619	7627
58	7634	7642	7649	7657	7664	7672	7679	7686	7694	7701
59	7709	7716	7723	7731	7738	7745	7752	7760	7767	7774
60	7782	7789	7796	7803	7810	7818	7825	7832	7839	7846
61	7853	7860	7868	7875	7882	7889	7896	7903	7910	7917
62	7924	7931	7938	7945	7952	7959	7966	7973	7980	7987
63	7993	8000	8007	8014	8021	8028	8035	8041	8048	8055
64	8062	8069	8075	8082	8089	8096	8102	8109	8116	8122
65	8129	8136	8142	8149	8156	8162	8169	8176	8182	8189
66	8195	8202	8209	8215	8222	8228	8235	8241	8248	8254
67	8261	8267	8274	8280	8287	8293	8299	8306	8312	8319
68	8325	8331	8338	8344	8351	8357	8363	8370	8376	8382
69	8388	8395	8401	8407	8414	8420	8426	8432	8439	8445
70	8451	8457	8463	8470	8476	8482	8488	8494	8500	8506
71	8513	8519	8525	8531	8537	8543	8549	8555	8561	8567
72	8573	8579	8585	8591	8597	8603	8609	8615	8621	8627
73	8633	8639	8645	8651	8657	8663	8669	8675	8681	8686
74	8692	8698	8704	8710	8716	8722	8727	8733	8739	8745
75	8751	8756	8762	8768	8774	8779	8785	8791	8797	8802
76	8808	8814	8820	8825	8831	8837	8842	8848	8854	8859
77	8865	8871	8876	8882	8887	8893	8899	8904	8910	8915
78	8921	8927	8932	8938	8943	8949	8954	8960	8965	8971
79	8976	8982	8987	8993	8998	9004	9009	9015	9020	9025
80	9031	9036	9042	9047	9053	9058	9063	9069	9074	9079
81	9085	9090	9096	9101	9106	9112	9117	9122	9128	9133
82	9138	9143	9149	9154	9159	9165	9170	9175	9180	9186
83	9191	9196	9201	9206	9212	9217	9222	9227	9232	9238
84	9243	9248	9253	9258	9263	9269	9274	9279	9284	9289
85	9294	9299	9304	9309	9315	9320	9325	9330	9335	9340
86	9345	9350	9355	9360	9365	9370	9375	9380	9385	9390
87	9395	9400	9405	9410	9415	9420	9425	9430	9435	9440
88	9445	9450	9455	9460	9465	9469	9474	9479	9484	9489
89	9494	9499	9504	9509	9513	9518	9523	9528	9533	9538
90	9542	9547	9552	9557	9562	9566	9571	9576	9581	9586
91	9590	9595	9600	9605	9609	9614	9619	9624	9628	9633
92	9638	9643	9647	9652	9657	9661	9666	9671	9675	9680
93	9685	9689	9694	9699	9703	9708	9713	9717	9722	9727
94	9731	9736	9741	9745	9750	9754	9759	9763	9768	9773
95	9777	9782	9786	9791	9795	9800	9805	9809	9814	9818
96	9823	9827	9832	9836	9841	9845	9850	9854	9859	9863
97	9868	9872	9877	9881	9886	9890	9894	9899	9903	9908
98	9912	9917	9921	9926	9930	9934	9939	9943	9948	9952
99	9956	9961	9965	9969	9974	9978	9983	9987	9991	9996

POWERS, ROOTS, AND RECIPROCALS 1—100

n	n^2	n^3	$\sqrt{n}$	$\sqrt[3]{n}$	$1/n$	n	n^2	n^3	$\sqrt{n}$	$\sqrt[3]{n}$	$1/n$
1	1	1	1.000	1.000	1.0000	51	2,601	132,651	7.141	3.708	.0196
2	4	8	1.414	1.260	.5000	52	2,704	140,608	7.211	3.733	.0192
3	9	27	1.732	1.442	.3333	53	2,809	148,877	7.280	3.756	.0189
4	16	64	2.000	1.587	.2500	54	2,916	157,464	7.348	3.780	.0185
5	25	125	2.236	1.710	.2000	55	3,025	166,375	7.416	3.803	.0182
6	36	216	2.449	1.817	.1667	56	3,136	175,616	7.483	3.826	.0179
7	49	343	2.646	1.913	.1429	57	3,249	185,193	7.550	3.849	.0175
8	64	512	2.828	2.000	.1250	58	3,364	195,112	7.616	3.871	.0172
9	81	729	3.000	2.080	.1111	59	3,481	205,379	7.681	3.893	.0169
10	100	1,000	3.162	2.154	.1000	60	3,600	216,000	7.746	3.915	.0167
11	121	1,331	3.317	2.224	.0909	61	3,721	226,981	7.810	3.936	.0164
12	144	1,728	3.464	2.289	.0833	62	3,844	238,328	7.874	3.958	.0161
13	169	2,197	3.606	2.351	.0769	63	3,969	250,047	7.937	3.979	.0159
14	196	2,744	3.742	2.410	.0714	64	4,096	262,144	8.000	4.000	.0156
15	225	3,375	3.873	2.466	.0667	65	4,225	274,625	8.062	4.021	.0154
16	256	4,096	4.000	2.520	.0625	66	4,356	287,496	8.124	4.041	.0152
17	289	4,913	4.123	2.571	.0588	67	4,489	300,763	8.185	4.062	.0149
18	324	5,832	4.243	2.621	.0556	68	4,624	314,432	8.246	4.082	.0147
19	361	6,859	4.359	2.668	.0526	69	4,761	328,509	8.307	4.102	.0145
20	400	8,000	4.472	2.714	.0500	70	4,900	343,000	8.367	4.121	.0143
21	441	9,261	4.583	2.759	.0476	71	5,041	357,911	8.426	4.141	.0141
22	484	10,648	4.690	2.802	.0455	72	5,184	373,248	8.485	4.160	.0139
23	529	12,167	4.796	2.844	.0435	73	5,329	389,017	8.544	4.179	.0137
24	576	13,824	4.899	2.884	.0417	74	5,476	405,224	8.602	4.198	.0135
25	625	15,625	5.000	2.924	.0400	75	5,625	421,875	8.660	4.217	.0133
26	676	17,576	5.099	2.962	.0385	76	5,776	438,976	8.718	4.236	.0132
27	729	19,683	5.196	3.000	.0370	77	5,929	456,533	8.775	4.254	.0130
28	784	21,952	5.292	3.037	.0357	78	6,084	474,552	8.832	4.273	.0128
29	841	24,389	5.385	3.072	.0345	79	6,241	493,039	8.888	4.291	.0127
30	900	27,000	5.477	3.107	.0333	80	6,400	512,000	8.944	4.309	.0125
31	961	29,791	5.568	3.141	.0323	81	6,561	531,441	9.000	4.327	.0123
32	1,024	32,768	5.657	3.175	.0312	82	6,724	551,368	9.055	4.344	.0122
33	1,089	35,937	5.745	3.208	.0303	83	6,889	571,787	9.110	4.362	.0120
34	1,156	39,304	5.831	3.240	.0294	84	7,056	592,704	9.165	4.380	.0119
35	1,225	42,875	5.916	3.271	.0286	85	7,225	614,125	9.220	4.397	.0118
36	1,296	46,656	6.000	3.302	.0278	86	7,396	636,056	9.274	4.414	.0116
37	1,369	50,653	6.083	3.332	.0270	87	7,569	658,503	9.327	4.431	.0115
38	1,444	54,872	6.164	3.362	.0263	88	7,744	681,472	9.381	4.448	.0114
39	1,521	59,319	6.245	3.391	.0256	89	7,921	704,969	9.434	4.465	.0112
40	1,600	64,000	6.325	3,420	.0250	90	8,100	729,000	9.487	4.481	.0111
41	1,681	68,921	6.403	3.448	.0244	91	8,281	753,571	9.539	4.498	.0110
42	1,764	74,088	6.481	3.476	.0238	92	8,464	778,688	9.592	4.514	.0109
43	1,849	79,507	6.557	3.503	.0233	93	8,649	804,357	9.644	4.531	.0108
44	1,936	85,184	6.633	3.530	.0227	94	8,836	830,584	9.695	4.547	.0106
45	2,025	91,125	6.708	3.557	.0222	95	9,025	857,375	9.747	4.563	.0105
46	2,116	97,336	6.782	3.583	.0217	96	9,216	884,736	9.798	4.579	.0104
47	2,209	103,823	6.856	3.609	.0213	97	9,409	912,673	9.849	4.595	.0103
48	2,304	110,592	6.928	3.634	.0208	98	9,604	941,192	9.899	4.610	.0102
49	2,401	117,649	7.000	3.659	.0204	99	9,801	970,299	9.950	4.626	.0101
50	2,500	125,000	7.071	3.684	.0200	100	10,000	1,000,000	10.000	4.642	.0100

ANSWERS

Chapter 1

EXERCISE 1.1 (page 4)

2. (a) Infinitely many.   (b) 1.   (c) None.

3. (a) Infinitely many.   (b) Infinitely many.   (c) One if the points are non-collinear, infinitely many otherwise.

4. 90°.   **5.** 17 in.   **6.** 14.3 in., 67°, 34°.

EXERCISE 1.3 (page 12)

1. $\overrightarrow{AB} = \overrightarrow{DC}$, $\overrightarrow{DA} = \overrightarrow{CB}$, $\overrightarrow{BC} = \overrightarrow{AD}$.

2. $\mathbf{u} + \mathbf{v} = \overrightarrow{QS} = \mathbf{v} + \mathbf{u}$, $\mathbf{u} - \mathbf{v} = \overrightarrow{RP}$, $\mathbf{v} - \mathbf{u} = \overrightarrow{PR}$.

3. (a) $\overrightarrow{RV}$.   (b) $\overrightarrow{RV}$.   (c) $\overrightarrow{RT}$.   (d) $\overrightarrow{RU}$. (e) $\overrightarrow{PS}$. (f) $\overrightarrow{RU}$. (g) $\overrightarrow{RU}$.
(h) $\overrightarrow{PS}$.

4. **0**.

8. (a) $\overrightarrow{DE}$.   (b) None.   (c) $\overrightarrow{CD}$.   (d) $\overrightarrow{AC}$.   (e) $\overrightarrow{EB}$.
(f) $\overrightarrow{AE}$.   (g) $\overrightarrow{AC}$.   (h) $\overrightarrow{AC}$.

9. 15, 16°.   **10.** 11, 52°.   **11.** 13, 13°.   **12.** 10.

EXERCISE 1.4 (page 16)

6. (a) $\overrightarrow{RT}$.   (b) $\overrightarrow{RW}$.

7. (a) $\overrightarrow{PS}$.   (b) **0**.   (c) $\overrightarrow{QR}$.   (d) $\overrightarrow{RQ}$.

EXERCISE 1.5 (page 21)

1. (a) 50 lb.   (b) 69 lb.   (c) 70 lb.   (d) 21 lb.   (e) 5 lb.   (f) 142 lb.

2. 44 lb., −7°.   **3.** 28 lb., −82°.   **4.** 28 lb.   **5.** 97 lb.

6. 30 lb., 78°.   **7.** 17 lb., −150° to the horizontal.

8. 13 lb., −154° to the horizontal.   **9.** 449 m.p.h., 56°.   **10.** 670 m.p.h., 63°.

11. 21 knots, 337°.   **12.** 18° to right of destination, 12 m.p.h.

13. 167°, 65 min.   **14.** 40 lb., 49°.   **15.** 40 lb., 49°.

EXERCISE 1.6 (page 25)

1. (a) 35 lb., 20 lb.   (b) 42 lb., 42 lb.   (c) 100 lb., 173 lb.
(d) 16 lb., 11 lb.   (e) 42 lb., 58 lb.   (f) 42 lb., 15 lb.

2. 21 lb., 28 lb.; 37°. **3.** 14 lb., 14 lb. **4.** 172 lb.
5. 42 lb. **6.** 785 lb. **7.** 34°, 40°. **8.** 35 lb.
9. 18 lb. **10.** 9,110 ft. per min.; 386 m.p.h.
11. 762,000 ft. per min.; 5000 m.p.h. **12.** 12,200 ft. per min.; 380 m.p.h.

EXERCISE 1.7 (page 30)

4. $\overrightarrow{PS} = 3\mathbf{v} - \mathbf{u}$, $\overrightarrow{RS} = -3\mathbf{u}$. **5.** $\overrightarrow{BD} = 2\mathbf{u} + \mathbf{v}$, $\overrightarrow{BC} = 2\mathbf{u} - \mathbf{v}$.
9. $2\mathbf{u} + \mathbf{v} + 5\mathbf{w}$; $\sqrt{41}$, $5\sqrt{17}$, 21.

EXERCISE 1.8 (page 39)

1. $\mathbf{w} = \dfrac{3\sqrt{3}}{5}\mathbf{u} + \tfrac{1}{2}\mathbf{v}$; $\mathbf{v} = 2\mathbf{w} - \dfrac{6\sqrt{3}}{5}\mathbf{u}$. **2.** 3.06, 2.06.

3. $\mathbf{w} = 2.88\mathbf{u} + 1.44\mathbf{v}$. **4.** $\overrightarrow{OB} = \tfrac{2}{5}\overrightarrow{OA} + \tfrac{3}{5}\overrightarrow{OC}$. **5.** $\mathbf{v} = \tfrac{4}{3}\mathbf{u} - \tfrac{1}{3}\mathbf{w}$.

REVIEW EXERCISE 1 (page 42)

1. (a) $\overrightarrow{PR}$. (b) $\overrightarrow{PT}$. (c) $\overrightarrow{QT}$. (d) $\overrightarrow{SP}$. (e) $\overrightarrow{PT}$. (f) $\overrightarrow{SR}$.
2. (a) $\overrightarrow{AG}$. (b) $\overrightarrow{EG}$. (c) $\overrightarrow{AC}$. (d) $\overrightarrow{BH}$. (e) $\overrightarrow{FC}$. (f) $\overrightarrow{CF}$.
  (g) $\overrightarrow{AF}$. (h) **0**. **3.** 6, 27°. **4.** $2\mathbf{u}$.
5. 87 pounds, 37° from the 40-pound force.
6. 61 gm., 141° from the 80-gram force.
7. 39 lb. **8.** 187 m.p.h., on a bearing of 135°. **9.** 203°, 20 knots.
10. 26 lb., 31 lb. **11.** 25 lb., 60 lb.; 23°.
12. 3,612 ft. per min.; 113 m.p.h. **13.** $\mathbf{v} = \dfrac{3\sqrt{3}}{5}\mathbf{u} + \tfrac{3}{8}\mathbf{w}$.
14. $\mathbf{u} = -3\mathbf{v} - \dfrac{3\sqrt{3}}{5}\mathbf{w}$. **18.** $\mathbf{v} = \tfrac{2}{3}\mathbf{w} + \tfrac{1}{3}\mathbf{u}$. **19.** $\overrightarrow{OQ} = \tfrac{5}{3}\overrightarrow{OP} - \tfrac{2}{3}\overrightarrow{OR}$.

Chapter 2

EXERCISE 2.1 (page 47)

2. All co-ordinates are positive in the first octant. By the signs $(+ + +)$,
  $(+ + -), (+ - +), (+ - -), (- + +), (- + -), (- - +), (- - -)$.
3. (a) $x = 0$. (b) $y = 0$. (c) $z = 0$.
4. (a) $y = z = 0$. (b) $x = z = 0$. (c) $x = y = 0$.
5. (a) $y = 0, z = 0$. (b) $x = 0, z = 0$. (c) $x = 0, y = 0$.

EXERCISE 2.2 (page 49)

1. (a) $(6, 9)$. (b) $(-2, 3)$. (c) $(4, 7)$. (d) $(5, -1, 5)$.
   (e) $(0, -2, -4)$. (f) $(4, 0, -5)$. (g) $(10, 40)$. (h) $(-12, -21)$.
   (i) $(0, 0)$. (j) $(-6, -3, 12)$. (k) $(8, 2, -6)$. (l) $(2, 1, -3)$.
   (m) $(0, 0)$. (n) $(1, 5)$. (o) $(1, 10)$. (p) $(2, 0, -2)$.
   (q) $(-7, 2, 4)$. (r) $(-5, 0, 6)$.
4. $(0, 15, 33)$. 5. $a = 2,\ b = 1$. 6. $a = -5,\ b = -\frac{1}{3},\ c = -20$.
7. $x = -\frac{23}{2},\ y = 1,\ z = \frac{32}{3}$. 8. $p = -\frac{7}{3},\ q = \frac{4}{3},\ r = 2$.

EXERCISE 2.3 (page 52)

3. (a) $(2, 5)$. (b) $(-3, 1)$. (c) $(-5, -2)$. (d) $(-2, -5)$.
   (e) $(3, -1)$. (f) $(5, 2)$. (g) $(2, 3)$. (h) $(-5, 9)$.
   (i) $(-2, -4)$. (j) $(-3, -5)$.
4. (a) $(-2, -2)$. (b) $(-11, 0)$. (c) $(8, 5)$. (d) $(-6, 1)$.
5. (a) $(3, -1, 4)$. (b) $(-3, -2, -4)$. (c) $(2, 1, 1)$.
   (d) $(4, -1, 0)$. (e) $(9, -2, 1)$. (f) $(0, -8, 0)$.
6. (a) $(-6, 1, 0)$. (b) $(2, 5, 5)$. (c) $(-2, -2, 4)$. (d) $(7, -2, -3)$.
7. The components of one are the additive inverses of the corresponding components of the other.
8. Equal in magnitude but opposite in direction. 9. The null vector.
10. (a) $b = c = 0$. (b) $a = c = 0$. (c) $a = b = 0$.
    (b) $a = 0$. (e) $b = 0$. (f) $c = 0$.

EXERCISE 2.4 (page 56)

1. (a) $(9, 3)$. (b) $(-2, 6)$. (c) $(-1, -2)$. (d) $(2, -6)$. (e) $(3, 0)$. (f) $(-7, 2)$.
2. (a) $(4, 9)$. (b) $(2, 4)$. (c) $(2, 0)$. (d) $(-4, -2)$.
3. (a) $(6, 0)$. (b) $(-4, -7)$.
7. (a) $(9, 5)$. (b) $(4, 1)$. (c) $(-5, 9)$. (d) $(-7, -\frac{9}{2})$.

1. For $k \in Re$ (a) $(k, 3k)$. (b) $(-3k, 4k)$. (c) $(3k, 5k, -2k)$.
   (d) $(-6k, -k, 5k)$. (e) $(k, -2k, 0)$. (f) $(-k, 2k, 3k)$.
2. (a) $(3k, 4k)$. (b) $(8k, -3k)$. (c) $(-7k, 2k)$.
   (d) $(-5k, 2k)$. (e) $(-5k, -2k, 4k)$. (f) $(4k, -3k, 2k)$.
3. (a) Yes. (b) No. (c) Yes. (d) No. (e) Yes. (f) No.
4. (a) -4. (b) Not possible. (c) -10.
   (d) $k = -\frac{1}{8},\ l = \frac{1}{8}$. (e) $k = 9,\ l = 12$. (f) $k = 0,\ l = -8$.

EXERCISE 2.6 (page 61)

1. For $k, l \in Re$ (a) $(k, 2l, 0)$. (b) $(k + 2l, 2k, -l)$.
(c) $(3k - 2l, 2k + 5l, 2k - 3l)$. (d) $(-3k + l, 2k, 4k + 3l)$.
(e) $(-2k, -2k - 3l, 5k + 4l)$. (f) $(-4k + 3l, -l, 5l)$.

2. (a) 5. (b) 0. (c) No solution. (d) 1.

3. (a) Yes. (b) Yes. (c) Yes. (d) Yes. (e) Yes. (f) Yes. (g) No.
(h) Yes. (i) No. (j) Yes. (k) Yes. (l) Yes. (m) No. (n) Yes.

4. (a) Yes. (b) Yes. (c) No. (d) Yes. 5. No.

6. (a) No. (b) No. (c) No. (d) No.

EXERCISE 2.7 (page 65)

1. (a) $(0,0) = 0(3, 5) + 0(2, -3)$. (b) $(3, -4) = 3(1, 0) - 4(0, 1)$.
(c) $(-3,3) = 0(4, 7) - 3(1, -1)$. (d) $(4, 4) = -4(-1, -1) + 0(-3, -3)$.
(e) $(0, 0) = 0(3, 7) + 0(2, 9)$. (f) $(4, 2) = 0(5, 9) + 2(2, 1)$.
(g) $(3, 2) = (1, 0) + 2(1, 1)$. (h) $(5, 2) = \frac{5}{3}(3, -2) + \frac{16}{3}(0, 1)$.
(i) $(5, 7) = \frac{11}{5}(-1, 1) + \frac{12}{5}(3, 2)$. (j) $(3, 1) = -\frac{17}{12}(-2, -1) + \frac{1}{12}(2, -5)$.

2. (a) No. (b) Yes; $(5, -2) = 5(1, 0) - \frac{2}{3}(0, 3)$.
(c) No. (d) Yes; $(5, -2) = -\frac{5}{2}(-2, 0) + \frac{2}{3}(0, -3)$.
(e) Yes; $(5, -2) = \frac{13}{6}(1, 3) + \frac{17}{12}(2, -6)$.
(f) Yes; $(5, -2) = \frac{13}{2}(2, -4) + 8(-1, 3)$.
(g) Yes; $(5, -2) = 0(3, -1) + 1(5, -2)$.
(h) Yes; $(5, -2) = \frac{9}{2}(2, 0) - 1(4, 2)$. (i) No.

3. (a) $(3, 2)$. (b) $(-1, 4)$. (c) $(6, 0)$. (d) $(-1, -2)$.

EXERCISE 2.8 (page 67)

1. (a) No. (b) Yes. (c) No. (d) No.

2. (a) Collinear.
(b) Not collinear; coplanar; $(-3, 3, 0) = -3(1, -1, 0) + 0(-1, 1, 1)$.
(c) Not collinear; coplanar; $(1, 1, 0) = (1, 0, 0) + (0, 1, 0)$.
(d) Not collinear; not coplanar. (e) Not collinear; not coplanar.
(f) Not collinear: coplanar; $(0, 4, 1) = 2(0, 2, \frac{1}{2}) + 0(0, -16, -18)$.
(g) Not collinear; not coplanar. (h) Not collinear; not coplanar.

3. (a) Collinear.
(b) Coplanar; $(-12, 4, 0) = 4(-3, 1, 0) + 0(2, 1, 4)$;
$(6, -2, 0) = -2(-3, 1, 0) + 0(2, 1, 4)$.
(c) Coplanar; $(-4, -6, 2) = -2(2, 3, -1) + 0(5, 1, 2)$;
$(-10, -2, -4) = 0(2, 3, -1) - 2(5, 1, 2)$.
(d) Coplanar; $(1, 2, 3) = (1, 0, 3) + (0, 2, 0)$;
$(-2, 0, -6) = -2(1, 0, 3) + 0(0, 2, 0)$.
(e) Noncoplanar. (f) Noncoplanar.
(g) Coplanar; $(4, 0, 3) = (2, 2, -1) + 2(1, -1, 2)$;
$(3, 1, 1) = (2, 2, -1) + (1, -1, 2)$.

EXERCISE 2.9 (page 70)

1. (a) Yes. (b) Yes. (c) Yes. (d) No. (e) No. (f) Yes.
2. (a) $(0, 1, 0) + (1, 0, 0) + \frac{1}{2}(0, 0, 2)$.
    (b) $-1(-1, 0, 0) + \frac{1}{3}(0, 3, 0) - \frac{1}{2}(0, 0, -2)$.
    (c) $-1(-1, 0, 1) + (0, 1, 0) + 2(0, 0, 1)$.
    (f) $(3, -1, 1) - \frac{4}{3}(2, -1, 1) + \frac{2}{3}(1, 1, 2)$.
3. (a) $(3, -2, 1)$. (b) $(-4, 0, 2)$. (c) $(5, -3, -1)$.
4. (a) $(-1, 2, 1) = -1(1, 0, 0) + (0, 2, 0) + \frac{1}{3}(0, 0, 3)$.
    (b) $(2, 2, 1) = \frac{17}{28}(3, 1, 0) + \frac{13}{28}(0, 3, 1) + \frac{5}{28}(1, 0, 3)$. (c) No solution.
    (d) $(1, 1, 4) = 4(4, -1, 1) - 5(3, 0, -1) + 5(0, 1, -1)$.
    (e) $(5, 2, 1) = (3, -3, 1) + \frac{1}{6}(2, 0, 0) + \frac{5}{3}(1, 3, 0)$.

REVIEW EXERCISE 2 (page 71)

1 (a) $(-3, 2)$. (b) $(15, -6, -21)$. (c) $(0, 18)$.
    (d) $(-8, 7, -12)$. (e) $(3, -5, 6)$. (f) $(6, -4, -5)$.
2. (a) $(-7, 7)$. (b) $(5, -2)$. (c) $(7, -2, 7)$. (d) $(4, -1, 11)$.
3. (a) $(1, 9)$. (b) $(2, 6)$. 4. (a) -2. (b) $k = -\frac{1}{3}, l = -\frac{2}{3}$.
5. (a) Yes. (b) No. (c) No. (d) No.
6. (a) Yes. (b) No. (c) No. (d) No.
7. (a) No. (b) Yes; $(4, -3) = -\frac{10}{7}(-1, 3) + \frac{9}{7}(2, 1)$.
    (c) No. (d) Yes; $(4, -3) = -\frac{1}{3}(3, -1) + \frac{5}{3}(3, -2)$.
    (e) Yes; $(4, -3) = 2(2, 0) - \frac{3}{5}(0, 5)$. (f) Yes; $(4, -3) = 18(1, 1) - 7(2, 3)$.
8. (a) Noncollinear, coplanar. (b) Collinear.
    (c) Noncollinear, noncoplanar. (d) Noncollinear, noncoplanar.
9. (a) Coplanar. (b) Noncoplanar. (c) Noncoplanar.
10. (a) Yes; $(5, 1, -2) = \frac{5}{3}(3, 0, 0) + \frac{1}{2}(0, 2, 0) + (0, 0, -2)$.
    (b) Yes; $(2, 2, -5) = \frac{7}{6}(3, -1, 0) + \frac{3}{2}(-1, 0, 3) - \frac{19}{6}(0, -1, 3)$.
    (c) Yes; $(3, 2, 3) = \frac{9}{2}(4, -1, 2) - 2(1, 0, 3) - \frac{13}{2}(2, -1, 0)$.

Chapter 3

EXERCISE 3.1 (page 76)

1. $3; 1; 2; 5; 0; 3; 2; 2; 5; 6$. 3. $6; 2\sqrt{5}; \sqrt{37}; 2\sqrt{26}; 3\sqrt{2}; 5; 3\sqrt{10}; 0$.
9. (a) Noncollinear. (b) Noncollinear. (c) Noncollinear.
10. (a) Right-angled. (b) Not right-angled. (c) Not right-angled.

EXERCISE 3.2 (page 78)

1. $3\sqrt{2}; \sqrt{29}; \sqrt{61}; \sqrt{29}; 0; \sqrt{74}; 2\sqrt{2}; \sqrt{61}; \sqrt{29}; \sqrt{122}$.
5. (a) Noncollinear. (b) Noncollinear. (c) Noncollinear.
6. (a) Right-angled. (b) Right-angled. (c) Not right-angled.

EXERCISE 3.3   (page 81)

1. (a) 2.   (b) 3.   (c) 6.   (d) 4.   (e) $\sqrt{26}$.   (f) $\sqrt{6}$.
   (g) 5.   (h) $3\sqrt{3}$.   (i) $2\sqrt{10}$.   (j) $\sqrt{53}$.   (k) $\sqrt{41}$.   (l) 3.
   (m) $2\sqrt{5}$.   (n) $\sqrt{11}$.   (o) $\sqrt{13}$.   (p) $\sqrt{14}$.

2. (a) $\sqrt{13}$.   (b) $\sqrt{65}$.   (c) $\sqrt{13}$.   (d) $\sqrt{26}$.   (e) $\sqrt{53}$.   (f) $\sqrt{65}$.

3. (a) $\sqrt{26}$.   (b) $\sqrt{6}$.   (c) $\sqrt{21}$.   (d) $5\sqrt{2}$.   (e) $3\sqrt{3}$.   (f) $\sqrt{77}$.
   (g) $\sqrt{101}$.   (h) $5\sqrt{2}$.   (i) $3\sqrt{10}$.

EXERCISE 3.4   (page 83)

1. (a) $\pm\left(\dfrac{\sqrt{2}}{2}, \dfrac{\sqrt{2}}{2}\right)$.   (b) $\pm\dfrac{1}{\sqrt{10}}(-3, 1)$.   (c) $\pm\dfrac{1}{\sqrt{29}}(-2, -5)$.

   (d) $\pm\sqrt{2}(\tfrac{1}{2}, -\tfrac{1}{2})$.   (e) $\pm\dfrac{1}{\sqrt{6}}(1, 1, 2)$.   (f) $\pm\dfrac{1}{\sqrt{11}}(-1, 3, 1)$.

   (g) $\pm\dfrac{1}{\sqrt{17}}(2, -2, 3)$.   (h) $\pm\dfrac{1}{\sqrt{34}}(-3, -3, 4)$.

2. (a) $\pm\left(\dfrac{1}{\sqrt{2}}, \dfrac{1}{\sqrt{2}}\right)$.   (b) $\pm\left(\dfrac{4}{\sqrt{52}}, \dfrac{-6}{\sqrt{52}}\right)$.   (c) $\pm\left(\dfrac{-3}{\sqrt{10}}, \dfrac{1}{\sqrt{10}}\right)$.

   (d) $\pm\left(\dfrac{-3}{\sqrt{14}}, \dfrac{1}{\sqrt{14}}, \dfrac{2}{\sqrt{14}}\right)$ (e) $\pm\left(\dfrac{4}{\sqrt{66}}, \dfrac{-1}{\sqrt{66}}, \dfrac{-7}{\sqrt{66}}\right)$.

   (f) $\pm\left(\dfrac{7}{\sqrt{58}}, 0, \dfrac{3}{\sqrt{58}}\right)$.

3. (a) $\pm\left(\dfrac{2}{\sqrt{14}}, \dfrac{-1}{\sqrt{14}}, \dfrac{3}{\sqrt{14}}\right)$.   (b) $\pm\left(\dfrac{2}{\sqrt{6}}, \dfrac{-1}{\sqrt{6}}, \dfrac{1}{\sqrt{6}}\right)$.   (c) $\pm\dfrac{1}{\sqrt{126}}(10, -5, -1)$

   (d) $\pm\dfrac{1}{\sqrt{46}}(6, -3, 1)$.   (e) $\pm\dfrac{1}{\sqrt{86}}(-2, 1, 9)$.   (f) $\pm\dfrac{1}{\sqrt{6}}(2, -1, 1)$.

   (g) $\pm\dfrac{1}{\sqrt{2206}}(-42, 21, 1)$.

EXERCISE 3.5   (page 84)

1. (a) 3.   (b) 5.   (c) -2.   (d) 17.   (e) $\tfrac{3}{2}$.   (f) $2ab$.   (g) 0.
   (h) 2.   (i) 0.   (j) 0.   (k) -1.   (l) 20.   (m) -5.   (n) 1.
   (o) $3ab$.   (p) $-a^2$.

2. (a) $\tfrac{15}{4}$.   (b) $-\tfrac{19}{2}$.   (c) 8.   (d) $-\tfrac{3}{2}$.

3. (a) 1.   (b) 1.   (c) 1.   4. (a) 0.   (b) 0.   (c) 0.

5. (a) 25.   (b) 14.   (c) $a^2 + b^2 + c^2$.

6. (a) 14.   (b) 14.   (c) -3.   (d) -3.   (e) 78.
   (f) 78.   (g) -348.   (h) -348.   (i) 312.

7. (a) -3.   (b) -3.   (c) -21.   (d) -21.   (e) -54.
   (f) -54.   (g) -36.   (h) -36.   (i) -216.

EXERCISE 3.7   (page 89)

7. (a) $2|\mathbf{u}|^2 + 5\mathbf{u}\cdot\mathbf{v} - 12|\mathbf{v}|^2$.   (b) $-6|\mathbf{u}|^2 - 12|\mathbf{v}|^2 + 17\mathbf{u}\cdot\mathbf{v}$.
8. (a) -130.   (b) -234.

EXERCISE 3.9   (page 94)

1. (a) $\dfrac{17}{5\sqrt{26}}$.   (b) $\dfrac{-12}{\sqrt{145}}$.   (c) $\dfrac{-4}{\sqrt{17}}$.

  (d) $\dfrac{9}{\sqrt{231}}$.   (e) $\dfrac{12}{5\sqrt{10}}$.   (f) $\dfrac{-22}{3\sqrt{114}}$.

2. (a) $122°$.   (b) $108°$.   (c) $23°$.   (d) $99°$.   (e) $80°$.   (f) $110°$.
3. (a) $51°$.   (b) $9°$.   (c) $112°$.   (d) $97°$.   (e) $141°$.   (f) $0°$.
4. (a) $135°$.   (b) $81°$.   (c) $72°$.
5. $\angle P = 75°,\ \angle Q = 38°,\ \angle R = 67°$.   **6.** $\angle P = 23°,\ \angle Q = 13°,\ \angle R = 144°$.
7. (a) $\frac{10}{21}$.   (b) $\frac{1}{2}$.   (c) -23.   (d) $-\frac{21}{2}$.   (e) 22.   (f) $\frac{11}{12}$.
8. Yes, $\angle PQR = 90°$.   **9.** No.   **10.** $h = -4,\ k = \frac{7}{2}$.

EXERCISE 3.10   (page 98)

1. (a) $\dfrac{6}{\sqrt{13}}$.   (b) $\frac{11}{5}$.   (c) 0.   (d) $\dfrac{1}{\sqrt{26}}$.   (e) $\dfrac{3}{\sqrt{10}}$.   (f) $\dfrac{7}{\sqrt{5}}$.

  (g) $\dfrac{11}{\sqrt{14}}$.   (h) $\dfrac{8}{\sqrt{14}}$.   (i) 0.   (j) $\dfrac{13}{\sqrt{21}}$.   (k) $\dfrac{12}{\sqrt{14}}$.   (l) $\dfrac{1}{\sqrt{14}}$.

2. (a) $\dfrac{35}{\sqrt{26}}$.   (b) $\dfrac{41}{\sqrt{33}}$.   **3.** When $\mathbf{u}$ and $\mathbf{v}$ are orthogonal.

4. (a) No.   (b) Yes; when $|\mathbf{u}| = |\mathbf{v}|$.

EXERCISE 3.11   (page 101)

1. (a) $(5, 0),\ (0, \frac{1}{2})$.   (b) $(-4, 0),\ (0, 7)$.   (c) $(6, 0),\ (0, -2)$.
  (d) $(-3, 0),\ (0, -4)$.
2. $\sqrt{29}$.   **3.** (a) $2\sqrt{5}$.   (b) $\sqrt{17}$.   **4.** $\sqrt{5}$.
5. $(3, 0),\ (0, -5)$.   **6.** $(3, 0),\ (0, -5)$.
7. $\mathbf{w}_1 = (-\frac{7}{5}, -\frac{14}{5}),\ \mathbf{w}_2 = (\frac{22}{5}, -\frac{11}{5})$.   **8.** $(-\frac{11}{5}, \frac{22}{5}),\ (-\frac{4}{5}, -\frac{2}{5})$.
9. $(\frac{51}{13}, \frac{-34}{13}),\ (\frac{14}{13}, \frac{21}{13})$.
10. Uphill force is 11 pounds.   Lift force is 11 pounds.
11. Uphill force is 2050 pounds.   Lift force is 900 pounds.
12. (a) $(-1, 0, 0),\ (0, 5, 0),\ (0, 0, 3)$.   (b) $(6, 0, 0),\ (0, -4, 0),\ (0, 0, 2)$.
  (c) $(-1, 0, 0),\ (0, -6, 0),\ (0, 0, 5)$.
13. $|\mathbf{F}_x| = 3$ lb.; $|\mathbf{F}_y| = 12$ lb.; $|\mathbf{F}_z| = 21$ lb.
14. $|\mathbf{F}_x| = 5$ lb.; $|\mathbf{F}_y| = 5$ lb.; $|\mathbf{F}_z| = 13$ lb.
15. $(2, -2, 0),\ (2, 2, 4),\ (-1, -1, 1)$.

EXERCISE 3.12   (page 105)

1. (a) 11 units.   (b) 11 units.   (c) 1 unit.   (d) None.
   (e) 17 units.   (f) 4 units.
3. 39 ft-lb.   **4.** $\sqrt{38}$ ft-lb.   **5.** 10,824,000 ft-lb.

REVIEW EXERCISE 3   (page 105)

1. (a) Noncollinear.   (b) Noncollinear.   (c) Noncollinear.
2. (a) Right-angled at Q.   (b) Not right-angled.   (c) Right-angled at Q.
4. (a) $\sqrt{29}$.   (b) $\sqrt{11}$.   (c) $\sqrt{21}$.   (d) $3\sqrt{10}$.   (e) $\sqrt{33}$.
5. (a) $\left(\dfrac{5}{\sqrt{29}}, \dfrac{-2}{\sqrt{29}}\right)$.   (b) $\left(\dfrac{-3}{\sqrt{11}}, \dfrac{1}{\sqrt{11}}, \dfrac{1}{\sqrt{11}}\right)$.   (c) $\dfrac{1}{\sqrt{21}}(4, 1, -2)$.
   (d) $\dfrac{1}{\sqrt{10}}(-3, 1)$.   (e) $\dfrac{1}{\sqrt{33}}(-2, -2, 5)$.
6. (a) $\sqrt{30}$.   (b) $\sqrt{34}$.   (c) $\sqrt{21}$.   (d) $\sqrt{97}$.
7. (a) -5.   (b) 7.   (c) -17.   (d) -22.   (e) -22.
   (f) 12.   (g) 65.   (h) 12.   (i) 68.   (j) -116.
8. (a) $-\frac{1}{42}\sqrt{105}$.   (b) $\frac{1}{6}\sqrt{6}$.   (c) $-\frac{17}{210}\sqrt{70}$.
9. (a) $\angle P = 72°, \angle Q = 52°, \angle R = 56°$.
   (b) $\angle P = 68°, \angle Q = 51°, \angle R = 61°$.
10. (a) 37°.   (b) 133°.   **11.** (a) $\dfrac{6}{\sqrt{65}}$.   (b) $\dfrac{7}{\sqrt{41}}$.
12. (a) 0.   (b) 5.   **13.** (a) $\dfrac{6\sqrt{65}}{13}$ ft-lb.   (b) 0.
14. $|\mathbf{F}_x| = \frac{7}{2}\sqrt{6}; |\mathbf{F}_y| = \sqrt{6}; |\mathbf{F}_z| = \frac{1}{2}\sqrt{6}.$ **15.** $-\frac{3}{5}\mathbf{v}_1, \frac{6}{5}\mathbf{v}_2, \frac{7}{4}\mathbf{v}_3.$

Chapter 4

EXERCISE 4.1   (page 110)

1. (a) $AP:PB = 1:2$.   (b) $AB:BP = 1:1$.   (c) $PA:AB = 1:1$.
   (d) $AB:BP = 4:1$.   (e) $PA:AB = 3:2$.
   (f) $AB:BP = 1:(\sqrt{2} - 1)$.
2. (a) $\frac{2}{5}$.   (b) 2.   (c) -1.
3. (a) $AP:PB = 1:1$.   (b) $AP:PB = 2:1$.   (c) $AP:PB = 4:1$.
   (d) $AB:BP = 1:1$.   (e) $AB:BP = 2:1$.   (f) $PA:AB = 2:1$.
8. (a) $k = \frac{1}{2}$.   (b) $k = \frac{2}{3}$.   (c) $k = \frac{4}{5}$.   (d) $k = 2$.
   (e) $k = \frac{3}{2}$.   (f) $k = -2$.

EXERCISE 4.2   (page 114)

1. (a) $(x, y) = (1 - k)(1, 1) + k(5, 2); \; x = 1 + 4k, y = 1 + k$.
   (b) $(x, y) = (1 - k)(3, 7) + k(-4, 2); \; x = 3 - 7k, y = 7 - 5k$.

(c) $(x, y) = (1 - k)(6, 6) + k(0, 0)$; $x = 6 - 6k$, $y = 6 - 6k$.

(d) $(x, y) = (1 - k)(-1, 0) + k(0, 7)$; $x = -1 + k$, $y = 7k$.

(e) $(x, y) = (1 - k)(3, -3) + k(0, 5)$; $x = 3 - 3k$, $y = -3 + 8k$.

(f) $(x, y) = (1 - k)(-2, 3) + k(-4, 7)$; $x = -2 - 2k$, $y = 3 + 4k$.

(g) $(x, y) = (1 - k)(-2, 4) + k(-5, -6)$; $x = -2 - 3k$, $y = 4 - 10k$.

(h) $(x, y) = (1 - k)(-3, -1) + k(-7, -2)$; $x = -3 - 4k$, $y = -1 - k$.

(i) $(x, y) = (1 - k)(4, \frac{1}{3}) + k(-\frac{1}{2}, 0)$; $x = 4 - \frac{9}{2}k$, $y = \frac{1}{3} - \frac{1}{3}k$.

(j) $(x, y) = (1 - k)(5, \sqrt{2}) + k(\sqrt{3}, 6)$; $x = 5 + k(\sqrt{3} - 5)$,
$y = \sqrt{2} + k(6 - \sqrt{2})$.

2. (a) $(3, \frac{3}{2})$.　　　(b) $(-\frac{1}{2}, \frac{9}{2})$.　　　(c) $(3, 3)$.　　　(d) $(-\frac{1}{2}, \frac{7}{2})$.

(e) $(\frac{3}{2}, 1)$.　　　(f) $(-3, 5)$.　　　(g) $(-\frac{7}{2}, -1)$.　　　(h) $(-5, -\frac{3}{2})$.

(i) $(\frac{7}{4}, \frac{1}{6})$.　　　(j) $\left(\dfrac{5}{2} + \dfrac{\sqrt{3}}{2}, 3 + \dfrac{\sqrt{2}}{2} \right)$.

3. (a) $(-\frac{1}{3}, 3)$.　　　(b) $(\frac{1}{4}, \frac{25}{3})$.　　　(c) $(-19, -1)$.　　　(d) $(23, 8)$.

4. (a) $AP : PB = 2 : 1$.　　　(b) $PA : AB = 1 : 1$.　　　(c) $PA : AB = 1 : 3$.

(d) $AB : BP = 1 : 4$.

5. (a) Line, $11x + 7y = 9$.　　　(b) Point, $(4, -5)$.

(c) Point, $(-3, 6)$.　　　(d) Point $(\frac{1}{2}, \frac{1}{2})$.

(e) Point, $(-10, 17)$.　　　(f) Three points, $(4, -5)$, $(-3, 6)$, $(-10, 17)$.

(g) Three points, $(11, -16)$, $(4, -5)$, $(-10, 17)$.　　　(h) Line segment.

(i) Ray.　　　(j) Ray.　　　(k) Two rays.

6. $(5, 4)$, $(2, 11)$ are on the line; $(14, -17)$ is on the line; $(-\frac{1}{2}, \frac{27}{2})$ is not.

8. (a) $(x, y) = (2, 3) + k(3, 5)$; $x = 2 + 3k$, $y = 3 + 5k$.

(b) $(x, y) = (2, 3) + k(-2, 1)$; $x = 2 - 2k$, $y = 3 + k$.

(c) $(x, y) = (2, 3) + k(0, -5)$; $x = 2$, $y = 3 - 5k$.

(d) $(x, y) = (2, 3) + k(-4, 0)$; $x = 2 - 4k$, $y = 3$.

(e) $(x, y) = (2, 3) + k(2, 6)$; $x = 2 + 2k$, $y = 3 + 6k$.

(f) $(x, y) = (2, 3) + k(-7, -4)$; $x = 2 - 7k$, $y = 3 - 4k$.

9. (a) $(3, 4)$, $(5, 1)$; $(2, -3)$.　　　(b) $(-1, 3)$, $(-3, 2)$; $(-2, -1)$.

(c) $(0, 1)$, $(4, -1)$; $(4, -2)$.　　　(d) $(3, -2)$, $(3, 3)$; $(0, -5)$.

(e) $(0, 0)$, $(1, -2)$; $(1, -2)$.　　　(f) $(4, -1)$, $(3, -1)$; $(-1, 0)$.

12. $x = kx_1$, $y = ky_1$.　　　13. (a) $x = x_1 + k$, $y = y_1$.　　　(b) $x = x_1$, $y = y_1 + k$.

EXERCISE 4.3 (page 120)

1. (a) $x + y = 10$.　　　(b) $x + y = -1$.　　　(c) $x - 4y = 34$.

(d) $-x + 2y = 2$.　　　(e) $3x - y = 30$.　　　(f) $2x + 3y = 13$.

(g) $x = 10$.　　　(h) $y = 9$.　　　(i) $3x + 2y = 13$.

(j) $2x + 5y = 3$.　　　(k) $3x + 7y = 0$.　　　(l) $2x - 5y = -25$.

2. (a) $3x + 5y = 34$.　　　(b) $3x - 7y = -58$.　　　(c) $2x + 7y = -53$.

(d) $y = 4$.　　　(e) Not determined.

3. (a) $3x + 4y = \pm 25$.　　　(b) $-2x + 7y = \pm 3\sqrt{53}$.

(c) $2x - 3y = \pm 10\sqrt{13}$.

4. (a) $(\frac{39}{25}, \frac{52}{25})$.   (b) $(\frac{7}{3}, 0)$.   (c) $(\frac{18}{29}, \frac{-45}{29})$.   (d) $(\frac{-9}{58}, \frac{21}{58})$.
(e) $(0, \frac{-5}{2})$.   (f) $(\frac{-3}{13}, \frac{9}{26})$.   (g) $(-3, 2)$.   (h) $(\frac{3}{26}, \frac{15}{26})$.

5. (a) $\frac{13}{5}$. (b) $\frac{7}{3}$. (c) $\frac{9\sqrt{29}}{29}$. (d) $\frac{3\sqrt{58}}{58}$. (e) $\frac{5}{2}$. (f) $\frac{3\sqrt{13}}{26}$. (g) $\sqrt{13}$. (h) $\frac{3\sqrt{26}}{26}$.

6. (a) $\frac{8}{\sqrt{5}}$.   (b) 0.   (c) $\frac{21}{\sqrt{34}}$.   (d) $\frac{28}{\sqrt{53}}$.

EXERCISE 4.4 (page 124)

1. (a) $(4, 6)$, $\dfrac{x-3}{2} = \dfrac{y-3}{3}$.   (b) $(10, -5)$, $\dfrac{x+2}{2} = \dfrac{y-5}{-1}$.

(c) $(1, 3)$, $\dfrac{x+3}{1} = \dfrac{y+2}{3}$.   (d) $(1, 1)$, $\dfrac{x+1}{1} = \dfrac{y+2}{1}$.

(e) $(7, -3)$, $\dfrac{x-1}{7} = \dfrac{y-1}{-3}$.   (f) $(9, 2)$, $\dfrac{x}{9} = \dfrac{y-2}{2}$.

(g) $(3, 4)$, $\dfrac{x-3}{3} = \dfrac{y}{4}$.   (h) $(3, -2)$, $\dfrac{x-4}{3} = \dfrac{y-6}{-2}$.

(i) $(-1, 0)$, no symmetric equation. (j) $(0, -3)$, no symmetric equation.

(k) $(4, 3)$, $\dfrac{x-5}{4} = \dfrac{y-2}{3}$.

2. (a) $x + 5y = -24$.   (b) $7x - 3y = 22$.   (c) $3x - 4y = 23$.
(d) $y + 5 = 0$.

3. $5x + 3y + 1 = 0$.   **4.** (a) Parallel to x-axis.   (b) Parallel to y-axis.

EXERCISE 4.5 (page 128)

1. (a) $56°, 34°$.   (b) $153°, -63°$.   (c) $72°, 18°$.   (d) $45°, 45°$.
(e) $157°, -67°$.   (f) $13°, 77°$.   (g) $53°, 37°$.   (h) $146°, -56°$.
(i) $180°, -90°$.   (j) $90°, 0°$.   (k) $37°, 53°$.

2. (a) $x - y = -1$. (b) $2\sqrt{3} + 3 = \sqrt{3}x + y$. (c) $.259x + .966y = 3.416$.

3. (a) $41°, 49°$.   (b) $109°, -19°$.   (c) $127°, -37°$.   (d) $67°, 23°$.

4. $\sqrt{3}x + y = \pm 10$.

EXERCISE 4.6 (page 131)

1. (a) $(x, y, z) = (1 - r)(1, 1, 1) + r(5, 5, 5)$; $x = k, y = k, z = k$; $x = y = z$.

(b) $\dfrac{x-1}{4} = \dfrac{y}{3} = \dfrac{z-4}{5}$.   (c) $x = 4 - 3r, y = 2, z = 1 + 3r$.

(d) $\dfrac{x+1}{8} = \dfrac{y-3}{4} = \dfrac{z-5}{-8}$.   (e) $\dfrac{x+4}{3} = \dfrac{y-1}{4} = \dfrac{z-7}{-5}$.

(f) $x = 4 + 2r, y = -3 + 10r, z = -3$.

(g) $x = 5 - 7r, y = -1, z = 3$.   (h) $\dfrac{x+6}{5} = \dfrac{y-2}{-3} = \dfrac{z-1}{-8}$.

(i) $x = -3, y = 1 + 5r, z = 6$.   (j) $x = 0, y = r, z = 1 - r$.

2. (a) $(3, 3, 3)$. (b) $(3, \frac{3}{2}, \frac{13}{2})$. (c) $(\frac{5}{2}, 2, \frac{5}{2})$. (d) $(3, 5, 1)$.
(e) $(-\frac{5}{2}, 3, \frac{9}{2})$. (f) $(5, 2, -3)$. (g) $(\frac{3}{2}, -1, 3)$. (h) $(-\frac{7}{2}, \frac{1}{2}, -3)$.
(i) $(-3, \frac{7}{2}, 6)$. (j) $(0, \frac{1}{2}, \frac{1}{2})$.

3. (a) $(2, \frac{1}{2}, 0)$. (b) $(\frac{13}{7}, \frac{5}{7}, \frac{2}{7})$. (c) No such point. (d) $(-2, \frac{13}{2}, 8)$.

4. (a) $AP : PB = 1 : 1$. (b) $AP : PB = 4 : 1$. (c) $PA : AB = 1 : 1$.
(d) $AP : PB = 4 : -3$. (e) $AB : BP = 1 : 1$. (f) $AP : PB = -4 : 5$.

6. (a) Parallel to y-axis through $(3, 0, -1)$.
(b) Parallel to x-axis through $(0, 4, -2)$.
(c) In the plane $z = 2$ through $(0, \frac{17}{2}, 2)$ and $(\frac{17}{3}, 0, 2)$.

7. (a) $x = x_1 + t, \; y = y_1, \; z = z_1$. (b) $x = x_1, \; y = y_1 + t, \; z = z_1$.
(c) $x = x_1, \; y = y_1, \; z = z_1 + t$.

8. $x = x_1 + ks_1, \; y = y_1 + ks_2, \; z = z_1 + ks_3$.

9. (a) $x = -2 - 3k, \; y = 5 + k, \; z = 3 - 4k$.
(b) $x = -2 + 4k, \; y = 5, \; z = 3 - 7k$.
(c) $x = -2, \; y = 5 - 2k, \; z = 3 + k$.

EXERCISE 4.7 (page 136)

1. (a) $55°, 55°, 55°$. (b) $16°, 79°, 79°$. (c) $45°, 90°, 45°$.
(d) $135°, 90°, 45°$. (e) $52°, 99°, 40°$. (f) $135°, 124°, 65°$.
(g) $29°, 103°, 64°$. (h) $126°, 79°, 38°$. (i) $146°, 90°, 33°$.
(j) $34°, 124°, 90°$.

2. (a) Parallel to z-axis. (b) Parallel to y-axis. (c) Parallel to x-axis.

3. (a) $\dfrac{x - 1}{4} = \dfrac{y - 1}{3} = \dfrac{z - 5}{-1}$. (b) $\dfrac{x + 3}{1} = \dfrac{y - 1}{-2} = \dfrac{z - 3}{4}$.
(c) $x = 4 + 3t, \; y = 2, \; z = 4 - 2t$. (d) $x = -1, \; y = 5 + 3t, \; z = 2$.
(e) $\dfrac{x - 4}{1} = \dfrac{y - 1}{-2} = \dfrac{z - 7}{2}$. (f) $x = 2 + k, \; y = -1 + 2k, \; z = 8$.
(g) $x = 4 + k, \; y = 1 + k, \; z = 0$. (h) $\dfrac{x + 2}{1} = \dfrac{y - 1}{-1} = \dfrac{z - 2}{\sqrt{2}}$.

REVIEW EXERCISE 4 (page 137)

1. (a) $AP : PB = 3 : 1$. (b) $AP : PB = -4 : 7$.
(c) Segment PB, where $AP : PB = 1 : 1$.
(d) Ray AP, where $PA : AB = 1 : 1$.

2. (a) $k = \frac{1}{5}$. (b) $k = -\frac{1}{2}$.

3. (a) P is A or B. (b) P is on ray BC with B between A and C.
(c) Line segment CB with $CA : AB = 1 : 1$.

4. (a) $\mathbf{r} = (1 - k)(4, 1) + k(3, 4); \; x = 4 - k, \; y = 1 + 3k$.
(b) $\mathbf{r} = (1 - k)(-2, 1) + k(3, -2); \; x = -2 + 5k, \; y = 1 - 3k$.
(c) $\mathbf{r} = (1 - k)(5, 0) + k(0, 2); \; x = 5 - 5k, \; y = 2k$.
(d) $\mathbf{r} = (1 - k)(-3, -4) + k(-2, 0); \; x = -3 + k, \; y = -4 + 4k$.

5. (a) $A(-3, 5), \; B(4, 0)$. (b) Ray AB. (c) Line AB.

6. (a) $\mathbf{r} = (2, -1) + k(3, -1)$; $x = 2 + 3k$, $y = -1 - k$.
(b) $\mathbf{r} = (5, 0) + k(-2, -3)$; $x = 5 - 2k$, $y = 0 - 3k$.

7. (a) $2x + 3y = 5$.   (b) $x = -2$.   (c) $5x - 2y = 0$.   (d) $x + y = 6$.

8. (a) $5x + 2y = 29$.   (b) $3x - y = -10$.   (c) $4x + 3y = -25$.

9. (a) $(\frac{9}{17}, \frac{36}{17})$.   (b) $(\frac{7}{2}, 0)$.   (c) $(\frac{-12}{13}, \frac{8}{13})$.   (d) $(\frac{3}{5}, -\frac{9}{5})$.

10. (a) $\frac{9}{17}\sqrt{17}$.   (b) $\frac{7}{2}$.   (c) $\frac{4}{13}\sqrt{13}$.   (d) $\frac{3}{5}\sqrt{10}$.

11. (a) $\frac{10}{17}\sqrt{17}$.   (b) $\frac{9}{2}$.   (c) $\frac{9}{13}\sqrt{13}$.   (d) $\frac{11}{5}\sqrt{10}$.

12. (a) $(7, -7)$; $\left(-\dfrac{1}{\sqrt{2}}, \dfrac{1}{\sqrt{2}}\right)$; $(135°, -45°)$; $\dfrac{x + 3}{1} = \dfrac{y - 4}{-1}$.

(b) $(2, 3)$; $\left(\dfrac{2}{\sqrt{13}}, \dfrac{3}{\sqrt{13}}\right)$; $(56°, 34°)$; $\dfrac{x - 4}{2} = \dfrac{y}{3}$.

(c) $(2, -1)$; $\left(-\dfrac{2}{\sqrt{5}}, \dfrac{1}{\sqrt{5}}\right)$; $(153°, -63°)$; $\dfrac{x - 5}{2} = \dfrac{y + 3}{-1}$.

(d) $(4, -3)$; $(-\frac{4}{5}, \frac{3}{5})$; $(143°, -53°)$; $\dfrac{x - 1}{4} = \dfrac{y - 1}{-3}$.

13. (a) $(x, y, z) = (1 - k)(3, -2, 3) + k(4, 0, -2)$; $x = 3 + k$, $y = -2 + 2k$,
$z = 3 - 5k$; $\dfrac{x - 3}{1} = \dfrac{y + 2}{2} = \dfrac{z - 3}{-5}$.

(b) $(x, y, z) = (1 - k)(5, 2, -1) + k(5, 2, 6)$; $x = 5$, $y = 2$, $z = -1 + 7k$.

(c) $(x, y, z) = (1 - k)(-1, 3, -2) + k(5, -3, -3)$; $x = -1 + 6k$,
$y = 3 - 6k$, $z = -2 - k$; $\dfrac{x + 1}{6} = \dfrac{y - 3}{-6} = \dfrac{z + 2}{-1}$.

(d) $(x, y, z) = (1 - k)(2, 1, 7) + k(-6, 1, -4)$; $x = 2 - 8k$, $y = 1$, $z = 7 - 11k$.

14. (a) $(\frac{7}{2}, -1, \frac{1}{2})$.   (b) $(5, 2, \frac{5}{2})$.   (c) $(2, 0, -\frac{5}{2})$.   (d) $(-2, 1, \frac{3}{2})$.

15. (a) $(-1, -2, 5)$; $\left(\dfrac{-1}{\sqrt{30}}, \dfrac{-2}{\sqrt{30}}, \dfrac{5}{\sqrt{30}}\right)$; $(101°, 111°, 24°)$.

(b) $(0, 0, 7)$; $(0, 0, 1)$; $(90°, 90°, 0°)$.

(c) $(6, -6, -1)$; $\left(-\dfrac{6}{\sqrt{73}}, \dfrac{6}{\sqrt{73}}, \dfrac{1}{\sqrt{73}}\right)$; $(135°, 45°, 83°)$.

(d) $(8, 0, 11)$; $\left(\dfrac{8}{\sqrt{185}}, 0, \dfrac{11}{\sqrt{185}}\right)$; $(54°, 90°, 36°)$.

16. (a) $(3, -7, 3)$; $\left(\dfrac{3}{\sqrt{67}}, \dfrac{-7}{\sqrt{67}}, \dfrac{3}{\sqrt{67}}\right)$; $(68°, 149°, 68°)$.

(b) $(5, 1, 0)$; $\left(\dfrac{5}{\sqrt{26}}, \dfrac{1}{\sqrt{26}}, 0\right)$; $(11°, 79°, 90°)$.

17. (a) $\dfrac{x - 4}{5} = \dfrac{y - 1}{1} = \dfrac{z + 2}{-4}$.   (b) $x = -2 + \frac{3}{5}k$, $y = 3$, $z = -1 + \frac{4}{5}k$.

(c) $x = 5 + k$, $y = -1 + \sqrt{2}k$, $z = 2 - k$.

Chapter 5

EXERCISE 5.1 (page 141)

2. (a) $m = \frac{1}{2}$.   (b) $k = -4$.   (c) $k + m = 3$.   (d) $k - m = -3$.

EXERCISE 5.2   (page 143)

1. (a) $(x, y, z) = (1 - k - m)(0, 0, 0) + k(1, 4, 9) + m(2, 2, 5)$;
   $x = k + 2m, \ y = 4k + 2m, \ z = 9k + 5m$.

   (b) $(x, y, z) = (1 - k - m)(0, 0, 0) + k(-1, -3, -1) + m(2, 5, -4)$;
   $x = -k + 2m, \ y = -3k + 5m, \ z = -k - 4m$.

   (c) $(x, y, z) = (1 - k - m)(1, 0, 0) + k(0, 1, 0) + m(0, 0, 1)$;
   $x = 1 - k - m, \ y = k, \ z = m$.

   (d) $(x, y, z) = (1 - k - m)(0, 0, 3) + k(0, -2, 0) + m(5, 0, 0)$;
   $x = 5m, \ y = -2k, \ z = 3 - 3k - 3m$.

   (e) $(x, y, z) = (1 - k - m)(5, 0, 0) + k(3, 2, -1) + m(4, 4, 0)$;
   $x = 5 - 2k - m, \ y = 2k + 4m, \ z = -k$.

   (f) $(x, y, z) = (1 - k - m)(-1, 3, -1) + k(0, 2, 0) + m(3, -1, 2)$;
   $x = -1 + k + 4m, \ y = 3 - k - 4m, \ z = -1 + k + 3m$.

   (g) $(x, y, z) = (1 - k - m)(2, 4, 3) + k(2, -1, 5) + m(2, 0, 6)$;
   $x = 2, \ y = 4 - 5k - 4m, \ z = 3 + 2k + 3m$.

3. (a) $x = x_1, \ y = k, \ z = m$.   (b) $x = k, \ y = y_1, \ z = m$.
   (c) $x = k, \ y = m, \ z = z_1$.

EXERCISE 5.3   (page 148)

1. (a) $5x + 5y + z = 15$.   (b) $y + 2z = 7$.
   (c) $5x + 2y = -13$.   (d) $x = 3$.   (e) $4x + 2y - z = 3$.
   (f) $-3x - 2y + 2z = -11$.   (g) $3x + 3y - 4z = 0$.
   (h) $x = 0$.   (i) $3x + 5y - 2z = 6$.   (j) $y = 0$.

2. (a) $y = \pm 4$.   (b) $x = \pm 2$.   (c) $5x - 3z = \pm 3\sqrt{34}$.
   (d) $5y - 2z = \pm\frac{1}{2}\sqrt{29}$.   (e) $3x - 3y + z = \pm\sqrt{57}$.
   (f) $2x - 3y - 5z = \pm\pi\sqrt{38}$.

3. (a) $2x + 2y + 3z = 17$.   (b) $-4x + 3y = 25$.   (c) $4x - y - 3z = 26$.

4. (a) $(0, 0, 0)$.   (b) $(\frac{5}{26}, \frac{15}{26}, \frac{10}{13})$.   (c) $(\frac{-10}{11}, \frac{30}{11}, \frac{10}{11})$.
   (d) $(\frac{80}{27}, \frac{-16}{27}, \frac{-16}{27})$.   (e) $(\frac{-24}{7}, \frac{36}{7}, \frac{-12}{7})$.   (f) $(\frac{-24}{13}, \frac{8}{13}, \frac{-32}{13})$.

5. (a) 0.   (b) $\frac{5}{26}\sqrt{26}$.   (c) $\frac{10}{11}\sqrt{11}$.   (d) $\frac{16}{9}\sqrt{3}$.   (e) $\frac{12}{7}\sqrt{14}$.   (f) $\frac{8}{13}\sqrt{26}$.

7. (a) $\frac{6}{7}\sqrt{14}$. (b) $\frac{1}{2}\sqrt{14}$. (c) $\frac{17}{19}\sqrt{38}$. (d) $\frac{1}{6}\sqrt{18}$. (e) $\frac{29}{14}\sqrt{14}$. (f) $\frac{37}{29}\sqrt{29}$.

REVIEW EXERCISE 5   (page 159)

3. (a) $x = 3k + 4m, \ y = 2k - m, \ z = -k + m$.
   (b) $x = 1 + 2k - 3m, \ y = 2 - 3k - m, \ z = -1 + 5k + 6m$.
   (c) $x = -3 + 9k, \ y = 1 - 2k + 4m, \ z = 4 - 5k - 4m$.
   (d) $x = 5 - 8k - m, \ y = -2 + 2k + 2m, \ z = -m$.

5. (a) $x + y + 5z = 14$.   (b) $4x - y = 6$.
   (c) $-x + 3y - z = -10$.   (d) $2x + 5z = 26$.

6. (a) $5x + y + 2z = \pm 3\sqrt{30}$.   (b) $2x - y - z = \pm 3\sqrt{2}$.

7. (a) $(\frac{3}{7}, \frac{-9}{7}, \frac{6}{7})$.   (b) $\frac{3}{7}\sqrt{14}$.

8. (a) $\frac{6}{13}\sqrt{26}$.   (b) $\frac{9}{41}\sqrt{41}$.   (c) $\frac{3}{5}\sqrt{10}$.   (d) 1.

Chapter 6

EXERCISE 6.1   (page 163)

1. $\{(-7, 15)\}$.   2. $\{(1, 2)\}$.   3. $\{(3, 5)\}$.   4. $\{(1, 2)\}$.
5. $\{(\frac{28}{19}, \frac{30}{19})\}$.   6. $\{(1, 3)\}$.   7. $\{(\frac{1}{2}, 1)\}$.   8. $\{(\frac{1}{2}, -\frac{11}{4})\}$.
9. $\{(6, -5)\}$.   10. $\{(-3, 5, 7)\}$.   11. $\{(2, -1, 1)\}$.   12. $\{(2, 3, 4)\}$.
13. $\{(-\frac{10}{17}, \frac{39}{17}, \frac{130}{17})\}$.   14. $\{(-1, -1, -1)\}$.
15. $\{(2, -2, \frac{1}{2})\}$.   16. $\{(\frac{1}{6}, \frac{1}{2})\}$.   17. $\{(\frac{1}{3}, \frac{1}{2})\}$.   18. $\{(0, 0, 0)\}$.
19. $\{(\frac{11}{2}, \frac{11}{30})\}$.   20. $\{(\frac{11}{140}, \frac{-11}{57})\}$.   21. $\{(0, 0, 0)\}$.

EXERCISE 6.2   (page 166)

1. $\{(\frac{29}{3}, 11)\}$.   2. Inconsistent.   3. Inconsistent.   4. Inconsistent.
5. $\{(\frac{18}{19}, \frac{28}{19}, \frac{31}{19})\}$.   6. Inconsistent.   7. Inconsistent.   8. $\{(2, -1)\}$.
9. Inconsistent.   10. Inconsistent.   11. Inconsistent.   12. $\{(\frac{4}{3}, \frac{4}{15}, \frac{-17}{15})\}$.
13. Inconsistent.   14. $\{(\frac{18}{7}, \frac{5}{7})\}$.   15. Inconsistent.

EXERCISE 6.3   (page 170)

1. Dependent; $\{(4 + 3k, k) \mid k \in Re\}$.

2. Dependent; $\left\{\left(-\dfrac{2k + 3}{3}, k\right) \middle| k \in Re\right\}$.

3. Dependent; $\{(3 - 2k + l, k, l) \mid k, l \in Re\}$.

4. Dependent; $\left\{\left(\dfrac{k - 3l - 1}{2}, k, l\right) \middle| k, l \in Re\right\}$.

5. Dependent; $\{(5 - k + l - m, k, l, m) \mid k, l, m \in Re\}$.
6. Dependent; $\{(3k - 2l + m - 2, k, l, m) \mid k, l, m \in Re\}$.
7. Independent; $\{(\frac{7}{5}, \frac{4}{5})\}$.   8. Inconsistent.
9. Dependent; $\{(3 - 2k, k) \mid k \in Re\}$.   10. Inconsistent.

11. Dependent; $\left\{\left(-5k - 13, -\dfrac{7k + 19}{2}, k\right) \middle| k \in Re\right\}$.

12. Independent; $\{(2, 1, -3)\}$.

13. Dependent; $\left\{\left(\dfrac{9 - 5k}{3}, -\dfrac{k}{3}, k\right) \middle| k \in Re\right\}$.

14. Dependent; $\left\{\left(\dfrac{31 - 4k}{7}, \dfrac{5k - 9}{7}, k\right) \middle| k \in Re\right\}$.

15. Dependent; $\left\{\left(\dfrac{8k - 8}{7}, \dfrac{26k - 19}{7}, k\right) \middle| k \in Re\right\}$.

16. Dependent; $\left\{\left(\dfrac{5k - 8l + 24}{7}, \dfrac{k - 3l + 9}{7\cdot}, k, l\right) \middle| k, l \in Re\right\}$.

17. Dependent; $\left\{\left(\dfrac{-17k + 13l - 20}{5}, \dfrac{-13k + 17l - 25}{5}, k, l\right) \middle| k, l \in Re\right\}.$

18. Dependent; $\left\{\left(\dfrac{-7 + 8k - 7l}{10}, \dfrac{9 - k + 4l}{5}, k, l\right) \middle| k, l \in Re\right\}.$

19. Dependent; $\left\{\left(\dfrac{11 - 2k - 7l + 13m}{5}, \dfrac{3k + 3l - 2m + 1}{5}, k, l, m\right) \middle| k, l, m \in Re\right\}.$

20. $\left\{\left(\dfrac{4 - 5k}{2}, k\right) \middle| k \in Re\right\}.$ 21. $\left\{\left(\dfrac{8-k}{3}, \dfrac{1 + 7k}{3}, k\right) \middle| k \in Re\right\}.$

22. $\left\{\left(\dfrac{6 - 2k}{5}, \dfrac{2 + 16k}{5}, k\right) \middle| k \in Re\right\}.$

EXERCISE 6.4   (page 173)

1. Dependent; $\{(5k, k) \mid k \in Re\}.$

2. Dependent; $\left\{\left(\dfrac{2k - l}{3}, k, l\right) \middle| k, l \in Re\right\}.$

3. Dependent; $\{(2k + l - 3m, k, l, m) \mid k, l, m \in Re\}.$
4. Independent; $\{(0, 0)\}.$ 5. Dependent; $\{(-3k, k) \mid k \in Re\}.$
6. Independent; $\{(0, 0)\}.$ 7. Dependent; $\{(2k, k, 0) \mid k \in Re\}.$
8. Dependent; $\{(2k - l, k, l) \mid k, l \in Re\}.$
9. Dependent; $\{(-k, -k, k) \mid k \in Re\}.$
10. Independent; $\{(0, 0, 0)\}.$ 11. Dependent; $\left\{\left(-\dfrac{k}{7}, \dfrac{4k}{7}, k\right) \middle| k \in Re\right\}.$
12. Dependent; $\{(-2k + l, k, l) \mid k, l \in Re\}.$
13. Dependent; $\{(l - k, k - 2l, k, l) \mid k, l \in Re\}.$
14. Dependent; $\{(4k - 3l, 11k - 7l, k, l) \mid k, l \in Re\}.$

15. Dependent; $\left\{\left(\dfrac{k + l - 2m}{2}, k, l, m\right) \middle| k, l, m \in Re\right\}.$

16. Dependent; $\left\{\left(\dfrac{-2k + l}{3}, k, l, 0\right) \middle| k, l \in Re\right\}.$

17. Dependent; $\{(-k, -k, k, 0) \mid k \in Re\}.$

18. Dependent; $\left\{\left(\dfrac{-9k}{28}, \dfrac{-43k}{28}, \dfrac{-87k}{28}, k\right) \middle| k \in Re\right\}.$

EXERCISE 6.5   (page 176)

1. (1) $[1 \quad -3 \quad 4].$ (2) $[3 \quad 2 \quad -3].$ (3) $[1 \quad 2 \quad -1 \quad 3].$
   (4) $[2 \quad -1 \quad 3 \quad -1].$ (5) $[1 \quad 1 \quad -1 \quad 1 \quad 5].$ (6) $[1 \quad -3 \quad 2 \quad -1 \quad -2].$

   (7) $\begin{bmatrix} 1 & 2 & 3 \\ 2 & -1 & 2 \end{bmatrix}.$ (8) $\begin{bmatrix} 1 & 2 & 3 \\ 3 & 6 & 6 \end{bmatrix}.$ (9) $\begin{bmatrix} 1 & 2 & 3 \\ 3 & 6 & 9 \end{bmatrix}.$

(10) $\begin{bmatrix} 1 & -2 & -2 & 6 \\ 3 & -4 & 1 & -1 \\ 5 & -8 & -3 & 12 \end{bmatrix}$. (11) $\begin{bmatrix} 1 & -2 & -2 & 6 \\ 3 & -4 & 1 & -1 \\ 5 & -8 & -3 & 11 \end{bmatrix}$. (12) $\begin{bmatrix} 1 & -2 & -2 & 6 \\ 3 & -4 & 1 & -1 \\ 2 & -5 & 3 & -10 \end{bmatrix}$.

(13) $\begin{bmatrix} 1 & -2 & 1 & 3 \\ 2 & -1 & 3 & 6 \end{bmatrix}$. (14) $\begin{bmatrix} 2 & 3 & -1 & 5 \\ 1 & 5 & -3 & -2 \end{bmatrix}$. (15) $\begin{bmatrix} 3 & -2 & 4 & 2 \\ 5 & -1 & -2 & -3 \end{bmatrix}$.

(16) $\begin{bmatrix} 1 & 2 & -1 & 2 & 6 \\ 3 & -1 & -2 & 3 & 9 \end{bmatrix}$. (17) $\begin{bmatrix} 2 & -3 & -1 & 5 & 7 \\ 3 & -2 & 5 & -1 & -2 \end{bmatrix}$.

(18) $\begin{bmatrix} 2 & 3 & -1 & -1 & 4 \\ 4 & 1 & -3 & 2 & -1 \end{bmatrix}$. (19) $\begin{bmatrix} 1 & -1 & 1 & 2 & -3 & 2 \\ 2 & 3 & -1 & 1 & -4 & 5 \end{bmatrix}$

(20) [2 5 4]. (21) $\begin{bmatrix} 1 & 1 & -2 & 3 \\ 2 & -1 & 3 & 5 \end{bmatrix}$. (22) $\begin{bmatrix} 3 & 1 & -2 & 4 \\ 2 & -1 & 4 & 2 \end{bmatrix}$.

2. (a) $\begin{bmatrix} 3 & -2 & 7 \\ 5 & 2 & 4 \end{bmatrix}$. (b) $\begin{bmatrix} 5 & 2 & 4 \\ 3 & -2 & 7 \end{bmatrix} \rightarrow \begin{bmatrix} 5 & 2 & 4 \\ 23 & 6 & 23 \end{bmatrix} \rightarrow \begin{bmatrix} 30 & 12 & 24 \\ 23 & 6 & 23 \end{bmatrix}$.

3. $\begin{bmatrix} 5 & 0 \\ 51 & -3 \end{bmatrix}$. **4.** $\begin{bmatrix} 1 & 1 \\ 18 & 0 \end{bmatrix}$. **5.** $\begin{bmatrix} 0 & 1 \\ 3 & 9 \end{bmatrix}$. **6.** $\begin{bmatrix} 0 & 1 & 3 \\ 12 & 15 & 24 \end{bmatrix}$.

7. $\begin{bmatrix} 4 & 1 & 6 \\ 42 & 12 & 48 \end{bmatrix}$. **8.** $\begin{bmatrix} 1 & 1 & 1 \\ 12 & 12 & 12 \end{bmatrix}$. **9.** $\begin{bmatrix} 2 & 1 & 5 & 2 \\ 27 & 6 & 60 & 18 \end{bmatrix}$.

10. $\begin{bmatrix} 0 & 4 & 1 & 5 \\ -9 & 39 & 12 & 51 \end{bmatrix}$. **11.** $\begin{bmatrix} 2 & 0 & 1 & 3 \\ 15 & 9 & 18 & 15 \end{bmatrix}$. **12.** $\begin{bmatrix} 10 & 2 & 4 \\ 0 & 1 & 5 \\ 33 & 5 & 16 \end{bmatrix}$.

13. $\begin{bmatrix} 2 & 2 & 4 \\ 5 & 3 & 1 \\ 8 & 5 & 18 \end{bmatrix}$. **14.** $\begin{bmatrix} 8 & 2 & 2 & -6 \\ 0 & 1 & 5 & 2 \\ 25 & 9 & 4 & -17 \end{bmatrix}$. **15.** $\begin{bmatrix} 1 & -1 & 4 \\ \frac{17}{2} & \frac{-9}{2} & 14 \\ 1 & 4 & -1 \end{bmatrix}$.

16. $\begin{bmatrix} 0 & -1 & -2 \\ 4 & -\frac{9}{2} & -5 \\ 3 & 1 & 5 \end{bmatrix}$. **17.** $\begin{bmatrix} 0 & -4 & 2 & -1 \\ 4 & 10 & -7 & -\frac{9}{2} \\ 2 & 1 & 3 & 5 \end{bmatrix}$. **18.** $\begin{bmatrix} -2 & 7 & 3 \\ 11 & -\frac{9}{2} & \frac{3}{2} \\ -2 & 1 & -1 \end{bmatrix}$.

19. $\begin{bmatrix} 4 & 2 & 0 \\ 10 & -11 & 12 \\ 3 & 1 & -4 \end{bmatrix}$. **20.** $\begin{bmatrix} -3 & 3 & -3 & -1 \\ \frac{29}{2} & -\frac{13}{2} & \frac{37}{2} & -\frac{9}{2} \\ 3 & -1 & 3 & 5 \end{bmatrix}$.

EXERCISE 6.6 (page 181)

1. $\begin{bmatrix} 1 & 3 \\ 0 & 1 \end{bmatrix}$. **2.** $\begin{bmatrix} 1 & \frac{3}{2} \\ 0 & 1 \end{bmatrix}$. **3.** $\begin{bmatrix} 1 & 3 \\ 0 & 0 \end{bmatrix}$. **4.** $\begin{bmatrix} 1 & 3 & -1 \\ 0 & 1 & -\frac{7}{2} \end{bmatrix}$.

5. $\begin{bmatrix} 1 & -4 & -7 \\ 0 & 1 & \frac{23}{11} \end{bmatrix}$. **6.** $\begin{bmatrix} 1 & \frac{-1}{2} & 3 \\ 0 & 1 & \frac{-22}{9} \end{bmatrix}$. **7.** $\begin{bmatrix} 1 & 3 \\ 0 & 1 \\ 0 & 0 \end{bmatrix}$.

8. $\begin{bmatrix} 1 & \frac{3}{2} \\ 0 & 1 \\ 0 & 0 \end{bmatrix}$. **9.** $\begin{bmatrix} 1 & -\frac{5}{2} \\ 0 & 1 \\ 0 & 0 \end{bmatrix}$. **10.** $\begin{bmatrix} 1 & -1 & 5 \\ 0 & 1 & -\frac{11}{4} \\ 0 & 0 & 1 \end{bmatrix}$.

11. $\begin{bmatrix} 1 & \frac{5}{2} & \frac{-1}{2} \\ 0 & 1 & \frac{-11}{19} \\ 0 & 0 & 0 \end{bmatrix}.$ **12.** $\begin{bmatrix} 1 & -\frac{3}{2} & -\frac{5}{2} \\ 0 & 1 & \frac{23}{19} \\ 0 & 0 & 0 \end{bmatrix}.$ **13.** $\begin{bmatrix} 1 & 3 & -1 & 2 \\ 0 & 1 & \frac{1}{12} & \frac{1}{3} \\ 0 & 0 & 1 & -2 \end{bmatrix}.$

14. $\begin{bmatrix} 1 & -\frac{3}{2} & -\frac{3}{2} & 0 \\ 0 & 1 & -\frac{7}{3} & -\frac{2}{3} \\ 0 & 0 & 1 & \frac{5}{13} \end{bmatrix}.$ **15.** $\begin{bmatrix} 1 & 7 & 1 & -3 \\ 0 & 1 & \frac{1}{6} & -\frac{5}{9} \\ 0 & 0 & 0 & 1 \end{bmatrix}.$ **16.** $\begin{bmatrix} 1 & \frac{5}{2} & \frac{3}{2} \\ 0 & 1 & -\frac{5}{17} \end{bmatrix}.$

17. $\begin{bmatrix} 1 & 4 & -3 \\ 0 & 1 & -\frac{11}{9} \\ 0 & 0 & 1 \end{bmatrix}.$ **18.** $\begin{bmatrix} 1 & \frac{1}{2} & -\frac{3}{2} & \frac{1}{2} \\ 0 & 1 & -\frac{7}{4} & \frac{5}{4} \\ 0 & 0 & 1 & \frac{13}{33} \end{bmatrix}.$ **19.** $\begin{bmatrix} 1 & \frac{1}{2} & \frac{1}{2} \\ 0 & 1 & \frac{1}{4} \end{bmatrix}.$

20. $\begin{bmatrix} 1 & -2 & 3 \\ 0 & 1 & -\frac{4}{9} \\ 0 & 0 & 1 \end{bmatrix}.$ **21.** $\begin{bmatrix} 1 & 3 & -1 & 1 \\ 0 & 1 & \frac{1}{8} & \frac{3}{4} \\ 0 & 0 & 1 & \frac{46}{69} \end{bmatrix}.$

EXERCISE 6.7 (page 186)

1. $x = 5$; $\{5\}$; independent.

2. $x + 3y = -2$; $\{(-3k - 2, k) \mid k \in Re\}$; dependent.

3. $x + 2y = -1, y = 6$; $\{(-13, 6)\}$; independent.

4. $x = 4, y = -3$; $\{(4, -3)\}$; independent.

5. $x + 3y = -1, y = 0$; $\{(-1, 0)\}$; independent.

6. $x = 5, 0y = 4$; ϕ; inconsistent.

7. $x + 3y = -2, 0x + 0y = 0$; $\{(-3k - 2, k) \mid k \in Re\}$ dependent.

8. $x + 3y = 0; y = 0$; $\{(0, 0)\}$; independent.

9. $x + 5y = 0, 0x + 0y = 0$; $\{(-5k, k) \mid k \in Re\}$; dependent.

10. $x + 2y - 3z = 1, z = 2$; $\{(7 - 2k, k, 2) \mid k \in Re\}$; dependent.

11. $x - y + 5z = 2, y + z = 4$; $\{(6 - 6k, 4 - k, k) \mid k \in Re\}$; dependent.

12. $x + 3y - 2z = 0, 0x + 0y + 0z = 4$; ϕ; inconsistent.

13. $x + y - 4z = 3, 0x + 0y + 0z = 0$; $\{(3 - k + 4l, k, l) \mid k, l \in Re\}$; dependent.

14. $x + 2y - z = 5, y + 3z = 1, z = 2$; $\{(17, -5, 2)\}$; independent.

15. $x + 3y + 3z = 2, y + 4z = -1; 0x + 0y + 0z = 1$; ϕ; inconsistent.

16. $x + 2y - z = 5, z = 4, 0x + 0y + 0z = 1$; ϕ; inconsistent.

17. $x + 2y - z = 5, z = 4, 0x + 0y + 0z = 0$; $\{9 - 2k, k, 4) \mid k \in Re\}$; dependent.

18. $x + 3y + z = 4, y + 5z = 2, 0x + 0y + 0z = 0$;
$\{(14k - 2, 2 - 5k, k) \mid k \in Re\}$; dependent.

19. $\{(\frac{18}{11}, \frac{5}{11})\}$, independent.   **20.** ϕ, inconsistent.

21. $\left\{\left(\frac{4 + k}{3}, k\right) \middle| k \in Re\right\}$, dependent.

22. $\left\{\left(\dfrac{1-k}{7}, \dfrac{24+4k}{7}, k\right) \,\middle|\, k \in Re\right\}$, dependent.

23. $\left\{\left(\dfrac{5-k}{2}, \dfrac{3k-5}{2}, k\right) \,\middle|\, k \in Re\right\}$, dependent

24. $\{(\frac{8}{7}, \frac{-19}{7})\}$, independent.　　　　**25.** $\{(1, \frac{2}{5}, \frac{-12}{5})\}$, independent.

26. ϕ, inconsistent.　　　**27.** $\left\{\left(\dfrac{8-5k}{11}, \dfrac{13+7k}{11}, k\right) \,\middle|\, k \in Re\right\}$, dependent.

EXERCISE 6.8 (page 190)

2. $\{(x, y) \mid x = -3k - 2, y = k, k \in Re\}$, line.

7. $\{(x, y) \mid x = -3k - 2, y = k, k \in Re\}$, line.

9. $\{(x, y) \mid x = -5k, y = k, k \in Re\}$, line.

10. $\{(x, y, z) \mid x = 7 - 2k, y = k, z = 2, k \in Re\}$, line.

11. $\{(x, y, z) \mid x = 6 - 6k, y = 4 - k, z = k, k \in Re\}$, line.

13. $\{(x, y, z) \mid x = 3 - k + 4l, y = k, z = l, k, l \in Re\}$, plane.

17. $\{(x, y, z) \mid x = 9 - 2k, y = k, z = 4, k \in Re\}$, line.

18. $\{(x, y, z) \mid x = 14k - 2, y = 2 - 5k, k, k \in Re\}$, line.

21. $\left\{(x, y) \,\middle|\, x = \dfrac{4+k}{3}, y = k, k \in Re\right\}$, line.

22. $\{(x, y, z) \mid x = \dfrac{1-k}{7}, y = \dfrac{24+4k}{7}, z = k, k \in Re\}$, line.

23. $\{(x, y, z) \mid x = \dfrac{5-k}{2}, y = \dfrac{3k-5}{2}, z = k, k \in Re\}$, line.

27. $\{(x, y, z) \mid x = \dfrac{8-5k}{11}, y = \dfrac{13+7k}{11}, z = k, k \in Re\}$, line.

EXERCISE 6.9 (page 193)

1. Yes. **2.** Yes. **3.** No. **4.** No. **5.** No. **6.** No. **7.** No. **8.** No. **9.** Yes. **10.** No.

REVIEW EXERCISE 6 (page 194)

1. (a) $\{(\frac{9}{4}, \frac{19}{4})\}$.　　　　(b) $\{(\frac{11}{13}, \frac{-18}{13})\}$.　　　　(c) ϕ.

(d) $\{(3k - 3, k) \mid k \in Re\}$.　　　(e) $\{(\frac{91}{11}, \frac{-4}{11})\}$.　　　(f) ϕ.

(g) $\{(\frac{-38}{7}, \frac{-6}{7}, -7)\}$.　　(h) ϕ.　　(i) $\left\{\left(\dfrac{k-1}{10}, \dfrac{7-2k}{5}, k\right) \,\middle|\, k \in Re\right\}$.

(j) $\{(-1, 0, -3)\}$.

2. (a) Dependent, $\left\{\left(\dfrac{k+7}{6}, k\right) \,\middle|\, k \in Re\right\}$.

(b) Dependent, $\{(6 + 3k - 2l, k, l) \mid k, l \in Re\}$.

(c) Dependent, $\left\{\left(\dfrac{24-5k}{20}, \dfrac{2+5k}{10}, k\right) \,\Big|\, k \in Re\right\}$.

(d) Dependent, $\left\{\left(\dfrac{18-2k}{7}, \dfrac{15+17k}{7}, k\right) \,\Big|\, k \in Re\right\}$.   (e) Inconsistent, ϕ.

(f) Dependent, $\left\{\left(\dfrac{k-2}{3}, k, 0\right) \,\Big|\, k \in Re\right\}$.

(g) Dependent, $\left\{\left(\dfrac{18+3k-l}{5}, \dfrac{1+k+8l}{5}, k, l\right) \,\Big|\, k, l \in Re\right\}$.

(h) Dependent, $\left\{\left(\dfrac{4+7k-13l}{21}, k, \dfrac{9+11l}{7}, l\right) \,\Big|\, k, l \in Re\right\}$.

3. (a) Dependent, $\left\{\left(\dfrac{-4k}{3}, k\right) \,\Big|\, k \in Re\right\}$.

(b) Dependent, $\{(-3k-3l, k, l) \mid k, l \in Re\}$.

(c) Independent, $\{(0, 0)\}$.   (d) Dependent, $\left\{\left(\dfrac{4k}{3}, k\right) \,\Big|\, k \in Re\right\}$.

(e) Dependent, $\left\{\left(\dfrac{3k}{8}, \dfrac{k}{16}, k\right) \,\Big|\, k \in Re\right\}$.

(f) Dependent, $\{(-2k, k, 0) \mid k \in Re\}$.   (g) Independent, $\{(0, 0, 0)\}$.

(h) Dependent, $\left\{\left(\dfrac{8k}{7}, \dfrac{10k}{7}, k\right) \,\Big|\, k \in Re\right\}$.   (i) Independent, $\{(0, 0)\}$.

(j) Independent, $\{(0, 0, 0)\}$.

(k) Dependent, $\left\{\left(\dfrac{k}{2}, \dfrac{5k-4l}{2}, k, l\right) \,\Big|\, k, l \in Re\right\}$.

(l) Dependent, $\left\{\left(\dfrac{3k-5l}{15}, \dfrac{k}{5}, k, l\right) \,\Big|\, k, l \in Re\right\}$.   4. No.

5. (a) $\begin{bmatrix} 1 & 1 & 7 \\ 3 & -1 & 2 \end{bmatrix}$.   (b) $\begin{bmatrix} 5 & -2 & 7 \\ 3 & 4 & -3 \end{bmatrix}$.

(c) $\begin{bmatrix} 3 & -2 & 7 \\ 6 & -4 & 21 \end{bmatrix}$.   (d) $\begin{bmatrix} 1 & -3 & -3 \\ -2 & 6 & 6 \end{bmatrix}$.

(e) $\begin{bmatrix} 2 & 3 & 10 \\ 1 & -4 & 7 \end{bmatrix}$.   (f) $\begin{bmatrix} 1 & 2 & 6 \\ 3 & 6 & 12 \end{bmatrix}$.

(g) $\begin{bmatrix} 1 & 3 & -2 & 6 \\ 2 & -1 & -1 & -3 \\ 3 & 2 & -4 & 10 \end{bmatrix}$.   (h) $\begin{bmatrix} 1 & -2 & 1 & -4 \\ 3 & -4 & 2 & 3 \\ 4 & -6 & 3 & 6 \end{bmatrix}$.

(i) $\begin{bmatrix} 6 & -1 & -1 & -2 \\ 2 & 3 & 1 & 4 \\ 2 & -7 & -3 & -10 \end{bmatrix}$.   (j) $\begin{bmatrix} 3 & 1 & -2 & 3 \\ 1 & 4 & 0 & -1 \\ 0 & 3 & -2 & 6 \end{bmatrix}$.

6. (a) $\begin{bmatrix} 1 & 2 \\ 0 & 1 \end{bmatrix}$.   (b) $\begin{bmatrix} 1 & \frac{2}{3} \\ 0 & 1 \end{bmatrix}$.   (c) $\begin{bmatrix} 1 & \frac{-4}{3} \\ 0 & 1 \end{bmatrix}$.   (d) $\begin{bmatrix} 1 & 2 & -5 \\ 0 & 1 & -3 \end{bmatrix}$.

(e) $\begin{bmatrix} 1 & 7 & 3 \\ 0 & 1 & \frac{2}{11} \\ 0 & 0 & 1 \end{bmatrix}$

(f) $\begin{bmatrix} 1 & 1 & 1 \\ 0 & 1 & -1 \\ 0 & 0 & 1 \end{bmatrix}.$

(g) $\begin{bmatrix} 1 & 4 \\ 0 & 1 \\ 0 & 0 \end{bmatrix}.$

(h) $\begin{bmatrix} 1 & 5 & -3 \\ 0 & 1 & -\frac{5}{6} \\ 0 & 0 & 0 \end{bmatrix}.$

(i) $\begin{bmatrix} 1 & 3 & -2 \\ 0 & 1 & -\frac{13}{11} \\ 0 & 0 & 1 \\ 0 & 0 & 0 \end{bmatrix}.$

(j) $\begin{bmatrix} 1 & -2 & -2 & -4 \\ 0 & 1 & \frac{1}{4} & -1 \\ 0 & 0 & 1 & \frac{4}{3} \\ 0 & 0 & 0 & 1 \end{bmatrix}.$

7. (a) Independent.   (b) Independent.   (c) Dependent.   (d) Dependent.

(e) Dependent.   (f) Inconsistent.   (g) Independent.   (h) Dependent.

(i) Dependent.   (j) Independent.

8. (c) $\{(2 + 3k, k) \mid k \in Re\}$, line.

(d) $\left\{\left(\dfrac{5k - 2}{10}, \dfrac{5k + 14}{10}, k\right) \;\middle|\; k \in Re\right\}$, line.

(e) $\{(2k - 6, k, 5) \mid k \in Re\}$, line.

(h) $\left\{\left(\dfrac{9 - 8k}{7}, \dfrac{8 - 11k}{7}, k\right) \;\middle|\; k \in Re\right\}$, line.

(i) $\left\{\left(\dfrac{-k}{7}, \dfrac{2k}{7}, k\right) \;\middle|\; k \in Re\right\}$, line.

Chapter 7

EXERCISE 7.1 (page 199)

1. (a), (b), (d), (e) are sets; (c), (f) are not.

2. (a) 16.   (b) 12.   (c) False, false, true.

3. (a) True, false, true.   (b) False, true.

EXERCISE 7.2 (page 200)

1. (a) $\{a, b, c, d, e, f, g, h\}$.   (b) $\{c, d\}$.   (c) $\{e\}$.

(d) $\{c, d, e\}$.   (e) $\{c, d, e\}$.

2. (a) $\{\frac{1}{5}\}$.   (b) $\{\frac{1}{5}\}$.   (c) $\{\frac{1}{2}, \frac{1}{4}, \frac{1}{5}, \frac{1}{6}, \frac{1}{8}, \frac{1}{10}\}$.

(d) $\{\frac{1}{2}, \frac{1}{4}, \frac{1}{5}, \frac{1}{6}, \frac{1}{8}, \frac{1}{10}\}$.   (e) $\{\frac{1}{3}, \frac{1}{4}, \frac{1}{6}, \frac{1}{7}, \frac{1}{9}, \frac{1}{10}\}$.

(f) $\{\frac{1}{3}, \frac{1}{5}, \frac{1}{7}, \frac{1}{9}\}$.   (g) $\{\frac{1}{2}, \frac{1}{4}, \frac{1}{6}, \frac{1}{8}, \frac{1}{10}\}$.   (h) $\{\frac{1}{3}, \frac{1}{7}, \frac{1}{9}\}$.

(i) $\{\frac{1}{3}, \frac{1}{7}, \frac{1}{9}\}$.   (j) $\{\frac{1}{4}, \frac{1}{6}, \frac{1}{10}\}$.   (k) $\{\frac{1}{4}, \frac{1}{6}, \frac{1}{10}\}$.

3. (a) $\{-4, -3, -2, 3, 4\}$.   (b) ϕ.   (c) $U = \{-4, -3, -2, -1, 0, 1, 2, 3, 4\}$.

(d) $\{-1, 0, 1, 2\} = P$.   (e) U.

6. P' = set consisting of all composite positive integers and the integer 1.
Q' = set of all odd positive integers.
$P \cap Q = \{2\}$.
$P \cup Q$ = set consisting of all positive prime integers and all positive even integers.

7. $\{(-1, 2)\}$.   8. ϕ.

EXERCISE 7.5 (page 212)

8. Dual identities: (1) $(S \cup \phi)' \cap S' = S'$. (2) $(U \cup A) \cap B = B$.
(3) $A' \cap (A \cup B) = A' \cap B$. (4) $X \cup Y \cup X' = U$.
(5) $(A \cup B')' \cap B = A' \cap B$.   (6) $(P \cap Q') \cup (P' \cup Q)' = P \cap Q'$.
(7) $(M' \cup U)' \cup M = M$.

9. U.   10. ϕ.   11. P.   12. $A' \cup B$.   13. N.   14. U.   15. ϕ.   16. B.

EXERCISE 7.7 (page 217)

1. $A \times B = \{(a, r), (a, s), (b, r), (b, s), (c, r), (c, s), (d, r), (d, s)\}$.
$B \times A = \{(r, a), (r, b), (r, c), (r, d), (s, a), (s, b), (s, c), (s, d)\}$.

2. $P \times P = \{(1, 1), (1, 2), (1, 3), (1, 4), (1, 5), (2, 1), (2, 2), (2, 3), (2, 4), (2, 5),$
$(3, 1), (3, 2), (3, 3), (3, 4), (3, 5), (4, 1), (4, 2), (4, 3), (4, 4), (4, 5),$
$(5, 1), (5, 2), (5, 3), (5, 4), (5, 5)\}$.

3. $\{(1, 2), (1, 3), (1, 4), (1, 5), (2, 1), (2, 3), (2, 4), (2, 5), (3, 1), (3, 2), (3, 4), (3, 5),$
$(4, 1), (4, 2), (4, 3), (4, 5), (5, 1), (5, 2), (5, 3), (5, 4)\}$.

4. 25, 20.

5. (a) $\{(-2, 0), (-2, 1), (0, 0), (0, 1), (-1, 0), (-1, 1), (1, 0), (1, 1), (2, 0),$
$(2, 1)\}$.
(b) $\{(1, 0), (2, 0), (3, 0)\}$.
(c) $\{(0, 1), (0, 2), (0, 3), (0, 4), (0, 5), (0, 6), (0, 7), (0, 8), (0, 9)\}$.
(d) $\{(2, 1), (2, 2), (2, 3), (3, 1), (3, 2), (3, 3), (5, 1), (5, 2), (5, 3), (7, 1), (7, 2),$
$(7, 3), (11, 1), (11, 2), (11, 3)\}$.

6. (a) 5, 2, 10.   (b) 3, 1, 3.   (c) 1, 9, 9.   (d) 5, 3, 15.   7. None.   8. None.

9. $A \times B \times C = \{(-1, 1, 0), (-1, 1, 1), (-1, 2, 0), (-1, 2, 1), (0, 1, 0), (0, 1, 1),$
$(0, 2, 0), (0, 2, 1), (1, 1, 0), (1, 1, 1), (1, 2, 0), (1, 2, 1)\}$.

$B \times A \times C = \{(1, -1, 0), (1, -1, 1), (2, -1, 0), (2, -1, 1), (1, 0, 0), (1, 0, 1),$
$(2, 0, 0), (2, 0, 1), (1, 1, 0), (1, 1, 1), (2, 1, 0), (2, 1, 1)\}$.

EXERCISE 7.8 (page 218)

1.

	$n(A \times B)$	$n(A \cap B)$	$n(A \cup B)$
(a)	25	3	7
(b)	12	0	7
(c)	15	3	5
(d)	30	1	10
(e)	0	0	9

2. $n(P \cup Q) = n(P) + n(Q)$,
$n(P \cap Q) = 0$.

3. $n(T \cap S) = n(T)$,
$n(T \cup S) = n(S)$.

4. $B \subseteq A$.   5. 0.

6. 5.

EXERCISE 7.9 (page 221)

1. 80 and 7.   **2.** (a) 40 and 6.   (b) 60 and 5.   (c) 18 and 8.   (d) 12 and 5.
(e) 0 and 3.   **3.** 64 and 4.   **4.** 5.   **5.** 24.   **6.** (i) 512.   (ii) 336.
7. $n(P) + n(Q) + n(R)$.   **8.** 216 and 6.   **9.** 5.

EXERCISE 7.10 (page 223)

1. 0.
2. From the data, the number of families using either A or B or C is 10,239 and this exceeds the total number of families.
3. (a) 75.   (b) 80.   (c) 28.   **4.** 84.   **5.** (a) 100. (b) 150.   **6.** 13.

REVIEW EXERCISE 7 (page 225)

1. $A \cap B = \{3, 5, 7, 11, 13\}$. $A \cup B = \{1, 2, 3, 5, 7, 11, 13\}$.
$C = \{3, 5, 7, 11, 13\}$.
2. (a) $\{3, 5, 7, 11, 13, 17, 19\}$.   (b) $\{1, 2, 3, 5, 7, 9, 11, 13, 15, 17, 19\}$.
(c) $\{1, 4, 6, 8, 9, 10, 12, 14, 15, 16, 18\}$.
(d) $\{2, 4, 6, 8, 10, 12, 14, 16, 18\}$.
(e) $\{1, 2, 4, 6, 8, 9, 10, 12, 14, 15, 16, 18\}$.
(f) $\{4, 6, 8, 10, 12, 14, 16, 18\}$.   (g) $\{2\}$.
4. (a) U.   (b) D.   (c) $P' \cap Q$.   (d) C'.   (e) $R \cup S$.
5. (a) (i), (iii), (v) are true.
6. (a) 12.   (b) 72.   (c) 4.   (d) 7.   (e) 2.   (f) 7.
7. 12   **9.** 20.   **10.** 231.

Chapter 8

EXERCISE 8.1 (page 229)

1. (i) 12.   (ii) 240.   (iii) 840.   (iv) 2730.   (v) 120.   (vi) 360.
2. 336.   **3.** 42.   **4.** 120.   **5.** 720.   **6.** 60.   **7.** 48.   **8.** 100.
9. 15.   **10.** 8.   **11.** (a) 40,320. (b) 10,080.   (c) 30,240. **12.** 40,320.
13. 120.   **14.** 504.   **15.** 12.   **16.** (a) 720.   (b) 480.   (c) 48.
17. 970,200.   **18.** 90.   **19.** 210.

EXERCISE 8.2 (page 233)

1. (a) 56.   (b) 20.   (c) 20.   (d) 56.   (e) 56.   (f) 1140.
2. (a) $(n + 1)!$ (b) $(n + 6)!$ (c) $(n - r + 1)!$
3. (a) $(n + 4)(n + 5)$. (b) n.   (c) $n + 1$.   (d) $n - r + 1$.
(e) $n - r$.   (f) $(n - r + 1)(n - r)$.
4. (a) 2.   (b) 3.   (c) 6.   (d) 4.   (e) 3.   (f) 8.

EXERCISE 8.3 (page 236)

1. (a) 60.   (b) 56.   (c) 2520. (d) 3960.
2. (a) 180.   (b) 420.   (c) 360.   (d) 2520. (e) 34,650.   (f) 840.
3. 30.   **4.** 120.   **5.** (a) 3360. (b) 360.   **6.** 300.   **7.** 12.
8. 84.   **9.** (a) 180.   (b) 60.   (c) 120.   (d) 12.   (e) 48.
10. (a) 48.   (b) 24.   **11.** 35.   **12.** 120.

EXERCISE 8.4 (page 241)

1. (a) 28.   (b) 10.   (c) 91.   (d) 1.   (e) 1.   (f) 1330.
   (g) 1326. (h) 100.   (i) 600.   (j) 5005.
2. 6.   **3.** 21.   **4.** 16.   **5.** (a) 220.   (b) 1320.   **6.** 91.

7. 54.   **8.** $\dfrac{n}{2}(n-3)$.   **9.** 45.   **10.** 840. **11.** 1316. **12.** 6167.

13. 153.   **14.** 1287. **15.** 55.   **16.** 91.   **17.** 27,720.   **18.** {2}.

19. {8}.   **20.** {20}. **23.** $\dfrac{52!}{13!\,39!}$.   **24.** $\dfrac{52!}{13!\,13!\,13!\,13!}$.   **25.** 56.

26. 35.

EXERCISE 8.5 (page 245)

1. 8, 32, 512, 16, 1024.
2. {ϕ, {a}, {b}, {c}, {d}, {a, b}, {a, c}, {a, d}, {b, c}, {b, d}, {c, d}, {a, b, c},
   {a, b, d}, {a, c, d}, {b, c, d}, {a, b, c, d}}.
3. 7.   **4.** 31.   **5.** 15.
6. (a) 4.   (b) 128.   (c) 64.   (d) 1024. (e) 1024. (f) 128.
7. 18.   **8.** 94.   **9.** 144.   **10.** 36.   **11.** 30.

EXERCISE 8.6 (page 246)

1. 864,000   **2.** 12,700,800. **3.** 1,814,400.   **4.** 28,800.   **5.** 64,800.
6. 11.   **7.** 43.   **8.** 85.   **9.** 918.   **10.** 19.

REVIEW EXERCISE 8 (page 248)

1. (a) 210.   (b) 2520.   (c) 9900.   (d) 1320.   (e) 35.   (f) 1.
   (g) 100.   (h) 792.   (i) 132.   (j) 140.   (k) 840.   (l) 6510.
2. (a) x.   (b) $x(x+1)$.   (c) $n-r$.
6. (a) 462   (b) 200.   (c) 461.   **7.** (a) 1,680.   (b) 20,160.
8. (a) 10,080.   (b) 720.   **9.** 210.   **10.** ~~140~~ 150
11. 495,000 (if letter is in first position).   **12.** 240.   **13.** 55.
14. 840.   **15.** 144.   **16.** 15.   **17.** 30.   **18.** 34.   **19.** 495.
20. 5,940.   **21.** 27,720. **22.** 5775.   **23.** 1440.   **24.** 20.   **25.** 10.
26. (a) {10}.   (b) {3}.   (c) {5}.   (d) {12, 3}.
27. 62.   **28.** 163.   **29.** 52.   **30.** 23.

Chapter 9

EXERCISE 9.1 (page 252)

1. (a) $1 + 2 + 3 + 4 + 5 + 6$. (b) $1 + 2 + 3 + 4 + 5 + 6$.
 (c) $1 + 0 + (-1) + (-2) + (-3) + (-4) + (-5)$.
 (d) $5 + 7 + 9 + 11 + 13 + 15 + 17 + 19$. (e) $3 + 6 + 9 + 12$.
 (f) $|1| + |0| + |-1| + |-2| + |-3| + |-4| + |-5|$.
 (g) $(-1) + (-1)^2 + (-1)^3 + (-1)^4 + (-1)^5 + (-1)^6$.
 (h) $1^2 + 2^2 + 3^2 + \cdots + (n-1)^2 + n^2$.
 (i) $\dfrac{1 \cdot 2}{2} + \dfrac{2 \cdot 3}{2} + \dfrac{3 \cdot 4}{2} + \cdots + \dfrac{(n-1)n}{2} + \dfrac{n(n+1)}{2}$.

3. (a) 36.   (b) 55.   (c) 31.   (d) 64.   (e) 0.   (f) -1.

4. (a) $\displaystyle\sum_{n=1}^{6} n$.   (b) $\displaystyle\sum_{n=1}^{7} n^2$. $\displaystyle\sum_{n=1}^{6} 2^n$.

 (d) $\displaystyle\sum_{n=1}^{6} (-1)^{n-1} 2^n$.   (e) $\displaystyle\sum_{i=1}^{n} a_i^2$.   (f) $\displaystyle\sum_{r=1}^{4} a^r b^r$.

 (g) $\displaystyle\sum_{n=1}^{5} a^n b^{n-1}$.   (h) $\displaystyle\sum_{n=1}^{6} (4n - 1)$.   (i) $\displaystyle\sum_{n=1}^{5} 2(3^{n-1})$.

EXERCISE 9.2 (page 256)

1. (a) $3\displaystyle\sum_{i=1}^{n} a_i + \sum_{i=1}^{n} b_i$.   (b) $2\displaystyle\sum_{k=1}^{10} k^2 - 6\sum_{k=1}^{10} k$.   (c) $\displaystyle\sum_{k=1}^{n} k^3 + 6\sum_{k=1}^{n} k^2 - 5n$.

 (d) $\displaystyle\sum_{p=1}^{n} 2^p + 3\sum_{p=1}^{n} p$.   (e) $\displaystyle\sum_{i=1}^{10} (-1)^i i^2 + 2\sum_{i=1}^{10} (-1)^i i$.

 (f) $2\displaystyle\sum_{k=1}^{n} k^3 - 6\sum_{k=1}^{n} k^2 + \sum_{k=1}^{n} k - 2n$.

2. (a) $6\displaystyle\sum_{k=1}^{n} k + 4n$.   (b) 0.

3. (a) $\displaystyle\sum_{k=1}^{9} (k + 11)$.   (b) $\displaystyle\sum_{a=1}^{11} \dfrac{a - 6}{a}$.   (c) $\displaystyle\sum_{n=1}^{6} \dfrac{n + 3}{n}$.

 (d) $\displaystyle\sum_{p=1}^{10} p$.   (e) $\displaystyle\sum_{k=1}^{4} 2(k + 6)^2$.   (f) $\displaystyle\sum_{i=1}^{6} (i^2 - 5i + 6)$.

EXERCISE 9.3 (page 259)

1. $\dfrac{n}{2}(n + 1)$.   **2.** $\dfrac{n}{n + 1}$.   **3.** $\dfrac{n}{3n + 1}$.   **4.** $\dfrac{2n}{2n + 1}$.

5. $\dfrac{n}{6n + 4}$.   **6.** $\dfrac{n}{2}(3n + 5)$.   **7.** $\dfrac{n}{4(2n + 1)}$.   **8.** $3n - 2$.

9. 2^{n-1}.   **10.** $\dfrac{n}{n + 1}$.   **11.** $2^{n+1} - 1$.

$\frac{n(n+2)}{n+1}$

12. $\frac{(n+1)^2-1}{n+1}=1-\frac{1}{n+1}.$ **13.** $\frac{2(3^n)+1}{3^n}=2+\frac{1}{3^n}.$

14. $\frac{n}{2}(n+1).$ **15.** $3^n-2^n.$

16. (a) $t_1=1,\ t_2=4,\ t_3=7,\ t_4=16,$ etc. (b) For example, $t_n=3n-2.$

EXERCISE 9.5 (page 270)

1. $\frac{n}{2}(3n+1).$ **2.** $2n(24-n).$ **3.** $n^2(n+1).$

4. $\frac{n}{6}(2n^2+9n+1).$ **5.** $\frac{n}{2}(n+1)(n^2+n-1).$ **6.** $\frac{n}{3}(n^2-3n+8).$

7. $\frac{n}{6}(n+1)(4n+5).$ **8.** $n(-2n^2+13n+5).$

9. $\frac{n}{4}(n+1)(n+2)(n+3).$ **10.** $\frac{n}{12}(n+1)(n+2)(9n-1).$

11. 1240.   **12.** 270.   **13.** 27,900.   **14.** 3741.   **15.** 1444.
16. 20,556.   **17.** 928.   **18.** 10,184   **19.** 317,660.   **20.** 48,020.

21. 3,491,040.   **22.** 1,546,230.   **23.** $\frac{n^2(n+1)^2}{4}.$

24. (a) $\frac{n(n+1)(2n+1)(3n^2+3n-1)}{30}.$ (b) $\frac{n^2(n+1)^2(2n^2+2n-1)}{12}.$

EXERCISE 9.6 (page 273)

1. $\frac{1}{x-1}+\frac{1}{x+2}.$ **2.** $\frac{1}{x-1}-\frac{1}{x+2}.$ **3.** $\frac{2}{x-3}+\frac{1}{x+2}.$

4. $\frac{-2}{x-2}+\frac{3}{x-1}.$ **5.** $\frac{3}{3-2x}+\frac{1}{1+x}.$ **6.** $\frac{3}{2k-1}-\frac{2}{2k+1}.$

7. $\frac{\frac{1}{3}}{3k-1}-\frac{\frac{1}{3}}{3k+2}.$ **8.** $\frac{1}{5k-2}-\frac{1}{5k+3}.$ **9.** $\frac{n}{n+1}.$

10. $\frac{n}{2n+1}.$ **11.** $\frac{4n}{3(4n+3)}.$ **12.** $\frac{n}{3(4n+3)}.$ **13.** $\frac{n}{3(5n+3)}.$

14. $\frac{3n}{2(3n+2)}.$ **15.** $\frac{4n}{1-4n^2}.$ **16.** $\frac{-3n(3n+5)}{4(3n-1)(3n+2)}.$

REVIEW EXERCISE 9 (page 274)

1. (a) $(-1)+1+3+5+7+9.$ (b) $8-10+12-14+16-18+20.$
  (c) $3+2+1+0+(-1)+(-2)+(-3)+(-4).$
  (d) $10+5+2+1+2+5+10.$

2. (a) $\sum_{p=1}^{8}(-1)^{p+1}p.$ (b) $\sum_{p=1}^{9}(4p-1).$ (c) $\sum_{p=1}^{7}3^{p-3}.$

  (d) $\sum_{p=1}^{5}(a+b)^{p-3}.$ (e) $\sum_{p=1}^{5}\frac{1}{(p+2)(p+3)}.$ (f) $\sum_{p=1}^{n}\frac{1}{p(2p+1)}.$

3. (a) $\sum\limits_{i=1}^{6} (2i + 3)$.   (b) $\sum\limits_{k=1}^{6} (k-3)^2$.   (c) $\sum\limits_{k=1}^{n+1} 2^{k-1}$.

(d) $\sum\limits_{p=1}^{n} p(p+2)$.   (e) $\sum\limits_{k=1}^{5} k$.   (f) $\sum\limits_{i=1}^{n} (-1)^i 3(i-2)$.

5. (a) $\frac{n}{2}(3n+1)$.   (b) $\frac{n}{2}(n+3)$.   (c) $\frac{n}{2}(2n^2+n+1)$.

(d) $\frac{n}{6}(4n^2+9n-1)$.   (e) $\frac{n}{4}(n-1)(n^2+3n-2)$.   (f) $n(n^3-n-3)$.

(g) 366.   (h) 2540.   (i) 5875.   (j) 1111.   (k) 37,680.   (l) 111,564.

9. (a) $\frac{2}{x-1} + \frac{3}{x+2}$.   (b) $\frac{2}{x+3} - \frac{1}{x-2}$.

(c) $\frac{2}{1-x} + \frac{2}{1+x}$.   (d) $\frac{4}{3(x-1)} - \frac{4}{3(x+2)}$.

10. (a) $\frac{n}{4(2n+1)}$.   (b) $\frac{n}{2(3n+2)}$.   (c) $\frac{5n}{4(5n+4)}$.

(d) $\frac{(n-1)(3n+2)}{2n(n+1)}$.   (e) $\frac{4n}{1-4n^2}$.   (f) $\frac{12}{65}$.

Chapter 10

EXERCISE 10.1 (page 279)

1. (a) 2.   (b) 5.   (c) 3.   (d) 5.

2. (a) $\sum\limits_{r=0}^{4} \binom{4}{r} a^{4-r} b^r = \binom{4}{0}a^4 + \binom{4}{1}a^3 b + \binom{4}{2}a^2 b^2 + \binom{4}{3}ab^3 + \binom{4}{4}b^4$
$= a^4 + 4a^3 b + 6a^2 b^2 + 4ab^3 + b^4$.

(b) $\sum\limits_{r=0}^{5} \binom{5}{r} a^{5-r} b^r = a^5 + 5a^4 b + 10a^3 b^2 + 10a^2 b^3 + 5ab^4 + b^5$.

(c) $\sum\limits_{r=0}^{8} \binom{8}{r} x^{8-r} y^r = x^8 + 8x^7 y + 28x^6 y^2 + 56x^5 y^3 + 70x^4 y^4 + 56x^3 y^5 + 28x^2 y^6$
$+ 8xy^7 + y^8$.

(d) $\sum\limits_{r=0}^{7} \binom{7}{r} p^{7-r} q^r = p^7 + 7p^6 q + 21p^5 q^2 + 35p^4 q^3 + 35p^3 q^4 + 21p^2 q^5 + 7pq^6$
$+ q^7$.

3. (a) 5.   (b) 6.   (c) 9.   (d) 8.

4. (a) 12.   (b) 16.   (c) 19.   (d) 21.

EXERCISE 10.2 (page 281)

1. (a) $\sum\limits_{r=0}^{12} \binom{12}{r} x^{12-r} y^r$.   (b) $\sum\limits_{r=0}^{9} (-1)^r \binom{9}{r} x^{9-r} y^r$.   (c) $\sum\limits_{r=0}^{7} \binom{7}{r} (2x)^{7-r} y^r$.

(d) $\sum\limits_{r=0}^{8} \binom{8}{r} (2x)^{8-r} \left(\frac{y}{2}\right)^r$.   (e) $\sum\limits_{r=0}^{10} \binom{10}{r} x^{20-2r}$.   (f) $\sum\limits_{r=0}^{15} (-2)^r \binom{15}{r} x^{2r}$.

2. (a) $a^5 - 5a^4b + 10a^3b^2 - 10a^2b^3 + 5ab^4 - b^5$.
   (b) $16a^4 + 32a^3b + 24a^2b^2 + 8ab^3 + b^4$.
   (c) $64x^6 - 96x^5y + 60x^4y^2 - 20x^3y^3 + \frac{15}{4}x^2y^4 - \frac{3}{8}xy^5 + \frac{1}{64}y^6$.

   (d) $x^8 + 4x^5 + 6x^2 + \dfrac{4}{x} + \dfrac{1}{x^4}$.   (e) $256x^8 - 128x^7 + 24x^6 - 2x^5 + \frac{1}{16}x^4$.

   (f) $243a^5 - 810\dfrac{a^4}{b} + 1080\dfrac{a^3}{b^2} - 720\dfrac{a^2}{b^3} + 240\dfrac{a}{b^4} - \dfrac{32}{b^5}$.

3. (a) $a^{10} + 10a^9b + 45a^8b^2 + \cdots$.   (b) $a^8 - 8a^7b + 28a^6b^2 + \cdots$.
   (c) $a^7 + 21a^6b + 189a^5b^2 + \cdots$.   (d) $1 - 45x + 945x^2 + \cdots$.
   (e) $243a^5 - 810a^4 + 1080a^3 \cdots$.   (f) $1 + 24b + 264b^2 + \cdots$.
   (g) $256x^8 - 256x^7y + 112x^6y^2 + \cdots$.   (h) $x^{12} - 12x^9 + 60x^6 + \cdots$.

   (i) $729x^{12} - 1458\dfrac{x^{11}}{y} + 1215\dfrac{x^{10}}{y^2} + \cdots$.

4. (a) $210a^4b^6$.   (b) $-280a^4b^3$.   (c) $\frac{15}{4}x^{10}$.   (d) $-960x^{11}$.

   (e) $\frac{280}{81}x^3y^4$.   (f) $4320x^3y^3$.   (g) 70.   (h) $\dbinom{2n}{n}$.

5. $84x^5y^2$.   **6.** $-448x^6y^5$.   **7.** $2160x^4y^{-8}$.   **8.** $a = 2, b = -\frac{1}{2}$.
9. $a = 1, b = -\frac{2}{3}, n = 8$.

EXERCISE 10.3 (page 286)

1. (a) $\dbinom{12}{r}x^r$.   (b) $(-1)^r 2^{8-r}\dbinom{8}{r}a^r$.   (c) $\dbinom{7}{r}x^{14-r}$.

   (d) $\dbinom{7}{r}a^{7-2r}$.   (e) $(-1)^r\dbinom{8}{r}p^{8-2r}$.   (f) $(-1)^r\dbinom{10}{r}x^{20-3r}$.

   (g) $\dbinom{10}{r}2^{10-r}a^{10-3r}$.   (h) $(-1)^r\dbinom{15}{r}2^{15-r}a^{15-4r}$.   (i) $\dbinom{n}{r}2^r a^{3n-5r}$.

2. 12, 220, 792.   **3.** $t_4 = 455$.   **4.** $t_2 = 5120x^8$; $t_6 = 8064$; $t_8 = 960x^{-4}$.
5. $t_3 = \frac{1215}{4}$; $t_5 = 540x^{-6}$.   **6.** -84; -126; no term of form ka^{-10}.
7. $t_7 = \frac{21}{2}$.   **8.** 8.   **9.** 9.   **10.** 10.

EXERCISE 10.4 (page 290)

1. (a) $1 - x + x^2 - x^3$, $|x| < 1$
   (b) $1 + 2x + 3x^2 + 4x^3$, $|x| < 1$
   (c) $1 - 2x + 3x^2 - 4x^3$, $|x| < 1$
   (d) $1 - x - \frac{1}{2}x^2 - \frac{1}{2}x^3$, $|x| < \frac{1}{2}$
   (e) $1 + 2x^2 + 3x^4 + 4x^6$, $|x| < 1$

   (f) $1 + 3x^2 + \frac{3}{2}x^4 - \frac{1}{2}x^6$, $|x| < \dfrac{1}{\sqrt{2}}$

   (g) $32 - 60x + \frac{135}{4}x^2 - \frac{405}{96}x^3$, $|x| < \frac{4}{3}$
   (h) $\frac{1}{3} + \frac{1}{27}x + \frac{1}{162}x^2 + \frac{5}{4374}x^3$, $|x| < \frac{9}{2}$
   (i) $2 - \frac{1}{4}x - \frac{1}{32}x^2 - \frac{5}{768}x^3$, $|x| < \frac{8}{3}$

(j) $1 + \frac{1}{3}x - \frac{1}{3^2}x^2 + \frac{5}{3^4}x^3$, $|x|<1$

(k) $8 + 6x + \frac{3}{4}x^2 - \frac{1}{16}x^3$, $|x|<2$

(l) $x^{-5} + 5x^{-4} + 15x^{-3} + 35x^{-2}$, $|x|<1$

2. (a) $(-1)^r x^r$, $|x|<1$

   (b) $(r+1)x^r$, $|x|<1$

   (c) $\frac{1}{2}(-1)^r (r+1)(r+2)x^r$, $|x|<1$

   (d) $\frac{1}{2}(r+1)(r+2)x^r$, $|x|<1$

   (e) $\dfrac{(-1)^{r+1} (1 \cdot 3 \cdot 5 \cdot 7 \cdots (2r-3))x^r}{2^r \, r!}$, $|x|<1$

   (f) $\dfrac{(-1)^r (1 \cdot 3 \cdot 5 \cdots (2r-1))x^r}{2^{\frac{4r+1}{2}} \, r!}$, $|x|<2$

   (g) $\dfrac{(-1)^r (5 \cdot 3 \cdot 1 \cdots (7-2r))x^r}{2^{2r-5} \, r!}$, $|x|<2$

   (h) $\dfrac{(3 \cdot 5 \cdot 7 \cdots (2r+1))x^r}{3^{2r+3} \, r!}$, $|x|<\frac{9}{2}$

   (i) $\dfrac{(-1)^{r+1} (2 \cdot 5 \cdot 8 \cdots \cdots (3r-4))x^r}{3^r \, 2^{2r-1} \, r!}$, $|x|<4$

   (j) $\dfrac{2^r (1 \cdot 4 \cdot 7 \cdots (3r-2))x^r}{3^{2r+1} \, r!}$, $|x|<\frac{3}{2}$

   (k) $\dfrac{(1 \cdot 4 \cdot 7 \cdots (3r-2))x^r}{3^{2r} r!}$, $|x|<3$

   (l) $\dfrac{(1 \cdot 3 \cdot 5 \cdots \cdot (2r-1))x^r}{2^{3r+1} \, r!}$, $|x|<4$

3. 66   **4.** 6   **5.** 0

6. (a) 5·100   (e) 0·980

   (b) 9·899   (f) 0·995

   (c) 3·107   (g) 0·100

   (d) 0·121

REVIEW EXERCISE 10 (page 291)

1. (a) $\displaystyle\sum_{r=0}^{7} \binom{7}{r} a^{7-r} b^r$.   (b) $\displaystyle\sum_{r=0}^{n} \binom{n}{r} 2^r x^{n-r} y^r$.

(c) $\sum_{r=0}^{10} (-1)^r \binom{10}{r} 2^{10-r} a^{10-r} b^r$.

(d) $\sum_{r=0}^{8} (-1)^r \binom{8}{r} x^{16-3r}$.

(e) $\sum_{r=0}^{15} \binom{15}{r} 2^{15-2r} x^{30-3r}$.

(f) $\sum_{r=0}^{n} (-1)^r \binom{n}{r} 2^{n-r} x^{2r}$.

2. (a) $a^6 + 6a^5b + 15a^4b^2 + 20a^3b^3 + 15a^2b^4 + 6ab^5 + b^6$.
   (b) $a^6 - 6a^5b + 15a^4b^2 - 20a^3b^3 + 15a^2b^4 - 6ab^5 + b^6$.
   (c) $32a^5 - 240a^4b + 720a^3b^2 - 1080a^2b^3 + 810ab^4 - 243b^5$

3. (a) $a^{12} + 24a^{11}b + 264a^{10}b^2 + \cdots$
   (b) $256x^8 - 1024x^7y + 1792x^6y^2 + \cdots$
   (c) $1024x^{20} + 2560x^{19} + 2880x^{18} + \cdots$
   (d) $729x^6 - 1458x^4 + 1215x^2 + \cdots$
   (e) $\frac{1}{1024}x^{10} + \frac{5}{128}x^8 + \frac{45}{64}x^6 + \cdots$
   (f) $a^{20}x^{40} + 20a^{19}bx^{38} + 190a^{18}b^2x^{36} + \cdots$
   (g) $1 - 2x + 4x^2 + \cdots$
   (h) $2 - \frac{1}{4}x - \frac{1}{64}x^2 + \cdots$
   (i) $\frac{1}{2^3} - \frac{3}{2^5}x + \frac{15}{2^8}x^2 + \cdots$

4. (a) $(-1)^r 3^r x^r$ (b) $\dfrac{(-1)^r(r+1)}{3^{r+4}} x^{2r}$ (c) $\dfrac{1\cdot4\cdot7\cdots(3r-2)}{2^{r+1}\,3^r\,r!} x^r$

5. $594x^{-8}$ 6. $210x^2$ 7. $t_9 = 180x^2$ 8. $32a^{13} + 176a^{12} + 336a^{11} + \cdots$
9. $16 - 80x + 136x^2 + \cdots$
10. $32,805;\ 252$
11. $t_3 = 240$
12. $t_6 = 252$
13. 9
14. $0\cdot1728$
15. (a) $10\cdot100$ (b) $243\cdot438$ (c) $0\cdot203$
16. $p = -3,\ n = 12$
17. $p = \frac{1}{2},\ n = 10$
18. $n = 8$
19. $a = 2,\ b = -\frac{1}{4}$
20. $a = 3,\ b = \frac{1}{3},\ n = 6$
21. nx^{n-1}
22. (a) $1 + 1 + \frac{1}{2!}(1 - \frac{1}{n}) + \frac{1}{3!}(1 - \frac{1}{n})(1 - \frac{2}{n}) + \frac{1}{4!}(1 - \frac{1}{n})(1 - \frac{2}{n})(1 - \frac{3}{n}) + \cdots$
    (b) $2\cdot7$

Chapter 11

EXERCISE 11.1 (page 295)

1. (a) $\frac{1}{6}$.   (b) $\frac{1}{3}$.   (c) $\frac{1}{2}$.   (d) $\frac{1}{2}$.   (e) $\frac{1}{2}$.   (f) $\frac{1}{2}$.

2. (a) $\frac{5}{8}$. (b) $\frac{3}{8}$. **3.** (a) $\frac{2}{7}$. (b) $\frac{3}{7}$. (c) $\frac{4}{7}$. **4.** $\frac{5}{9}$.

5. (a) $\frac{19}{63}$. (b) $\frac{4}{21}$. (c) $\frac{32}{63}$. **6.** (a) $\frac{1}{15}$. (b) $\frac{1}{30}$. (c) $\frac{1}{5}$.

7. (a) $\frac{4}{9}$. (b) $\frac{5}{9}$. (c) $\frac{1}{9}$. **8.** $\frac{3}{8}$. **9.** (a) $\frac{1}{22}$. (b) $\frac{9}{22}$.

10. (a) $\frac{1}{36}$. (b) $\frac{1}{12}$. **11.** $\frac{1}{8}$. **12.** (a) $\frac{1}{17}$. (b) $\frac{1}{221}$. (c) $\frac{25}{102}$. (d) $\frac{1}{1326}$.

EXERCISE 11.2 (page 299)

1. $S_1 = \{(0, 3), (1, 2), (2, 1), (3, 0)\}$, number of heads and tails.
   $S_2 = \{HHH, HHT, HTH, HTT, THH, THT, TTH, TTT\}$.

2. One in S_1, three in S_2.

3.

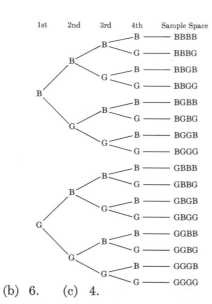

(a) 1.   (b) 3.

4.

(a) 4.   (b) 6.   (c) 4.

5. $S = \{$RBG, RBW, RBY, RGW, RGY, RWY, BGW, BGY, BWY, GWY$\}$.
   (a) 6.   (b) 4.   (c) 3.   (d) 9.

6. $S = \{$BB, BG, BR, GB, GG, GR, RB, RG, RR$\}$.   (a) 3.   (b) 2. (c) 8.

7. $\{$1234, 3124, 1234, 3142, 1324, 3214, 1342, 3241, 1423, 3412, 1432, 3421, 2134, 4123, 2143, 4132, 2314, 4213, 2341, 4231, 2413, 4312, 2431, 4321.$\}$
   (a) 6.   (b) 7.   (c) 9.

EXERCISE 11.3 (page 305)

1. (a) $\frac{2}{9}$.   (b) $\frac{1}{6}$.   (c) $\frac{5}{12}$.   (d) $\frac{5}{12}$.   (e) $\frac{5}{36}$.   (f) $\frac{1}{6}$.
   (g) $\frac{1}{3}$.   (h) $\frac{1}{18}$.   (i) $\frac{4}{9}$.   (j) $\frac{7}{18}$.   (k) $\frac{1}{3}$.   (l) 0.
2. $\frac{74}{299}$.   (b) $\frac{225}{299}$.   (c) $\frac{37}{598}$.   (d) $\frac{75}{299}$.
3. (a) $\frac{1}{8}$.   (b) $\frac{3}{8}$.   (c) $\frac{1}{2}$.   (d) $\frac{7}{8}$.
4. (a) $\frac{1}{3}$.   (b) $\frac{1}{15}$.   (c) $\frac{8}{15}$.   (d) $\frac{1}{5}$.
5. (a) $\frac{1}{4}$.   (b) $\frac{3}{8}$.   (c) $\frac{1}{4}$.
6. (a) $\frac{1}{4}$.   (b) $\frac{7}{24}$.   (c) $\frac{3}{8}$.   (d) $\frac{1}{24}$.
7. (a) $\frac{3}{5}$.   (b) $\frac{3}{10}$.   (c) $\frac{2}{5}$.   (d) $\frac{9}{10}$.

EXERCISE 11.4 (page 309)

1. (a) 7 to 4.   (b) 4 to 7.   2. (a) 1 to 5.   (b) 1 to 2.   (c) 5 to 1.
3. (a) 3 to 4.   (b) 5 to 2.   4. 4 to 3.   5. 14 to 25.
6. 1 to 3.   7. 7 to 1.   8. (a) 25 to 77.   (b) 188 to 33.   (c) 1 to 220.
9. (a) 1 to 8.   (b) 31 to 5.   (c) 5 to 7.   (d) 5 to 1.
10. 6 to 1.   11. 2 to 7.   12. 1 to 1.

EXERCISE 11.5 (page 313)

1. (a) $\frac{1}{9}$.   (b) $\frac{5}{9}$.   (c) $\frac{3}{4}$.   (d) $\frac{2}{9}$.
2. (a) $\frac{1}{4}$.   (b) $\frac{1}{2}$.   (c) $\frac{11}{20}$.   (d) $\frac{4}{5}$.
3. (a) $\frac{5}{19}$.   (b) $\frac{11}{19}$.   4. $\frac{8}{15}$.
5. (a) $\frac{1}{2}$.   (b) $\frac{4}{5}$.   (c) $\frac{13}{20}$.   (d) $\frac{2}{5}$.   (e) $\frac{7}{20}$.
6. $\frac{11}{28}$.   7. $\frac{55}{221}$.   8. (a) $\frac{8}{15}$.   (b) $\frac{1}{8}$.   (c) $\frac{2}{15}$.
9. 22%; 121.   10. $\frac{9}{20}$.

EXERCISE 11.6 (page 315)

1. (b), (e). 2. (b). 3. (d), (e). 4. No. $P(A \cup B) = \frac{1}{2}$. 5. Yes. $P(A \cup B) = \frac{2}{3}$.
6. (a) $\frac{11}{36}$.   (b) $\frac{5}{18}$.   (c) $\frac{1}{2}$.   (d) $\frac{11}{36}$.   (e) $\frac{2}{3}$.   (f) $\frac{5}{9}$.
7. (a) $\frac{3}{4}$.   (b) $\frac{3}{4}$.   (c) $\frac{1}{2}$.   (d) 1.
8. (a) $\frac{3}{8}$.   (b) $\frac{3}{4}$.   (c) $\frac{5}{8}$.   (d) $\frac{5}{8}$.   (e) $\frac{5}{8}$.
9. (a) $\frac{1}{17}$.   (b) $\frac{25}{102}$.   (c) $\frac{1}{221}$.   (d) $\frac{1}{1326}$.   (e) $\frac{55}{221}$.   10. $\frac{79}{1326}$.

EXERCISE 11.7 (page 320)

1. (a) Independent.   (b) Dependent.   (c) Mutually exclusive.
   (d) Dependent.   (e) Dependent.   (f) Dependent.

2. $\frac{1}{72}$.   **3.** $\frac{1}{64}$.   **4.** (a) $\frac{4}{9}$.   (b) $\frac{1}{9}$.   (c) $\frac{4}{9}$.
5. (a) Independent.   (b) Mutually exclusive.   (c) Dependent.
6. (a) $\frac{8}{225}$.   (b) $\frac{8}{125}$.   (c) $\frac{1}{27}$.   (d) $\frac{16}{375}$.
7. (a) $\frac{1}{8}$.   (b) $\frac{1}{8}$.   (c) $\frac{5}{8}$.   **8.** No.   **9.** No.   **10.** Yes.

EXERCISE 11.8 (page 325)

1. (a) $\frac{25}{216}$.   (b) $\frac{5}{324}$.   (c) $\frac{671}{1296}$.   **2.** (a) $\frac{5}{16}$.   (b) $\frac{1}{2}$.   (c) $\frac{1}{32}$.
3. (a) $\frac{5}{16}$.   (b) $\frac{1}{2}$.   (c) $\frac{1}{32}$.   (d) $\frac{31}{32}$.   **4.** (a) $\frac{1}{16}$.   (b) $\frac{135}{512}$.
5. $\frac{233}{729}$.   **6.** (a) $\frac{1}{216}$.   (b) $\frac{25}{72}$.   (c) $\frac{91}{216}$.   (d) $\frac{919}{5832}$.
7. (a) $\frac{27}{64}$.   (b) $\frac{3}{64}$.   (c) $\frac{243}{256}$.   (d) $\frac{1}{256}$.   **8.** $\frac{4547}{8192}$.
9. $\frac{1}{4}$.   **10.** $\frac{1}{6}$.   **11.** $\frac{27}{125}$.   **12.** 0.189.   **13.** 0.000547034.

EXERCISE 11.9 (page 330)

1. $\frac{1}{4}, \frac{1}{3}$ **7.** $\frac{2}{5}$ (d) $\frac{2}{7}$
2. $\frac{1}{5}, \frac{1}{2}$ **8.** $\frac{1}{4}$ (e) $\frac{1}{7}$
4. $\frac{2}{3}$ **9.** (a) $\frac{1}{4}$
5. $\frac{8}{23}$ (b) $\frac{1}{16}$
6. $\frac{1}{4}$ (c) $\frac{4}{7}$

17. 0
18. $\frac{1}{6}$
19. $\frac{2}{7}, \frac{2}{7}$
20. $\frac{6}{25}$
21. $\frac{5}{32}$

REVIEW EXERCISE 11 (page 332)

1. (a) {ABCD, ABCE, ABCF, ABDE, ABDF, ABEF, ACDE, ACDF, ACEF, ADEF, BCDE, BCDF, BCEF, BDEF, CDEF}.
  (b) {A, A A, K A, Q A, J A, 10 K, A K, K K, Q K, J K, 10 Q, A Q, K Q, Q Q, J Q, 10 J, A J, K J, Q J, J J, 10 10, A 10, K 10, Q 10, J 10, 10}.

2. (a) $\frac{3}{5}$.   (b) $\frac{3}{10}$.   (c) $\frac{9}{10}$.   (d) $\frac{1}{2}$.   (e) $\frac{3}{5}$.   (f) $\frac{1}{10}$.
3. (a) $\frac{5}{18}$.   (b) $\frac{1}{36}$.   (c) $\frac{5}{36}$.   (d) $\frac{1}{12}$.   (e) $\frac{1}{6}$.   (f) $\frac{2}{3}$.   (g) $\frac{1}{3}$.
4. (a) $\frac{1}{13}$.   (b) $\frac{1}{26}$.   (c) $\frac{1}{4}$.   (d) $\frac{2}{13}$.   (e) $\frac{5}{13}$.
5. (a) $\frac{1}{100}$.   (b) $\frac{21}{46}$.   (c) $\frac{6}{115}$.   **6.** $\frac{43}{91}$.
7. (a) $\frac{7}{33}$.   (b) $\frac{4}{165}$.   (c) $\frac{28}{55}$.   (d) $\frac{14}{55}$.   **8.** 38,916 to 15,229.
9. 14 to 25.
10. (a) Independent. (b) Dependent. (c) Mutually exclusive. (d) Independent.
11. $\frac{3}{400}$.   **12.** $\frac{2072}{3125}$.   **13.** (a) $\frac{80}{243}$.   (b) $\frac{20}{243}$.   (c) $\frac{716}{729}$.   (d) $\frac{73}{729}$.   **14.** $\frac{821}{3125}$.
15. (a) $\frac{15}{64}$.   (b) $\frac{57}{64}$.   (c) $\frac{7}{64}$.   (d) $\frac{1}{64}$.   **16.** 0.5786.

Chapter 12

EXERCISE 12.1 (page 336)

	Declarative	Statement	Open sentence		Declarative	Statement	Open sentence
1.	Yes	False	No	14.	Yes	True	No
2.	No	No	No	15.	Yes	No	Yes
3.	Yes	No	Yes	16.	No	No	No
4.	Yes	True	No	17.	No	No	No
5.	Yes	True	No	18.	Yes	True	No
6.	Yes	True	No	19.	Yes	No	Yes
7.	Yes	False	No	20.	Yes	False	No
8.	Yes	True	No	21.	Yes	False	No
9.	Yes	False	No	22.	Yes	False	No
10.	Yes	False	No	23.	Yes	False	No
11.	No	No	No	24.	Yes	False	No
12.	Yes	No	Yes	25.	Yes	No	Yes
13.	Yes	True	No				

EXERCISE 12.2 (page 339)

3. (a) Set, point, line, on, between.   (b) Line segment, joining, point, on, circle.
(c) Person, citizen, Canada.   (d) Number, *Re*.   (e) Polygon, sides.

EXERCISE 12.3 (page 341)

	Conjunction	Disjunction		Conjunction	Disjunction
1.	True	True	7.	False	False
2.	True	True	8.	True	True
3.	False	True	9.	False	True
4.	False	False	10.	False	True
5.	False	False	11.	False	False
6.	True	True	12.	True	True

EXERCISE 12.4 (page 343)

1. $4 + 5 \neq 20$.
2. Not all right angles are equal.
3. The world will not end on Jan. 16, 2176.
4. The sum of two consecutive integers is not an even integer.
5. -3 is not a positive integer.
6. π is not a rational number.
7. $3 + 1 \leq 2$.

The true one is negation.
Statement.
Truth unknowable.

Negation.
Negation.
Negation.
Statement.

8. $x^2 + y^2 = 16$ is not the equation of a line.   Negation.
9. $\sqrt{2}$ is a rational number.   Statement.
10. Toronto is not the capital city of Canada.   Negation.
11. $2 + 3 \neq 5$ or not all dogs have four legs.   Negation.
12. Not all right angles are equal or the graph
    of $y = 3x^2$ is not a circle.   Negation.
13. $2 + 3 \neq 5$ and dogs do not have four legs.   Statement.
14. Not all right angles are equal and the graph
    of $y = 3x^2$ is not a circle.   Statement.
15. Not all similar triangles are congruent and
    -3 is not a natural number.   Negation.
16. 100 is not 20% of 800 or the angle in a
    semicircle is not a right angle.   Negation
17. π is not a rational number and $\sqrt{2}$ is not a
    rational number.   Negation.
18. Alexander the Great was not a Roman
    citizen or $2x + 1 \neq 3$.   Negation.

EXERCISE 12.5 (page 345)

	$p \Rightarrow q$	$q \Rightarrow p$			$p \Rightarrow q$	$q \Rightarrow p$
1. (a)	True	True		(e)	True	True
(b)	True	True		(f)	True	True
(c)	True	False		(g)	False	True
(d)	True	True		(h)	False	True

3. (a) Statement.   (b) Statement.   (c) Statement.   (d) Statement.
   (e) Statement.   (f) Negation.   (g) Statement.   (h) Statement.

4. Yes.   5. Yes.   6. No.

EXERCISE 12.7 (page 351)

1. (a) For all x.   (b) For some x.   (c) For some x.   (d) For some x.
   (e) For all parallelograms.   (f) All triangles are not parallelograms.
   (g) Some triangles are not isosceles.   (h) For all x.
   (i) For all cyclic quadrilaterals.   (j) Some rectangles are not squares.

2. (a) For some $x \in Re$, $|x| \neq x$.   (b) For all $x \in N$, $x^2 \neq 2$.
   (c) Some rational numbers are not real numbers.
   (d) For some $n \in N$, $n^2 - n + 41$ is not a prime integer.
   (e) Some triangles are isosceles.   (f) All triangles are isosceles.
   (g) All students are clever.   (h) Some students are clever.
   (i) Some students are stupid.
   (j) For all numbers x, y, $x^2 - y^2 \neq (x - y)^2$.
   (k) For all $x \in Re$, $x^2 \neq -4$.
   (l) For some positive integer x, $x + 4 \geq 10$.

EXERCISE 12.8 (page 356)

1. Substitution. **2.** Detachment. **3.** Invalid.
4. Disjunction. **5.** Invalid. **6.** Contrapositive.
7. Syllogism. **8.** Invalid. **9.** Invalid.
10. Contrapositive.

EXERCISE 12.10 (page 362)

1. (a) $p \Rightarrow q$.   (b) $r \Rightarrow q$.   (c) $q \wedge r$.   (d) $p \vee r$.
   (e) $(r \wedge q) \Rightarrow p$. (f) $\sim r \wedge q$. (g) $\sim r \Rightarrow \sim p$.
   (h) $r \Rightarrow (\sim q \vee \sim p)$. (i) $q \Leftrightarrow (\sim r \wedge p)$.
3. (a) $\sim p \vee q$.   (b) $p \wedge (\sim q \vee \sim r)$.
   (c) $\exists_x, x \in N(2x$ is odd$)$; $\sim \forall_x, x \in N(2x$ is even$)$.
   (d) $p \wedge \sim q$; $\sim (p \Rightarrow q)$.
   (e) $\sim \exists_x, x \in Re$ $(2x^2 + 7 = 3)$; $\forall_x, x \in Re$, $(2x^2 + 7 \neq 3)$.
   (f) $\sim \forall_x (P_x \Rightarrow Q_x)$; $\exists_x(P_x \not\Rightarrow Q_x)$; $\exists_x(P_x \wedge \sim Q_x)$.
   (g) $\sim \exists_x(S_x \Rightarrow P_x)$; $\forall_x(\sim(S_x \Rightarrow P_x))$; $\forall_x(S_x \wedge \sim P_x)$.
4. (a) All even integers are divisible by 2.
   (b) There exists an integer both prime and even.
   (c) There exists no integer both prime and even.
   (d) Every integer is composite or divisible by 2.
   (e) If an integer is prime, it is not divisible by 2.
   (f) There exists an integer that is prime if and only if it is even.

REVIEW EXERCISE 12 (page 363)

4. (a) Syllogism. (b) Disjunction. (c) Invalid. (d) Syllogism.
   (e) Contrapositive. (f) Invalid. (g) Substitution.
   (h) Invalid. (i) Equivalence. (j) Invalid.
7. (a) True. (b) False. (c) True.
9. $\forall_\epsilon, \epsilon > 0(\exists_\delta, \delta > 0(|x - y| < \delta \Rightarrow |f(x) - f(y)| < \epsilon))$.

Chapter 13

EXERCISE 13.2 (page 369)

1. $\begin{pmatrix} A\ B \\ A\ B \end{pmatrix}$ and $\begin{pmatrix} A\ B \\ B\ A \end{pmatrix}$.

2. $\left\{ \begin{pmatrix} 1\ 2\ 3 \\ 1\ 2\ 3 \end{pmatrix}, \begin{pmatrix} 1\ 2\ 3 \\ 1\ 3\ 2 \end{pmatrix}, \begin{pmatrix} 1\ 2\ 3 \\ 2\ 1\ 3 \end{pmatrix}, \begin{pmatrix} 1\ 2\ 3 \\ 2\ 3\ 1 \end{pmatrix}, \begin{pmatrix} 1\ 2\ 3 \\ 3\ 1\ 2 \end{pmatrix}, \begin{pmatrix} 1\ 2\ 3 \\ 3\ 2\ 1 \end{pmatrix} \right\}$.

3. $\left\{ \begin{pmatrix} A\ B\ C\ D \\ A\ B\ C\ D \end{pmatrix}, \begin{pmatrix} A\ B\ C\ D \\ A\ B\ D\ C \end{pmatrix}, \begin{pmatrix} A\ B\ C\ D \\ A\ C\ B\ D \end{pmatrix}, \begin{pmatrix} A\ B\ C\ D \\ A\ C\ D\ B \end{pmatrix}, \begin{pmatrix} A\ B\ C\ D \\ A\ D\ B\ C \end{pmatrix}, \begin{pmatrix} A\ B\ C\ D \\ A\ D\ C\ B \end{pmatrix}, \right.$

$\begin{pmatrix} A\ B\ C\ D \\ B\ A\ C\ D \end{pmatrix}, \begin{pmatrix} A\ B\ C\ D \\ B\ A\ D\ C \end{pmatrix}, \begin{pmatrix} A\ B\ C\ D \\ B\ C\ A\ D \end{pmatrix}, \begin{pmatrix} A\ B\ C\ D \\ B\ C\ D\ A \end{pmatrix}, \begin{pmatrix} A\ B\ C\ D \\ B\ D\ A\ C \end{pmatrix}, \begin{pmatrix} A\ B\ C\ D \\ B\ D\ C\ A \end{pmatrix},$

$\begin{pmatrix} A\ B\ C\ D \\ C\ A\ B\ D \end{pmatrix}, \begin{pmatrix} A\ B\ C\ D \\ C\ A\ D\ B \end{pmatrix}, \begin{pmatrix} A\ B\ C\ D \\ C\ B\ A\ D \end{pmatrix}, \begin{pmatrix} A\ B\ C\ D \\ C\ B\ D\ A \end{pmatrix}, \begin{pmatrix} A\ B\ C\ D \\ C\ D\ A\ B \end{pmatrix}, \begin{pmatrix} A\ B\ C\ D \\ C\ D\ B\ A \end{pmatrix},$

$$\left.\begin{pmatrix}A\,B\,C\,D\\D\,A\,B\,C\end{pmatrix},\begin{pmatrix}A\,B\,C\,D\\D\,A\,C\,B\end{pmatrix},\begin{pmatrix}A\,B\,C\,D\\D\,B\,A\,C\end{pmatrix},\begin{pmatrix}A\,B\,C\,D\\D\,B\,C\,A\end{pmatrix},\begin{pmatrix}A\,B\,C\,D\\D\,C\,A\,B\end{pmatrix},\begin{pmatrix}A\,B\,C\,D\\D\,C\,B\,A\end{pmatrix}\right\}.$$

4. $\begin{pmatrix}1\,2\,3\,4\\1\,4\,3\,2\end{pmatrix}$ and $\begin{pmatrix}1\,2\,3\,4\\3\,4\,1\,2\end{pmatrix}$.

5. (a) $\begin{pmatrix}A\,B\,C\,D\,E\\A\,B\,C\,D\,E\end{pmatrix},\begin{pmatrix}A\,B\,C\,D\,E\\A\,B\,D\,C\,E\end{pmatrix},\begin{pmatrix}A\,B\,C\,D\,E\\A\,C\,B\,D\,E\end{pmatrix},$

$\begin{pmatrix}A\,B\,C\,D\,E\\A\,C\,D\,B\,E\end{pmatrix},\begin{pmatrix}A\,B\,C\,D\,E\\A\,D\,B\,C\,E\end{pmatrix},\begin{pmatrix}A\,B\,C\,D\,E\\A\,D\,C\,B\,E\end{pmatrix}.$

(b) Same as (a) but with A and E interchanged on the second line of each symbol.

(c) $\begin{pmatrix}A\,B\,C\,D\,E\\A\,B\,C\,D\,E\end{pmatrix}$ and $\begin{pmatrix}A\,B\,C\,D\,E\\E\,B\,C\,D\,A\end{pmatrix}.$

(d) $\begin{pmatrix}A\,B\,C\,D\,E\\A\,C\,D\,B\,E\end{pmatrix}$ and $\begin{pmatrix}A\,B\,C\,D\,E\\E\,C\,D\,B\,A\end{pmatrix}.$

6. (a) $\begin{pmatrix}1\,2\,3\,4\,5\\1\,2\,3\,4\,5\end{pmatrix}$ and $\begin{pmatrix}1\,2\,3\,4\,5\\1\,2\,5\,4\,3\end{pmatrix}.$

(b) $\begin{pmatrix}1\,2\,3\,4\,5\\a\,b\,3\,c\,5\end{pmatrix}$ with abc replaced by $1\,2\,4,\,1\,4\,2,\,2\,1\,4,\,\,2\,4\,1,\,4\,1\,2,\,4\,2\,1.$

(c) $\begin{pmatrix}1\,2\,3\,4\,5\\a\,b\,c\,5\,4\end{pmatrix}$ with abc replaced by $1\,2\,3,\,1\,3\,2,\,2\,1\,3,\,2\,3\,1,\,3\,1\,2,\,3\,2\,1.$

(d) $\begin{pmatrix}1\,2\,3\,4\,5\\3\,5\,1\,4\,2\end{pmatrix}.$ (e) $\begin{pmatrix}1\,2\,3\,4\,5\\3\,2\,5\,4\,1\end{pmatrix}$ and $\begin{pmatrix}1\,2\,3\,4\,5\\3\,4\,5\,2\,1\end{pmatrix}.$

7. (a) $\begin{pmatrix}1\,2\,3\,4\,5\,6\\a\,b\,c\,4\,5\,6\end{pmatrix}$ with abc replaced by $1\,2\,3,\,1\,3\,2,\,2\,1\,3,\,2\,3\,1,\,3\,1\,2,\,3\,2\,1.$

(b) $\begin{pmatrix}1\,2\,3\,4\,5\,6\\1\,2\,3\,a\,b\,c\end{pmatrix}$ with abc replaced by $4\,5\,6,\,4\,6\,5,\,5\,4\,6,\,5\,6\,4,\,6\,4\,5,\,6\,5\,4.$

(c) $\begin{pmatrix}1\,2\,3\,4\,5\,6\\4\,5\,6\,1\,2\,3\end{pmatrix}.$ (d) $\begin{pmatrix}1\,2\,3\,4\,5\,6\\6\,5\,3\,4\,2\,1\end{pmatrix}$ and $\begin{pmatrix}1\,2\,3\,4\,5\,6\\6\,5\,4\,3\,2\,1\end{pmatrix}.$

8. $(n-2)!.$

EXERCISE 13.3 (page 371)

1. Only the identity. $\begin{pmatrix}A\ B\ C\\A\ B\ C\end{pmatrix}.$

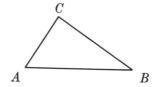

2. Identity and rotation of 180° about the median from A.

$\begin{pmatrix}A\ B\ C\\A\ B\ C\end{pmatrix}$ and $\begin{pmatrix}A\ B\ C\\A\ C\ B\end{pmatrix}.$

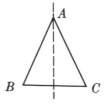

3. Only the identity. $\begin{pmatrix} A & B & C & D \\ A & B & C & D \end{pmatrix}$.

4. Identity; rotations of 120° and 240° about the centre; rotations of 180° about the three medians.

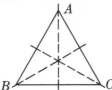

$\begin{pmatrix} A & B & C \\ A & B & C \end{pmatrix}$, $\begin{pmatrix} A & B & C \\ C & A & B \end{pmatrix}$, $\begin{pmatrix} A & B & C \\ B & C & A \end{pmatrix}$,

$\begin{pmatrix} A & B & C \\ A & C & B \end{pmatrix}$, $\begin{pmatrix} A & B & C \\ C & B & A \end{pmatrix}$, $\begin{pmatrix} A & B & C \\ B & A & C \end{pmatrix}$.

5. Identity; rotation of 180° about centre; rotations of 180° about lines H and V.

$\begin{pmatrix} A & B & C & D \\ A & B & C & D \end{pmatrix}$, $\begin{pmatrix} A & B & C & D \\ C & D & A & B \end{pmatrix}$,

$\begin{pmatrix} A & B & C & D \\ D & C & B & A \end{pmatrix}$, $\begin{pmatrix} A & B & C & D \\ B & A & D & C \end{pmatrix}$.

6. Identity; rotation of 180° about centre; rotations of 180° about lines D_1 and D_2.

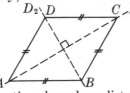

$\begin{pmatrix} A & B & C & D \\ A & B & C & D \end{pmatrix}$, $\begin{pmatrix} A & B & C & D \\ C & D & A & B \end{pmatrix}$,

$\begin{pmatrix} A & B & C & D \\ A & D & C & B \end{pmatrix}$, $\begin{pmatrix} A & B & C & D \\ C & D & A & B \end{pmatrix}$.

7. The motions have been listed in the text.

$R_0 = \begin{pmatrix} A & B & C & D \\ A & B & C & D \end{pmatrix}$, $R_{90} = \begin{pmatrix} A & B & C & D \\ B & C & D & A \end{pmatrix}$, $R_{180} = \begin{pmatrix} A & B & C & D \\ C & D & A & B \end{pmatrix}$, $R_{270} = \begin{pmatrix} A & B & C & D \\ D & A & B & C \end{pmatrix}$

$H = \begin{pmatrix} A & B & C & D \\ D & C & B & A \end{pmatrix}$, $V = \begin{pmatrix} A & B & C & D \\ B & A & D & C \end{pmatrix}$, $D_1 = \begin{pmatrix} A & B & C & D \\ A & D & C & B \end{pmatrix}$, $D_2 = \begin{pmatrix} A & B & C & D \\ C & B & A & D \end{pmatrix}$.

8. Identity; rotations of 72°, 144°, 216°, 288° about O; rotations of 180° about M_1, M_2, M_3, M_4, M_5.

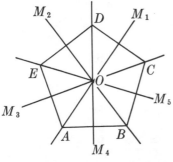

$R_0 = \begin{pmatrix} A & B & C & D & E \\ A & B & C & D & E \end{pmatrix}$, $R_{72} = \begin{pmatrix} A & B & C & D & E \\ B & C & D & E & A \end{pmatrix}$,

$R_{144} = \begin{pmatrix} A & B & C & D & E \\ C & D & E & A & B \end{pmatrix}$, $R_{216} = \begin{pmatrix} A & B & C & D & E \\ D & E & A & B & C \end{pmatrix}$,

$R_{288} = \begin{pmatrix} A & B & C & D & E \\ E & A & B & C & D \end{pmatrix}$, $M_1 = \begin{pmatrix} A & B & C & D & E \\ A & E & D & C & B \end{pmatrix}$,

$M_2 = \begin{pmatrix} A & B & C & D & E \\ C & B & A & E & D \end{pmatrix}$, $M_3 = \begin{pmatrix} A & B & C & D & E \\ E & D & C & B & A \end{pmatrix}$,

$M_4 = \begin{pmatrix} A & B & C & D & E \\ B & A & E & D & C \end{pmatrix}$, $M_5 = \begin{pmatrix} A & B & C & D & E \\ D & C & B & A & E \end{pmatrix}$.

9. Identity; rotations of 60°, 120°, 180°, 240°, 300° about the centre; rotations of 180° about each of the three diagonals joining opposite vertices; rotations of 180° about each of the three lines joining midpoints of opposite sides. Altogether there are 12 such motions.

10. Identity; rotations of 45°, 90°, 135°, 180°, 225°, 270°, 315° about the centre; rotations of 180° about each of the four diagonals joining opposite vertices; rotations of 180° about each of the four joining midpoints of opposite sides. Altogether there are 16 such motions.

11. $2n$.

12. The sixteen permutations listed in the answer to question (3) of Exercise 8.1 which do not appear in the answer to question (7) of this Exercise.

EXERCISE 13.4 (page 374)

1. (a) $(x, y) \rightarrow (x + 3, y + 4)$ or $T_{3,4}\begin{bmatrix} x \\ y \end{bmatrix} = \begin{bmatrix} x + 3 \\ y + 4 \end{bmatrix}$.

(b) $(x, y) \rightarrow (x - 2, y + 1)$. (c) $(x, y) \rightarrow (x, y)$.

(d) $(x, y) \rightarrow (x, y - 3)$. (e) $(x, y) \rightarrow (x - 3, y - 3)$.

(f) $(x, y) \rightarrow \left(\frac{1}{2}x - \frac{\sqrt{3}}{2}y, \frac{\sqrt{3}}{2}x + \frac{1}{2}y\right)$ or $R_{(\pi/3)}\begin{bmatrix} x \\ y \end{bmatrix} = \begin{bmatrix} \frac{1}{2}(x - \sqrt{3}y) \\ \frac{1}{2}(\sqrt{3}x + y) \end{bmatrix}$.

(g) $(x, y) \rightarrow (-y, x)$. (h) $(x, y) \rightarrow (-x, -y)$.

(i) $(x, y) \rightarrow \left(\frac{x + y}{\sqrt{2}}, \frac{-x + y}{\sqrt{2}}\right)$. (j) $(x, y) \rightarrow (y, -x)$.

2. (a) $T_{-3,-2}$. (b) $T_{5,-2}$. (c) $T_{4,0}$. (d) $T_{-2,3}$. (e) $T_{3,3}$.

3. $T_{-3,0}$; $T_{0,-2}$; $T_{3,0}$; $T_{0,2}$.

4. (a) $R_{(-\pi/3)}$. (b) $R_{(\pi/3)}$. (c) $R_{(-\pi/3)}$. (d) $R_{(\pi/3)}$.

5. (a) $R_{(\pi/3)}$. (b) $R_{(-\pi/3)}$. (c) $R_{(\pi/3)}$. (d) $R_{(-\pi/3)}$.

6. $f_{2,0}$; $f_{-2,0}$; $f_{0,2}$; $f_{0,-2}$.

$x \rightarrow 2x$ $x \rightarrow -2x$ $x \rightarrow 2$ $x \rightarrow -2$

7. $\begin{bmatrix} 0 & 0 \\ 0 & 0 \end{bmatrix}, \begin{bmatrix} 1 & 0 \\ 0 & 0 \end{bmatrix}, \begin{bmatrix} 2 & 0 \\ 0 & 2 \end{bmatrix}$, etc. 29 matrices.

EXERCISE 13.5 (page 337)

	(i)	(ii)	(iii)	(iv)	(v)	(vi)
1. (a)	3	-3	-3	0	-6	7
(b)	29	29	45	50	850	205
(c)	49	49	81	100	2704	961
(d)	16	19	24	25	47	51
(e)	$\frac{5}{2}$	$\frac{2}{5}$	$\frac{1}{2}$	1	$\frac{2}{15}$	9
(f)	5	5	6	5	5	6
(g)	10	10	6	5	30	6
(h)	5	2	3	5	2	6
(i)	2	5	6	5	3	3
(j)	$\frac{7}{2}$	$\frac{7}{2}$	$\frac{9}{2}$	5	$\frac{13}{4}$	$\frac{17}{4}$
(k)	25	32	729	3125	32^3	6^8
(l)	-5	-8	-15	-20	16	30
(m)	1	2	3	0	2	0
(n)	2	1	0	0	0	1

2. $A + B = B + A$ $\qquad$ AB $\qquad$ BA

(a) $\begin{bmatrix} 4 & 0 \\ 4 & 3 \end{bmatrix}$ $\begin{bmatrix} 4 & 6 \\ 8 & -24 \end{bmatrix}$ $\begin{bmatrix} 8 & 5 \\ -16 & -28 \end{bmatrix}$

(b) $\begin{bmatrix} 5 & -4 \\ 9 & 5 \end{bmatrix}$ $\begin{bmatrix} -21 & -14 \\ 26 & 10 \end{bmatrix}$ $\begin{bmatrix} 8 & -18 \\ 17 & -19 \end{bmatrix}$

(c) $\begin{bmatrix} 5 & 0 \\ 8 & 1 \end{bmatrix}$ $\begin{bmatrix} 9 & -4 \\ 8 & -3 \end{bmatrix}$ $\begin{bmatrix} 1 & 0 \\ 20 & 5 \end{bmatrix}$

(d) $\begin{bmatrix} -1 & 2 \\ & 8 & 3 \end{bmatrix}$ $\begin{bmatrix} -1 & 4 \\ -4 & 5 \end{bmatrix}$ $\begin{bmatrix} -3 & -2 \\ 16 & 7 \end{bmatrix}$

(e) $\begin{bmatrix} 7 & 4 \\ 9 & 1 \end{bmatrix}$ $\begin{bmatrix} 20 & 8 \\ 19 & 10 \end{bmatrix}$ $\begin{bmatrix} 22 & 8 \\ 16 & 8 \end{bmatrix}$

(f) $\begin{bmatrix} 1 & 1 \\ -1 & -1 \end{bmatrix}$ $\begin{bmatrix} 0 & 1 \\ 1 & 0 \end{bmatrix}$ $\begin{bmatrix} 0 & -1 \\ -1 & 0 \end{bmatrix}$

(g) $\begin{bmatrix} \frac{5}{2} & 0 \\ 0 & \frac{17}{4} \end{bmatrix}$ $\begin{bmatrix} 1 & 0 \\ 0 & 1 \end{bmatrix}$ $\begin{bmatrix} 1 & 0 \\ 0 & 1 \end{bmatrix}$

EXERCISE 13.6 (page 382)

1. $P \theta Q$ $Q \theta P$ P^2 Q^2

(a) $\begin{pmatrix} 1 & 2 & 3 \\ 3 & 2 & 1 \end{pmatrix}$ $\begin{pmatrix} 1 & 2 & 3 \\ 1 & 3 & 2 \end{pmatrix}$ $\begin{pmatrix} 1 & 2 & 3 \\ 2 & 3 & 1 \end{pmatrix}$ $\begin{pmatrix} 1 & 2 & 3 \\ 1 & 2 & 3 \end{pmatrix}$

(b) $\begin{pmatrix} 1 & 2 & 3 & 4 \\ 4 & 2 & 1 & 3 \end{pmatrix}$ $\begin{pmatrix} 1 & 2 & 3 & 4 \\ 1 & 4 & 2 & 3 \end{pmatrix}$ $\begin{pmatrix} 1 & 2 & 3 & 4 \\ 3 & 4 & 1 & 2 \end{pmatrix}$ $\begin{pmatrix} 1 & 2 & 3 & 4 \\ 1 & 2 & 3 & 4 \end{pmatrix}$

(c) $\begin{pmatrix} 1 & 2 & 3 & 4 & 5 \\ 5 & 2 & 3 & 4 & 1 \end{pmatrix}$ $\begin{pmatrix} 1 & 2 & 3 & 4 & 5 \\ 1 & 5 & 3 & 4 & 2 \end{pmatrix}$ $\begin{pmatrix} 1 & 2 & 3 & 4 & 5 \\ 2 & 5 & 3 & 4 & 1 \end{pmatrix}$ $\begin{pmatrix} 1 & 2 & 3 & 4 & 5 \\ 1 & 2 & 3 & 4 & 5 \end{pmatrix}.$

(d) $\begin{pmatrix} a & b & c & d & e \\ d & a & e & b & c \end{pmatrix}$ $\begin{pmatrix} a & b & c & d & e \\ e & d & a & b & c \end{pmatrix}$ $\begin{pmatrix} a & b & c & d & e \\ d & b & a & c & e \end{pmatrix}$ $\begin{pmatrix} a & b & c & d & e \\ c & d & e & a & b \end{pmatrix}.$

(e) $\begin{pmatrix} 1 2 3 4 5 6 7 8 9 \\ 3 5 2 7 6 8 9 4 1 \end{pmatrix}$ $\begin{pmatrix} 1 2 3 4 5 6 7 8 9 \\ 8 1 9 2 4 3 6 7 5 \end{pmatrix}$ $\begin{pmatrix} 1 2 3 4 5 6 7 8 9 \\ 3 4 1 2 6 9 5 7 8 \end{pmatrix}$ $\begin{pmatrix} 1 2 3 4 5 6 7 8 9 \\ 1 2 8 7 5 3 6 4 9 \end{pmatrix}.$

2. (a) $\begin{pmatrix} 1 & 2 & 3 \\ 1 & 2 & 3 \end{pmatrix}$ (b) $\begin{pmatrix} 1 & 2 & 3 & 4 \\ 1 & 3 & 2 & 4 \end{pmatrix}$ (c) $\begin{pmatrix} 1 & 2 & 3 & 4 & 5 \\ 5 & 3 & 4 & 1 & 2 \end{pmatrix}$ (d) $\begin{pmatrix} a & b & c & d & e \\ e & b & d & c & a \end{pmatrix}.$

3. Multiplication of permutations is associative.

4. (a) E_2.   (b) R_{120}.   (c) E_3.

5. (a) R_{270}.   (b) R_{270}.   (c) R_{180}.   (d) R_0.   (e) R_{180}.   (f) R_{180}.
   (g) H.   (h) V.   (i) R_{180}.   (j) R_{180}.   (k) R_{90}.   (l) D_2.

6.

θ	I	R_x	R_y	R_{xy}
I	I	R_x	R_y	R_{xy}
R_x	R_x	I	R_{xy}	R_y
R_y	R_y	R_{xy}	I	R_x
R_{xy}	R_{xy}	R_y	R_x	I

EXERCISE 13.7 (page 386)

1. (a) $T_{4,5}$.   (b) $T_{8,0}$.   (c) $T_{0,0}$.   (d) $T_{-3,1}$.

3.
	$f \ominus g$	$g \ominus f$
(a)	$x \rightarrow 6x - 1$	$x \rightarrow 6x + 17$
(b)	$x \rightarrow 18x + 1$	$x \rightarrow 18x - 23$
(c)	$x \rightarrow 9x^2 - 12x + 7$	$x \rightarrow 3x^2 + 7$
(d)	$x \rightarrow x^4 + 2x^3 + 2x^2 + x + 1$	$x \rightarrow x^4 - 2x^3 + 4x^2 - 3x + 3$

EXERCISE 13.8 (page 388)

The following are groupoids.
1 (a), (b), (c); 2 (a), (b), (e), (f); 3 (a), (c); 4 (a), (b), (c), (e), (f); 5 (a), (b), (c), (d); 6 (a), (b), (c), (d), (e); 7 (b), (c), (d), (f), (g), (h), (i), (j), (l), (n); 8 (a), (b), (c), (d), (e); 9 (a), (b); 10 (a), (c), (e); 11 (a), (b), (c); 12 (a), (b), (c); 13 (a), (b), (c), (d); 14; 15.

EXERCISE 13.9 (page 393)

The following groupoids of Exercise 13.8 are semigroups.
1 (a), (b); 2 (a), (b), (e), (f); 3 (a), (c); 4 (a), (b), (e); 5 (a), (b), (c), (d); 6 (a), (b), (c), (d), (e); 7 (f), (g), (h), (i), (j), (n); 8 (a), (b), (c), (d) (e); 9 (a), (b); 10 (a), (c), (e); 11 (a), (b), (c); 12 (a), (b), (c); 13 (a), (c), (d); 14; 15.

EXERCISE 13.10 (page 395)

The following algebraic systems in Exercise 13.8 have
(a) no identities:
   2 (b), (c), (d); 4 (b), (d); 7 (a), (b), (c), (d), (h), (k), (m), (n), (o), (p), (q); 10 (b), (d).
(b) right but not left identities:
   1 (c); 4 (c), (f); 6 (f); 7 (e), (i), (l).
(c) left but not right identities:
   7 (j); 13 (c).
(d) both left and right identities:
   1 (a), (b); 2 (a), (e) (f); 3 (a), (b), (c); 4 (a), (e); 5 (a), (b), (c), (d); 6 (a), (b), (c), (d), (e); 7 (f), (g); 8 (a), (b), (c), (d), (e); 9 (a), (b); 10 (a), (c), (e); 11 (a), (b), (c); 12 (a), (b), (c); 13 (a), (b), (d); 14; 15.

EXERCISE 13.11 (page 400)

1. The following algebraic systems of Exercise 13.8 with identities (see Answers for (1d) of Exercise 13.10) have inverses for *all* elements.
   1 (a); 2 (a); 4 (a), (e); 5 (a), (c);
   6 (a) [1 and -1 are their own inverses; i and $-i$ are inverses of each other];
   6 (b), (d), (e);
   8 (a) each element is its own inverse;
      (b) each element is its own inverse;
      (c) R_0, R_{180}, D_1, D_2, H, V are their own inverses;
         R_{90} and R_{270} are inverses of each other;
      (d) each element is its own inverse;
      (e) R_0, E_1, E_2, E_3 are their own inverses; R_{120} and R_{240} are inverses.

9 (a); 10 (c); (e) f_1, f_2, f_3, f_6 are their own inverses; f_4 and f_5 are inverses;
11 (a), (b), (c); 12 (a), (b), (c);
13 (a) A is its own inverse; B and C are inverses;
   (b) each element is its own inverse;
   (d) each element is its own inverse.

2. (a) $\begin{pmatrix} 1 & 2 & 3 \\ 2 & 1 & 3 \end{pmatrix}$.
   (b) $\begin{pmatrix} A & B & C & D \\ C & D & B & A \end{pmatrix}$.
   (c) $\begin{pmatrix} 1 & 2 & 3 & 4 & 5 \\ 3 & 1 & 4 & 5 & 2 \end{pmatrix}$.

   (d) $\begin{pmatrix} A & B & C & D & E \\ B & E & A & C & D \end{pmatrix}$.
   (e) $\begin{pmatrix} 1 & 2 & 3 & 4 & 5 & 6 \\ 2 & 4 & 6 & 5 & 1 & 3 \end{pmatrix}$.

3. (a) $f^{-1} : x \to \frac{1}{4}x + \frac{1}{4}$.
   (b) $f^{-1} : x \to 2x - 6$.
   (c) $f^{-1} : x \to -\frac{1}{2}x + \frac{3}{2}$.
   (d) $f^{-1} : x \to -\frac{1}{4}x - \frac{7}{4}$.

EXERCISE 13.12 (page 404)

1. The following systems of Exercise 13.8 are groups.
1 (a); 2 (a); 4 (a), (e); 5 (a), (c); 6 (a), (b), (d), (e); 8 (a), (b), (c) (d), (e);
9 (a); 10 (c), (e); 11 (a), (b), (c); 12 (a), (b), (c); 13 (a), (d).

2. The following systems of Exercise 13.8 are commutative groups.
1 (a); 2 (a); 4 (a), (e); 5 (a), (c); 6 (a), (b), (d), (e); 8 (a), (b), (d); 9 (a);
10 (c); 11 (a), (b), (c); 13 (a), (d).

3. (b) and (d) are groups.
    4. Rhombus.

EXERCISE 13.13 (page 406)

1. (a) $AB = \begin{bmatrix} 7 & 2 \\ 14 & 4 \end{bmatrix}$, $BA = \begin{bmatrix} 3 & 6 \\ 4 & 8 \end{bmatrix}$.

   (b) $AB = \begin{bmatrix} -9 & 3 \\ -2 & 2 \end{bmatrix}$, $BA = \begin{bmatrix} -4 & 24 \\ 1 & -3 \end{bmatrix}$.

   (c) $AB = \begin{bmatrix} 10 & -2 \\ 9 & 19 \end{bmatrix}$, $BA = \begin{bmatrix} 13 & 0 \\ 14 & 16 \end{bmatrix}$.

   (d) $AB = \begin{bmatrix} 15 & -6 \\ 9 & -9 \end{bmatrix}$, $BA = \begin{bmatrix} -5 & 13 \\ 2 & 11 \end{bmatrix}$.

2. $(AB)C = A(BC)$
   (a) $\begin{bmatrix} 3 & 29 \\ 6 & 58 \end{bmatrix}$.
   (b) $\begin{bmatrix} -15 & -15 \\ -6 & 2 \end{bmatrix}$.
   (c) $\begin{bmatrix} 14 & 22 \\ -29 & 103 \end{bmatrix}$.
   (d) $\begin{bmatrix} 27 & 21 \\ 27 & -9 \end{bmatrix}$.

3. (a) A^{-1} does not exist; $B^{-1} = \begin{bmatrix} \frac{1}{3} & 0 \\ -\frac{2}{3} & 1 \end{bmatrix}$.

   (b) $A^{-1} = \begin{bmatrix} -1 & \frac{5}{2} \\ 0 & \frac{1}{2} \end{bmatrix}$; $B^{-1} = \begin{bmatrix} \frac{1}{6} & -\frac{1}{3} \\ \frac{1}{6} & \frac{2}{3} \end{bmatrix}$.

   (c) $A^{-1} = \begin{bmatrix} \frac{3}{13} & \frac{1}{13} \\ -\frac{1}{13} & \frac{4}{13} \end{bmatrix}$; $B^{-1} = \begin{bmatrix} \frac{3}{8} & -\frac{1}{16} \\ -\frac{1}{8} & \frac{3}{16} \end{bmatrix}$.

   (d) $A^{-1} = \begin{bmatrix} \frac{2}{3} & -1 \\ \frac{1}{3} & 0 \end{bmatrix}$; $B^{-1} = \begin{bmatrix} \frac{2}{27} & \frac{5}{27} \\ \frac{5}{27} & -\frac{1}{27} \end{bmatrix}$.

7. No; the inverse of such a matrix does not necessarily have integral components.

11.

	I	R_x	R_y	R_{xy}
I	I	R_x	R_y	R_{xy}
R_x	R_x	I	R_{xy}	R_y
R_y	R_y	R_{xy}	I	R_x
R_{xy}	R_{xy}	R_y	R_x	I

EXERCISE 13.14 (page 410)

1. The following systems are rings. (a), (b), (c), (g), (i), (k), (l), (m).
2. Yes. **3.** Yes. **4.** (a) Yes. (b) Yes. (c) Yes. (d) No. (e) No. **5.** Yes.
6. (a) Commutative rings are 1 (a), (b), (c), (g), (i), (k), (l), (m); 2; 4 (b), (c); 5.
   (b) Rings with units are 1 (c), (g), (i), (k), (m); 2; 3; 4 (a), (b), (c); 5.
   (c) Commutative rings with unit are 1 (c), (g), (i), (m); 2; 4 (b), (c); 5.
7. In 3, 4 (a), (b).　　**9.** Example 4; also (5) of the Exercise.

EXERCISE 13.15 (page 413)

1. The following systems of Exercise 8.14 are fields. 1(c), (g), (i), (k), (m); 5 .
2. No.　　**4.** No.

EXERCISE 13.16 (page 417)

1. (a) $\begin{pmatrix}1\,2\,3\,4\,5\,6\,7\,8\\5\,6\,2\,1\,8\,7\,3\,4\end{pmatrix}$, $\begin{pmatrix}1\,2\,3\,4\,5\,6\,7\,8\\8\,7\,6\,5\,4\,3\,2\,1\end{pmatrix}$, $\begin{pmatrix}1\,2\,3\,4\,5\,6\,7\,8\\4\,3\,7\,8\,1\,2\,6\,5\end{pmatrix}$, I.

  (b) $\begin{pmatrix}1\,2\,3\,4\,5\,6\,7\,8\\2\,3\,4\,1\,6\,7\,8\,5\end{pmatrix}$, $\begin{pmatrix}1\,2\,3\,4\,5\,6\,7\,8\\3\,4\,1\,2\,7\,8\,5\,6\end{pmatrix}$, $\begin{pmatrix}1\,2\,3\,4\,5\,6\,7\,8\\4\,1\,2\,3\,8\,5\,6\,7\end{pmatrix}$, I.

  (c) $\begin{pmatrix}1\,2\,3\,4\,5\,6\,7\,8\\1\,5\,6\,2\,4\,8\,7\,3\end{pmatrix}$, $\begin{pmatrix}1\,2\,3\,4\,5\,6\,7\,8\\1\,4\,8\,5\,2\,3\,7\,6\end{pmatrix}$, I.

  (d) $\begin{pmatrix}1\,2\,3\,4\,5\,6\,7\,8\\3\,2\,6\,7\,4\,1\,5\,8\end{pmatrix}$, $\begin{pmatrix}1\,2\,3\,4\,5\,6\,7\,8\\6\,2\,1\,5\,7\,3\,4\,8\end{pmatrix}$, I.

  (e) $\begin{pmatrix}1\,2\,3\,4\,5\,6\,7\,8\\8\,4\,3\,7\,5\,1\,2\,6\end{pmatrix}$, $\begin{pmatrix}1\,2\,3\,4\,5\,6\,7\,8\\6\,7\,3\,2\,5\,8\,4\,1\end{pmatrix}$, I.　(f) $\begin{pmatrix}1\,2\,3\,4\,5\,6\,7\,8\\5\,8\,7\,6\,1\,4\,3\,2\end{pmatrix}$, I.

  (g) $\begin{pmatrix}1\,2\,3\,4\,5\,6\,7\,8\\2\,1\,5\,6\,3\,4\,8\,7\end{pmatrix}$, I.　　　　(h) $\begin{pmatrix}1\,2\,3\,4\,5\,6\,7\,8\\7\,8\,4\,3\,6\,5\,1\,2\end{pmatrix}$, I.

  (i) $\begin{pmatrix}1\,2\,3\,4\,5\,6\,7\,8\\4\,8\,5\,1\,3\,7\,6\,2\end{pmatrix}$, I.　　　　(j) $\begin{pmatrix}1\,2\,3\,4\,5\,6\,7\,8\\7\,3\,2\,6\,8\,4\,1\,5\end{pmatrix}$, I.

2. (a) $\begin{pmatrix}1\,2\,3\,4\\2\,1\,4\,3\end{pmatrix}$, I.　(b) $\begin{pmatrix}1\,2\,3\,4\\4\,3\,2\,1\end{pmatrix}$, I.　(c) $\begin{pmatrix}1\,2\,3\,4\\1\,3\,4\,2\end{pmatrix}$, $\begin{pmatrix}1\,2\,3\,4\\1\,4\,2\,3\end{pmatrix}$, I.

  (d) $\begin{pmatrix}1\,2\,3\,4\\4\,2\,1\,3\end{pmatrix}$, $\begin{pmatrix}1\,2\,3\,4\\3\,2\,4\,1\end{pmatrix}$, I.　　　(e) $\begin{pmatrix}1\,2\,3\,4\\2\,4\,3\,1\end{pmatrix}$, $\begin{pmatrix}1\,2\,3\,4\\4\,1\,3\,2\end{pmatrix}$, I.

3. In 1(a), the first and third rotations listed in the answer are inverses, the second and fourth are their own inverses. In 1(c), the first two rotations listed are inverses. In 2(a), each rotation is its own inverse. In 2(c), the first two are inverses.

1. (a) Closure, associativity.   (b) Closure.   (c) All.   (d) All.
   (e) Closure, associativity.   (f) All.   (g) Closure, identity.
2. (a) All.
   (b) Abelian group under addition; associativity of multiplication, distributivity.
   (c) Associativity, identity and inverses under addition; closure, associativity under multiplication, distributivity.
   (d) Abelian group under addition; associativity of multiplication, distributivity.
   (e) All.
   (f) Abelian group under addition; closure under multiplication.
3. (a) All.   (b) 2(b), (c), (f).
4. 2(a) not a field; no multiplicative identity or inverses.
   2(b) not a field; no closure under multiplication.
   2(c) not a field; no closure under addition.
   2(d) not a field; no closure under multiplication, no multiplicative identity or inverses.
   2(e) not a field; no multiplicative identity or inverses.
   2(f) not a field; no associativity of multiplication, no distributivity.

INDEX